The Induction of Flowering
SOME CASE HISTORIES

EDITED BY

L. T. Evans

CORNELL UNIVERSITY PRESS
ITHACA, NEW YORK

First published in the United States of America by

CORNELL UNIVERSITY PRESS
1969

Library of Congress Catalog Card Number: 69-16522

COMPOSED IN AUSTRALIA, PRINTED IN HONG KONG

Contents

The Contributors

L. H. Aung, *Dept. of Horticulture, Michigan State University, East Lansing, Michigan, U.S.A.*

L. A. T. Ballard, *CSIRO Division of Plant Industry, Canberra, Australia.*

G. Bernier, *Institut de Botanique, Université de Liège, Liège, Belgium.*

H. M. Cathey, *Crops Research Division, U.S.D.A., Plant Industry Station, Beltsville, Maryland, U.S.A.*

B. G. Cumming, *Dept. of Botany, University of Western Ontario, London, Ontario, Canada.*

L. T. Evans, *CSIRO, Division of Plant Industry, Canberra, Australia.*

D. J. C. Friend, *Dept. of Botany, Universtiy of Hawaii, Honolulu, Hawaii, U.S.A.*

C. G. Guttridge, *Dept. of Horticulture, Long Ashton Research Station, Bristol, U.K.*

K. C. Hamner, *Dept. of Botany, University of California, Los Angeles, California, U.S.A.*

W. Haupt, *Botanisches Institut der Universität Erlangen-Nürnberg, W. Germany.*

J. and Y. Heslop-Harrison, *Dept. of Botany, University of Wisconsin, Madison, Wisconsin, U.S.A.*

W. S. Hillman, *Biology Dept., Brookhaven National Laboratory, Upton, New York, U.S.A.*

K. Napp-Zinn, *Botanisches Institut, Köln-Lindenthal, W. Germany.*

R. M. Sachs, *Dept. of Landscape Horticulture, University of California, Davis, California, U.S.A.*

F. B. Salisbury, *Plant Science Dept., Utah State University, Logan, Utah, U.S.A.*

W. W. Schwabe, *Dept. of Horticulture, Wye College, Kent, England.*

A. Takimoto, *Laboratory of Applied Botany, Kyoto University, Kyoto, Japan.*

S. J. Wellensiek, *Laboratorium voor Tuinbouwplantenteelt, Landbouwhogeschool, Wageningen, Netherlands.*

S. H. Wittwer, *Dept. of Horticulture, Michigan State University, East Lansing, Michigan, U.S.A.*

J. A. D. Zeevaart, *M.S.U./A.E.C. Plant Research Laboratory, Michigan State University, East Lansing, Michigan, U.S.A.*

Abbreviations

A	acceptor partner in a graft union
Amo-1618	2-isopropyl-4 dimethylamino-5-methyl phenyl-1-piperidine-carboxylate methyl chloride
ATP	adenosine triphosphate
B9, B995	N, N-dimethylamino succinamic acid
CCC	(2-chloroethyl) trimethyl ammonium chloride
CFL	cyclic fluorescent light
CIPC	isopropyl N-(3-chlorophenyl) carbamate
CL	continuous light
D	donor partner in a graft union
2,4-D	2,4-dichlorophenoxyacetic acid
DCMU	3(3,4 dichlorophenyl)-1, 1 dimethyl urea
DNP	2,4-dinitrophenol
DT	day temperature
EDTA	ethylene diamine tetracetic acid
f.c.	foot candle (1 f.c. = 10.8 lux). The luminous efficiency of lamps varies greatly with their type, age, temperature etc., but the energy flux for radiation between 4000 and 7700Å at a light intensity of 1 f.c. is commonly about 5.5 μW cm^{-2} for incandescent lamps and 3.1–3.6 μW cm^{-2} for fluorescent lamps.
5FDU	5-fluorodeoxyuridine
FPA	p-fluorophenylalanine
FR	far-red light (7000–7700Å)
5FU	5-fluorouracil
GA3	gibberellic acid
hr	hours
IAA	3-indoleacetic acid
IBA	indolebutyric acid
LD	long days
LDP	long-day plant
LSDP	long-short-day plant
MH	maleic hydrazide
mμ	1 mμ = 10 Angstroms
NAA	1-naphthalene acetic acid
nm	nanometer (1nm = 10Å)
NT	night temperature

Phosfon	2,4-dichlorobenzyl-tributylphosphonium chloride
P_{fr}	phytochrome in the far-red (λmax 7200Å) absorbing form
P_r	phytochrome in the red (λmax 6600Å) absorbing form
R	red light (6000–7000Å)
RGR	relative growth rate
RQ	respiratory quotient
SD	short days
SDP	short-day plant
SK & F7997	tris-(2-diethylaminoethyl) phosphate trihydrochloride
SLDP	short-long-day plant
TIBA	tri-iodobenzoic acid
2TU	2-thiouracil
μw	microwatt
	($1\ \mu\text{w cm}^{-2} = 10\ \text{erg sec}^{-1}\ \text{cm}^{-2} = 1.43 \times 10^{-5}\ \text{cal min}^{-1}\ \text{cm}^{-2}$)

'And bathed every veyne in swich licour,
Of which vertu engendered is the flour'

Geoffrey Chaucer, 1387

Preface

Six hundred years ago Chaucer wrote confidently of the 'vertu' which engendered the flower. Since the recognition in 1918 of the controlling influence on flowering of daylength and temperature, a multitude of experiments and publications has pinned down, though not identified, this 'vertu'.

Much of our understanding of flowering concerns the earliest steps towards it, the induction of flowering. And much of it has come from work with a small number of plants. Those steps, in some of these plants, is the subject of this book.

A powerful trend in biology today is the increasing emphasis on the similarities between organisms, and on the development of concepts applicable to all. Faced with this, it may be valuable to be reminded, occasionally, of the rich and subtle diversity of behaviour through which organisms adapt to their environment.

Such diversity is only too apparent in the flowering processes of higher plants, to the frustration of reviewers and to the confusion of readers. Yet the unique or apparently anomalous features of the flowering process in each plant may become both consistent and significant when viewed in the context of the behaviour of that plant.

This book, therefore, aims to expose the diversity of flowering behaviour rather than to neglect it or confine it within a few generalizations.

The following case histories by no means cover the full range of flowering behaviour. Some plants which have played a significant role in the development of our concepts are not included, two because the induction of authors proved to be a reversible process. Each editor would make a different selection of case histories, and I will not attempt to justify mine, except to note the emphasis on plants requiring exposure to only one day of appropriate length, and on plants which can be induced to flower as seedlings, since these are likely to be of increasing importance in future work on the induction of flowering.

The case histories are built on a common plan, to aid comparison between plants. The plan was agreed to by all authors, but was not equally suited to all plants, hence the occasional missing sections.

Suggestions from many of my colleagues, particularly Dr L. A. T. Ballard, and from the authors of the case histories, have shaped the book. I am very grateful to them, to Mrs V. Ronning for her careful typing and proof reading, and to Miss A. E. Grant Lipp who also helped with the proof reading. Material on Tournois was kindly provided by Professors L. Plantefol, J. Heslop-Harrison and K. Napp-Zinn, and on Garner and Allard by Drs H. A. Borthwick, R. A. Steinberg, J. E. McMurtrey, and the Director of the Southern Historical Collection in the University of North Carolina Library at Chapel Hill, to all of whom I owe thanks.

I am indebted also to the Editors of the following periodicals for permission to reproduce diagrams which have been published previously: *American Journal of Botany, Annals of Botany, Australian Journal of Biological Sciences, Botanical Gazette, Botanical Review, Canadian Journal of Botany, Journal of Experimental Botany, Journal of Horticultural Science, Nature, Plant & Cell Physiology, Plant Physiology, Planta, Proceedings of the American Society of Horticultural Science, Zeitschrift fur Pflanzenphysiologie*; and to Professor A. E. Murneek for permission to cite a private communication to him from Dr. W. W. Garner.

The authors wish to acknowledge the support of the U.S. Atomic Energy Commission for the preparation of Chapters 5, 7 and 21, of the National Research Council of Canada for Chapter 6, and of Deutsche Forschungsgemeinschaft for Chapter 12.

L. T. Evans

Outline For Each Case History

1   *History of Use*
2   *Growing Techniques and Growth Habit*
3   *Inflorescence Structure and Criteria of Flowering Response*
4   *Effects of Plant Age*
5   *Vernalization and Devernalization*
6   *Short Day Vernalization*
7   *Photoperiod Response*
8   *Spectral Dependence*
9   *Endogenous Rhythms*
10   *Fractional Induction*
11   *Photoperiodic Inhibition*
12   *Dual Photoperiod Responses*
13   *Effects of Temperature*
14   *Effects of Mineral Nutrition*
15   *Effects of Gas Composition*
16   *Translocation of the Floral Stimulus*
17   *Grafting Experiments*
18   *Effects of Growth Substances and Growth Retardants*
19   *Effects of Metabolic Inhibitors*
20   *Florigenic Extracts*
21   *Induction of Excised Apices*
22   *Chemical, Histochemical, and Ultrastructural Changes at Induction*
23   *Inflorescence Differentiation.*

1

A Short History of the Physiology of Flowering

By L. T. Evans

As an experimental study, the physiology of flowering is about 50 years old. Between 1910 and 1920 the controlling influence of daylength on flowering in many plants was established, as was the need by others for a period at low temperatures. At this time too, the experiments of Fischer,[35] of Klebs,[50] and of Kraus and Kraybill[54] indicated that nutritional conditions may also have a marked influence on flowering in some plants, and for a while preoccupation with the carbohydrate/nitrogen ratio overshadowed work on the effects of daylength and of low temperature vernalization.

The Role of Daylength

Beginning with A. Henfrey in 1852,[47] several nineteenth century writers considered the possibility that daylength might influence plant distribution and development. Following the invention of a practical incandescent lamp by Edison in 1879, experiments in 'electrohorticulture' by Bailey[3] and others showed that flowering of several horticultural plants could be accelerated by extending natural daylengths with incandescent light.

That daylength was the controlling factor was first realised by Julien Tournois (Fig. 1–1). Born in 1884, he began his experiments on flowering and sexuality in hops and in hemp at Paris in 1910, for his doctoral thesis. His choice of plants, partly inspired by his father's interest, could hardly have been more fortunate. His first experiments,[80] published in 1911, described the extremely early flowering that occurred in plants sown during winter. In subsequent experiments, he eliminated temperature, humidity and seed origin as causal factors for this precocious flowering, and began his critical experiment in April 1912. In this, plants were exposed from sowing to either natural spring daylengths, continuous light, or days shortened to 6 hours. Although the plants in short days grew most slowly, they flowered most rapidly. The results of this experiment were published in July 1912.[81] Near the beginning of this paper, Tournois mentioned daylength as a possible causal factor, but concluded at the end that 'the flowering of hemp and of hops is the more precocious the smaller the quantity of light which plants receive after germination'. These two papers of Tournois are the ones cited by Garner and Allard[37] and many others, and leave it open to debate whether Tournois had grasped the importance of daylength. However, his last paper[82], on sexuality in hops, is quite explicit on this point. The experiments he carried out in 1913 eliminated various factors as the cause of precocious flowering. Most importantly, he showed that reduced light intensity led to only a slight acceleration of flowering, and concluded that 'precocious flowering in young plants of hemp and hops occurs when, from germination, they are exposed to very short periods of daily illumination'. He also concluded that 'precocious flowering is not so much caused by shortening of the days as by lengthening of the nights'. Although Tournois was a modest, reticent man who spoke little of his work, it was clear to his friends[23,29] that he was excited by his findings and had planned further experiments. However, he was killed at the front shortly after the publication of his major paper.

In Germany, at the same time, G. Klebs came tantalizingly close to realizing the significance of daylength in the control of flowering, when he made plants of *Sempervivum funkii* flower by exposing them to several days of continuous light. Klebs concluded[49] that the additional light was acting catalytically and not as a nutritional factor.

The recognition of daylength as a major factor controlling flowering, and many other responses, in a wide array of plants, and of the different kinds of response to daylength, dates from the publication in 1920 of a classic paper by W. W. Garner and H. A. Allard.[37] Like Tournois, Garner and Allard approached the possible influence of daylength with extreme diffidence, as the following account by Garner[36] shows:

'The two cardinal observations with which we started were that, in contrast with other tobaccos, the new Maryland Mammoth variety always continued a purely vegetative type of growth through the open growing season at Washington, and that successive plantings of certain varieties of soybeans made at short intervals through the spring and early summer all tended to flower at the same date. In the case of tobacco, it was not at first realized that a seasonal effect was definitely involved in the very unusual behaviour of the new variety. It was thought that perhaps the "shock" of transplanting to the greenhouse was a major factor, possibly aided by increasing age of the plants. We were temporarily misled by the observation that seedlings grown in small pots in winter and early spring flowered and fruited freely, thus suggesting a nutritional angle. The big lead came after several years with the observation that with the advance of spring new shoots developing on stumps that had been producing flowering shoots suddenly swung over to the indeterminate vegetative type of growth. It was then perfectly clear that a seasonal factor was involved. Since the plants were growing in a warm greenhouse, it appeared that temperature could be excluded. With respect to light, we naturally reasoned that intensity and composition might be involved. However, fairly extensive investigations were being conducted on other problems with both tobacco and soybeans that seemed to preclude intensity and spectral composition of light as important factors. At this stage the problem appeared to assume a somewhat hopeless trend, but after much deliberation it was concluded that the only remaining seasonal phenomenon that could be a factor was change in relative length of day and night. The importance of this conclusion, of course, lies in the fact that length of day was dissociated from the factor of amount of solar radiation. The decisive test was then made in the simplest possible way but without great hope of success, mainly for the reason that there appeared to be no accepted basis in plant physiology for consideration of day length as other than a purely quantitative factor.'

Garner and Allard's decisive test, which originated at a lunchtime conversation, began on July 10th, 1918, when Allard placed three pots with persistently vegetative Mammoth tobacco plants and a box of Peking soybeans into what he described as a primitive dog house of his own devising[1]. These plants received only 7 hours of light each day while comparable plants remained in the full summer daylengths of Washington D.C. The tobacco plants which were enclosed each day promptly flowered, while those outside stayed vegetative. The soybeans also showed accelerated development in short days (c.f. Fig. 3–1).

That four short-day plants—hops, hemp, soybeans and Maryland Mammoth tobacco—played a key role in the recognition of the importance of daylength was probably due to more than chance. Kjellmann, Bailey, Rane, Corbett, and Klebs had all observed an acceleration of flowering in long-day plants under extended daylengths, but this seemed due to a general acceleration of growth with additional light. A short-day response was less readily explained in this way, and the lack of effect of reduced light intensities compelled the conclusion that daylength was involved. Tournois eliminated light intensity as the operative factor after doing his critical daylength experiment, whereas Garner and Allard did so before.

(a) Julien Tournois (1884–1914) of France.

(b) M. Chailahjan of U.S.S.R.

(c) H. A. Borthwick (left) with H. A. Allard (1880–1963) of U.S.A.

FIGURE 1–1 Some founders of flowering physiology

If Garner and Allard began their daylength experiments diffidently in 1918, they were certainly emboldened by 1919. Allard (Fig. 1–1) was a keen observer and a naturalist with an extremely wide range of knowledge. His earlier work on tobacco included pioneer studies on the nature of the mosaic disease[1,4,83] and he made equally original analyses of the stridulations of insects.[43] His contribution to the experiments of 1919 is evident in the plants used and the range of responses observed.

Garner, who trained as a chemist, was also a man of broad perspective. He did not have Allard's enormous knowledge of plants, but his systematic approach, displayed in the extensive experiments eliminating light intensity as the crucial factor and in the serial planting of soybean varieties, nicely complemented Allard's more impulsive nature. Their first paper[37] is a classic not only in the range of species, of kinds of experiments, and of plant responses used to establish that daylength influences plant behaviour, but also in the breadth of the discussion which includes consideration of the effects of daylength on plant distribution, on crop yields, and on the behaviour of algae and the migration of birds. They also introduced the terms photoperiod for daylength and photoperiodism for the response of organisms to the relative length of day and night. Yet, despite the power and sweep of this paper, it was almost rejected by the editorial panel to which it was submitted, as being insufficiently novel.[2]

Vernalization

Many biennial and winter annual plants require prolonged exposure to low temperatures before they can flower. Such exposure brings them to the condition they would normally reach in spring, and is therefore known as vernalization.

Like photoperiodism and many other phenomena, vernalization was known long before it was recognized. In an essay written in 1857 Klippart[51] wrote:

'To convert winter into spring wheat, nothing more is necessary than that the winter wheat should be allowed to germinate slightly in the fall or winter, but kept from vegetation by a low temperature or freezing, until it can be sown in the spring. This is usually done by soaking and sprouting the seed, and freezing it while in this state and keeping it frozen until the season for spring sowing has arrived. Only two things seem requisite, germination and freezing. It is probable that winter wheat sown in the fall, so late as only to germinate in the earth, without coming up, would produce a grain which would be a spring wheat, if sown in April instead of September. The experiment of converting winter wheat into spring wheat has met with great success. It retains many of its primitive winter wheat qualities, and produces at the rate of 28 bushels per acre.'

McKinney[65] also cites even earlier writings indicating that the idea of vernalization was well known in the USA in Klippart's time.

Gassner[40] was the first to make a systematic analysis of the phenomenon of vernalization. He sowed seeds of both spring and winter forms of Petkus rye on a series of occasions, and held them at 1–2°C, 5–6°C, 12°C or 24°C, until they appeared above the ground, after which they were planted out. He found that whereas spring rye did not have any 'chilling requirement' for flowering, winter rye would not flower unless it was held at low temperatures for a prolonged period.

Gassner's work was extended by Maximov, and by several other Russian investigators, particularly Lysenko, who first coined the name jarovizacija, the anglicized equivalent of which is vernalization. Lysenko contributed more than a dramatic name, however. Several investigators had obtained conflicting results in attempting to repeat Gassner's experiments and it appears to have been

Lysenko who first recognized,[63] as a result of experiments by Meljnik, that many winter cereals would flower only when vernalization was followed by exposure to long-day conditions. Previously, in 1928, Lysenko had postulated[62] that the processes of development in plants are independent of growth, and take place in a series of irreversible steps or phases, which must be completed in a strict sequence. This was his theory of phasic development.

Lysenko's idea that reproductive development was separate from growth was by no means new. MacDougal in 1903[64] had indicated that they were distinct processes capable of separation. Similarly, Lysenko's idea that development proceeded in a series of steps each with its own environmental requirements had been clearly enunciated by Klebs in 1918.[50] What was new was Lysenko's attempt to provide a single all-embracing scheme for the development of all plants. He could hardly have chosen a more perverse field to which to apply his rigid generalizations, and exceptions soon appeared. For example, Gregory and Purvis[42] showed that the effects of vernalization could, under some conditions, be reversed by subsequent high temperatures, in the process of devernalization. At the time this finding was of greatest significance in showing that progress in development is not irreversible as Lysenko had postulated. However, the phenomenon of devernalization subsequently proved to be most useful in further analysis of the nature of the process of vernalization.

While critical assessment of the theory of phasic development flourished outside the USSR, it was for long stifled within that country, as was criticism of Lysenko's plant breeding methods. The imprisonment of the great Russian geneticist N. I. Vavilov for contradicting Lysenko is well known. Less known are the persecutions of plant physiologists such as D. A. Sabinin,[21] who tried to present a balanced assessment of Lysenko's contribution to the physiology of development. This was indeed a chilling phase in the development of biology.

Thirty Years in Search of a Hormone

In 1930 Curtis and Chang[27] showed that the shoot tip of celery plants was the tissue that responded to low temperature vernalization, and this was subsequently confirmed for sugar beet and chrysanthemum. On the other hand, experiments by Garner and Allard[38] with *Cosmos* and by Razumov[75] on photoperiodic control of tuberization in potatoes suggested that it was the leaves which initially respond to daylength. Ingenious experiments with spinach by Knott,[52] using thimbles to impose short-day conditions on the shoot apex alone, and light pipes to expose it to long days, clearly established that it was the leaves which initially responded to daylength. Knott concluded that 'the part played by the foliage of spinach in hastening the response to a photoperiod favourable to reproductive growth may be in the production of some substance, or stimulus, that is transported to the growing point'.

Julius Sachs had suggested the existence of flower-forming substances which could move within a plant as early as 1865.[76] Whether they were nutritive or hormonal was not clear. The isolation by Went in 1928[84] of a plant hormone which controlled extension growth and meristematic activity stimulated the search for a flowering hormone. Experiments like those of Knott with spinach were carried out in Russia in 1936 by Chailahjan[17] and Moshkov[66] with chrysanthemum and by Psarev[74] with soybeans and all showed that, while it was the shoot apex which ultimately responded to the inductive daylength, it was the leaves which perceived the photoperiod. Chailahjan (Fig. 1–1) advocated the existence of a floral hormone, as a result of these experiments, and named it florigen in 1937.[18]

Support for the concept of a flowering hormone followed quickly from grafting experiments, in which it was shown that receptor plants under non-inductive conditions could be induced to flower by grafting them to donor plants of the same strain which had previously been kept under inductive daylength conditions. Experiments of this kind were first carried out by Kuijper and Wiersum[55] in Holland and by Chailahjan and Yarkovaya[22] in Russia. Even more striking evidence for a floral hormone came from experiments in which donors of one daylength response type could induce flowering in receptors of a different response type. Chailahjan[19] induced flowering in the short-day plant *Helianthus tuberosus* in long days by grafting to day neutral *H. annuus* donors. Moshkov[67] went even further and induced flowering in Maryland Mammoth tobacco in long days by grafting to the long-day plant *Nicotiana sylvestris*. These experiments not only provided strong evidence for the existence of a floral hormone, but also suggested that the hormone was common to both long and short-day plants. Chailahjan's ardent advocacy of florigen seemed justified and the name was used widely despite strictures on its poor etymology.[24] This baptism of the flowering hormone aided belief in its existence in the face of many unsuccessful attempts to extract it. Recently, some progress in this direction has been made, and the stimulus has been renamed florigenic acid.[58]

Although we know nothing of the identity of the floral stimulus, indirect evidence has been obtained of the time when it moves from leaves to shoot apex, and of the velocity of its movement. This comes from the technique, first used on *Xanthium* in 1954, of exposing plants with one leaf to a single inductive cycle and removing the leaf at various times after.[48,77,79] Such treatments can be used to estimate when the floral stimulus reaches the shoot apex, which is essential to an understanding of early changes at the apex in response to the stimulus.

The indirect nature of the evidence for a specific flowering hormone, and the continued failure to extract and identify it, have at times led some workers to question whether flower induction might not as properly be considered as removal of a photoperiodic inhibition which prevents the shoot apex from forming flowers. Gregory[41] first raised this query in 1936, and it was developed more fully by Lona[59,60] and von Denffer.[28] De-inhibition is insufficient on its own as an explanation of the control of flowering by daylength, but flower induction may well involve an interaction between inhibitors and stimuli whose production is controlled by daylength, as may be seen in some of the chapters that follow.

More Darkness Than Light

Photoperiodism is the response of plants to the relative length of the daily light and dark periods. Experiments by Garner and Allard[39] with alternating light and dark periods of equal duration, from 15 seconds to 12 hours, indicated that whereas long-day plants flowered rapidly under short light-dark cycles, short-day plants remained vegetative unless they received long uninterrupted dark periods.

The central role of the dark period in the photoperiodic processes of *Xanthium* was clearly established by Hamner and Bonner,[45] from three kinds of evidence. With light-dark cycles 24 hours in length they showed that *Xanthium* would flower only when the dark period was $8\frac{1}{2}$ hours or longer. With light-dark cycles both shorter and longer than 24 hours they showed that it was not the relative length of the light and dark periods that controlled flowering, nor the length of the light period, but that it was the duration of the dark period, which had to exceed a critical length to be effective. Secondly, they showed that exposure to light for one minute in the middle of a dark period of more than critical length rendered it ineffective. Thirdly, whereas the temperature during the photoperiod had little effect, the temperature during the dark period had a marked effect on the flowering response.

The importance of the dark period in the flowering of long-day plants was emphasized by Lang and Melchers[57] from their work with *Hyoscyamus niger*. In this case, long dark periods had an inhibitory rather than a stimulatory role. Such was the emphasis on the central role of the dark period for both long and short-day plants that it was suggested that they should be referred to as short and long-night plants respectively. However, further analysis has restored some importance to the light period as well, justifying the retention of Garner and Allard's original terminology.

With Biloxi soybeans, Borthwick and Parker[6] showed that exposure to a single prolonged dark period was insufficient for flower induction, and that for short days to be effective they had to include a period in light. The required duration in light depended on the number of short-day cycles, and on the light intensity.[7] Moshkov obtained comparable results with *Perilla*.[68] With *Kalanchöe*, light for one second in each 24 hours was sufficient to meet the light requirement.[46]

In 1940 Hamner[44] extended the analysis of light and dark requirements for flower induction in soybeans, and concluded that processes in the light (A), processes in the dark (B), and processes from an interaction between the two (C), govern flower induction. Here began an activity which characterized the forties, devoted to the ABC of photoperiodism. Many schemes were presented, for both long and short-day plants, in attempts to reduce the rapidly accumulating phenomenology to sequences of processes common to many plants. The array of facts, the close argument, and the ingenuity encompassed by these schemes are impressive, and the framework lives on in current analyses of induction into a series of partial processes.

Note that a concept implicit in most of these schemes was that the time requirement for the light and dark processes was simply a matter of how long it took them to reach completion, or at least threshold levels. With this hourglass concept one was free to vary the duration of the light and dark periods independently, and a great deal of work of this kind was done.

As early as 1936 Bünning[11] had suggested that time measurement in photoperiodic reactions was associated with endogenous rhythms and that the flowering response depended on the time at which plants were exposed to light or darkness in relation to the oscillation of the rhythm. Re-assertion of this idea in 1944,[12,13] when the hourglass concept was at full tide, led only to the scepticism which often greets highly original ideas. However, by giving light breaks at various times to *Kalanchöe* plants grown in 72-hour cycles of 12 hours light—60 hours darkness, Carr[16] obtained some evidence in support of Bünning's hypothesis, and other evidence followed. Several of the chapters in this book present evidence of endogenous circadian (= about one day) rhythms in photoperiodic responses. Whether these are an integral component of time measurement in photoperiodism, or merely modulate the photoperiodic responses obtained under certain experimental conditions, remains an open question.

Master Pigment

In 1936, while Garner and Allard were continuing their experiments at Arlington, a new unit within the United States Department of Agriculture was set up at Beltsville to examine the anatomical and physiological changes in plants under different daylengths. H. A. Borthwick (Fig. 1–1) and M. W. Parker analysed the effects of such factors as plant age, temperature, carbon dioxide concentration, and plant variety on flowering response and meristematic differentiation in soybeans, as was suggested at the establishment of their project. The insight into the flowering physiology of soybeans gained from this work was an essential prelude to the later advances. In 1944 they began a collaboration with S. B. Hendricks, the object of which was to characterize the light active in photoperiodism. Within 8 weeks a spectrograph was constructed, largely out of reject equipment. The experimental technique grew out of the finding by Hamner and Bonner in 1938[45] that exposure to light for one minute during the middle of a long dark period could nullify its inductive effect. The wavelength-dependence of this light break effect in soybean was published in 1945,[71] and a very similar action spectrum was soon found for another short-day plant, *Xanthium*.[72] More surprisingly, it was found that the action spectra for light breaks promoting flowering in the long-day plants barley and *Hyoscyamus* were similar,[8,70] implying that one pigment mediated the photoperiodic processes of both long and short-day plants. The reach of this pigment was extended still further when it was found that it could also control de-aetiolation[73] and seed germination.[10] Since germination experiments could be carried out more rapidly and on a greater scale than could flowering experiments, germination displaced flowering as the preferred response system for further study of the photomorphogenic pigment.

The next major advance in understanding how this pigment acted came in 1952 when it was found that the light reaction controlling seed germination could be reversibly potentiated and suppressed by red and far-red light respectively.[10] The pigment was deduced to exist in two forms, one with an absorption peak in the red region of the spectrum (P_r) and the other, probably biologically active, form with peak absorption in the far red region (P_{fr}). It was also deduced that the P_{fr} form could revert in darkness to the inactive P_r form, at a rate depending on the temperature.

These deductions were applied to a further analysis[9] of the effect of a light break on flowering in *Xanthium*, in which it was shown that the inhibitory effect of a light break was reversible by subsequent exposure to far red light. Brief exposure to far red light at the end of the main light period reduced the length of the dark period needed for flowering, while exposure to red light increased it. The interpretation of these results was that the pigment was predominantly in the active P_{fr} form at the end of the light period, and this had to revert to the P_r form before the dark reactions could begin. Exposure to far red light at the beginning of the dark period converted most of the pigment to the P_r form, and thereby shortened the length of the dark period required for flowering in *Xanthium*. Thus, dark reversion of the pigment was one component of time-measurement.

Further major steps in work on the photomorphogenic pigment were its physical detection in 1959[15] when it was named phytochrome, and the identification of its chromophore in 1966.[78]

The 1952 paper on phytochrome control of flowering in *Xanthium*[9] shaped much of the thinking about how daylength controlled flowering for many years. Long-day plants were thought to need P_{fr} action during the night, while short-day plants had to await reversion to P_r before their dark reactions could begin. This simple antithesis is no longer an adequate explanation. Nakayama[69] found that in at least one short-day plant, *Pharbitis*, phytochrome in the P_{fr} form is required during the early hours of an effective dark period. In the same year Konitz[53] obtained evidence with *Chenopodium amaranticolor* suggesting that changes in sensitivity to P_{fr} action are linked to an endogenous rhythm, a theme expanded in several of the following chapters.

The Central Mystery

Molecular biology has its central dogma, but in flowering physiology we have two terminal dogmas and a central mystery. The dogmas are that one pigment, phytochrome, mediates the initial photoperiodic reactions in all plants, and one hormone, florigen, concludes them. The central mystery is how, with a common beginning and a common end, the intermediate reactions require darkness in short-day plants and light in long-day plants.

Most of the little we know about the biochemical nature of these intermediate reactions has come from work with plants requiring exposure to only one short or long day for flower induction. *Xanthium* was the first such plant known and became the preferred object of study, not only because of the convenience of one cycle induction, but also because it permitted kinds of experiments not possible with plants requiring prolonged induction. As a result, the events contributing to photoperiodic induction in *Xanthium* could be analysed in terms of a series of partial processes, whose timing was known, if not their nature. Some insight into their nature has been gained from experiments in which growth regulators or specific antimetabolites are applied at various times during induction to either the leaf or the shoot apex.

Salisbury[77] pioneered this approach in his work on the role of auxin during induction in *Xanthium*. In 1937 Dostal and Hosek[30] with the long-day plant *Circaea lutetiana*, and Hamner and Bonner[45] with *Xanthium*, had shown that auxin applications could reduce the flowering response to inductive daylengths. Then in 1942 Clark and Kerns[25] and Cooper[26] found that auxin promoted flowering in the pineapple, and Zimmerman and Hitchcock[85] found that tri-iodobenzoic acid promoted it in the tomato. There followed a great deal of work on the effect of auxin on flower induction in many plants. However, Salisbury's experiments, and other similar work, suggest that although auxin may modify the flowering response, changes in endogenous auxins do not play a central role in the processes of induction.

Unlike the animal hormones, none of the known plant hormones is organ-specific in its action. All act on many plant tissues. On this basis one may query the specific action of the putative flowering hormone, as Cholodny[24] did when Chailahjan[18] postulated florigen. An alternative is that induction requires only a particular sequence and combination of changes in several hormones, none specifically concerned with flower induction.

The finding by Lang[56] in 1956 that gibberellic acid could induce flowering in *Hyoscyamus niger*, quickly extended to other long-day plants by Lona[61] and by Bünsow and Harder,[14] seemed at first to support the view that flowering was not under the control of a specific floral hormone, since gibberellins inhibited rather than promoted flowering in short-day plants. Chailahjan[20] put forward an ingenious theory that florigen consisted of two components, gibberellins, lacking in long-day plants in short days, and anthesins, lacking in short-day plants in long days. There are several difficulties with this theory, one being that there is little evidence from grafting experiments that non-induced long and short-day plants can complement each other, as they should. Moreover, although gibberellins may substitute for long days, we still lack evidence that endogenous gibberellins play a role in the inductive processes of long-day plants.

Another endogenous growth regulator which influences flower induction is abscisin. This substance, like the auxins and gibberellins, has a broad spectrum of action in plants, affecting growth, tuberization, senescence, abscission and bud dormancy.[32] It occurs in higher concentration in both shoot apices and leaves under short-day conditions,[31] inhibits flowering in some long-day plants[34] and can induce it in some short day plants.[32]

Thus, there are several endogenous growth regulators known to have a marked influence on flower induction. Further, the level of their occurrence in plants is known to be controlled by daylength. Evidence of more specific substances, exclusively concerned with flower induction, is sparse, but experiments with specific inhibitors suggest that the synthesis of a steroid may be an essential component of the photoperiodic processes in the leaves of both short and long-day plants.[5,33] However, the reactions involved in flower induction remain a dark continent on biochemical maps, and we still have only the slightest of clues as to the nature of the terrain.

Shoot Apex Response

The three most important questions we can ask in flowering physiology are: How is the time in light or darkness measured in leaves? What is the nature of the hormone(s) which controls flowering and is produced in leaves as a result of this time measurement? How does this hormone initiate the differentiation of flowers instead of leaves at the shoot apex? Most of the flowering work to date has been concerned with the first two questions, which contain the essence of photoperiodism, but can still not be answered. Partly by default, and partly because of intense current interest in the mechanisms of hormone action and of differentiation, the third question is now also being considered in studies of flower induction. The shoot apex may have little to commend it as a tissue for the study of differentiation, because of its small size and inaccessibility, but the experimental advantages of strict environmental control of the course and timing of differentiation may sometimes outweigh the disadvantages. Histochemistry, electron microscopy, autoradiography and other techniques are being used to elucidate the nature of the early changes at the shoot apex during flower induction. With these new techniques come new kinds of experimenters, whose involvement with the physiology of flowering may well alter the whole framework of our approaches to the induction of flowering.

REFERENCES

[1] Allard, H. A. Unpublished letter of January 19, 1931 to Paul de Kruif, in the Southern Historical Collection, University of North Carolina Library, Chapel Hill, N.C.

[2] Allard, H. A. 'A bit of history of long ago.' Unpublished manuscript in possession of Dr H. A. Borthwick.

[3] Bailey, L. H. (1893). Greenhouse notes for 1892–93. I. Third report upon electro-horticulture. *N.Y. Agric. Exp. Sta. Bull.* **55**, 147.

[4] Bawden, F. C. (1964). *Plant viruses and virus diseases*. 4th edn. Ronald Press, N.Y.

[5] Bonner, J., Heftmann, E. and Zeevaart, J. A. D. (1963). Suppression of floral induction by inhibitors of steroid biosynthesis. *Plant Physiol.* **38**, 81.

[6] Borthwick, H. A. and Parker, M. W. (1938). Influence of photoperiods upon the differentiation of meristems and the blossoming of Biloxi soybeans. *Bot. Gaz.* **99**, 825.

[7] Borthwick, H. A. and Parker, M. W. (1938). Photoperiodic perception in Biloxi soybeans. *Bot. Gaz.* **100**, 374.

[8] Borthwick, H. A., Hendricks, S. B. and Parker, M. W. (1948). Action spectrum for photoperiodic control of floral initiation of a long day plant, Wintex barley (*Hordeum vulgare*) *Bot. Gaz.* **110**, 103.

[9] Borthwick, H. A., Hendricks, S. B. and Parker, M. W. (1952). The reaction controlling floral initiation. *Proc. Nat. Acad. Sci.* **38**, 929.

[10] Borthwick, H. A., Hendricks, S. B., Parker, M. W., Toole, E. M. and Toole, V. K. (1952). A reversible photoreaction controlling seed germination. *Proc. Nat. Acad. Sci.* **38**, 662.

[11] Bünning, E. (1936). Die endonome Tagesrhythmik als Grundlage der photoperiodischen Reaktion. *Ber. dtsch. bot. Ges.* **54**, 590.

[12] Bünning, E. (1944). Endonome Tagesrhythmik und Photoperiodismus bei Kurztagpflanzen. *Biol. Zbl.* **64**, 161.

13 Bünning, E. (1944). Die allgemeinen Grundlagen der photoperiodischen Empfindlichkeit. *Flora* **38**, 93.

14 Bünsow, R. and Harder, R. (1956). Blütenbildung von *Lapsana* durch Gibberellin. *Naturwiss.* **43**, 527.

15 Butler, W. L., Norris, K. H., Siegelman, H. W. and Hendricks, S. B. (1959). Detection, assay, and preliminary purification of the pigment controlling photoresponsive development of plants. *Proc. Nat. Acad. Sci.* **45**, 1703.

16 Carr, D. J. (1952). A critical experiment on Bünning's theory of photoperiodism. *Zeit. Naturf.* **76**, 570.

17 Chailahjan, M. K. (1936). On the hormonal theory of plant development. *C.R. (Dokl.) Acad. Sci. U.R.S.S.* **3**, 442.

18 Chailahjan, M. K. (1937). Concerning the hormonal nature of plant development processes. *C.R. (Dokl.) Acad. Sci. U.R.S.S.* **16**, 227.

19 Chailahjan, M. K. (1937). (Hormone theory of plant development.) Moscow, Leningrad. Acad. Sci. U.R.S.S.

20 Chailahjan, M. K. (1958). Hormonale Faktoren des Pflanzenblühens. *Biol. Zbl.* **77**, 641.

21 Chailahjan, M. K. (1965). The life and scientific work of Professor D. A. Sabinin. *Soviet Plant Physiol.* **12**, 669.

22 Chailahjan, M. K. and Yarkovaya, L. M. (1937). (Influence of the stock on the flowering of the scion in *Perilla*). *Tr. Inst. Fisiol. Rast. im K. A. Timiriazeva (Moscow)* **2** (1), 133.

23 Chatelet, A. (1920). Tournois (Julien). Annuaire 1920 de l'Association amicale de Secours des anciens Elèves de l'Ecole normale supérieure, 59–62.

24 Cholodny, N. G. (1939). The internal factors of flowering. *Herbage Rev.* **7**, 223.

25 Clark, M. F. and Kerns, K. R. (1942). Control of flowering with phytohormones. *Science* **95**, 536.

26 Cooper, W. C. (1942). Effect of growth substances on flowering of the pineapple under Florida conditions. *Proc. Amer. Soc. hort. Sci.* **41**, 93.

27 Curtis, O. F. and Chang, H. T. (1930). The relative effectiveness of the temperature of the crown as contrasted with that of the rest of the plant upon the flowering of celery plants. *Amer. J. Bot.* **17**, 1047.

28 von Denffer, D. (1950). Blühhormon oder Blühhemmung? Neue Gesichtspunkte zur Physiologie der Blütenbildung. *Naturwiss.* **37**, 296, 317.

29 Desroche (1915). Chroniques et nouvelles. *Rev. gén. Bot.* **27**, 31.

30 Dostal, R., and Hosek, M. (1937). Über den Einfluss von Heteroauxin auf die Morphogenese bei *Circaea* (das Sachssche Phänomen) *Flora (Jena)* **131**, 263.

31 Eagles, C. F. and Wareing, P. F. (1964). The role of growth substances in the regulation of bud dormancy. *Physiol. Plantar.* **17**, 697.

32 El-Antably, H. M. M., Wareing, P. F. and Hillman, J. (1967). Some physiological responses to D, L Abscisin (Dormin). *Planta* **73**, 74.

33 Evans, L. T. (1964). Inflorescence initiation in *Lolium temulentum* L. VI. Effects of some inhibitors of nucleic acid, protein, and steroid biosynthesis. *Aust. J. Biol. Sci.* **17**, 24.

34 Evans, L. T. (1966). Abscisin II: Inhibitory effect on flower induction in a long day plant. *Science* **151**, 107.

35 Fischer, J. (1916). Zur Frage der Kohlensäureernährung der Pflanze. *Gartenflora* **65**, 232.

36 Garner, W. W. (1944). Private communication cited by Murneek, A. E. In *Vernalization and photoperiodism*, p. 41. Eds A. E. Murneek and R. O. Whyte. Chronica Botanica, Waltham, Mass. 1948.

37 Garner, W. W. and Allard, H. A. (1920). Effect of the relative length of day and night and other factors of the environment on growth and reproduction in plants. *J. Agric. Res.* **18**, 553.

38 Garner, W. W. and Allard, H. A. (1925). Localization of the response in plants to relative length of day and night. *J. Agric. Res.* **31**, 555.

39 Garner, W. W. and Allard, H. A. (1931). Effect of abnormally long and short alternations of light and darkness on growth and development of plants. *J. Agric. Res.* **42**, 629.

40 Gassner, G. (1918). Beiträge zur physiologischen Charakteristik sommer- und winterannueller Gewächse, insbesondere der Getreidepflanzen. *Zeit. Bot.* **10**, 417.

41 Gregory, F. G. (1936). The effect of length of day on the flowering of plants. *Sci. Hort.* **4**, 143.

42 Gregory, F. G. and Purvis, O. N. (1936). Devernalization of winter rye by high temperature. *Nature* **138**, 1013.

[43] Gurney, A. (1964) Harry A. Allard; his life and work (1880–1963). *Torrey Bot. Club Bull.* **91**, 151.

[44] Hamner, K. C. (1940). Inter-relation of light and darkness in photoperiodic induction. *Bot. Gaz.* **101**, 658.

[45] Hamner, K. C. and Bonner, J. (1938). Photoperiodism in relation to hormones as factors in floral initiation and development. *Bot. Gaz.* **100**, 388.

[46] Harder, R. and Gümmer, G. (1947). Über die untere kritische Tageslänge bei der Kurztagpflanze *Kalanchöe blossfeldiana*. *Planta* **35**, 88.

[47] Henfrey, A. (1852). *The vegetation of Europe* cited by Allard, H. A. (1944) An interesting reference to length of day as affecting plants. *Science* **99**, 263.

[48] Khudairi, A-K. and Hamner, K. C. (1954). The relative sensitivity of *Xanthium* leaves of different ages to photoperiodic induction. *Plant Physiol.* **29**, 251.

[49] Klebs, G. (1913). Über das Verhältnis der Aussenwelt zur Entwicklung der Pflanze. *Sitz. ber. Acad. Wiss. Heidelb. Ser. B.* No. 5.

[50] Klebs, G. (1918). Über die Blütenbildung bei *Sempervivum*. *Flora (Jena)* **111/112**, 128.

[51] Klippart, J. H. (1857). An essay on the origin, growth, diseases, varieties, etc. of the wheat plant. *Ohio State Bd. Agr. Ann. Rept.* **12**, 562. Cited by McKinney.[65]

[52] Knott, J. E. (1934). Effect of a localized photoperiod on spinach. *Proc. Amer. Soc. Hort. Sci.* **31**, 152.

[53] Konitz, W. (1958). Blühhemmung bei Kurztagpflanzen durch Hellrot- und Dunkelrotlicht in der photo- und skotophilen Phase. *Planta* **51**, 1.

[54] Kraus, E. J. and Kraybill, H. R. (1918). Vegetation and reproduction with special reference to tomato. *Ore. Agr. Expt. Stat. Bull.* No. 149.

[55] Kuijper, J. and Wiersum, L. K. (1936). Occurrence and transport of a substance causing flowering in the soya bean (*Glycine Max* L.) *Proc. Kon. nederl. Akad. Wet.* **39**, 1114.

[56] Lang, A. (1956). Induction of flower formation in biennial *Hyoscyamus* by treatment with gibberellin. *Naturwiss.* **43**, 284.

[57] Lang, A. and Melchers, G. (1943). Die photoperiodische Reaktion von *Hyoscyamus niger*. *Planta* **33**, 653.

[58] Lincoln, R. G., Cunningham, A. and Hamner, K. C. (1964). Evidence for a florigenic acid. *Nature* **202**, 559.

[59] Lona, F. (1948). La fioritura della brevidiurna *Chenopodium amaranticolor* Coste et Reyn. coltivata in soluzione nutritizia con saccarosio, in assenza di stimolo fotoperiodico euflorigeno. *Nuov. Giorn. botan. Ital.* **56**, 559.

[60] Lona, F. (1949). La fioritura delle brevidiurne a notte continua. *Nuov. Giorn. botan. Ital.* **56**, 479.

[61] Lona, F. (1956). Osservazioni orientative circa l'effetto dell'acido Gibberellico sullo sviluppo riproduttivo di alcune longidiurne e brevidiurne. *L'Ateneo Parmense* **27**, 867.

[62] Lysenko, T. D. (1928). (Effect of the thermal factor on the duration of the developmental phases of plants. Experiments with cereals and cotton). *Trudy Azerbaidzh. tsentr. opytno-selekts. Stants. Im. Tov. Ordzhonikidze (Baku)* No. 3.

[63] Lysenko, T. D. (1932). *Bull. Jarov.* **4**, 3, cited by R. O. Whyte (1939). Phasic development of plants. *Biol. Rev.* **14**, 65.

[64] MacDougal, D. T. (1903). The influence of light and darkness upon growth and development. *Mem. N.Y. Bot. Gard.* **2**, 1. cited by Garner, W. W., and Allard, H. A.[37]

[65] McKinney, H. H. (1940). Vernalization and the growth phase concept. *Bot. Rev.* **6**, 25.

[66] Moshkov, B. S. (1936). Role of leaves in photoperiodic reaction of plants. *Bull. Appl. Bot. Genet. & Plant Breed.* A**17**, 25.

[67] Moshkov, B. S. (1937). (Flowering of short day plants in continuous light as a result of grafting). *Tr. prikl. Bot., Genet. i Selekts. Ser. A., Sotsialist, Rastenievodstvo* **21**, 145.

[68] Moshkov, B. S. (1939). Minimum intervals of darkness and light to induce flowering in short day plants. *C.R. (Dokl.) Acad. Sci. U.R.S.S.* **22**, 456.

[69] Nakayama, S. (1958). Studies on the dark process in the photoperiodic response of *Pharbitis* seedlings. *Sci. Rep. Tohoku. Univ.* **24**, 137.

[70] Parker, M. W., Hendricks, S. B. and Borthwick, H. A. (1950). Action spectrum for the photoperiodic control of floral initiation of the long day plant *Hyoscyamus niger*. *Bot. Gaz.* **111**, 242.

[71] Parker, M. W., Hendricks, S. B., Borthwick, H. A. and Scully, N. J. (1945). Action spectrum for the photoperiodic control of floral initiation in Biloxi soybean. *Science* **102**, 152.

[72] Parker, M. W., Hendricks, S. B., Borthwick, H. A. and Scully, N. J. (1946). Action spectra for photoperiodic control of flower initiation in short day plants. *Bot. Gaz.* **108**, 1.

[73] Parker, M. W., Hendricks, S. B., Borthwick, H. A. and Went, F. W. (1949). Spectral sensitivities for leaf and stem growth of etiolated pea seedlings and their similarity to action spectra for photoperiodism. *Amer. J. Bot.* **36**, 194.

[74] Psarev, G. M. (1936). Localization of the photoperiodic stimulus in soybean. *Sovetsk. Bot.* 1936 (3) 88.

[75] Razumov, V. (1931). On the localization of photoperiodical stimulation. *Bull. Appl. Bot. Genet. Plant Breed.* **27**, 249.

[76] Sachs, J. (1865). Wirkung des Lichts auf die Blüthenbildung unter Vermittlung der Laubblätter. *Bot. Ztg.* **23**, 117, 125, 133.

[77] Salisbury, F. B. (1955). The dual role of auxin in flowering. *Plant Physiol.* **30**, 327.

[78] Siegelman, H. W., Turner, B. C. and Hendricks, S. B. (1966). The chromophore of phytochrome. *Plant Physiol.* **41**, 1289.

[79] Skok, J. and Scully, N. J. (1954). Characteristics and movement of the flowering stimulus from the induced leaf of *Xanthium*. *Bot. Gaz.* **116**, 142.

[80] Tournois, J. (1911). Anomalies florales du Houblon japonais et du Chanvre déterminées par des semis hâtifs. *C.R. Acad. Sci.* **153**, 1017.

[81] Tournois, J. (1912). Influence de la lumière sur la floraison du Houblon japonais et du Chanvre. *C.R. Acad. Sci.* **155**, 297.

[82] Tournois, J. (1914). Sexualité du Houblon. *Ann. Sci. Nat. Bot.* (*Paris*) 9ᵉ ser. **19**, 49.

[83] Walker, J. C. (1950). *Plant Pathology.* 2nd edn. McGraw Hill, N.Y.

[84] Went, F. W. (1928). Wuchstoff und Wachstum. *Rec. Trav. Bot. Néerl.* **25**, 1.

[85] Zimmerman, P. W. and Hitchcock, A. E. (1942). Flowering habit and correlation of organs modified by TIBA. *Contrib. Boyce Thompson Inst.* **12**, 491.

2

Xanthium strumarium L.

By Frank B. Salisbury

1 History of Use

Taxonomy

It is possible to find a wide variety of species names in the literature on the flowering of members of the genus *Xanthium*. In many cases different names have been applied to identical material, sometimes even from the same seed source. As a rule, these ambiguities have arisen because taxonomists have not even approached agreement on the scientific terminology. Löve and Dansereau[102] present a table in which they compare the synonyms for different *Xanthium* species given in several common floras in which there is virtually no agreement among the authors. Names used in studies on the physiology of flowering are equally varied: *Xanthium achinatum*,[191] *X. canadense*,[10] *X. chinense*,[16] *X. commune*,[42] *X. italicum*,[160,99] *X. pen(n)sylvanicum*,[56] *X. saccharatum*,[141] *X. strumarium*.[88]

Linnaeus[91] named two species in the genus *Xanthium*: *strumarium* and *spinosum*. The thorny *spinosum* is an easily identifiable and highly stable species which has seldom been used in flowering research.[97] Since Linnaeus' time, *strumarium* has been splintered into a multitude of species. In the early work on flowering at the Plant Industry Station at Beltsville, Maryland,[51] the plant was referred to as *X. pen(n)sylvanicum*, Wallr. (The second n was unfortunately omitted by Wallroth who proposed the name.) The name *X. pensylvanicum* was used by the researchers at the University of Chicago,[56] and they, their students, and others have continued to use it. It is the most frequently encountered species name in the flowering literature.

In 1946 the workers at Beltsville reinvestigated the taxonomy of *Xanthium*. S. F. Blake[141] found that Wallroth[206] had in 1844 described *X. pensylvanicum* and *X. saccharatum* as distinct species, and that Widder[211] had combined these in 1923 under the term *X. saccharatum*. Thus *pensylvanicum* was apparently a synonym, and the workers at Beltsville began to use the term *saccharatum*. In 1956 Downs,[43] then a student at Beltsville, reported that Millspaugh and Sherff[126] had, in 1918, combined *saccharatum* and *pensylvanicum* under the term *pensylvanicum*. At that time workers at Beltsville returned to the use of the term *pensylvanicum*. As early as 1946 the Beltsville scientists had obtained seeds from Hamner in Chicago and found that the resulting plants exhibited exactly the same morphology and flowering response as those produced from seeds collected in the Beltsville area.

In the late 1930s and at intervals up to the present time, seeds have been collected in the Chicago area by Hamner and others. (Usually, boys have been paid for collecting the seeds.) Plants from these, called *Xanthium pen(n)sylvanicum* Wallr., have long been propagated and utilized in studies on photoperiodism and are referred to as the Chicago strain.

It has long been known that *X. pensylvanicum* was in doubt. For example, H. A. Harrington, a taxonomist at Colorado State University, classified my plants as *X. italicum*,[160] using the latest floras of Illinois. Specimens of plants which I used are on file in the herbarium at Colorado State University,[160] and Hamner has filed specimens at the University of California in Los Angeles.[74]

By far the best recent paper on the taxonomy of *Xanthium* is that of Löve and Dansereau.[102] They conclude that Linneaus' *X. strumarium* should remain as one highly variable species, native to both Europe and North America. They illustrate eight complexes of this single species: *achinatum, Cavanillesii, chinense, italicum, orientale, oviforme, pensylvanicum, strumarium.* They are convinced that these represent only high points in a continuum of hybridization within the entire species, and they state that intermediate types are often encountered.

They agree with Millspaugh and Sherff[126] in considering *saccharatum* as a synonym of *pensylvanicum.* They emphasize that *pensylvanicum* is closely related to *italicum*, and that often it is quite impossible to distinguish between members of the two complexes.

It is evident from their illustrations that the Chicago strain is clearly in the *pensylvanicum* complex, although the fruits which we use resemble their *italicum* nearly as closely as they resemble *pensylvanicum.* They do not resemble the other six complexes. The paper of Löve and Dansereau is presented as a tentative study, and other methods of modern taxonomy should be applied. Apparently the entire *X. strumarium* species (all 8 complexes) is tetraploid with 2n = 36 chromosomes.

Löve and Dansereau propose the subspecies *Cavanillesii*, within which the complexes *pensylvanicum* and *italicum* have the status of notomorphs. Thus the plant most often used in studies on flowering should at the moment be classified as *Xanthium strumarium* L. ssp. *Cavanillesii* (Shouw.) D. Löve and P. Dansereau, notomorph *pensylvanicum* (Wallr.) or possibly *italicum* (Mor.). In view of all this, it is comforting to realize that the English language common name cocklebur has never been in dispute!

Although the various complexes may be members of the single species *X. strumarium*, their flowering response is highly variable.[92,145] Hence, physiologists working with *Xanthium* species would do well to describe their seed source carefully and to file herbarium specimens.

History of use in studies on photoperiodism

According to Gilbert,[51] Garner and Allard listed *X. pensylvanicum* as a short-day species, although we have been unable to find such a listing in Garner and Allard's early papers. Gilbert's paper reports the first attempt to use *Xanthium* as a test object for the study of the mechanism of photoperiodism. He attempted to use temperature as a tool to study photoperiodism, and he was concerned with the then-current controversy relating to the initiation of flowers in response to the carbohydrate-nitrogen ratio. Because his controls all flowered at a high level, his results are nearly without value for us.

Shull, who worked on germination of *Xanthium* seeds throughout his lifetime, mentioned in 1927[184] a number of observations which he had made relating to flowering of *Xanthium.* Although research on photoperiodism was very active during the late 1920s and early 1930s, I could find only one paper referring to flowering of *Xanthium.* Ramaley[143] in 1934 at the University of Colorado surveyed a large number of species for their flowering response to photoperiod. *X. commune* was said to be delayed in its flowering by extended days.

Upon arriving at the University of Chicago in 1937, Karl Hamner looked for a suitable plant for studies in photoperiodism. He noticed that *Xanthium* plants being used in the greenhouse by Shull produced burs in the winter when they were extremely small, indicating that they were short-day plants. He instigated a study with a student, Edith Neidle,[132] on flowering in *Xanthium* as influenced by mineral nutrition. In the course of this experiment the lights were inadvertently left off one night, and all of the plants in the greenhouse flowered, indicating clearly that *Xanthium* would respond to a single inductive cycle.[53] Hamner was joined by James Bonner in 1938 for an intensive summer of experimentation. The published results[56] appeared in the December issue of the Botanical Gazette. This paper is a classic in research on photoperiodism using *Xanthium*, as will become evident in the following pages. It was shown that the leaves perceive the light-dark cycle (many previous papers showing this with other plants are cited), that the plant apparently responds to the length of the dark instead of the light period, that a light interruption of the dark period will inhibit flowering, and that old leaves are inhibitory to flowering. Translocation of the stimulus was studied in several ways, and much time was spent in an unsuccessful attempt to extract the flowering hormone or find some substance which would cause flowering.

This work initiated a great burst of interest and activity in Hamner's group at the University of Chicago. Long[101] in 1939 reported successful leaf grafts and studies on the effects of age and temperature upon the critical dark period. Hamner[54] in 1940 presented some classical experiments on depletion of the high-intensity light product by brief intervals of darkness separated from each other by a few minutes of light. Here he presented his scheme: A, B → C, suggesting that the products of a light reaction (A) combine with those of a dark reaction (B) to produce the flowering stimulus (C). Snyder[190] continued this work with experiments on the effects of light intensity on flowering. Mann,[110] reporting experiments with light intensity and temperature, emphasized the light conditions following the inductive dark period. Aubrey Naylor[128] described nutritional experiments, indicating that nitrogen or phosphorus levels did not influence the critical dark period, although high nitrogen promoted rate of floral bud development. His wife, Frances Naylor,[131] published a classical description of the development of the flowers following different levels of induction.

Robert and Alice Withrow[214] reported in 1940 that, of various colored lights used, red was most effective in inhibiting the effects of a dark period on flowering of *Xanthium*. They published in 1943[213] their classical paper on translocation of the flowering stimulus in *Xanthium*, in which they showed that the stimulus moves only in living tissue (contrary to a preliminary suggestion of Hamner and Bonner[56]). Alice Withrow[212] published another nutrition study, again indicating that flowering was controlled only by photoperiod and not by nutrient levels. Because of the interest in the carbohydrate-nitrogen theory of flowering, this topic was often studied during these years, and work with *Xanthium* was clear-cut in rejecting the carbohydrate-nitrogen ratio as the controlling factor in flowering.

In 1946 Parker, Hendricks, Borthwick, and Scully[141] presented a detailed action spectrum for inhibition of flowering in *Xanthium* by interruption of an inductive dark period with light, confirming and extending the work of the Withrows. This was followed in 1952 by the classical paper[15] showing that the effects of red light upon flowering of *Xanthium* could be overcome by immediate illumination with far-red.

From the mid-1940's on, it is cumbersome to consider work on the flowering of *Xanthium* from a historical viewpoint. Hence other important findings are considered in relation to specific subjects as discussed below. Some reviews on photoperiodism emphasize *Xanthium* rather strongly.[92,130,161,166,167]

Uses other than in flowering research

Xanthium has been used in laboratory studies relating to a wide variety of topics in plant physiology. Of about 180 papers in my early file reporting work with *Xanthium*, 56 included topics unrelated to flowering. In at least 40 there was no mention of flowering whatsoever. The number could be expanded considerably since we arbitrarily decided to exclude papers relating to a toxic principle present in *Xanthium* cotyledons.

Table 2–1 summarizes some topics of research other than flowering. A few of these topics are of considerable interest, and some might conceivably contribute to our understanding of flowering in *Xanthium*. For example, the considerable efforts spent by Mansfield and his collaborators[116,122] on stomatal mechanisms in *Xanthium* has, among other things, postulated an endogenous rhythm in control of these mechanisms. Such a rhythm could also be important in time measurement in the flowering process. In many cases, *Xanthium* was used in the studies of Table 2–1 simply because plants were available in the greenhouse from experiments on flowering.

Since flowering may readily be thought of in an ecological context, studies on the ecology of *Xanthium* could also be of importance to an ultimate understanding of flowering in this plant. In this respect a paragraph in the summary of Löve and Dansereau[102] is of interest: 'Ecologically, in eastern North America at least, *Xanthium* is primarily a beach plant, which perfers open habitats and succumbs to crowding. The seeds are most often dispersed by water and wind. It enters easily into ruderal habitats, but only as long as these are open and unshaded.' Because of its ready adaptability to cultivated and well-watered ground, *Xanthium* has been a weed of some importance in many crops. Since the advent of 2,4-D, however, *Xanthium* is not very important as a weed, and indeed, it is no longer even listed in many weed manuals.

TABLE 2–1

Some topics of research with *Xanthium*. References are not exhaustive.

Topics	References
Dormancy of the seed	39, 40, 71, 118, 137, 182, 187, 202, 208, 209
Substances toxic to animals	23, 45, 60, 144
Plant growth inhibitors	5, 8, 49, 72, 152
Stomatal movements	61, 111, 112, 113, 114, 115, 116, 121, 122
Leaf growth and chloroplasts	46, 66, 103, 104, 105, 106, 107, 108
Clinostat rotation	67, 68, 69
Effects of ultraviolet irradiation	33, 34, 142
Leaf temperatures	44, 123
Nucleic acid and protein metabolism	30, 35, 36, 124, 155, 156, 157
Leaf senescence and kinetin-like compounds	29, 75, 77, 135, 136, 147
Morphological studies	48, 184, 185, 192, 204
Implanted lettuce seeds	3, 120
Ecological studies	102, 183, 186, 195
Taxonomic studies	43, 51, 91, 102, 126, 141, 160, 206, 211

2 Growing Techniques and Growth Habit

Detailed growing techniques for *Xanthium* may be nearly as varied as the people who have used the plant in studies on flowering. A few basic approaches are, of course, common to all workers. Procedures followed at Colorado State University have been outlined in detail.[167,171]

Germination of the seed

Crocker[39] published in 1906 the results of an excellent study relating to dormancy in the seeds of *Xanthium*. He confirmed the folk tale that of the two seeds in the cocklebur fruit, the lower one germinates more readily than the upper one. He correctly diagnosed the dormancy of the upper seed as an exclusion by the testa (seed coat) of oxygen. The lower seed also exhibits a dormancy but less pronounced than the upper. Dormancy of the upper seed could be overcome by high oxygen partial pressures or by high temperatures. The nature of this dormancy has been analysed extensively (references in Table 2–1), but for experimental purposes the best procedure now appears to be simply to plant the fruits in sand, preferably using burs which are at least a year old, watering them profusely, and allowing germination to take place at high temperatures (between 32° and 38°C). Even relatively young seeds will germinate rapidly and uniformly if temperatures are high enough. Incidentally, this procedure is suggested by Crocker's[39] 1906 paper, although many subsequent papers seemed to complicate the situation.

FIGURE 2–1. (a) Photograph of vegetative plant of *Xanthium strumarium* L. Both 2.1 (a) and (b) show plants as they appear when grown in the greenhouse. In the field, plants branch profusely at the axillary nodes.

Care of the plants

When the first true leaves begin to appear, the young seedlings may be conveniently transplanted. If they are transplanted into soil, larger plants will be produced if pots contain at least half a liter of soil. Smaller pots produce smaller plants, but pots which are very large become inconvenient to handle. Several workers have utilized sand, vermiculite, perlite, or some other medium watered with a complete nutrient solution. If soil is used, it should be previously sterilized, primarily to kill weed seeds. Soil with high salt concentrations will not produce good plants. A well-aerated soil may seem important, but we have occasionally grown plants in pots with no drainage hole, noticing only after plants are mature that they had been growing with their roots completely submerged in water. Such plants seemed normal in every way. *Xanthium* plants do require relatively large quantities of water and wilt easily without it. Fertilization is very important.

FIGURE 2–1. (b) Photograph of flowering plant of *Xanthium strumarium* The arrow (right) indicates a male inflorescence; female flowers have developed into burs (fruit) shown in inset.

Many studies[128,132,167,212] have shown that high nitrogen (and to a lesser extent phosphorus) levels promote the flowering response to an inductive dark period. Both rate of development of the flower and uniformity of development for the plants in a group are promoted. In one study,[167] uniformity and rate of floral development increased with addition of fertilizer right to the point where plants were badly damaged by the high salt concentration.

Light and temperature

To maintain plants in a vegetative condition, the daily photoperiod must be extended to at least 16 hours. A single interruption during the dark period would probably also be suitable but is seldom used. It is convenient for lights to go off at 10:00 p.m. and come on again at 4:00 a.m., ensuring that the times of dusk and dawn will be the same all year. Both incandescent and fluorescent lamps have been used. Intensities at the leaf level should be about 50 f.c. It has been shown by several workers[27,41,95,101,110,158,190] that plants respond best when exposed to high-intensity light during the normal photoperiod. Thus if plants are grown under heavily shaded glass or in growth chambers with low light intensities, results will not be optimal.

In one study at least,[167] in which plants were grown in growth chambers with adequate light intensities, flowering response was still increasing with increasing day and night temperatures at 27°C, the highest temperature tested. Hence for optimal response it is important to maintain greenhouse growing temperatures relatively high both summer and winter.

Preparation of plants for experimentation

We prepare plants for an experiment by removing all leaves below the half-expanded one and at least one leaf above it. Using plants defoliated to a single leaf greatly facilitates experiments in which it is desirable to illuminate leaf tissue with known intensities of light or to dip leaves in solutions of various chemicals. Such defoliated plants respond virtually as well as those which have not been defoliated.

It is important to note that greenhouse-grown plants do not have the growth habit typical of those grown out-of-doors. Plants in the field branch heavily, while axillary buds of greenhouse-grown plants remain dormant, producing a plant with a single stem. Although research has been done on this,[4] reasons for the differences between greenhouse and field-grown plants remain to be completely discerned.

3 Inflorescence Structure and Criteria of Flowering Response

Xanthium is a monoecious plant. The terminal inflorescence is staminate, while the axillary reproductive buds are pistillate. Frequently, axillary buds will become branches with a terminal staminate inflorescence and axillary pistillate flowers. Figure 2–1b illustrates this situation. A few studies of the morphology of the staminate and pistillate flowers have been published.[48,131,210]

Several criteria of the flowering response have been used. Gilbert[51] observed plants at intervals with a dissecting microscope, recording the number of days until the staminate inflorescence first became apparent. In most modern studies this would be quite unsatisfactory, since floral primordia appear two or three days after the first inductive dark period. Hamner[54] and many of his students at Chicago[56,101,128] differentiated only between plants which were strictly vegetative, those which exhibited an inflorescence primordium but no flower primordia, those with flower primordia, and those with macroscopic flowers and fruits. Mann[110] refined this somewhat by measuring the diameter of the staminate inflorescence primordium. His scoring system utilized tenths of a millimeter for primordia larger than 0.7 mm in diameter, although he would reduce the score somewhat when primordia with large diameters seemed less mature than was typical for their size. Vegetative primordia were assigned the value of 0, and those less than 0.7 mm were apparently scored on a scale of 1 to 6 depending upon experience.

Some workers[141] have argued that scoring systems might be influenced by conditions during the development of the floral bud rather than by conditions causing induction. Thus they have recorded only whether plants were vegetative or flowering. Other workers have assumed that effects upon floral bud development will be expressed the same in control plants as in those receiving special treatments, and thus they have developed scoring systems such as that described above. The system of Salisbury[159,167] is illustrated in Figure 2–2 and described in Table 2–2, where it is also compared with those mentioned above and with the system of Downs,[43] Lincoln, Raven, and Hamner[89] and Searle.[178]

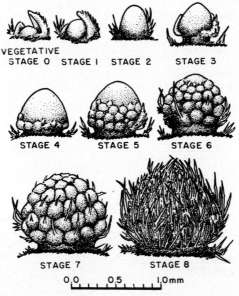

FIGURE 2–2. Floral stages according to Salisbury.[159,167] See Table 2–2.

The Salisbury system has the valuable property of producing nearly straight lines on a graph when results of two kinds of experiments are plotted. In the one case, plants are observed at daily intervals following a single inductive dark period. In the other case, plants are given single inductive dark periods varying in length from 8 to 16 or more hours. Floral stages are determined 7 to 10 days following this treatment and plotted as a function of the length of the inductive dark period. Since floral stage is proportional to time after induction, floral stage observed at some arbitrary time following induction is a measure of rate of floral development. As should be apparent from Table 2–2, the scoring systems of Downs[43] and of Lincoln, Raven, and Hamner[89] would not be expected to be linear. The system of Searle[177,178] is a refinement of that of Salisbury and should be linear.

Searle's more recent bioassay[178] compares the status of the terminal inflorescence (usually on 4 axillary branches) with the weight of these branches and the expansion of the donor leaf tissue. He further suggests use of a percent floral response system of scoring in which the estimated percentage of the area of the receptacle occupied by floret primordia is recorded. This system compared with Salisbury's stages is also non-linear. Furthermore, it begins at Salisbury's stage 3, assuming that earlier stages do not really represent floral bud development. It is true that such stages have been known to revert to the vegetative condition,[131] but it is equally true that they appear only in response to floral induction. There seems to be little reason to adopt Searle's percent floral response, since this merely replaces a linear system with a non-linear one. His measurements of donor leaf growth and final receptor branch weight could be valuable in certain applications.

TABLE 2–2

Descriptions of several floral stage systems, each compared with the Salisbury system.

Salisbury[159,167]	Hamner and Bonner[56]	Mann[110]	Hamner and Nanda[57]
0. Vegetative. Shoot apex relatively flat and small.	Strictly vegetative.	0. Vegetative.	0. Vegetative.
1. First clearly visible swelling of the shoot apex.	Inflorescence primordia.	1. First indication of floral initiation.	1. Spherical inflorescence primordium.
2. Floral apex at least as high as broad, but not yet constricted at the base.		2.	
3. Floral apex constricted at the base, but no flower primordia yet visible.		3.	
4. First visible flower primordia, covering up to the lower one quarter of the floral apex.	Flower primordia.	Arbitrary stages used but not defined.	2. Flower primordia covering basal one third of inflorescence primordium.
5. Flower primordia covering from one to three quarters of the floral apex.		4.	3. Flower primordia covering basal two thirds of inflorescence primordium.
6. Flower primordia covering all but the upper tip of the floral apex.		5.	
7. Floral apex completely covered by flower primordia. Slightly to moderately pubescent.			4. Flower primordia completely covering inflorescence primordium.
8. Very pubescent and showing some differentiation of flower parts. At least one millimeter basal diameter.	Macroscopic flowers and fruits.	6. Macroscopic flowers.	5. Diameter of inflorescence 1 mm.

(Each successive stage is 0.25 mm larger than the preceding one.)

4 Effects of Plant Age and Leaf Size

Maximum response can sometimes be obtained with plants 30 days after transplanting,[158] but in other experiments (unpublished) plants had to be at least 60 days old before they would respond maximally. Much more effort has gone into the study of the size and age of the leaf which will respond maximally and the quantity of leaf tissue required to give a measurable response.

Hamner and Bonner[56] showed that the leaf perceived the inductive conditions (short day). When a single leaf was darkened for a period longer than the critical

Lincoln, Raven and Hamner[89]	Downs[43]	Searle[179]	
		Salisbury Stages	% Floral* Response
0. Vegetative stem primordia.	0. Vegetative.	0.	
1. Youngest recognizable inflorescence; smooth dome several times size of vegetative apex.	1. Some differentiation of terminal meristem; dome shaped appearance.		
		2.5	0
	2. Receptacle enlarged, constricted at base, floral primordia at base	3.0	1
		3.5	3
2. Smooth dome flanked by a few staminate floret primordia on basal periphery of inflorescence apex. (0.25 mm.)	3. Individual floral primordia visible on lower half of receptacle, each flower subtended by a bract.	4.0	10
		4.5	30
3. Lower three-fourths of inflorescence covered with floret primordia. (0.50 mm.)		5.0	60
		5.5	80
	4. Flowers visible more than half way up the receptacle; do not cover the top.	6.0	90
		6.5	97
4. Floret primordia cover entire inflorescence (0.75 mm.).	5. Flower primordia completely cover receptacle; lobes of corolla differentiated on lower flowers.	7.0	100
5. Floret primordia cover entire inflorescence (1.0 mm.).	6. Corolla lobes differentiated in all flower primordia except at top of receptacle.	* The estimated percentage of the area of the receptacle that is observed to be occupied by floret primordia; an average of the terminal and four axillary buds.	
	7. All flower primordia with differentiated corolla lobes; primordia of five stamens present in lowermost flowers.		

night, flowering of the entire plant was the result, even though other leaves remained in continuous light. Long[101] showed that leaves so induced could be grafted to vegetative plants, causing them to flower. Hamner and Bonner[56] also showed that plants remained vegetative if young leaves were continually removed as they began to expand. It was tacitly assumed that the fully-expanded leaf was most sensitive to induction. Naylor[128] had studied the critical dark period of individual leaves, but beginning with the first fully expanded one. Its critical night was 9 hours, and in older leaves this increased to 10.5 to 15 hours.

Some 13 years after Naylor's experiments, the problem was re-examined by Khudairi and Hamner[74] and Salisbury.[159] Plants were defoliated to a single leaf and induced with a long dark period. It became quite apparent that the half-expanded leaf was by far the most sensitive, i.e. the most rapidly expanding one on the plant.[159,167]

Hamner and Bonner[56] had cut leaves to smaller and smaller areas, attempting to discover the smallest area which would still permit photoperiodic induction. They found that as little as 2–3 cm^2 would respond to three photoinductive cycles when the rest of the defoliated plant remained in continuous light. Searle[178] found with his system that less than about 7 cm^2 of leaf tissue was not sufficient to respond to a single inductive dark period. Khudairi and Hamner[74] cut off the stem of a mature plant just above the cotyledons, removing also the cotyledons and one cotyledonary bud. When the remaining cotyledonary bud began to grow, they tested the sensitivity of the developing shoot at various times after it began to develop. They found a maximum flowering response with 13 to 16-day-old shoots. The leaf tissue on these shoots was only about 1.5 cm^2. A minimal response occurred with a total leaf area of only 0.2 cm^2 (response to a single 16-hour dark period). They concluded that actual leaf area is less important than physiological age. The first leaves on their developing shoots remained small, but again they were highly sensitive while they were most rapidly expanding.

The cotyledons on *Xanthium* seedlings are green, expand to a total area of 9 or 10 cm^2, and remain on the plant for several days to a few weeks. Yet they were completely insensitive to induction of flowering by exposure to repeated 16-hour dark periods.[70]

5 Vernalization

While the flowering of *Xanthium* is influenced in many interesting ways by both low and high temperature treatments (see section 13), there is no vernalization in the usual sense, nor does prolonged exposure to low temperatures promote the subsequent response to photoinduction.

7 Photoperiod Response

In this section emphasis is upon the component steps of the flowering process, the partial processes. In the next section, emphasis is upon the pigment and its action, and in the following section the discussion revolves around the problem of time measurement.

Since *Xanthium* flowers in response to a single dark period, both preceded and followed by continuous light and constant temperature, we may think of three phases to the photoperiodic response of this plant: the light before the dark period, the dark period itself, and the light following the dark period.

Light preceding the dark period

Students of Hamner[110,190] showed in 1940 that flowering is promoted by high intensities of light, both preceding and following the inductive dark period. In these studies both the length and the intensity of the photoperiod were directly correlated with the degree of flowering. Hamner himself[54] devised the experiment which allowed the most penetrating analysis of the importance of light preceding the inductive dark period. He realized that one could hardly precede an inductive dark period with a long period of darkness! To make this approach possible, he interrupted the first dark period at 3-hour intervals with brief periods of relatively low-intensity light. After 24 or 36 hours of these short dark periods, plants could then be exposed to a final uninterrupted long dark period to ascertain whether they were capable of responding to it. If the inductive dark period followed the short cycles immediately, it proved to be ineffective, but if three hours of sunlight were inserted just before the inductive dark period, then it was fully effective. Hence it appeared that high-intensity light was essential if an inductive dark period was to be effective. Hamner also found, however, that 10 hours of relatively low-intensity light (100 f.c.) would also allow response to a following inductive dark period, but this finding is usually overlooked.

Liverman and Bonner[93] proposed that the assumed need for high-intensity light preceding an inductive dark period was a need for the accumulation of photosynthates. Hamner had suggested[57] that flowering resulted from the interaction between a light product (A) and a dark product (B) which produced the flowering stimulus (C). Liverman and Bonner suggested that the light product (A) was merely photosynthate. The requirement for light, then, would be a requirement for energy substrates which could be used in carrying out the reactions of the dark period. They reported evidence supporting this idea in that the inhibitory effects of the short dark cycles could be at least partially overcome if leaves were submerged in a sucrose solution during the final inductive dark period (24 hours long in their experiments). Untreated plants or plants with leaves submerged in water remained vegetative, while control plants receiving three hours of sunlight previous to the inductive dark period flowered at 53 percent, and those with leaves submerged in a 1 percent sucrose solution flowered at 44 percent. Sucrose was also applied by placing cuttings in test tubes of sucrose solution. Krebs cycle intermediates and other sugars besides sucrose were also effective in these experiments. Lang[81] found in a preliminary experiment that certain reducing substances (glutathione, cysteine, cystine, and ascorbic acid) also tended to overcome the inhibition due to the short dark periods.

Salisbury[169] has questioned the conclusion that photosynthates are of immediate importance and provide the explanation for the results of Hamner.[54] He repeated the experiments of Liverman and Bonner[93] and did find slight increases in the percentage of plants flowering in response to sucrose treatment. The differences were erratic and always very small when compared on a floral stage basis, however. A new experimental approach was devised. Plants were given 7.5 hours of darkness (phasing dark period), a period of light from a few seconds to 12 hours or longer (intervening light period), and then a subsequent inductive dark period (test dark period), often 12 hours long. If the intervening light period was not longer than about 3 to 5 hours, then flowering in response to the final inductive dark period failed. Thus the situation seemed to be closely analogous to the experiment of Hamner, and the intervening light period seemed to be a way to study the importance of light preceding the inductive dark period. No response to increasing intensity was observed beginning at intensities of only a few foot-candles (25 Watt incandescent bulb about 2 m away). Furthermore, red light seemed to be most promotive during this period and far-red least promotive. Salisbury explained his results more in terms of time measurement (see section 9 below) than in terms of photosynthesis. Of course, it is obvious that photosynthesis is of importance, since the existence of the plant, and all plant reactions including those of the dark period, ultimately depend upon photosynthates. Apparently these usually remain at adequate levels unless a prolonged short-cycle treatment is given as in the experiments of Hamner[54] (36 hours) or Liverman and Bonner[93] (24 hours). There would appear to be a definite requirement for light preceding the inductive dark period, but this requirement is related most directly to time measurement and less so to the production of photosynthates. In Salisbury's[169] experiments sucrose did not overcome the inhibitory effects of intervening light periods shorter than 3 hours.

Reactions of the dark period: the critical night

Hamner and Bonner[56] established the critical dark period for *Xanthium* as being between 8 and 9 hours. They further showed that the dark period was more important than the photoperiod in controlling flowering in this plant. To do so, they used 12-hour cycles, 48-hour cycles, exposure to a short photoperiod plus a short dark period, or a short photoperiod plus a long dark period, or a long photoperiod plus a long dark period. In all of these combinations, flowering occurred only when the dark period was longer than about 8.5 hours, irrespective of whether the photoperiod was short or long. Their work was done without a detailed series of floral stages, but quantitative differences did appear between the various treatments such that not all photoperiods were exactly equal in effectiveness. Nevertheless, the conclusion seemed quite justified that an un-interrupted long dark period was essential to induction in *Xanthium* and that the length of the photoperiod was of only secondary importance.

Mann[110] measured the quantitative aspects of the response to a long dark period using his scoring system. With this approach he was able to plot the degree of flowering as a function of the length of a single inductive dark period. The critical night becomes very apparent in curves of this type, and the optimum or saturating dark period proves to be between 12 and 15 hours. This work has been substantiated by many subsequent studies.[127,167,168,174] It was also shown by several workers[56,159] that increasing the number of photoinductive cycles increased the flowering response.

Hamner and Bonner[56] also showed that low temperatures during the dark period were inhibitory to flowering. Their work has been substantiated, and effects of temperature on critical night have also been studied.[94,101,110,168] As we shall see in subsequent sections (9 and 13), effects of temperature on the critical dark period are relatively minor in *Xanthium*. At quite low temperatures (e.g., 5°C) there is an extension of the critical dark period of 2 or 3 hours, but over the range of 15 to 35°C, the critical dark period may be changed as little as 20 minutes. Actually, as demonstrated as early as 1940 by Long,[101] the length of the critical dark period is influenced by a number of factors including plant age, shade, humidity, and temperature. Long seems to be the only worker who mentions humidity as a factor influencing flowering. There is a strong effect of leaf age on critical night as shown by Naylor[128] and by Salisbury.[158]

Reactions of the dark period: effects of a light interruption

Hamner and Bonner[56] in their experiments with *Xanthium*, discovered the so-called light break phenomenon which has since been used in many experiments with many species. They showed that a 1-minute light interruption in the middle of a 9-hour dark period would completely prevent flowering. Since that time, many other workers have studied this phenomenon (e.g.[14,15,43,47,141,146,168,169,174]). Light interruptions are typically most effective when applied about 8 hours after the beginning of the dark period. Red light is most effective, and this is reversed by far-red light, although far-red is also inhibitory under certain conditions.[47,109,146]

The threshold intensities for inhibition of the inductive dark period have been investigated by workers at Beltsville[141] and others.[168] Flowering was inhibited to a detectable degree by light from an incandescent bulb when the intensity was about 5 μW/cm^2, and an intensity of 20 μW/cm^2 completely suppressed the flowering response.[158] The red-wavelength portion of this incandescent light is about 0.4 μW/cm^2. Inhibitory intensities were measured at Beltsville[141] as 0.01 to 0.02 f.c., using again an incandescent light bulb. Total quantities of threshold inhibitory light during an entire dark period were about 10 to 100 f.c. minutes, approximately equal to the quantity of energy required to suppress flowering when it is given in a single, brief (seconds to minutes) light interruption during the middle of the dark period.

The intensity of so-called threshold light is about equivalent to that of moonlight, although the quantity of red light in moonlight would be somewhat less than that present in the equivalent foot-candles of incandescent light. It is reasonable to assume that *Xanthium* plants respond at most only marginally to the light of the full moon at the zenith.

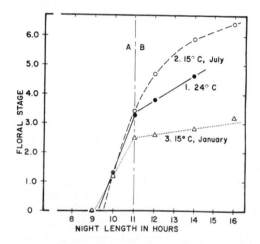

FIGURE 2–3. Flowering stage 9 days after a single inductive dark period as a function of the length of the inductive dark period. Curves 2 and 3 represent plants exposed to darkness at 15°C; curve 1 at 24°C. Curves 1 and 3 were from the same experiment. Note sharp break at about 11 hours which is much less noticeable when the experiment is performed in summer. In experiments using a single dark period, critical night often exceeds 9 hours but see Figure 2–8 (data from Salisbury[168]).

Based upon figures such as those quoted above, attempts have been made to calculate the intensity of light during evening twilight when plants begin to respond as though they were in total darkness – or during the morning as though they were in full light. Takimoto and Ikeda[197] attacked the problem directly. Control plants were left in the open exposed to both evening and morning twilight. Other controls were exposed to the entire evening twilight period but covered until well after dawn (or vice-versa). To study evening twilight, other plants were covered at various times during evening twilight and the covers were removed at the same time as their comparable controls well after dawn. Flowering of treated plants was compared with controls to discover the time during twilight when covering the plants had no effect upon flowering compared to controls. *Xanthium* plants responded as though darkness were total when twilight had dropped to *ca.* 0.1 to 1.0 f.c. in the evening, and they responded as though the night were at an end when morning twilight intensities had reached *ca.* 1.0 to 5.0 f.c.

Hamner and Bonner[56] suggested that, since the dark period was demonstrably most important in induction of *Xanthium*, and since this period was sensitive both to temperature and to light, flowering must be in response to some chemical reaction occurring during this dark period. Flowering of *Xanthium* has been discussed in these terms by many workers since this time.[15,43,54,110,168] Salisbury[174] proposed a set of three reactions which might account for the reactions of the dark period. The first of these was postulated to be conversion of phytochrome from the far-red (P_{fr}) to the red-receptive (P_r) form (now referred to as pigment shift – see below). The second was called preparatory reaction(s) and was based upon the assumption that pigment shift went to completion in the first one to three hours of the dark period, while other essential reaction(s) had to go on to complete the critical dark period. This interval of time is now referred to as time measurement (see below). Following completion of the critical dark period, it was proposed that synthesis of flowering hormone was initiated. This seemed to be implied by results of experiments on the critical night (Fig. 2–3). Salisbury[168] has also suggested that synthesis of flowering hormone consists of two phases, an initial very rapid one and a slower one following saturation.

Light following the inductive dark period

As indicated above, there were several early indications[110] that light following the inductive dark period, to be maximally effective, should be of high intensity. Skok and Scully[188] suggested, in view of their results on experiments relating to translocation of the flowering stimulus, that light following the dark period was at least not harmful to the flowering hormone.

Lockhart and Hamner[95,96] studied post-inductive conditions in some detail. Plants were given a single inductive dark period (preceded by several hours of high-intensity light); this inductive dark period was terminated by a brief period of light, and then plants were given another short (typically 4-hour) dark period. Plants so treated often flowered less than comparable controls which did not receive the second dark period. There was considerable variability, but if plants were treated with IAA immediately before the second dark period, this variability tended to disappear and inhibition was high. The longer the second dark period, the greater the inhibition, but if the second dark period was separated from the first one by an interval of several hours of high-intensity light, no inhibition could be observed. It was suggested that the product(s) of the inductive dark period was only a precursor to the flowering stimulus, and its final conversion or stabilization required exposure to high-intensity light for several hours.

Salisbury[166,167] suggested the alternative that the product(s) of the dark period might, indeed, be the final flowering stimulus, but that the leaf may be capable of destroying this material until exposure of the leaf to high-intensity light removes this capability for destruction. The variability in response might indicate that the ability of the leaf to destroy the flowering stimulus might depend upon its previous environmental history. Carr[27] found that sucrose would completely overcome the inhibitory effect of the second dark period. (Salisbury had failed in an attempt to demonstrate this,[158] but his methods were somewhat different.) Carr suggested that the effect of the sucrose was upon translocation of the flowering stimulus out of the leaf, and that stabilization of a precursor was not a part of the flowering process.

It is interesting to note that translocation alone will not account for the results of Lockhart and Hamner.[95,96] Unless there is some hormone or precursor destruction in the leaf, inhibition of translocation would merely delay flowering by a few hours but not otherwise inhibit it. Furthermore, Carr's results fit any of the three schemes presented here. Sucrose might promote translocation of the stimulus out of the leaf, provide an energy source for stabilization of a precursor, or change the metabolic status of the leaf so that it was not capable of destruction of stimulus.

All of this reasoning, with no possible satisfactory conclusion, illustrates the difficulty and the pitfalls of understanding experiments of this type. Results nearly always can be interpreted in several different ways, and a number of new and different experiments are required to allow one to differentiate between the available explanations.

A further pitfall is illustrated by the work and the discussion of Searle.[177] A special system of experimentation with *Xanthium* was devised. Plants (Chicago strain) were grown under continuous light of relatively low intensity (2,000 to 2,200 f.c.), and only those which grew well were selected for use under these conditions, resulting in a special strain. Induction was brought about by placing single leaves in light-tight air-conditioned aluminium boxes. Four small openings in the top of a box could be shaded to allow different light intensities to fall on the leaf. The terminal bud and all but one axillary bud were removed. The leaf by this bud was induced in the box, and the axillary branch which grew out was used to assess the flowering response. Two leaves were left on the plant below the one subjected to the dark period.

Searle was never able to observe an inhibition of flowering when the induced leaf was subjected to low light intensity or a second dark period, as in the experiments of Lockhart and Hamner. It is interesting that Searle (and later Zeevaart in a review[217]) interpreted these results to imply that Lockhart and Hamner's second high-intensity light process didn't so much as exist. Because Searle failed to observe it, the extensive and detailed results of Lockhart and Hamner,[95,96] Carr[27] and Salisbury[158] were essentially ignored.

The question is not whether an inhibition due to a second dark period can be observed. Obviously, it was observed. The question is why it could be observed in some experiments but not in the experiments of Searle. Several possible answers are apparent. Perhaps the leaves of Searle's special strain were never capable of destroying flowering stimulus. Or perhaps the leaves left in the light in Searle's experiments transported sufficient substrate into the leaf in the dark that it was able to stabilize hormone, translocate it out, or be changed so that it could not destroy it. Indeed, Searle[178] in a later paper reports that the leaves left in the light do have a promotive effect for several hours after the inductive dark period (after this time they become inhibitory).

Attempting to understand the biochemistry of the flowering response in *Xanthium* without biochemical experimentation is certainly a challenging pastime!

8 Spectral Dependence

Kinetics of the light break

Before learning which wavelengths of light are most effective in the inhibition of flowering due to a light interruption of an inductive dark period, it is essential to know something about the times when a light interruption is most effective and about the reciprocity relationship. For many years it was assumed[141] that the middle of the inductive dark period was the most effective time for inhibition by a light interruption – regardless of the length of the dark period. This was found not to be true.[174] With dark periods of 10, 12, 16, and 20 hours, maximum time of effectiveness was always about 8 hours after the beginning of darkness. With the shorter dark periods (10 to 12 hours), complete inhibition also occurred before 8 hours, so that the middle of short dark periods is always a sensitive time. Even with a very long night, however, a time of maximum effectiveness at 8 hours can always be observed.[146] This occurs independently of temperature (Fig. 2–4). The kinetics of the light-interruption phenomenon are important to our consideration of timing and will be discussed in the next section.

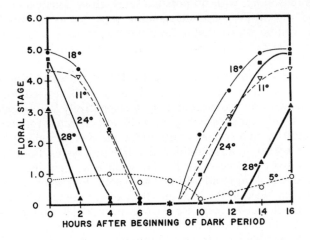

FIGURE 2–4. Flowering of plants 9 days after induction as a function of the time at which a single inductive dark period, at various temperatures, was interrupted with 5 minutes of red light. All plants except those at 5°C were completely inhibited by the interruption at 8 hours. (Data obtained by the graduate plant physiology class at Colorado State University, Spring, 1966.)

Reciprocity was studied in connection with the determination of the spectral dependence of the light-break phenomenon.[141] The Beltsville group studied the two hours in the middle of a 12-hour dark period (end of the 5th hour until end of the 7th hour). In view of the discussion above, the 6th to the 8th hour may have been somewhat better. An attempt was made to see if the product of intensity × duration of light exposure remained a constant for a given level of inhibition; namely, that inhibition required to inhibit flowering about 50 percent (admittedly a rather rough approximation, since only 6 plants were used in each replication). Using 8 levels of total energy (intensity × duration) given, in each case, for several durations from 30 seconds to 64 minutes, results seemed to indicate that the reciprocity law did hold within a factor of about 1.5.

Reciprocity has since been tested[172] by determining the saturating quantity of light about 4 hours after the beginning of a 16-hour dark period, using different intensities and durations. At this time, saturating light quantities do not inhibit flowering completely to the vegetative level. These experiments were only preliminary, but reciprocity did not hold well (a factor of 4 or 5).

The saturating quantity of light is of interest.[174] It was shown that this saturating quantity remained constant for light interruptions given at 3.75, 5, and 10 hours after the beginning of a single 16-hour inductive dark period. At 8 hours, plants were completely vegetative with about 1/3 of the saturating exposure time. If, as seems reasonable, the saturating quantity of light is a measure of the available photoreceptor pigment, then these results would indicate that the quantity of pigment remains quite constant throughout the dark period beginning at least as early as 3.75 hours after the beginning of darkness. These experiments have been successfully repeated in other contexts.[162,172]

Spectral dependence

Withrow and Withrow,[214] using *Xanthium* and other plants, found that red light was most effective in inhibiting flowering when it replaced an inductive dark period. Blue was almost equivalent to darkness. The only detailed measurement of an action spectrum for the light-break interruption in *Xanthium* was performed in 1946 at Beltsville by Parker, Hendricks, Borthwick, and Scully.[141] Their work might be improved somewhat by utilizing a suitable system of floral stages, but the results are sufficiently clear-cut that they have not seemed to require duplication in the more than 20 years since they were first obtained. Single leaves were illuminated at various points in the spectrum at various energy levels and for various durations, near the middle of a 12-hour inductive dark period. Minimal energies required to prevent floral initiation were determined for many narrow regions of the spectrum. Maximum effectiveness occurred in the 6000 to 6800 Å range with minimum effectiveness at 4800 Å (the ideal safe light region for experiments on flowering of *Xanthium*). There was a slight effectiveness at wavelengths shorter than 4800 Å.

In 1952, Borthwick, Hendricks, and Parker[15] at Beltsville extended the recent findings of reversibility of the red promotion of germination of lettuce seeds with far-red to the light-break phenomenon in flowering of *Xanthium*. An inhibition of flowering due to an interruption of the dark period with red light was reversed by subsequent exposure to far-red. *Xanthium* was the only plant used in these experiments and was thus the first species in which the red-far-red reversible system was demonstrated to be a part of the flowering process. It was in this paper and the associated one on germination of lettuce seed that the reversible pigment system, later named phytochrome, was first postulated. Plants were given an extended dark period which was interrupted in the middle with incandescent light. They were then exposed on the spectrograph to different regions of the spectrum, obtaining an action spectrum for the reversal effect. Wavelengths in the region of 7215 to 7450 Å were effective, with the peak of effectiveness at about 7300 Å.

It was also in this paper that results of an experiment were reported in which irradiation with far-red at the beginning of an inductive dark period shortened the critical night by an hour or two. The far-red light was obtained by filtering sunlight through Corning red-purple ultra filters. Based upon this experiment and reasoning in relation to the reversible pigment system, they postulated that the critical night was controlled by the time required for the thermal (metabolic) conversion of P_{fr} to P_r in the dark. Most of the pigment would exist as P_{fr} at the beginning of the dark period, but since red light is maximally effective in inhibition, most of the pigment must exist as Pr later in the dark period. This experiment on shortening of the critical night by exposure to far-red light at the beginning of the dark period could never be repeated in the Beltsville laboratory nor anywhere else. The reason for this has never become apparent, but it may be related to the question of time measurement discussed in the next section.

The work on the reversible pigment system in *Xanthium* was further pursued in a series of experiments by Downs.[43] Perhaps his most significant finding was that the effectiveness of far-red reversal following red irradiation declined, so that far-red light was ineffective in reversal when given 30 minutes after red irradiation. Based upon this experiment, Downs postulated that P_{fr} is the biologically active form of phytochrome, in this case inhibiting flowering of *Xanthium*. Its inhibitory act would, according to this interpretation, be complete within 30 minutes.

Downs also found that short exposures to far-red were more effective in reversing the red inhibition than long exposures. This has since been confirmed,[109] and the overlapping absorption spectra for the two forms of phytochrome are considered to be the basis for an explanation.[63] That is, P_{fr} also absorbs somewhat in the red region of the spectrum, and P_r absorbs somewhat in the far-red region. Thus when plants are illuminated with far-red light, most of the pigment is converted to P_r, but some of this is converted back to P_{fr} by absorption of far-red light. The result is that, under continuous irradiation with far-red light, a certain portion of the pigment continues to exist as P_{fr}. If plants are immediately returned to the dark, this will decay or be converted to P_r; in any case, disappear. If plants are continually illuminated with far-red light, the pigment will not be allowed to disappear, and it may inhibit flowering.

This explanation for the inhibitory effect of far-red light introduces an interesting but important complication in the interpretation of virtually all results utilizing red or far-red irradiation. Lona,[100] for example, found that extension of the day with far-red light (8 hours sunlight, 8 hours far-red, 8 hours dark) was inhibitory compared to 8 hours light followed by 16 hours of darkness. This is what would be expected on the basis of the overlapping absorption spectra, but such an explanation was not readily apparent to Lona.

Complications due to timing

In recent years, it has become increasingly apparent that spectral dependence in the flowering of *Xanthium* is strongly influenced by the time at which the experiment is performed. This is an important clue to solution of the problem of time measurement, but the basic facts will be presented here.

The papers of Downs[43] and Mancinelli and Downs[109] indicate the importance of the duration of exposure in determining the effect of far-red; short exposures are promotive in that they reverse the inhibitory effects of red, while long exposures are themselves inhibitory. Since Downs' work, several other phenomena have been described. Borthwick and Downs[14] studied the effects of several repeated cycles made up of short (1.5 to 3-hour) photoperiods with very long dark periods (21 to 22.5 hours). Following the short light period, light interruptions had virtually no effect for 6 to 8 hours (P_{fr} was innocuous). Then, for about 2 hours, red light (P_{fr}) was highly promotive. After about 10 hours, red light (P_{fr}) became inhibitory. Esashi and Oda[47] discuss the inhibitory effects of far-red light. With a single inductive cycle, far-red was never inhibitory, but when cycles were repeated, a strong inhibitory effect of far-red at the beginning of the dark period could be observed. This was reversible by red. With a single inductive cycle, far-red would reverse the inhibitory effect of red as in the early experiments,[15,43] but with repeated cycles, the inhibitory effect of far-red was itself so pronounced that a reversal of the red inhibition could only be observed with very brief far-red exposures. Longer exposures were always inhibitory when several inductive cycles were given but not necessarily when a single cycle was given. Whether all this can be explained in terms of the overlapping absorption spectra as discussed above remains to be seen.

In a recent paper, Reid, Moore, and Hamner[146] found that far-red light was not inhibitory in short (less than 15-hour) inductive dark periods but was inhibitory when the dark period exceeded 15 hours. They used dark periods as long as 72 hours. Inhibition was especially pronounced during the first 15 hours but was also apparent when far-red was given in the latter part of an extended dark period. The inhibitory effect of far-red could be overcome by giving red light at any time during the first 30 hours of darkness (again in extended dark periods).

Salisbury[169] developed an approach to the study of time measurement in the flowering of *Xanthium* in which plants are first maintained for several days in continuous light at constant temperature, after which they are exposed to a phasing dark period, an intervening light period, and a test dark period (see above). Flowering occurred only when the intervening light period was longer than 3 to 5 hours, with a maximum at 12 hours, and low intensities during this period were sufficient to saturate the response. A rough action spectrum was determined, indicating a peak of promotion in the red and a minimal effect in the far-red. Further experiments using red and far-red filters showed that red light was highly promotive during the intervening light period while far-red was innocuous or inhibitory. When plants were given a brief interruption with white light, terminating the phasing dark period, and then a test dark period 24 hours long, interruptions of this test dark period with red and with far-red light indicated an inhibition due to far-red light during the first 20 hours, while red light was inhibitory only about 14 hours after the beginning of the dark period. There even appeared to be a slight promotive effect of red light during the first few hours of this extended test dark period. Salisbury concluded that normal flowering in *Xanthium* requires completion of a cycle, during part of which red light (P_{fr}) is promotive or at least innocuous, and during the other part of which, P_{fr} is inhibitory.

9 Endogenous Rhythms and Time Measurement

Hourglass vs. oscillator timing

When the reversible nature of the phytochrome system was discovered in 1952,[15] the postulated dark conversion was immediately presented as an explanation for time measurement in the flowering of *Xanthium*. If the pigment exists as P_{fr} at the beginning of the dark period, but P_{fr} is inhibitory some hours later, there must be a change in the pigment within the plant from P_{fr} to P_r. Borthwick Hendricks, and Parker[15] suggested that the time for this change controlled the critical dark period, and the suggestion has been reiterated since then.[62,63] Recent work[21,65] seems to indicate that the phytochrome pigment does not convert in all plants from P_{fr} to P_r in darkness. Rather P_{fr} may simply be destroyed, while P_r is synthesized anew. The end result is the same, whether actual conversion takes place or not.

Bünning had suggested as early as 1936[18] (and in more recent reviews[19]) that the endogenous circadian rhythm, which had been clearly demonstrated in plants and animals and which required some sort of time measuring system within the organism, was also responsible for time measurement in photoperiodism. Bünning had developed a theory, according to which plants oscillated on a daily cycle through a phase in which light was promotive (photophil) to a phase in which light was inhibitory (to flowering and to other processes). He had suggested that in short-day plants the light-inhibitory phase (skotophil) was somewhat accelerated so that flowering was promoted if the photoperiod was short. In long-day plants, on the other hand, this phase was delayed, requiring a long photoperiod. The phases were supposedly reset by dawn during each cycle.

As a result of many hypotheses and much experimentation, the original theory of Bünning was rejected. Advances or delays in leaf-movement rhythms were not observed as predicted. Furthermore, the theory would not explain the overwhelming importance of the dark period in the flowering of a plant such as

Xanthium. Nevertheless, oscillating timers do apparently exist in plants, and it is conceivable that time measurement in the flowering process might in some way be coupled to these oscillators. A timer such as phytochrome shift would be more closely analogous to an hourglass than to an oscillator.

Hamner has often defended the oscillating or circadian clock as the mechanism of time measurement in flowering.[59] Defence of this hypothesis with *Xanthium* as the test plant is not particularly easy, however. Plants may be grown under continuous light at constant temperature from the time they are seedlings until induction is brought about by a single dark period longer than about 8.3 hours. Following this dark period, plants are returned to continuous light and constant temperature. How could rhythms play a role in this? One can also interrupt an extended dark period (e.g. 72 hours) with brief intervals of light, or utilize increasingly longer dark periods, looking again for circadian cycles in sensitivity to light or something comparable to the total-cycle-length experiments which work so well with soybeans. Marginal observations of this type have been made,[55,163] but as a rule, attempts to observe such oscillations have failed. Two recent detailed studies, both of them negative, illustrate the point rather well.[127,177]

It is conceivable, however, that manifestations of rhythm as in the experiments of Hamner might not be the only proof of the participation of an oscillating timer in photoperiodism. The clock which measures time in the photoperiodism of *Xanthium* might be the same clock (or the same kind of clock) which normally controls leaf movements and other circadian rhythms, but it might be rapidly damped out in a constant environment so that only one cycle is completed. The primary question is not necessarily: 'Does the clock always oscillate?' Rather we may ask: 'Is the clock which is normally capable of controlling circadian oscillations the same one (or the same kind) which controls time measurement in photoperiodism?' The clock which has been studied in relation to its controlled circadian rhythms has several characteristics besides rhythmicity. After considering some problems connected with the phytochrome hypothesis of time measurement, we will then examine three similarities between photoperiodic time measurement in *Xanthium* and in the circadian rhythms.

The inadequacy of phytochrome in time measurement

As indicated above, Salisbury and Bonner[174] observed that the saturating quantity of red light during a 16-hour dark period remained constant after 3.75 hours. If this indicates that P_r has reached its maximum level by that time, then pigment shift could hardly require the 8.3 hours which constitute the critical dark period for *Xanthium*. It has also been suggested[166,167] that a half-time decay curve which might approximate the change in phytochrome status could not account for a sharp critical dark period, since such a curve is typically quite flat by the time decay has progressed very far.

The most telling argument against phytochrome changes as constituting time measurement is the lack of effect of threshold light upon time measurement. Light intensities adequate to inhibit flowering to a level of about 50 percent of the controls when plants are left under the light during the entire dark period do not influence the critical night[168] or the time of maximum sensitivity to a light interruption.[138,171] The fact that flowering is inhibited by light of these intensities indicates that a certain level of P_{fr} must be maintained in the plant. Yet time measurement is not influenced. Thus time measurement cannot be the decrease in P_{fr} to levels below that which inhibits flowering.

In view of these observations, it would be difficult to imagine that a simple lowering in the level of P_{fr} could account for time measurement in flowering of

Xanthium. It is equally clear, however, that some other reaction rate might account for time measurement. The concept of hourglass timing is not eliminated by the inadequacy of phytochrome as the hourglass. There are other evidences, however, which seem to suggest that the time measuring mechanism in photoperiodism is at least similar to that which controls the circadian rhythms.

Temperature independence

One of the most striking things about the circadian clocks in both plants and animals is their virtual temperature independence.[19] Such a temperature independence is also apparent in the time measurement of *Xanthium.* We have discussed this as it can be observed in effects of temperature upon the critical dark period.[94,168] Salisbury[169] also studied temperature effects during the intervening light period, in which temperature independence was again apparent. A more sensitive way to study time measurement is by observing the time of maximum sensitivity to a light perturbation of an inductive dark period. From 11° to 28°C, the time of maximum sensitivity is uninfluenced by temperature.[170, 171] It was delayed somewhat at 5°C (see Fig. 2–4).

Alternating phases in sensitivity to red light

In the experiments of Salisbury[168] mentioned above, red light was promotive and far-red inhibitory during the intervening light period. Immediately after, during the test dark period, red light became increasingly inhibitory while far-red was innocuous (for short dark periods). In other experiments, far-red has been shown to be inhibitory during part of a 24-hour inductive cycle but not during the other part.[14,47,146] In any case, it is apparent that even in *Xanthium,* although rhythmical oscillations exhibiting several cycles are seldom observed, changes in sensitivity to light are not difficult to demonstrate. These may not be rhythmical in the sense that several cycles are exhibited, but they do display the changing sensitivity characteristic of a single cycle and predicted by Bünning.[18]

Clock resetting

The results of a series of experiments performed by Papenfuss and Salisbury[138,140] open up a number of possibilities for interpretation of time measurement in photoperiodism. In studies of circadian rhythms in leaf movements (or other manifestations), it has often been shown that the phases of a cycle may be shifted (either advanced or delayed) by a light perturbation given at appropriate times.[19,20] Rhythms are delayed, for example, as light breaks are given later and later after the beginning of a dark period (they are acting as dusk). Finally a point is reached after which rhythms are advanced by light perturbations (they are acting as dawn).[20]

Papenfuss and Salisbury investigated this phenomenon in the flowering of *Xanthium.* As indicated in Figure 2–5, light interruptions given two or four hours after the beginning of an inductive dark period did not greatly influence the following time of maximum sensitivity to a second light interruption, although there was a delayed inhibition of up to two or four hours. If the critical dark period was studied, the delay was quite apparent, but somewhat less than might be expected. When the first light interruption was given after 6 hours, however, then the result was strikingly different. Rather than a delay of 6 hours or less in time of maximum sensitivity, there was a delay of 16 hours, or 10 hours following the light perturbation. If the first light interruption was given 7.5 hours after the beginning of darkness, then the delay was 14 hours after the light interruption or 21.5 hours after the beginning of the dark period (not shown in the figure). There was a clear-cut phase shift. Light interruptions before 5 hours tended to act as dusk, while those after 5 hours acted as dawn.

In another series of experiments, plants were given a 7.5-hour phasing dark period followed by intervening light periods of various lengths from 1 minute to several hours. The intervening light period was then followed by a test dark period of 16 hours or longer, and this was interrupted at various times to determine the time of maximum sensitivity. With intervening light periods of 5 hours

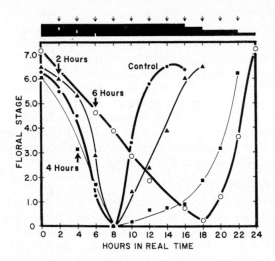

FIGURE 2–5. Flowering after 9 days as a function of time of interruption of a long dark period for controls, given only one interruption, and for plants given an interruption at 2, 4, or 6 hours followed by a second interruption given at various times. Bars at the top illustrate the plan of experiment, arrows indicating the time of the second light interruption (except for controls) and white breaks indicating time of the first interruption (data from Papenfuss and Salisbury[140]).

or less, time of maximum sensitivity remained constant in terms of real time (time after beginning of the phasing dark period or, since this was constant, time after termination of the phasing dark period by a light flash). Of course, time of maximum sensitivity came at decreasing time intervals after the beginning of the test dark period for intervening light periods of increasing length up to five hours (Fig. 2–6). As the intervening light period increased beyond 5 hours, the time of maximum sensitivity to a light interruption of the test dark period was delayed in terms of real time but remained, to a first approximation, constant at about 8 hours after the beginning of the test dark period. These results indicate that the light interruption terminating the phasing dark period acted as a dawn signal, rephasing the cycle so that time of maximum sensitivity came 13 to 14 hours after this light flash. This dawn signal remains the over-riding factor as it was extended to a duration of about 5 hours of light. Following this, termination of the intervening light period acted as a dusk signal, establishing the time of maximum sensitivity at 8 hours following this signal. It appears that in *Xanthium* the clock may go into a state of suspension during the light period, being restarted at any time after a 5-hour intervening light period by termination of this light period. This ability to be suspended and restarted may prove to be unique with plants which can respond to a single inductive cycle. It may be the characteristic which allows them so to respond.

There is an interesting complication in Figure 2–6. This is the dip in the curve between 9 and 14 hours. Salisbury[168] had found that with intervening light periods of 12 hours, the critical dark period of the following test dark period was shortened from the usual 8.3 hours to 6.5 or 7.0 hours. This phenomenon also appears in the dips in the curves in Figure 2–6. Time of maximum sensitivity is advanced to about 6.5 hours after beginning of the test dark period when the intervening light period is 12 hours long.

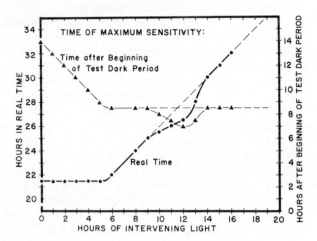

FIGURE 2–6. Plants were given a phasing dark period of 7.5 hours followed by an intervening light period of various durations and a test dark period during which a light interruption was given at various times to determine the time when it was maximally effective. The figure shows this time of maximum effectiveness as a function of the length of the intervening light period. Heavy line indicates time of maximum effectiveness in terms of real time, measuring from the beginning of the phasing dark period. Lighter line indicates time of maximum effectiveness measuring from the beginning of the test dark period. Dashed lines are interpolations and extrapolations (data from Papenfuss and Salisbury[140]).

Although other explanations are possible (e.g. an inhibitor produced after 12 hours of light[168]), these data may provide another demonstration of the oscillating nature of the photoperiodism clock. It is as though the oscillator, phased to the daytime oscillation by the dawn signal, completes this phase after about 9 hours and begins to move into the dark phase. After 12 hours of light, it might have gone as far as possible into the dark phase, after which the continued presence of light tends to entrain or phase shift the clock back into the suspended light phase. If plants are placed in the dark after a 12-hour intervening light period, the clock might continue to oscillate into the dark phase, reaching the time of maximum sensitivity to a light interruption about 6.5 hours later.

An oscillating photoperiodism clock

Although considerable work remains to be done, there is some interesting evidence in favor of an oscillating timer in the photoperiodism response, even of *Xanthium*. Although the rhythmical patterns observable with plants requiring several inductive cycles are much less apparent with *Xanthium*, characteristics of temperature independence, alternating phases of sensitivity to light, and clock resetting are similar to or identical with these characteristics as they have been described in relation to the usual circadian rhythms.

Further studies on circadian clocks in *Xanthium* would seem to be justified. Bonde[6,7] has examined effects of various total cycle lengths upon growth of this plant, but his experiments were not designed to investigate the presence of an endogenous circadian clock. Mansfield and his coworkers[61,113,114,115,121] have investigated stomatal activities in *Xanthium* and report evidence in favor of an endogenous circadian clock exercising some degree of control over these mechanisms. It is not readily apparent, however, how their studies may relate to the photoperiodism clock.

A number of workers have attempted to study leaf movement rhythms in *Xanthium*, although most of their results remain unpublished. Bünning[17] reported in 1932 that leaf movements in *Xanthium* were more easily induced by the dusk signal than the dawn signal. The problem is made initially difficult by the fact that leaf movements in *Xanthium* cannot be clearly observed with the kymograph methods developed for bean and other plants (due to continued movements and growth of the stem). Nevertheless, Christensen,[32] working in my laboratory, developed an automated time-lapse photography system in which plants were photographed while silhouetted against a green luminescent panel during the dark period. There was a clear-cut circadian rhythm in leaf movements in *Xanthium*, observable sometimes for five or six cycles under constant light. Furthermore, this rhythm disintegrates and essentially disappears under conditions inhibitory to flowering such as a 12-hour test dark period following a 3-hour intervening light period. The rhythm is extremely strong under conditions highly promotive of flowering, such as a 12-hour intervening light period followed by a 12-hour test dark period. Hamner and Reid[58] have essentially duplicated these results, although in their experiments the rhythm faded rapidly in continuous light. Bünning[20] has shown that bean leaf-movement rhythms fade rapidly in continuous far-red wavelengths. Christensen used only fluorescent light, which contains virtually no far-red light.

Christensen's study was disappointing in at least two respects. There was an extreme amount of variability in the leaf movement rhythm of *Xanthium*, in contrast to a high degree of uniformity in the flowering response. Furthermore, some of the responses which might have been predicted from the studies of Papenfuss and Salisbury[140] could not be observed. There was no sharp change in the leaf movement rhythm, for example, following light perturbation given six hours after the beginning of darkness. It may be that we have yet to learn how to interpret the leaf movement rhythms in *Xanthium*, or it is possible that these movements are controlled by a circadian clock different from the photoperiodism clock, even though the photoperiodism clock may have the characteristics of circadian clocks in other organisms.

One implication of the studies of Papenfuss and Salisbury[140] could be of considerable significance. Based upon the observations of delaying, rephasing, suspending, and restarting the photoperiodism clock in *Xanthium*, it has been possible to explain several results of light perturbation experiments with this plant by assuming only that the photoperiodism clock is being influenced by these light perturbations. That is, we might imagine that synthesis of flowering hormone in *Xanthium* is dependent only upon the photoperiodism clock being in a certain phase, and that light interruptions (i.e., the phytochrome system) influence only the phase of the clock and not flowering hormone synthesis itself. If this is true, then our speculations about the effects of P_{fr} on the synthesis of flowering hormone become relatively meaningless, since we need be concerned only with the effects of P_{fr} (and perhaps P_r) on the status of the clock.

We had previously assumed that clock resetting could only be a delay, so that a flash of light during a dark period could only terminate and then reinitiate such a dark period. Several experiments could not be explained on this assumption. For example, a light interruption given 8 hours after the beginning of a 20-hour dark period inhibits flowering completely.[174] If its only effect were to terminate and reinitiate the dark period, why are the 12 hours following the light flash ineffective? Normally 12 hours of darkness are optimal for flowering of *Xanthium*. Knowing now that light flashes given after 5 hours not only reinitiate the dark period but cause a phase shift, these results are easily understood. A light interruption 8 hours after the beginning of the dark period will rephase the clock so that flowering hormone will not begin to be synthesized for another 13 or 14 hours.

With these ideas in mind, some of the results of other workers are easier to understand. Wareing[207] reported, for example, that 'a light break given during the early part of a long dark period inhibits flowering in . . . *Xanthium* regardless of the duration of the main photoperiod'. Bünning's original hypothesis postulated that dawn was always controlling, but the work of Papenfuss and Salisbury[140] makes it clear that with light periods longer than 5 hours the clock is essentially suspended, to be reinitiated in its activity again by the dusk signal. With light periods longer than 5 hours, duration of the light period will be relatively unimportant (except for the complication of the 12-hour intervening light period discussed above). Carr[24] reported that light interruptions near the beginning and near the end of a 36-hour dark period were inhibitory. The inhibition at the beginning is easy to understand in terms of the above discussion, and the inhibition near the end could be an example of the inhibitory effects of a brief interval of darkness following a light flash which might act as the dawn signal. In any case, the effect is similar to that reported by Lockhart and Hamner.[95,96]

It is not apparent at the moment how effects of threshold light might be explained in terms of the above assumptions, and the experiments on far-red light[47,100,109,146] are also far less easy to understand. It seems quite conceivable, however, that the inhibitory effects of far-red light applied during the early part of an inductive dark period may influence the clock in many ways which would make these experimental results appear somewhat less baffling. Perhaps far-red only suspends the clock and does not rephase it, always depending upon the time it is given. Experiments such as those performed above might be carried out to obtain such information.

10 . Fractional Induction

Since *Xanthium* will respond at a near maximum level with a single inductive dark period, few studies have been carried out to see whether a series of consecutive dark periods will be as effective as the same number of dark periods separated by long days (or continuous light). Long[101] did report that four 15-hour dark periods at *ca.* 5°C resulted in a residual flowering effect which could be observed longer than 24 hours after the last inductive dark period. Lincoln, Raven, and Hamner[90] reported that repeated short-day treatment of a single leaf is more effective than the division of the same number of inductive cycles between two leaves. They further found that a lapse of several days between short-day treatments lessens their total effectiveness. Such experiments with *Xanthium* are difficult to interpret, however, since leaf sensitivity to induction is known to be a strong function of leaf age. A leaf remains at its maximum sensitivity only for two or three days, and thus cycles given consecutively when the leaf was most sensitive would be expected to be more effective than cycles separated by a few days so that all did not fall during the time of the leaf's maximum sensitivity.

In view of the above discussion on time measurement, it would not be at all surprising if various combinations of long and short days would influence flowering of *Xanthium* in ways not unlike those observed in fractional induction experiments with other plants.

11 Photoperiodic Inhibition

Hamner and Bonner[56] indicated that fully-expanded leaves on receptor branches (2-branched plants) subjected to long photoperiods may exert some influence inhibitory to the floral initiation brought about by donor branches on short photoperiod. Under similar circumstances, young expanding leaves exerted a promotive effect on floral initiation and flower development. This phenomenon was thoroughly studied in 1956 by Lincoln, Raven, and Hamner.[89] These authors found an inhibition in the flowering of a receptor branch of a 2-branched *Xanthium* plant which was quantitatively related to the leaf area which was exposed to long days. The greater the leaf area, the less flowering of the receptor branch. This could be partially overcome by placing the receptor branch in deep shade, creating a carbohydrate-deficient condition in this branch. Apparently the increased flow of carbohydrate to the receptor branch under these conditions resulted in increased movement of flowering stimulus. Shading the donor branch decreased flowering of the receptor.

Although at least part of the phenomenon could be ascribed to effects on translocation of the stimulus, there are several factors which indicate that the entire inhibitory effect of leaves on long day cannot be explained in terms of translocation. Immature leaves were also slightly capable of exhibiting the inhibitory effect.[89] Most impressive was the observation that the length of the day which is critical for effective inhibition is appreciably longer than that which is critical for photoinduction. Leaves receiving less than 7.25 hours of darkness could nevertheless act in an inhibitory way. The inhibitory effect was also observed when the dark period was interrupted. This is not readily explicable in terms of translocation. A single light interruption of the dark period was only effective at fairly high intensities, but much lower quantities of light were effective when the interruptions were given at several intervals during the dark period.

In view of these experiments, it appears that mature leaf tissue on long photoperiods exhibits an inhibitory effect upon flowering which is not simply an effect upon translocation of the floral stimulus and which may involve production of a substance or substances which are inhibitory to flowering. Incidentally, Lam[76] has further studied these effects, demonstrating that even photoperiodically-insensitive leaves (too old) can still exert the inhibitory effect on flowering. In Searle's[178] special system, the presence of non-induced leaves proved to be inhibitory beginning 42 hours after the beginning of induction. Before this time they were promotive.

12 Dual Photoperiod Responses

In the usual sense of the term, *Xanthium* is clearly a short-day plant and does not exhibit a dual photoperiod response. In a special sense, however, a long-day response can be observed. In the experiments of Salisbury[169] described above, when the intervening light period was shorter than 3 to 5 hours, plants remained vegetative, but as its length increased beyond 5 hours, floral stage increased. Since *Xanthium* was responding with increased flowering to increased photoperiod, it was responding as a long-day plant. The situation is complicated, however, since the critical day depended upon the length of the test dark period (usually 12 hours). The results are better understood in terms of clock resetting[140] than by recourse to definitions of short-day or long-day plants.

13 Effects of Temperature

We have already discussed temperature effects in several other contexts. Gilbert's[51] 1926 paper indicated that flowering response of *Xanthium* to short day was reduced by low temperatures, but his results are virtually worthless since his long-day controls varied from 13.4 to 15.2 hours! Snyder[190] demonstrated a general promotion by high temperatures, and Long[101] found that more inductive cycles were required at low temperatures (*ca.* 5°C) than at higher temperatures (*ca.* 21°C). Mann[110] found that the critical dark period was extended to 12–15 hours at 10°C as compared to the usual 8.3 hours at temperatures above 20°C. More recently Salisbury[168] studied the critical dark period at several temperatures, using a single inductive night. Although the critical dark period was prolonged at temperatures as low as 5° to 10°C, it varied by only about 20 minutes at temperatures from 15° to 35°C. This was confirmed by Lockhart.[96] Salisbury[170,171] also found no effect of temperature with *Xanthium* upon time of maximum sensitivity to a light break, agreeing with earlier results with *Pharbitis.*[196]

In the late 1950's de Zeeuw[41] and Nitsch and Went,[134] using the controlled environment facilities at the California Institute of Technology, discovered an interesting effect of temperature upon flowering of *Xanthium*. They found that when plants were exposed during half of a 16-hour photoperiod to 4°C, flowering would occur even though the dark period was only 8.0 hours long (instead of the usual 8.3). The effect could be observed with two cycles but was best observed when several inductive cycles were given. It was also most readily observed when the 8 hours of low temperature came during the second half rather than the first half of the photoperiod.

Interestingly enough, the titles of both papers included 'flowering of *Xanthium* under long-day conditions'. Of course, they did not mean to imply that flowering increased as daylength increased; only that flowering occurred on daylengths longer than might be expected. Salisbury[168] studied the critical dark period under comparable conditions. It was found that with a single inductive cycle, the critical dark period was extended when the low temperature followed the inductive dark period. With 5 cycles (low temperature during the second half of the photoperiod), the critical dark period was shortened to about 7 hours (Fig. 2–7).

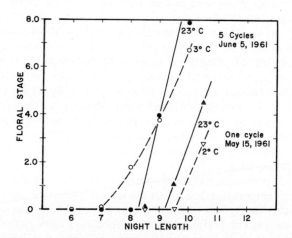

FIGURE 2–7. Flowering after 9 days as a function of night length for plants induced at 23°C with one or 5 dark periods followed by temperatures in the light of 2°, 3°, or 23°C (data from Salisbury[168]).

There are at least two possible explanations for this interesting effect of low temperature during the photoperiod upon the subsequent critical night. An inhibitor may be synthesized during the latter hours of extended photoperiods (e.g. 12 to 16 hours after beginning of the photoperiod), and low temperatures might prevent the synthesis of this inhibitor, allowing the subsequent inductive dark period to be more effective. Alternatively, the effects of low temperature may be upon the timing mechanism. It was observed (Fig. 2–4 and 2–8) that

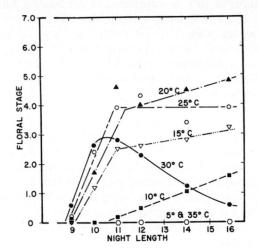

FIGURE 2–8. Flowering after 9 days as a function of night length for plants induced at several temperatures with a single dark period (data from Salisbury[168]).

time measurement was upset (longer critical night or time to maximum sensitivity) when temperatures during the inductive dark period approached the freezing point. This was also true for temperatures during an intervening light period.[169] It is conceivable then, that low temperatures during the photoperiod slow the clock so that, as described above in section 9 on timing, the clock has begun to oscillate into the dark phase and not yet been re-entrained to the light phase at the time plants go into the dark.

Salisbury's[168] study of temperature effects on the critical dark period (Fig. 2–8) also provided information about the effects of temperature upon synthesis of flowering hormone. Plotting floral stage as a function of night length, a rapid increase in flowering is observed for two or three hours following the critical night. The slopes of the curves indicate a remarkable insensitivity to temperature (Q_{10} of about 1.3). Following this rapid initial synthesis, there appears to be a saturation point after which the curves tend to level out. At temperatures of 15° to 25°C, slopes remain somewhat positive, but at 30°C, the slope becomes highly negative, indicating a destruction of flowering hormone at high temperatures with increasing time.

Another kind of temperature experiment supports these results.[94,168] Intervals of high and low temperature are given during an inductive dark period. Low temperatures have little effect on flowering, and high temperatures (40°C) are also ineffective during the first 6 hours of an inductive dark period. There is an incomplete inhibition of flowering when plants are exposed to high temperatures from the 6th to the 8th hour, however, and flowering is inhibited nearly to zero when high temperatures are given between the 8th and the 10th hour. Inhibition decreases from the 10th to the 16th hour. These results may be interpreted on the assumption that the clock is temperature-insensitive, but synthesis of flowering hormone and destruction once it has been synthesized are accentuated by elevated temperatures.

Although the clock measuring the critical dark period may be temperature-insensitive, it would seem reasonable to imagine that phytochrome shift, which must occur metabolically during the first part of the inductive dark period, would be sensitive to temperature. This was tested by measuring the critical night with a set of control plants in the usual way and repeating treatments with two other sets of plants, one of which was exposed to low temperature (10°C) during the first two hours of the dark period, the other of which was exposed to these temperatures between the 5th and the 7th hour after the beginning of the dark period. Plants which were exposed to the low temperature during the first two hours of darkness exhibited an increase in the critical night of nearly an hour, while plants exposed to the low temperature between the 5th and the 7th hours exhibited the same critical night as the controls.[168] These results are in agreement with the interpretation that phytochrome shift is a temperature-sensitive process occurring in the first part of the dark period, although subsequent time measurement is not.

14 Effects of Mineral Nutrition

During the 1920's and 1930's, there was much speculation about the importance of nutrition to flowering. It was postulated that accumulation of carbohydrates promoted flowering while high nitrogen levels promoted vegetative growth at the expense of flowering. Gilbert[51] considered the problem at length in his paper but contributed little to its solution. Hamner's student Neidle[132] first used Xanthium in an experiment designed to investigate this problem. She found that high nitrogen levels greatly promoted induction of flowering in Xanthium as well as subsequent development of flowers and fruits, providing always that plants were exposed to a suitable photoperiod. No adjustment of nitrogen level would induce flowering unless plants were given the usual long dark period. The results clearly indicated, then, that flowering in Xanthium was completely under control of photoperiod, and that high nitrogen was promotive rather than inhibitory as had been postulated. Subsequent work[212] has substantiated this conclusion, and indeed it is easy to observe a promotive effect of high nitrogen levels upon flowering of Xanthium plants which have been properly induced by photoperiod.[167] Naylor[128] found that the critical dark period was not influenced by low nitrogen, potassium, or phosphate levels, while an abundance of these compounds promoted flowering.

Effects of iron deficiency on flowering of Xanthium have been studied.[189] It was found that iron-deficient plants could not be induced to flower, or they flowered abnormally, even though they were placed in normal nutrient solutions immediately following the photoinductive period. This result was apparently not due to lower carbohydrate levels, since applied sucrose failed to overcome the inhibitory effects of iron deficiency. If plants were allowed to recover from iron deficiency in normal nutrient solutions previous to induction, they flowered normally.

Plants which have been induced to flower fail to exhibit boron deficiency symptoms under conditions which cause symptoms in vegetative plants.[193] It was suggested that the decrease in cambial activity associated with floral induction caused the reduction in deficiency symptoms. Mobility of boron in Xanthium has also been studied.[119]

15 Effects of Gas Composition

Khudairi and Hamner[73] reported that ethylene chlorohydrin vapor promoted flowering of Xanthium under long-day conditions. These conditions were obtained by preceding an 8-hour dark period with 8 hours of low-intensity incandescent light. Controls remained vegetative, but these conditions are obviously very near to the threshold for induction in *Xanthium*. Abeles[1] strongly inhibited flowering with ethylene concentrations of 10 and 100 ppm applied in bell jars during a 16-hour inductive dark period. Khudairi and Hamner speculate that ethylene chlorohydrin promoted flowering in their experiments because of a postulated inhibition in synthesis of auxin. Abeles, on the other hand, expected ethylene to be inhibitory, because application of auxin induces its formation and auxin inhibits flowering. Of course, final interpretation of these results will depend not only upon a more complete understanding of the effects of ethylene chlorohydrin and of ethylene upon metabolism in *Xanthium*, but also perhaps upon an understanding of the effects of auxin or other products of ethylene or ethylene chlorohydrin metabolism on flowering.

Langston and Leopold[83] reported that induction in *Xanthium* required the presence of CO_2 during the dark period. A night interruption reduced the rate of CO_2 fixation during the inductive dark period. Sen and Leopold[181] studied dark fixation during an inductive night as well as effects of induction upon photosynthetic fixation of CO_2. They observed effects of the light period upon dark fixation; i.e. the longer the interval after the beginning of the dark period, the lower the rate of dark fixation. Furthermore, a dark period influenced the subsequent photosynthetic CO_2 fixation; i.e. the longer the preceding dark period, the lower the photosynthetic rate. Light fixation products (using $^{14}CO_2$) changed rapidly during the inductive dark period. There was a rapid depletion of sugars, a rise in organic and amino acids, and a very rapid depletion in alanine. Sen[179] continued this work. A red or a far-red interruption of the inductive dark period resulted in rapid decarboxylation and then significant hydrolysis of the ethanol-insoluble fraction. Indeed red and far-red treatments markedly altered the composition of products in the leaves at the end of the dark period following the interruption.

Campbell and Leopold[22] exposed plants to high CO_2 pressures following an inductive dark period. This treatment resulted in flowering of plants on dark periods shorter than those required to induce flowering in controls. The experiment is somewhat analogous to those utilizing low temperatures during the photoperiod, as described above, and may have the same explanation.

16 Translocation of the Floral Stimulus

Since Hamner and Bonner[56] postulated the existence of a flowering stimulus synthesized in the leaves, they were naturally concerned with the translocation of this stimulus from the leaves to the bud. Using two-branched plants produced by removing the main stem above the cotyledonary buds and allowing these to grow out, they investigated this problem. They found that the stimulus would move from a donor branch to a receptor branch maintained on long days, but that the presence of mature leaves on the receptor branch inhibited the translocation of the stimulus, while the presence of immature leaves promoted translocation. They showed that even a small portion of a mature leaf on the receptor branch left on long days would act in an inhibitory fashion.

Withrow and Withrow[213] investigated the movement of the stimulus, showing that it would not pass through a stem from which the bark had been removed or through dead petiole tissue. They concluded that it moved primarily in the phloem and only in living tissue.

In the early 1950s, three groups of investigators[74,159,188] independently developed a technique for studying movement of the flowering stimulus from an induced leaf of *Xanthium*. Plants were defoliated at various time intervals following an inductive dark period. If leaves were removed immediately following the dark period, plants usually remained completely vegetative; when leaves were removed several hours (typically 24) after induction, flowering was nearly equivalent to that of control plants from which the leaves had not been removed. Intermediate defoliation times resulted in intermediate levels of flowering (Fig. 2–9). Salisbury[158] found that the time for translocation of the stimulus as

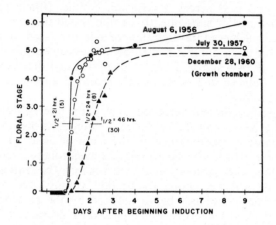

FIGURE 2–9. Three examples of flowering as a function of defoliation time, showing the range of translocation times which can be observed (from Salisbury[167]).

measured by this defoliation technique was much longer in winter than in summer and ascribed the difference to light intensity. He later showed[167] that translocation was accelerated by increasing temperature, and that the Q_{10} for this reaction was between 2 and 3, as might be expected for metabolic processes. Skok and Scully[188] found that the stimulus moved out of the leaf even when plants were left in continuous darkness for several days, but that returning plants to light greatly accelerated movement of the stimulus. Carr[27] confirmed the effects of light on movement of the stimulus and reported that the depressing effects of low light intensities were overcome by application of sucrose to the induced leaf. He concluded that the flowering stimulus moved in the mass flow stream of assimilate from the leaf, and that the requirement for high-intensity light was a requirement for photosynthesis which provided the assimilate.

Searle[177] disputed these findings, claiming that light intensity following induction had no effect upon subsequent flowering. His highly specialized system, however, was not really comparable to that used in the above work. A single leaf was induced in a small box, but two leaves exposed to continuous light remained on the plant. It is conceivable that these extra leaves supplied assimilate or in some other way influenced translocation.

Lam[76] altered the direction of movement of the flower stimulus by application of gibberellic acid and by removal of plant organs. The stimulus was forced down by decapitation and disbudding, causing dormant buds to respond.

Salisbury[160,163] studied the effects of certain growth regulators upon translocation. He found that auxins inhibit flowering when applied during the period of translocation of the flowering stimulus but not when applied after this time. Nevertheless, when plants were treated with auxin and defoliated at intervals following induction, the initial time of translocation was not influenced, although the level of flowering was decreased. A few other compounds besides auxin also seemed to inhibit during the translocation.[37]

17 Grafting Experiments and Necessity for an Active Bud

This topic is intimately related to the last one. Many grafting experiments were performed in an attempt to study the nature and translocation properties of the floral stimulus. Hamner and Bonner[56] initially demonstrated the movement of stimulus across a contact graft between two plants. They further reported that the stimulus would pass across a diffusion contact (tissue paper), although Withrow and Withrow[213] subsequently demonstrated that a living tissue union had probably been achieved through the pores in the tissue paper. They further showed that direct tissue contact had to be uninterrupted for more than 4 days if stimulus were to pass across. Long[101] demonstrated that leaves of *Xanthium* plants could be induced and subsequently removed and grafted to a receptor plant, causing it to flower.

Lona[98] followed up these experiments with some interesting studies in which it was shown that very small *Xanthium* leaves would, as they enlarged, become induced in response to the presence on the plant of older, previously induced leaves. These leaves which were far too small (primordia to a few millimeters) to respond to the long dark periods could, when mature, be grafted to a vegetative plant, causing it to flower. Lona found that young leaves of other species (particularly *Perilla*) could not be so induced by the presence of previously induced mature leaves. This work was repeated by Zeevaart.[216]

Bonner and Thurlow[12] found that auxin inhibited flowering and that plants so inhibited would not induce receptor plants to flower. Thurlow[203] transmitted the flowering stimulus through several graft generations.

There have been a number of attempts to ascertain the role of active buds in induction of *Xanthium* and other plants. Carr[25,26] attempted to induce detached leaves which were subsequently grafted to receptor plants or disbudded plants which were subsequently grafted to receptors. In both cases induction failed, but he did not include as controls detached leaves with buds. This was first substantiated by Zeevaart,[215] although he later[216] reported as high as 40 percent induction of detached leaves. Other workers[86,90,159] found a requirement for active buds, but the requirement could easily be for a stabilization of hormone and not for its initial production in the leaves. In any case, the requirement could be overcome by the presence of young leaves,[86] particularly if plants were treated with gibberellic acid, or by application of auxin (NAA).[159] There is a possibility that auxin treatment increased the rate at which the buds became active,[27] but this was not apparent in the experiments.

18 Effects of Growth Substances and Growth Retardants

Considerable effort has been expended in an attempt to inhibit or promote flowering by application of growth regulators. Work with auxin has been reviewed by Lang.[82]

Hamner and Bonner[56] applied several substances, including vitamins and IAA, to *Xanthium* plants, but found no promotive effect on flowering. Their experiments were not designed to detect inhibitory effects, but Bonner and Thurlow[12] found an inhibition of flowering due to applied IAA or NAA. These auxins were applied as sprays, or cuttings were placed in test tubes containing the auxin solutions, or leaves were submerged in auxin solution during the inductive dark period. Concentrations as low as 1 mg per liter (*ca.* 5×10^{-6}M) were inhibitory when leaves were submerged. If the auxin was removed (e.g. using cuttings) plants could subsequently be induced normally. The auxin antagonist, 2,4-dichloroanisole, suppressed the effect of auxin and hastened development of the floral buds. Bonner[9] reported that 2,4-dichloroanisole and triiodobenzoic acid (TIBA) would induce the formation of flower buds when plants were maintained on long days (days extended by low-intensity light so that controls just remained vegetative). The buds which were induced had the appearance of flower buds but did not continue to develop normally. Salisbury[172] has repeated these experiments but found the promotion of flowering by antiauxins to be very marginal. Struckmeyer and Roberts[194] extracted from flowering *Xanthium* plants a material which they referred to as anti-auxin. It overcame auxin-induced callus formation, for example. It was reported to have flower-promoting properties. Naylor[129] studied the effects of several auxins upon flowering of *Xanthium* and concluded that while these compounds could suppress flowering, they never prevented it completely.

Liverman[92] found that some auxin inhibition could be observed even when the material was applied after the end of the inductive dark period. These findings were confirmed and extended.[158,159,173,174] There was no effect of auxin upon the length of the critical dark period (time measurement), and the auxin inhibition was additive to but not synergistic with inhibition due to a light interruption. It was suggested that applied auxin causes a destruction of flowering hormone and that the native auxin had at most a relatively minor effect in the normal flowering process. Carr[27] suggested that, since effects of auxin could be observed during the period of translocation of the flowering stimulus, the effect of applied growth regulators might be upon translocation. Salisbury[163] found, however, that applied auxin, although it inhibited flowering, did not influence the initial time of translocation nor the shape of the translocation curve.

Salisbury[159] reported that auxin inhibits flowering only while the flowering hormone is in the leaf, and that a promotion of flowering by auxin can be observed; e.g. when auxin is applied immediately following removal of the leaves. Auxin promotion was also more evident under low light intensities, and applied auxin overcame the need for active buds. de Zeeuw and Leopold[42] observed a promotion of flowering at low concentrations of applied auxin (1 to 5 ppm NAA). Such a slight promotion is also evident in Salisbury's figures.[158,159,160,174]

Cooke[38] measured auxin levels in extracts of *Xanthium* using the *Avena* test. He found that as soon as flowers appeared, auxin levels dropped. Transfer of plants to short-day conditions resulted in an increase in auxin level, but after a few days plants under long-day conditions had more auxin. He interpreted his results as an indication that natural auxin levels within the plant had little effect on the normal flowering process.

Lockhart and Hamner[95,96] found that applied IAA increased the inhibitory effectiveness of a short dark period (4 hours) given following a light break after a normal inductive dark period. Hamner and Nanda[57] found that more IAA was required for inhibition if the high intensity light period previous to the inductive dark period was longer. They suggested that a product of the high intensity light reacted with IAA.

Brown and Taylor[16] found that X-rays inhibited flowering when given during the inductive dark period but not when given before. X-rays after the dark period gave a temporary promotion to flowering. It is conceivable that this observation may be related to effects of growth regulators upon flowering (e.g. by a destruction or stimulation of growth regulator synthesis). Effects of ethylene were discussed above.

Salisbury[160,163] developed a new approach to the study of the effects of growth regulators upon flowering in *Xanthium*. Compounds were tested by dipping plants in a concentration series just before an inductive dark period. Effective compounds were applied at various times before, during, and after a single inductive dark period to document their time of effectiveness in the flowering process (Fig. 2–10). Materials which were effective when applied during the inductive dark period but not when applied later might be inhibiting either time measurement or synthesis of flowering hormone, and their effects upon time measurement were studied by observing their effect upon critical dark period.

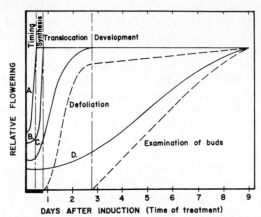

FIGURE 2–10. Summary of results of experiments in which a chemical is applied to plants at various times during and following a single inductive dark period. Postulated steps in the flowering process are indicated, and broken lines show results of translocation (defoliation) and bud development (examination of buds) experiments for comparison (data after Salisbury[167]).

Cobaltous ion (Co^{++}) inhibited flowering, but only when applied before the end of the critical dark period.[160,163] Co^{++} extended the critical night, but no other compound used in Salisbury's experiments had this effect. Dinitrophenol (DNP) inhibited flowering when applied during the inductive dark period but not when applied after. This seemed to imply a need for ATP in the synthesis of flowering hormone. IAA and NAA inhibited during the translocation period, and dalapon (2,2-dichloropropionic acid), maleic hydrazide, and 2,4-D inhibited development of the floral bud, even when they were applied only a day before examination of the bud.

Salisbury[162] and Salisbury and Eichhorn[176] further studied the effects of cobaltous ion. This ion was effective in the presence of various anions, but K^+ and Mn^{++} had no effect upon flowering. The effect of Co^{++} was not reversed by DNP but was completely reversed by cysteine and glutathione, leading Salisbury[162] to postulate that sulfhydryl groups might be involved in time measurement in the flowering process. In later experiments,[176] many other compounds known to chelate with Co^{++} reversed the Co^{++} inhibition. These were not sulfhydryl compounds. There was no interaction of Co^{++} with red or far-red light given at various times and for various durations during an inductive dark period, except that the time of maximum sensitivity to a red light interruption was delayed by about 2 hours following application of Co^{++} (Fig. 2–11). In the case of cysteine, at least, reversal of the Co^{++} inhibition was not due to a prevention of penetration of Co^{++}. Cysteine would reverse the Co^{++} effect even when applied two or three hours after Co^{++} had penetrated the leaf. Some of the compounds which chelate most strongly with Co^{++} would even prevent the vegetative damage usually caused by Co^{++}. It was postulated that Co^{++} retards the time measuring process in flowering by reacting with some substance involved in this process, and that materials which will form a strong enough chelate with Co^{++} will prevent this combination. Some substances known to form weak chelates with Co^{++} were ineffective in reversing its effect on flowering.

It has been shown by several workers[2,52,79,80,86,163] that gibberellic acid will not induce flowering in *Xanthium*, although stem elongation is strongly promoted. It has been reported[52] that GA_3 promotes floral development in *Xanthium*, providing two or three normal inductive cycles are given. There is also a slight promotion of flowering when GA is applied before the end of the critical night

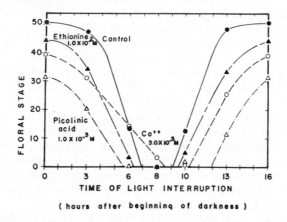

FIGURE 2–11. Effects of various chemicals upon level of flowering for plants given a single 16-hour inductive dark period and a single interruption of light at various times as indicated. Cobaltous ion changes the time of maximum sensitivity to the light interruption; ethionine and picolinic acid do not, although they do extend the critical dark period as shown by other experiments (data from Collins *et al.*[37]).

in a 16-hour (inductive) dark period.[163] Furthermore, the ability of young leaves to preserve the flowering stimulus in debudded plants is strongly enhanced by application of GA_3.[86]

19 Effects of Metabolic Inhibitors

At the Botanical Congress in 1959, Salisbury[164,165] suggested that the approach described above for growth regulators be used to study the biochemistry of flowering hormone synthesis by application of metabolic inhibitors (such as DNP, see above). He reported on preliminary results with 5-fluorouracil (5-FU), using the three tests of effective concentration, time of application, and effect on critical dark period. A fourth test was added: reversal by simultaneous application of a suspected metabolite. An inhibitory concentration of 5-FU was applied in the presence of increasing concentrations of orotic acid, the orotic acid overcoming the 5-FU inhibition. Uracil and thymidine failed to reverse the 5-FU inhibition.

Salisbury and Bonner[175] found that 5-FU inhibited flowering when applied before or during the inductive dark period but not when applied later. Inhibition was brought about when a given concentration of 5-FU was applied to the apical bud as well as when it was applied to the leaves. Since the bud is much smaller, less 5-FU per plant produced an inhibition when the substance was applied to the bud than when it was applied to the leaves. All other information relating to the flowering process seems to imply that the reactions of the inductive dark period are occurring in the leaves, but the results with 5-FU were interpreted as an indication that some essential process goes on in the bud during the inductive dark period. It is possible, but unlikely in view of the studies described in the next paragraph, that 5-FU requires several hours to be absorbed, this lag accounting for the apparent effectiveness during the dark period. The reversal of the 5-FU effect by orotic acid but not by thymidine or uracil suggested that RNA synthesis was the essential process involved.

Bonner and Zeevaart[13] confirmed the earlier results with 5-FU and reported that labeled 5-FU will move readily from the leaf to the bud but not in the reverse direction, indicating even more strongly that its effect must be in the bud. They found that labeled 5-FU was incorporated into RNA in the bud, and that this incorporation was decreased by concurrent application of orotic acid. Presumably RNA containing 5-FU would be fraudulent. 5-Fluorodeoxyuridine (5-FDU) also inhibited flowering when applied to the bud, but its effect was reversed by thymidine applied at the end of the inductive dark period. Apparently DNA synthesis was being inhibited by 5-FDU, and Bonner and Zeevaart concluded that RNA synthesis was the process inhibited by 5-FU. Cherry and van Huystee[30] also studied effects of 5-FU. They concluded that since high concentrations (10^{-2} molar) are required to completely inhibit flowering, the effect was not a specific one. This conclusion would hardly seem to be justified, since they knew nothing about the quantities which actually penetrated into the cells. They found that synthesis of ribosomal RNA in the bud was inhibited more by 5-FU than was synthesis of messenger RNA.

Collins, Salisbury, and Ross[37] applied several antimetabolites to *Xanthium* plants and found that many, including a number of amino acid analogs, had no effect upon flowering, although in a few cases, vegetative growth was inhibited. Ethionine, p-fluorophenylalanine, benzimidazole, 2,6-diaminopurine, α-picolinic acid, and quercetin inhibited flowering only when they were applied before the end of the inductive dark period. Effects of these compounds, except picolinic acid and quercetin, were at least partially reversed by certain amino acids or pyrimidines, suggesting that protein or nucleic acid synthesis was essential during the inductive dark period. In most cases inhibition was readily observed when the substances were applied to the leaves, but in several instances compounds were also effective when applied to the buds. No role for picolinic acid or quercetin has been suggested, although a quercetin derivative has been reported in cocklebur.[199] α-Methylmethionine, 2-thiouracil, 6-azauracil, and 5-bromo-3-isopropyl-6-methyluracil inhibited flowering when applied during the dark period or during the time of hormone translocation. Effects of thiouracil were overcome by additions of uracil or orotic acid, and uridine incompletely reversed the inhibitions of azauracil and 5-bromo-3-isopropyl-6-methyluracil. α-Methylmethionine inhibition was reversed by methionine. Effects appeared to be in the leaf, but since translocation to the bud may be assumed, these preliminary observations are not conclusive. Ethionine and picolinic acid increased the length of the critical night but did not change the time of maximum sensitivity to a red-light interruption. Thioproline retarded flowering regardless of when it was applied, and its effect was not reversed by L-proline. Effects of thioproline must be non-specific and upon development of the floral bud.

It is interesting that effects of several compounds upon flowering may be clearly separated in time from effects of these same compounds upon vegetative growth of the plant. In general most compounds which inhibit flowering also influence vegetative growth, although a few do not, while a few others may influence vegetative growth without inhibiting flowering. Most of those which inhibit both flowering and vegetative growth will fail to inhibit flowering when applied after some time (e.g. end of the dark period or end of the translocation period). Thus it would appear that development of the floral bud is far more resistant to metabolic inhibitors than is growth of the leaves.

Some workers[64,178] have failed to grasp the significance of the time-of-application test. Searle,[178] for example, found effects of 6-azauracil and 5-bromo-3-isopropyl-6-methyluracil on vegetative growth of the plant and concluded that their effects on flowering could therefore not be specific. Both of these compounds inhibit flowering only when they are applied before the end of the translocation period.[37] When they are applied after this time, effects on vegetative growth may still be noted, but development of the floral bud is as rapid as that of controls to which no chemical has been applied. Thus we cannot conclude anything about the action of a compound in the flowering process from its effects upon vegetative growth of the plant. The point is not whether vegetative growth is influenced, but whether flowering is affected in a specific or a non-specific way.

Collins[35,36] studied the floral inhibition due to ethionine and α-methylmethionine. Since known methyl donors (betaine, choline, and dimethylthetin) did not reverse the ethionine effects, he concluded that methyl donation was not a significant part of the flowering process. Ethionine inhibited incorporation of methionine into protein, sometimes becoming incorporated itself, producing fraudulent protein. Since most amino acid analogs do not inhibit flowering. Collins suggested that the flowering hormone might be a relatively small peptide containing only a few amino acids.

Miller and Ross[124] studied the inhibition due to p-fluorophenylalanine (FPA). The inhibition was reversed by L-phenylalanine but not by tyrosine. FPA strongly inhibited the absorption of phenylalanine, leucine, and glycine by *Xanthium* leaf discs, but the three amino acids did not inhibit absorption of FPA. FPA inhibited incorporation of phenylalanine into protein, and Miller and Ross concluded that its effect on flowering was probably an effect upon synthesis of enzymes essential to the process. In terms of Collins' suggestion,[36] the small peptide might at least include methionine and phenylalanine.

Ross[155,156,157] studied the effects of 6-azauracil on nucleic acid metabolism in *Xanthium* leaves. He found that conversion of orotic acid to RNA is inhibited by 6-azauracil, and that the pathways of nucleotide synthesis in *Xanthium* are much like those in other organisms.

Co^{++}, mentioned above,[162,163,176] may be considered to be a metabolic inhibitor rather than a growth regulator. Ross[153] studied effects of Co^{++} upon metabolism of acetate and mevalonic acid. In view of his results (which are complex and not obviously related to flowering), he suggested that Co^{++} inhibits conversion of acetate to mevalonic acid.

Bonner, Heftmann, and Zeevaart[11] studied effects of various sterol inhibitors produced by the Smith, Kline, and French Laboratories of Philadelphia. They found that SK & F 3301, 7732, and 7997 inhibit flowering. These compounds are known to inhibit cholesterol biosynthesis as well as the synthesis of other steroids in rat liver. Effects of SK & F 7997 on flowering were studied most intensively. The compound was active when applied before or at the beginning of the inductive dark period but not when applied after the end of the critical night. It appeared to be effective in the leaves and not in the buds, and no cholesterol or steroid precursor would reverse its inhibition of flowering. It was found that there was much incorporation of both labeled acetate and labeled mevalonic acid into nonsaponifiable material of both leaves and buds, but this appeared to be identical in induced and non-induced plants. SK & F 7997 inhibited sterol biosynthesis in *Xanthium*, but β-sitosterol and stigmasterol were the same in both vegetative and induced leaves. It was concluded that steroid synthesis may be a part of the flowering process, but that results so far do not demonstrate this unequivocally.

20 Florigenic Extracts

Hamner and Bonner,[56] in their brief summer's work, tested some 246 different kinds of extracts and extract fractions in an attempt to find the floral-initiating substance in induced *Xanthium* leaves. All of their results were negative. There have also been several efforts to extract auxins and anti-auxins (growth inhibitors).[5,8,38,49,152,194] Only Roberts *et al.*[148,150,152,194] claim any flower-inducing activity for these materials (see below).

Some experiments of Bogorad and McIlrath[3,120] are difficult to classify in this chapter but may apply here. Light-sensitive lettuce seeds were embedded in *Xanthium* petioles and wrapped with aluminium foil so that they remained in the dark. The seeds germinated when plants were held on short days but not when plants were on long days, indicating, perhaps, a germination promoting substance produced under conditions which promote flowering. This obviously suggests some relationship between florigen and the germination promoter, but a light interruption of the inductive dark period inhibited flowering but not germination.

In 1948 Bonner and Bonner[10] made a water extract of a large flower primordium of a palm tree (*Washingtonia robusta*). This extract was given to *Xanthium* plants through a downward pointing flap of stem inserted into a test tube. Fifty-eight of 68 test plants treated with this extract flowered, while water controls remained strictly vegetative. Several attempts were made to duplicate this experiment, but all failed. For one thing, Bonner and Bonner were unable to obtain another flowering primordium identical to the one used in the successful experiment.

For nearly 20 years Roberts[148,150,151,194] has been reporting a successful extraction of flower-promoting substances from *Xanthium*. Initially, he would not divulge his methods, since he was applying for a patent (since granted, US 2,937,206). When the procedures were finally explained,[150] other workers were unable to duplicate them (although few have tried). He has now accumulated a complex series of fractions from his extracts and an equally complex theory of flowering. He no longer claims that his substances are equivalent to the flowering hormone; that is, that they will induce flowering in purely vegetative plants. He does feel that they will strongly influence the flowering of plants already induced, and, in some cases, that they will influence the sex of the developing flowers. His work could eventually prove to be highly significant, although it is badly in need of confirmation by other laboratories.

Lincoln, Mayfield, and Cunningham[87] reported in 1961 the preparation of an extract from lyophilized tissue of flowering *Xanthium* plants, which initiated development of floral buds when applied to test plants maintained on long-day conditions (even continuous light). Buds failed to develop beyond an early stage, but the experiment was nevertheless clear-cut and reproducible. It was shown that extracts from vegetative plants failed to yield flower-inducing substances,[117] and active materials have been extracted from flowering day-neutral plants (sunflower[88]) and from a fungus culture.[85] The extract has been purified somewhat,[117] and its acidic nature has been demonstrated.[84] Lincoln and his coworkers consider their extract to be the flowering hormone, florigen, and it was suggested that the material be called florigenic acid. Whether the extract proves to be the long-sought florigen or not, its flower-promoting characteristics are of the utmost interest and significance. The work of Lincoln's group has been fully confirmed by Carr.[28]

Biswas, Paul, and Henderson[2] have extracted flowering *Xanthium* plants, putting emphasis on the sterol components of the extracts. Some fractions induced floral bud initiation in both chrysanthemum and *Xanthium*. Attempts are being made to identify the active principles.

21 Induction of Excised Apices

Some attempts have been made by Phillips at Colorado State University to culture excised apices of *Xanthium* and to study their induction, and experiments have also been performed at the University of Chicago. This work is inconclusive and has not been published. Phillips excised control apices and apices induced by three short days. About 15 percent grew on a wick in a special liquid medium in test tubes. Vegetative tips produced roots, stems and leaves but remained vegetative even on short days, but induced tips grew into greatly modified floral structures.

22 Chemical, Histochemical, and Ultrastructural Changes

Struckmeyer[191] found a decrease in the number of cambial cells with a resulting decrease in the formation of vascular tissue in the stems of induced *Xanthium* plants. If induction was stopped before it was complete (5 days were required), tissues reverted back to the non-induced condition.

Khudairi and Bonde[72] studied an *Avena* curvature inhibitor in *Xanthium* leaves and found that it decreased with increasing induction. Taylor[198,200] found significant changes in phenylpropane derivatives, particularly chlorogenic acid. Light breaks during the inductive dark period had only slight effects on these changes, however, and so they are not obviously related to induction.

Sen[179,180,181] studied several metabolic components as they are influenced by induction and particularly as this might be influenced by light interruption of the dark period.[179] Many effects were observed, such as an increase in malic acid following red light treatment. The findings may some day be of interest in relation to flowering.

Nitsan[133] studied the electrophoretic patterns of *Xanthium* leaf extracts as affected by photoperiod. While he found changes in the patterns, he did not use a light break, and his results must remain ambiguous along with those of others who have studied general metabolic components as they might correlate with induction.

Considerable effort has been expended in an attempt to understand the nucleic acid status of induced and non-induced *Xanthium* plants. Both leaves and buds have been studied. Ross[154] found no significant differences between nucleotide composition (base ratios) of vegetative and floral buds. This finding was substantiated by Cherry and van Huystee[30] who also found[31] that induced *Xanthium* buds synthesize relatively more messenger RNA than do vegetative buds. Thomas[201] studied the mitotic index in the apical region of *Xanthium* buds, finding that it doubled within 24 hours immediately following a single inductive dark period. He postulates that flowering hormone causes an increase in the rate of DNA synthesis as would, of course, be expected.

Vergara and McIlrath[205] studied the influence of induction on water uptake of *Xanthium*. Peaks in water absorption appeared coincident with the appearance of macroscopic flowers and with anthesis. But water absorption by debudded plants under inductive photoperiods were similar to that of intact photoinduced plants, and thus it was concluded that the observation was merely a parallel occurrence and not an indication of cause and effect. Krizek, McIlrath, and Vergara[75] observed an increase in senescence when plants were held under an inducing photoperiod, again whether buds were present or not.

Roberts[149] attempts to differentiate between induction of flowers and subsequent floral development. Since both are promoted by essentially the same condition (long dark periods), his arguments are not convincing. There are clearly different properties exhibited between induction and development, but these could be due to the secondary changes which take place upon conversion to the reproductive state.

Gifford[50] has studied histochemical and ultrastructural changes at induction with *Xanthium* and several other plants. He observed the increase of cell division mentioned by Thomas.[201] He also observed an increase in RNA shortly after induction, as indicated by staining with pyronin. Histones, as indicated by alkaline Fast Green, seemed to increase in the cytoplasm following induction. This was of particular interest, since histones are usually thought to occur only in the nucleus.

23 Inflorescence Differentiation

Development of the inflorescence of *Xanthium* was described as early as 1915 by Farr.[48] His study did not include the immediate changes which occur upon induction, however. Naylor[131] did study development of both male and female flowers following 1, 4, 8, and continuous photoinductive cycles. She found that the rate of bud development was strongly increased by increasing induction, and that increasing induction also stimulated the production of carpellate more than staminate inflorescences. The vegetative stem tip has been described in some detail,[78,125,210] and some initial descriptions have been published on the histology of the developing terminal inflorescence.[210] The layer of cells immediately below the tip seemed to be the first to become mitotically active upon conversion from the vegetative to the flowering state.

Although much remains to be discovered, it is apparent that *Xanthium strumarium L.*, primarily the notomorph *pensylvanicum*, has contributed an extensive body of information relating to the flowering of plants in response to photoperiod.

REFERENCES

[1] Abeles, F. B. (1967). Inhibition of flowering in *Xanthium pensylvanicum* by ethylene. *Plant Physiol.* **42**, 608.
[2] Biswas, P. K., Paul, K. B. and Henderson, J. H. (1966). Effect of *Chrysanthemum* plant extract on flower initiation in short-day plants. *Physiol. Plantar.* **19**, 875.
[3] Bogorad, L. and McIlrath, W. J. (1959). A correlation of photoperiodic response of *Xanthium* and germination of implanted lettuce seed. In *Photoperiodism and Related Phenomena in Plants and Animals*, 301. Ed. R. B. Withrow. Amer. Assoc. Adv. Science, Washington, D. C.
[4] Bogorad, L. and McIlrath, W. J. (1960). Effect of light quality on axillary bud development in *Xanthium. Plant Physiol.* **35**, xxxii.
[5] Bonde, E. K. (1953). Growth inhibitors and auxin in leaves of cocklebur. *Physiol. Plantar.* **6**, 234.
[6] Bonde, E. K. (1955). The effect of various cycles of light and darkness on the growth of tomato and cocklebur plants. *Physiol. Plantar.* **8**, 913.
[7] Bonde, E. K. (1956). Further studies on the effect of various cycles of light and darkness on the growth of tomato and cocklebur plants. *Physiol. Plantar.* **9**, 51.
[8] Bonde, E. K. and Khudairi, A. K. (1954). Further experiments with a growth inhibitor extracted from *Xanthium* leaves. *Physiol. Plantar.* **7**, 66.
[9] Bonner, J. (1949). Further experiments on flowering in *Xanthium. Bot. Gaz.* **110**, 625.
[10] Bonner, J. and Bonner, D. (1948). Note on induction of flowering in *Xanthium. Bot. Gaz.* **110**, 154.
[11] Bonner, J., Heftmann, E. and Zeevaart, J. A. D. (1963). Suppression of floral induction by inhibitors of steroid biosynthesis. *Plant Physiol.* **38**, 81.
[12] Bonner, J. and Thurlow, J. (1949). Inhibition of photoperiodic induction in *Xanthium* by applied auxin. *Bot. Gaz.* **110**, 613.
[13] Bonner, J. and Zeevaart, J. A. D. (1962). Ribonucleic acid synthesis in the bud an essential component of floral induction in *Xanthium. Plant Physiol.* **37**, 43.
[14] Borthwick, H. A. and Downs, R. J. (1964). Roles of active phytochrome in control of flowering of *Xanthium pensylvanicum. Bot. Gaz.* **125**, 227.
[15] Borthwick, H. A., Hendricks, S. B. and Parker, M. W. (1952). The reaction controlling floral initiation. *Proc. Nat. Acad. Sci.* **38**, 929.
[16] Brown, G. N. and Taylor, F. G., (1966). Interaction of radiation and photoperiodism in *Xanthium chinense*. Effects of variation in time of radiation with respect to photoinduction. *Radiation Bot.* **6**, 145.

[17] Bünning, E. (1932). Über die Erblichkeit der Tagesperiodizität bei den *Phaseolus*— Blättern. Jahrb. *Wiss. Bot.* **77**, 283.

[18] Bünning, E. (1936). Die endogene Tagesrhythmik als Grundlage der photoperiodischen Reaktion. *Ber. dtsch. bot. Ges.* **54**, 590.

[19] Bünning, E. (1960). Opening Address: Biological Clocks. *Symposia on Quantitative Biology* **25**, 1.

[20] Bünning, E. (1964). *The Physiological Clock.* Springer-Verlag, Berlin, Göttingen, Heidelberg (Translated from the German *Die Physiologische Uhr*).

[21] Butler, W. L. and Lane, H. C. (1965). Dark transformations of phytochrome in vivo. II. *Plant Physiol.* **40**, 13.

[22] Campbell, C. W. and Leopold, A. C. (1958). Modification of photoperiodic response in cocklebur by CO_2. *Plant Physiol.* **33**, xix.

[23] Campori, A. S. (1945). El "Abrojo grande" es toxico para el cerdo. *An. Soc. Rural Argentina* **79**, 293.

[24] Carr, D. J. (1952). The photoperiodic behaviour of short-day plants. *Physiol. Plantar.* **5**, 70.

[25] Carr, D. J. (1953). On the nature of photoperiodic induction. I Photoperiodic treatments applied to detached leaves. *Physiol. Plantar.* **6**, 672.

[26] Carr, D. J. (1953). Ibid II Photoperiodic treatments of de-budded plants. *Physiol. Plantar.* **6**, 680.

[27] Carr, D. J. (1957). Ibid IV Preliminary experiments on the effect of light following the inductive long dark period in *Xanthium pensylvanicum*. *Physiol. Plantar.* **10**, 249.

[28] Carr, D. J. (1966). The relationship between florigen and the flower hormones. Conference on Plant Growth Regulators. *Ann. New York Acad. Sci.* **44**, 305.

[29] Carr, D. J. and Burrows, W. J. (1966). Evidence of the presence in xylem sap of substances with kinetin-like activity. *Life Sciences* **5**, 2061.

[30] Cherry, J. H. and van Huystee, R. B. (1965). Effects of 5-fluorouracil on photoperiodic induction and nucleic acid metabolism of *Xanthium. Plant Physiol.* **40**, 987.

[31] Cherry, J. H. and van Huystee, R. B. (1965). Comparison of messenger RNA in photoperiodically induced and noninduced *Xanthium* buds. *Science* **150**, 1450.

[32] Christensen, O. V. (1967). Leaf-movement rhythms and flowering in *Xanthium*. Master's thesis, Colorado State University, Ft. Collins.

[33] Cline, M. G. and Salisbury, F. B. (1966). Effects of ultraviolet radiation on the leaves of higher plants. *Radiation Bot.* **6**, 151.

[34] Cline, M. G. and Salisbury, F. B. (1966). Effects of ultraviolet alone and simulated solar ultraviolet radiation on the leaves of higher plants. *Nature* **211**, 484.

[35] Collins, W. T. (1962). Methionine-ethionine relationship to flowering of *Xanthium. Plant Physiol. Supplement* **37**, xxviii.

[36] Collins, W. T. (1963). Studies on the biochemistry of flowering of *Xanthium pensylvanicum. Diss. Abs.* **23**, 3091.

[37] Collins, W. T., Salisbury, F. B. and Ross, C. W. (1963). Growth regulators and flowering. III Antimetabolites. *Planta* **60**, 131.

[38] Cooke, A. R. (1954). Changes in free auxin content during the photoinduction of short-day plants. *Plant Physiol.* **29**, 440.

[39] Crocker, W. (1906). Role of seed coats in delayed germination. *Bot. Gaz.* **42**, 265.

[40] Davis, W. E. (1930). The development of dormancy in seeds of cocklebur (*Xanthium*). *Amer. J. Bot.* **17**, 77.

[41] de Zeeuw, D. (1957). Flowering of *Xanthium* under long-day conditions. *Nature* **180**, 558.

[42] de Zeeuw, D. and Leopold, A. C. (1956). The promotion of floral initiation by auxin. *Amer. J. Bot.* **43**, 47.

[43] Downs, R. J. (1956). Photoreversibility of flower initiation. *Plant Physiol.* **31**, 279.

[44] Drake, B. G. (1967). Heat transfer studies in *Xanthium*. Master of Science Thesis, Colorado State University, Fort Collins.

[45] Egley, G. H. (1962). Zootoxicity of cocklebur (*Xanthium pensylvanicum*) *Diss. Abs.* **22**, 2143.

[46] Erickson, R. O. (1966). Relative elemental rates and anisotropy of growth in area: a computer programme. *J. Expt. Bot.* **17**, 390.

[47] Esashi, Y. and Oda, Y. (1964). Inhibitory effect of far-red light on the flowering of *Xanthium pensylvanicum. Plant & Cell Physiol.* **5**, 507.

[48] Farr, C. H. (1915). The origin of the inflorescences of *Xanthium. Bot. Gaz.* **59**, 136.

[49] Geissman, T. A., Deuel, P., Bonde, E. K. and Addicott, F. A. (1954). Xanthinin: a plant growth-regulating compound from *Xanthium pennsylvanicum. J. Amer. Chemical Soc.* **76**, 685.

[50] Gifford, E. M., Jr. (1963). Developmental studies of vegetative and floral meristems. In *Meristems and Differentiation*. Brookhaven Symp. Biol. No. 16, 126.

[51] Gilbert, B. E. (1926). Interrelation of relative day length and temperature. *Bot. Gaz.* 81, 1.

[52] Greulach, V. A. and Haesloop, J. G. (1958). Influence of gibberellin on *Xanthium* flowering as related to number of photoinductive cycles. *Science* 127, 646.

[53] Hamner, K. C. (1938). Correlative effects of environmental factors on photoperiodism. *Bot. Gaz.* 99, 615.

[54] Hamner, K. C. (1940). Interrelation of light and darkness in photoperiodic induction. *Bot. Gaz.* 101, 658.

[55] Hamner, K. C. (1960). Photoperiodism and circadian rhythms. *Cold Spring Harbor Symposia on Quant. Biol.* 25, 269.

[56] Hamner, K. C. and Bonner, J. (1938). Photoperiodism in relation to hormones as factors in floral initiation and development. *Bot. Gaz.* 100, 388.

[57] Hamner, K. C. and Nanda, K. K. (1956). A relationship between applications of indoleacetic acid and the high-intensity light reaction of photoperiodism. *Bot. Gaz.* 118, 13.

[58] Hamner, K. C. and Reid, H. B. (1967). Relation of the circadian rhythm of leaf movement and the flowering response of *Xanthium*. Paper presented at the Western Section, Amer. Soc. of Plant Physiol., Univ. of Calif. at Los Angeles.

[59] Hamner, K. C. and Takimoto, A. (1964). Circadian rhythms and plant photoperiodism. *Amer. Nat.* 902, 295.

[60] Harvey, R. B., Larson, A. H., Landon, R. H., Boyd, W. L. and Erickson, L. C. (1945). Weeds poisonous to livestock. *Bull. Minn. Agric. Expt. Sta.* 388, 1.

[61] Heath, O. V. S., Mansfield, T. A. and Meidner, H. (1965). Light-induced stomatal opening (in *Xanthium pennsylvanicum*) and the postulated role of glycollic acid. *Nature* 207, 960.

[62] Hendricks, S. B. (1960). Rates of change of phytochrome as an essential factor determining photoperiodism in plants. *Cold Spring Harbor Symposia on Quantitative Biology* 25, 245.

[63] Hendricks, S. B. and Borthwick, H. A. (1963). Control of plant growth by light. In *Environmental Control of Plant Growth*, 233. Ed. L. T. Evans. Academic Press, N.Y.

[64] Hillman, W. S. (1962). *The Physiology of Flowering*. Holt, Rinehart and Winston, N.Y.

[65] Hillman, W. S. (1967). The physiology of phytochrome. *Ann. Rev. Plant Physiol.* 18, 301.

[66] Holowinshy, A. W., Moore, P. B. and Torrey, J. G. (1965). Regulatory aspects of chloroplast growth in leaves of *Xanthium pensylvanicum* and etiolated red kidney bean seedling leaves. *Protoplasma* 60, 94.

[67] Hoshizaki, T., Carpenter, B. H. and Hamner, K. C. (1964). The interaction of plant hormones and rotation around a horizontal axis on the growth and flowering of *Xanthium pensylvanicum*. *Planta* 61, 178.

[68] Hoshizaki, T. and Hamner, K. C. (1962). An unusual stem bending response of *Xanthium pensylvanicum* to horizontal rotation. *Plant Physiol.* 37, 453.

[69] Hoshizaki, T. and Hamner, K. C. (1962). Effect of rotation on flowering response of *Xanthium pensylvanicum*. *Science* 137, 535.

[70] Jennings, P. R. and Zuck, R. K. (1954). The cotyledon in relation to photoperiodism in cocklebur. *Bot. Gaz.* 116, 199.

[71] Khan, A. A. (1966). Breaking of dormancy in *Xanthium* seeds by kinetin mediated by light and DNA-dependent RNA synthesis. *Physiol. Plantar.* 19, 869.

[72] Khudairi, A. K. and Bonde, E. K. (1954). Growth inhibitor activity in *Xanthium* in relation to photoperiodism. *Plant Physiol.* 29, 533.

[73] Khudairi, A. K. and Hamner, K. C. (1954). Effect of ethylene chlorohydrin on floral initiation in *Xanthium*. *Bot. Gaz.* 115, 289.

[74] Khudairi, A. K. and Hamner, K. C. (1954). The relative sensitivity of *Xanthium* leaves of different ages to photoperiodic induction. *Plant Physiol.* 29, 251.

[75] Krizek, D. T., McIlrath, W. J. and Vergara, B. S. (1966). Photoperiodic induction of senescence in *Xanthium* plants. *Science* 151, 95.

[76] Lam, S. L. (1965). Movement of the flower stimulus in *Xanthium*. *Amer. J. Bot.* 52, 924.

[77] Lam, S. L. and Leopold, A. C. (1960). Reversion from flowering to the vegetative state in *Xanthium*. *Amer. J. Bot.* 47, 256.

[78] Lance, A. (1957). Récherches cytologiques sur l'évolution de quelques méristèmes apicaux et sur ses variations provoquées par des traitements photopériodiques. *Ann. Sci. Nat. Bot.* 18, 91.

79 Lang, A. (1956). Gibberellin and flower formation. *Naturwiss.* **43**, 544.
80 Lang, A. (1957). The effect of gibberellin upon flower formation. *Proc. Nat. Acad. Sci.* **43**, 709.
81 Lang, A. (1958). Induction of reproductive growth in plants. Fourth International Congress of Biochemistry. *VI–Biochemistry of Morphogenesis*, 126.
82 Lang, A. (1961). Auxins in flowering. In *Encyclopedia of Plant Physiology* **14**, 909. Ed. W. Ruhland. Springer-Verlag, Berlin.
83 Langston, R. and Leopold, A. C. (1954). The dark fixation of carbon dioxide as a factor in photoperiodism. *Plant Physiol.* **29**, 436.
84 Lincoln, R. G. and Cunningham, A. (1964). Evidence for a florigenic acid. *Nature* **202**, 559.
85 Lincoln, R. G., Cunningham, A., Carpenter, B. H., Alexander, J. and Mayfield, D. L. (1966). Florigenic acid from fungal culture. *Plant Physiol.* **41**, 1079.
86 Lincoln, R. G. and Hamner, K. C. (1958). An effect of gibberellic acid on the flowering of *Xanthium*, a short-day plant. *Plant Physiol.* **33**, 101.
87 Lincoln, R. G., Mayfield, D. L. and Cunningham, A. (1961). Preparation of a floral initiating extract from *Xanthium*. *Science* **133**, 756.
88 Lincoln, R. G., Mayfield, D. L., Hutchins, R. O., Cunningham, A., Hamner, K. C. and Carpenter, B. H. (1962). Floral initiation of *Xanthium* in response to application of an extract from a day-neutral plant. *Nature* **195**, 918.
89 Lincoln, R. G., Raven, K. A. and Hamner, K. C. (1956). Certain factors influencing expression of the flowering stimulus in *Xanthium*. Part I. Translocation and inhibition of the flowering stimulus. *Bot. Gaz.* **117**, 193.
90 Lincoln, R. G., Raven, K. A. and Hamner, K. C. (1958). Certain factors influencing expression of the flowering stimulus in *Xanthium*. Part II. Relative contribution of buds and leaves to effectiveness of inductive treatment. *Bot. Gaz.* **119**, 179.
91 Linnaeus, C. (1753). *Species Plantarum*. Stockholm.
92 Liverman, J. L. (1955). The physiology of flowering. *Ann. Rev. Plant Physiol.* **6**, 177.
93 Liverman, J. L. and Bonner, J. (1953). Biochemistry of the photoperiodic response: The high-intensity-light reaction. *Bot. Gaz.* **115**, 121.
94 Lockhart, J. A. (1961). Mechanism of the photoperiodic process in higher plants. *Encyclopedia of Plant Physiol.* **16**, 390.
95 Lockhart, J. A. and Hamner, K. C. (1954). Effect of darkness and indoleacetic acid following exposure to short day on the floral response of *Xanthium*, a short-day plant. *Bot. Gaz.* **116**, 133.
96 Lockhart, J. A. and Hamner, K. C. (1954). Partial reactions in the formation of the floral stimulus in *Xanthium*. *Plant Physiol.* **29**, 509.
97 Lona, F. (1946). Sul comportamento fotoperiodico di alcune specie di *Xanthium*. Brevidiurne che fioriscono a luce continua. *Nuovo G. bot. ital.* **53**, 635.
98 Lona, F. (1946). Sui fenomeni di induzione, posteffetto e localizzazione fotoperiodica. L'induzione antogena indiretta delle foglie primordiali di *Xanthium italicum* Moretti. *Nuovo G. bot. ital.* **53**, 548.
99 Lona, F. (1947). Esigenze fotoperiodiche dei poliploidi e loro significato ecologico e fitogeografico. Nota preventiva. *Nuovo G. bot. ital.* **54**, 793.
100 Lona, F. (1959). Some aspects of photothermal and chemical control of growth and flowering. In *Photoperiodism and Related Phenomena in Plants and Animals*, 351. Ed. R. B. Withrow. Amer. Assoc. Adv. Sci., Washington, D.C.
101 Long, E. M. (1939). Photoperiodic induction as influenced by environment factors. *Bot. Gaz.* **101**, 168.
102 Löve, D. and Dansereau, P. (1959). Biosystematic studies on *Xanthium*: taxonomic appraisal and ecological status. *Can. J. Bot.* **37**, 173.
103 Maksymowych, R. (1962). An analysis of leaf elongation in *Xanthium pensylvanicum* presented in relative elemental rates. *Amer. J. Bot.* **49**, 7.
104 Maksymowych, R. (1963). Cell division and cell elongation in leaf development of *Xanthium pensylvanicum*. *Amer. J. Bot.* **50**, 891.
105 Maksymowych, R. and Blum, M. K. (1966). Incorporation of H³-thymidine in leaf nuclei of *Xanthium pensylvanicum*. *Amer. J. Bot.* **53**, 134.
106 Maksymowych, R., Blum, M. K. and Devlin, R. G. (1966). Autoradiographic studies of the synthesis of nuclear DNA in various tissues during leaf development of *Xanthium pennsylvanicum*. *Develop. Biol.* **13**, 250.
107 Maksymowych, R. and Erickson, R. O. (1960). Development of the lamina in *Xanthium italicum* represented by the plastochron index. *Amer. J. Bot.* **47**, 451.
108 Maksymowych, R. and Mark, R. E. (1962). Architecture of cell elongation in leaf development of *Xanthium pensylvanicum*. Abst. of papers. *Amer. J. Bot.* **49**, 655.

[109] Mancinelli, A. L. and Downs, R. J. (1967). Inhibition of flowering of *Xanthium pensylvanicum* Wallr. by prolonged irradiation with far-red. *Plant Physiol.* **42**, 95.

[110] Mann, L. K. (1940). Effect of some environmental factors on floral initiation in *Xanthium. Bot. Gaz.* **102**, 339.

[111] Mansfield, T. A. (1964). A stomatal light reaction [in *Xanthium pennsylvanicum*] sensitive to wavelengths in the region of 700 mμ. *Nature* **201**, 470.

[112] Mansfield, T. A. (1965). Responses of (*Xanthium pennsylvanicum*) stomata to short duration increases in carbon dioxide concentration. *Physiol. Plantar.* **18**, 79.

[113] Mansfield, T. A. (1965). The low intensity light reaction of stomata. Effects of red light on rhythmic stomatal behavior in *X. pensylvanicum. Proc. Roy. Soc. Ser. B.* **162**, 567.

[114] Mansfield, T. A. (1965). Studies in stomatal behaviour XII Opening in high temperature in darkness. *J. Expt. Bot.* **16**, 721.

[115] Mansfield, T. A. and Heath, O. V. S. (1963). Studies in stomatal behaviour IX Photoperiodic effects on rhythmic phenomena in *Xanthium pennsylvanicum. J. Expt. Bot.* **14**, 334.

[116] Mansfield, T. A. and Meidner, H. (1966). Stomatal opening in light of different wavelengths: Effects of blue light independent of carbon dioxide concentration. *J. Expt. Bot.* **17**, 510.

[117] Mayfield, D. L., Lincoln, R. G., Hutchins, R. O. and Cunningham, A. (1963). Concentration of a floral-inducing entity from plant extracts. *J. Agr. Food Chem.* **11**, 35.

[118] McHargue, J. S. (1921). Some points of interest concerning the cocklebur and its seeds. *Ecology* **2**, 110.

[119] McIlrath, W. J. (1965). Mobility of boron in several dicotyledonous species. *Bot. Gaz.* **126**, 27.

[120] McIlrath, W. J. and Bogorad, L. (1958). Photoperiodic floral induction of *Xanthium* and germination of lettuce seeds implanted in the petioles. *Bot. Gaz.* **119**, 186.

[121] Meidner, H. and Mansfield, T. A. (1965). Studies in stomatal behaviour. XI. Further observations on responses to night length. *J. Expt. Bot.* **16**, 145.

[122] Meidner, H. and Mansfield, T. A. (1966). Rates of photosynthesis and respiration in relation to stomatal movements in leaves treated with α-hydroxysulphonate and glycollate. *J. Expt. Bot.* **17**, 502.

[123] Mellor, R. S., Salisbury, F. B. and Raschke, K. (1964). Leaf temperatures in controlled environments. *Planta* **61**, 56.

[124] Miller, J. and Ross, C. W. (1966). Inhibition of leaf processes by p-fluorophenyl-alanine during induction of flowering in the cocklebur. *Plant Physiol.* **41**, 1185.

[125] Millington, W. F. and Fisk, E. L. (1956). Shoot development in *Xanthium pennsylvanicum* I The vegetative plant. *Amer. J. Bot.* **43**, 655.

[126] Millspaugh, C. F. and Sherff, E. E. (1918). New species of *Xanthium* and *Solidago. Field Museum Natural History, Chicago. Bot. Ser.* **4**, 1.

[127] Moore, P. H., Reid, H. B. and Hamner, K. C. (1967). Flowering responses of *Xanthium pensylvanicum* to long dark periods. *Plant Physiol* **42**, 503.

[128] Naylor, A. W. (1941). Effect of nutrition and age upon rate of development of terminal staminate inflorescences of *Xanthium pennsylvanicum. Bot. Gaz.* **103**, 342.

[129] Naylor, A. W. (1950). Some effects of growth substances on floral initiation and development in *Xanthium. Amer. J. Bot.* **37**, 681.

[130] Naylor, A. W. (1952). The control of flowering. *Sci. Amer.* **186**, 49.

[131] Naylor, F. L. (1941). Effect of length of induction period on floral development of *Xanthium pennsylvanicum. Bot. Gaz.* **103**, 146.

[132] Neidle, E. K. (1939). Nitrogen nutrition in relation to photoperiodism in *Xanthium pennsylvanicum. Bot. Gaz.* **100**, 607.

[133] Nitsan, J. (1962). Electrophoretic patterns of *Xanthium* leaf extracts as affected by physiological age of leaf, photoperiod, and age of plant. *Plant Physiol.* **37**, 291.

[134] Nitsch, J. P. and Went, F. W. (1959). The induction of flowering in *Xanthium pennsylvanicum* under long days. In *Photoperiodism and Related Phenomena in Plants and Animals*, 311. Ed. R. B. Withrow. Amer. Assoc. Advanc. Sci., Washington.

[135] Osborne, D. J. (1962). Effect of kinetin on protein and nucleic acid metabolism in *Xanthium* leaves during senescence. *Plant Physiol.* **37**, 595.

[136] Osborne, D. J. and McCalla, D. R. (1961). Rapid bioassay for kinetin and kinins using senescing leaf tissue. *Plant Physiol.* **36**, 219.

[137] Ota, J. (1925). Continuous respiration studies of dormant seeds of *Xanthium. Bot. Gaz.* **80**, 288.

[138] Papenfuss, H. D. (1966). Time measurement in flowering of *Xanthium*. Ph.D. Dissert., Colorado State University, Fort Collins.

[139] Papenfuss, H. D. and Salisbury, F. B. (1966). Light promotion of flowering and time measurement in *Xanthium*. Z. *Pflanzenphysiol.* **54**, 195.

[140] Papenfuss, H. D. and Salisbury, F. B. (1967). Properties of clock resetting in flowering of *Xanthium*. *Plant Physiol.* **42**, 1562.

[141] Parker, M. W., Hendricks, S. B., Borthwick, H. A. and Scully, N. J. (1946). Action spectrum for the photoperiodic control of floral initiation of short-day plants. *Bot. Gaz.* **108**, 1.

[142] Pirschle, K. and von Wettstein, F. (1940). Einige vorläufige Beobachtungen über die Wirkung verschiedener Lichtintensitaten und qualitäten auf höhere pflanzen unter konstanten bedingungen. *Biol. Zentralbl.* **60**, 626.

[143] Ramaley, F. (1934). Influence of supplemental light on blooming. *Bot. Gaz.* **96**, 165.

[144] Rastelli, G. and Giberri, C. (1930). Sul principio attivo dello *Xanthium spinosum*. *Boll. Soc. Ital. Biol. Sper.* **5**, 549.

[145] Ray, P. M. and Alexander, W. E. (1966). Photoperiodic adaptation to latitude in *Xanthium strumarium*. *Amer. J. Bot.* **53**, 806.

[146] Reid, H. B., Moore, P. H. and Hamner, K. C. (1967). Control of flowering of *Xanthium pensylvanicum* by red and far-red light. *Plant Physiol.* **42**, 532.

[147] Richmond, A. E. and Lang, A. (1957). Effect of kinetin on protein content and survival of detached *Xanthium* leaves. *Science* **125**, 650.

[148] Roberts, R. H. (1951). The induction of flowering with a plant extract. In *Plant Growth Substances*, 347. Ed. F. Skoog. Univ. Wisconsin Press.

[149] Roberts, R. H. (1951). Induction and blossoming of *Xanthium*. *Science* **113**, 726.

[150] Roberts, R. H. (1964). The use of natural extracts in sex regulation of plants. In *Fifth International Conference on Plant Growth Substances* **123**, 611. Ed. J. P. Nitsch. CNRS, Paris.

[151] Roberts, R. H. and Struckmeyer, B. E. (1964). The lipid hormones of the reproductive cycle. *Plant Physiol.* **39**, xxxvi.

[152] Roberts, R. H., Struckmeyer, B. E. and Fogelberg, S. O. (1957). Chemically induced cell proliferation and its inhibition by a naturally occurring antiauxin. *Science* **126**, 206.

[153] Ross, C. W. (1962). Effects of cobaltous chloride on metabolism of *Xanthium pennsylvanicum* leaves. *Plant Physiol. Supplement* **37**, xxxvii.

[154] Ross, C. W. (1962). Nucleotide composition of ribonucleic acid from vegetative and flowering cocklebur-shoot tips. *Biochim. Biophys. Acta* **55**, 387.

[155] Ross, C. W. (1964). Influence of 6-azauracil on pyrimidine metabolism of cocklebur leaf discs. *Biochim. Biophys. Acta* **87**, 564.

[156] Ross, C. W. (1964). Metabolism of 6-azauracil and its incorporation into RNA in the cocklebur. *Phytochem.* **3**, 603.

[157] Ross, C. W. (1965). Comparison of incorporation and metabolism of RNA pyrimidine nucleotide precursors in leaf tissues. *Plant Physiol.* **40**, 65.

[158] Salisbury, F. B. (1955). Kinetic studies on the physiology of flowering. Ph.D. Dissert., Calif. Institute of Tech., Pasadena, California.

[159] Salisbury, F. B. (1955). The dual role of auxin in flowering. *Plant Physiol.* **30**, 327.

[160] Salisbury, F. B. (1957). Growth regulators and flowering. I Survey methods. *Plant Physiol.* **32**, 600.

[161] Salisbury, F. B. (1958). The flowering process. *Sci. Amer.* **198**, 109.

[162] Salisbury, F. B. (1959). Growth regulators and flowering. II The cobaltous ion. *Plant Physiol.* **34**, 598.

[163] Salisbury, F. B. (1959). Influence of certain growth regulators on flowering of cocklebur. In *Photoperiodism and Related Phenomena in Plants and Animals*, 381. Ed. R. B. Withrow. Amer. Assoc. Adv. Sci., Washington, D.C.

[164] Salisbury, F. B. (1959). Metabolic approaches to flower induction. Reprinted from *IX International Botanical Congress, Proceedings*, Vols. II, IIA.

[165] Salisbury, F. B. (1961). Metabolic approaches to flower induction. *Recent Adv. Bot.* **11**, 1294.

[166] Salisbury, F. B. (1961). Photoperiodism and the flowering process. *Ann. Rev. Plant Physiol.* **12**, 293.

[167] Salisbury, F. B. (1963). *The Flowering Process*. Pergamon Press, Oxford.

[168] Salisbury, F. B. (1963). Biological timing and hormone synthesis in flowering of *Xanthium*. *Planta* **59**, 518.

[169] Salisbury, F. B. (1965). Time measurement and the light period in flowering. *Planta* **66**, 1.

[170] Salisbury, F. B. (1966). Die Blütenbildung. *Naturwiss. Medizin* **12**, 48.

[171] Salisbury, F. B. (1968). *The Biology of Flowering*. In Press.

[172] Salisbury, F. B. Unpublished data.

[173] Salisbury, F. B., and Bonner, J. (1955). Interaction of light and auxin in flowering. *Beitr. Biol. Pflanz.* **31**, 419.

[174] Salisbury, F. B. and Bonner, J. (1956). The reactions of the photoinductive dark period. *Plant Physiol.* **31**, 141.

[175] Salisbury, F. B. and Bonner, J. (1960). Inhibition of photoperiodic induction by 5-fluorouracil. *Plant Physiol.* **35**, 173.

[176] Salisbury, F. B. and Eichhorn, G. L. (1963). Chelates of cobaltous ion and flowering of *Xanthium*. *Planta* **60**, 145.

[177] Searle, N. E. (1961). Persistence and transport of flowering stimulus in *Xanthium*. *Plant Physiol.* **36**, 656.

[178] Searle, N. E. (1965). Bioassay of floral stimulus in *Xanthium*. *Plant Physiol.* **40**, 273.

[179] Sen, S. P. (1962). The role of carbon dioxide fixation in photoperiodism–the effect of dark interruption treatments. *Indian J. Plant Physiol.* **5**, 202.

[180] Sen, S. P. (1964). Tracer studies on the biochemical aspects of flowering: translocation of photosynthates and metabolic changes in the shoot apex. *Indian J. Plant Physiol.* **7**, 1.

[181] Sen, S. P. and Leopold, A. C. (1956). Influence of light and darkness upon carbon dioxide fixation. *Plant Physiol.* **31**, 323.

[182] Shull, C. A. (1911). The oxygen minimum and the germination of *Xanthium* seeds. *Bot. Gaz.* **52**, 453.

[183] Shull, C. A. (1915). Physiological isolation of types in the genus *Xanthium*. *Bot. Gaz.* **69**, 474.

[184] Shull, C. A. (1927). Nature of the multiple seeded *Xanthium*. *Bot. Gaz.* **83**, 385.

[185] Shull, C. A. (1928). The multiple-seeded *Xanthium*. *Bot. Gaz.* **86**, 240.

[186] Shull, C. A. (1934). Persistence of subspecific types of *Xanthium* under field conditions. *Bot. Gaz.* **96**, 175.

[187] Shull, C. A. and Davis, W. B. (1923). Delayed germination and catalase activity in *Xanthium*. *Bot. Gaz.* **75**, 268.

[188] Skok, J. and Scully, N. J. (1954). Characteristics and movement of the flowering stimulus from the induced leaf of *Xanthium*. *Bot. Gaz.* **116**, 142.

[189] Smith, H. J., McIlrath, W. J. and Bogorad, L. (1956). Some effects of iron deficiency on flowering of *Xanthium*. *Bot. Gaz.* **118**, 174.

[190] Snyder, W. E. (1940). Effect of light and temperature on floral initiation in cocklebur and Biloxi soybean. *Bot. Gaz.* **102**, 302.

[191] Struckmeyer, B. E. (1941). Structure of stems in relation to differentiation and abortion of blossom buds. *Bot. Gaz.* **103**, 182.

[192] Struckmeyer, B. E. (1949). Effect of alpha-naphthalene acetamide upon the anatomical structures of cocklebur grown in a nutrient medium deficient in calcium. *Bot. Gaz.* **111**, 130.

[193] Struckmeyer, B. E. and MacVicar, R. (1948). Further investigations on the relation of photoperiod to the boron requirement of plants. *Bot. Gaz.* **109**, 237.

[194] Struckmeyer, B. E. and Roberts, R. H. (1955). The inhibition of abnormal cell proliferation with antiauxin. *Amer. J. Bot.* **42**, 401.

[195] Symons, J. L. (1926). Studies in the genus *Xanthium*. *Bot. Gaz.* **81**, 121.

[196] Takimoto, A. and Hamner, K. C. (1965). Studies on red light interruption in relation to timing mechanisms involved in the photoperiodic response of *Pharbitis nil*. *Plant Physiol.* **40**, 952.

[197] Takimoto, A. and Ikeda, K. (1961). Effect of twilight on photoperiodic induction in some short-day plants. *Plant & Cell Physiol.* **2**, 213.

[198] Taylor, A. O. (1965). Some effects of photoperiod on the biosynthesis of phenylpropane derivatives in *Xanthium*. *Plant Physiol.* **40**, 273.

[199] Taylor, A. O. and Wong, E. (1965). Quercetagetin 3, 6-dimethyl ether (in *Xanthium*). *Tetrahedron Letters* **41**, 3675.

[200] Taylor, A. O. and Zucker, M. (1966). Turnover and metabolism of chlorogenic acid in *Xanthium* leaves and potato tubers. *Plant Physiol.* **41**, 1350.

[201] Thomas, R. G. (1963). Floral induction and the stimulation of cell division in *Xanthium*. *Science* **140**, 54.

[202] Thornton, N. C. (1935). Factors influencing germination and development of dormancy in cocklebur seeds. *Contrib. Boyce Thompson Inst.* **7**, 477.

[203] Thurlow, J. F. (1948). Certain aspects of photoperiodism. Master's Thesis, Calif. Institute of Tech., Pasadena, California.

[204] Trivedi, B. S. and Sharma, P. C. (1964). Morphology of the bur of *Xanthium*. *Can. J. Bot.* **42**, 1235.

[205] Vergara, B. S. and McIlrath, W. J. (1960). Influence of photoperiod on water uptake of *Xanthium*. *Bot. Gaz.* **122**, 96.

[206] Wallroth, K. F. W. (1844). Monographischer Versuch uber die Gewachsgattung *Xanthium*. *Beitr. Bot.* **1**, 228.

[207] Wareing, P. F. (1954). Experiments on the 'light-break' effect in short-day plants. *Physiol. Plantar.* **7**, 157.

[208] Wareing, P. F. and Foda, H. A. (1956). Possible role of growth inhibitors in the dormancy of seed of *Xanthium* and lettuce. *Nature* **178**, 908.

[209] Wareing, P. F. and Foda, H. A. (1957). Growth inhibitors and dormancy in *Xanthium* seed. *Physiol. Plantar.* **10**, 266.

[210] Wetmore, R. H., Gifford, E. M., Jr. and Green, M. C. (1959). Development of vegetative and floral buds. In *Photoperiodism and Related Phenomena in Plants and Animals*, 255. Ed. R. B. Withrow. Amer. Assoc. Advanc. Sci., Washington.

[211] Widder, F. J. (1923). Die Arten der Gattung *Xanthium*. *Repertorium Spec. Nov. Reg. Veget. Beihefte* **20**, 1.

[212] Withrow, A. P. (1945). The interrelationship of nitrogen supply and photoperiod on the flowering, growth and stem anatomy of certain long-day and short-day plants. *Butler Univ. Bot. Stud.* **7**, 40.

[213] Withrow, A. P. and Withrow, R. B. (1943). Translocation of the floral stimulus in *Xanthium*. *Bot. Gaz.* **104**, 409.

[214] Withrow, R. B. and Withrow, A. P. (1940). The effect of various wavebands of supplementary radiation on the photoperiodic response of certain plants. *Plant Physiol.* **15**, 609.

[215] Zeevaart, J. A. D. (1957). Studies on flowering by means of grafting. II Photoperiodic treatment of detached perilla and *Xanthium* leaves. *Koninkl. Nederl. Akademie Van Wetenschappen-Amsterdam, Proc.*, Series C, **60** (3).

[216] Zeevaart, J. A. D. (1958). Flower formation as studied by grafting. *Mededelingen van de Landbouwhogeschool* **58**, 1.

[217] Zeevaart, J. A. D. (1962). Physiology of flowering. *Science* **137**, 723.

3

Glycine max (L.) Merrill

By Karl C. Hamner

1 History of Use

Taxonomy

Frequently, the soybean has been referred to by the scientific name *Soya max*. Ricker and Morse[97] contend, in accordance with the International Code of Botanical Nomenclature, the correct name is *Glycine max* (*L.*) Merrill. According to Johnson and Bernard,[56] *Glycine max* and *G. ussuriensis* are both known to have 40 chromosomes and to behave as diploids. They are cross-fertile and the hybrids usually have normal fertility. In at least one species, *G. javanica*, there are some types reported to have 20 pairs of chromosomes while some other types have 10. Johnson and Bernard cite references which indicate that the basic number of chromosomes in the genus is 10.

Origin and cultivation

A recent book entitled *The Soybean*[81] contains chapters on genetics, breeding, physiology, nutrition, and the management of the plant, including a good discussion of the origin and cultivation of soybeans. While the origin of the cultivated form of soybean is uncertain, it is likely to have been in north central China. There seems to be agreement that *G. ussuriensis* was the progenitor of the cultivated form. It has been proposed that the soybean was received by Korea from North China between 200 B.C. and the Third Century. From Korea it was then introduced into Japan. Morse[72] reports that the plant appeared in the United States as early as 1804. Since 1898, introductions of numerous varieties from Manchuria, China, Korea, and Japan, have been made by the U.S.D.A. and have been used in soybean breeding in this country.

Cartter and Hartwig[13] cite several reviews that have appeared on soybean management since 1908. These authors discuss recent research on culture and management of soybean as a major crop in the United States. According to the most recent reports[117] soybeans now rank third among the cash crops in this country and first among the oil seed crops of the Western Hemisphere. The United States produces approximately 73 per cent of the total world crop.

2 Growing Techniques and Growth Habit

General

The literature on the culture of soybean as a commercial crop is very extensive. One may wish to contrast a paper by Morse in 1927[71] with that by Nagata in 1960[75] in which the problems of the culture of different varieties of soybean are discussed in relation to latitude, time of planting, etc.

Because of these varietal differences, agronomists have classified soybean varieties into 10 maturity classes, ranging from Group 00, adapted to northern United States and southern Canada, to Group VIII, adapted to the Gulf Coast area.[56] After each variety mentioned in this review, I have attempted to show the group to which the particular variety belongs.

Several varieties of soybean were used by Garner and Allard[38,39] in the original experiments (Fig. 3–1) from which they proposed a dependence on daylength. This led to extensive experimentation on the photoperiodic control of floral induction in soybeans.

In growing soybeans for experimentation, difficulties are often encountered during germination and early growth. Soybean seeds do not remain viable for more than a few years. The proper soil moisture content may be critical in seed germination.[54,82] Soybeans often go through a period of nitrogen deficiency during the early stages of development, when the stores of nitrogen in the seed are exhausted and before nitrogen fixation has developed sufficiently to supply nitrogen requirements. Fred *et al.*[29] point out that under certain conditions when maximum opportunity for photosynthesis exists, plants may remain in this condition in spite of the development of nodules on the roots. Under these circumstances, plants may be induced to recover by shading or supplying nitrogen fertilizer.

FIGURE 3–1. Biloxi soybean plants, from the experiments of Garner and Allard in 1919. The plants on the left, with pods, were exposed to only 12 hours of light each day (from Garner and Allard[39]).

When soybeans are grown in pots on greenhouse benches, root temperatures may become high. Early and Cartter[22] found that soybean plants can tolerate a wide range of root temperatures, 22° to 27°C being most favorable for maximum dry weight production of shoots and roots. Temperatures as low as 17° may reduce development.

Withrow and Withrow[115] used soybean as one test plant in a rather comprehensive study of artificial sources of radiant energy. They concluded that fluorescent lamps are the best single source of artificial illumination. Parker and Borthwick[88] on the other hand, concluded that radiation from a carbon

arc lamp burning 'sunshine' carbons supplemented with radiation from incandescent filament lamps was superior to any other type for growing soybeans.
Excellent growth in soybeans occurs under artificial illumination of cool white
fluorescent lamps supplemented with incandescent light if the illuminance at
the leaf surface approaches 2000 f.c.

Growing techniques

The following procedure is satisfactory in growing Biloxi soybeans (VIII) for
experimental purposes. Pots (10 cm.) are filled with a mixture of two parts
autoclaved sandy loam soil and one part vermiculite. The mixture is watered
and four seeds are placed on the soil surface in each pot. The seeds are then
covered with about an inch of dry soil mixture and placed on the greenhouse
bench. The pots are not watered again until the seeds germinate. At this time
the pots are sprinkled with a suspension of nitrogen-fixing bacteria obtained by
soaking the root systems of plants from previous experiments in tapwater. The
plants are then watered as required, and about once a week are supplied with a
balanced nutrient solution. After the primary leaves expand on most of the
plants, the seedlings are thinned to leave two uniform plants per pot. The plants
are allowed to grow in the greenhouse under long-day conditions until two or
three trifoliate leaves are fully expanded. Long-day conditions are obtained by
extending the natural day to approximately 20 hours by incandescent light of
approximately 50 f.c. The plants are then given an experimental treatment and
returned to the long-day conditions in the greenhouse until examined for floral
development some time later. The pots are placed about 5 inches apart on the
greenhouse bench and the plants become fairly crowded as they grow. If the
plants are given too much growing space or too much fertilizer, they will tend to
produce branches. When a branched plant is given a photoperiodic treatment,
each branch may respond by producing floral buds, and such plants may not
show a direct correlation between flower bud production and effectiveness of
treatment. If one uses crowded conditions and limits fertilizer, the plants rarely
produce branches and may grow to a height of several feet before dissection.
As plants grow and become fairly tall, they are staked to give them support.
Plants must be checked periodically to prevent an infestation with red spider to
which they are very susceptible.

Growth habit

It is generally considered that exposure to short days induces flower bud formation while decreasing the rate of vegetative growth in many short-day plants
including soybean. However, some reports indicate that short days may stimulate localized growth. Psarev[92] noted that short days retarded growth in height
of the plant, and reduced the number and length of internodes produced. He
also noted that length of day affected the structural characteristics of the plant.
The size of the parenchyma cells in the upper part of the stems was particularly
reduced in plants exposed to short days. He later reported[93] that plants abscised
leaves earlier if exposed to long photoperiods followed by short photoperiods
than did plants exposed to short photoperiods throughout their life. Furthermore, while the height of the plants increased when they were exposed to long
days, the diameter at the internodes decreased.[94] The increase in stem diameter
of the plants maintained on short days was attributed to increased growth and
differentiation of the xylem. In comparing an early variety of soybean, Krushal,
with a late variety, Illini (III), Psarev and Neuman[95] found a greater cambial
activity and greater xylem development in both varieties when they were grown
on short days. However, cambial growth was affected by daylength more in

Illini than in Krushal. Psarev and Veselovskaja[96] also report the positive influence of short days on cambial activity in 12 varieties of soybeans with induction periods of 3 to 15 short days. Three short days stimulated flowering, and in some varieties, 3 to 5 short days increased growth in height but additional short days inhibited it. Withrow[114] found that a limitation of nitrogen could interact with daylength markedly to alter the anatomy of the stem. Under limited nitrogen supply, cell size decreased and cell wall thickness and lignification increased even when the plants were exposed to long photoperiods. Under short photoperiods, similar nitrogen limitations caused a smaller ratio of phloem to xylem cells in the flowering stems than in the vegetative stems. A greater proportion of undifferentiated cells was found in the vegetative stem. These results may indicate that short days stimulate cambial activity, thereby producing a greater amount of xylem. Langer and Bussell[64] exposed Biloxi soybean plants to just enough short days to induce flowering. They found that during the induction period, the rate of leaf initiation was significantly greater in flowering shoots than in vegetative ones.

3 Inflorescence Structure and Criteria of Flowering Response

Anatomical studies

Guard[46] has described in detail the development of flowers in the Manchu (III) variety of soybean. The flowers are borne in axillary (rarely terminal) racemes, usually of 5 to 16 flowers each, but with as many as 35 flowers in a single inflorescence. The first indication of floral development is the appearance of a knob-like primordium in the axil of a bract which is still developing. The calyx tube, at this time, develops rapidly. While the petals are still very small, the primordia of the outer circle of stamens appear. When the last primordium of the first circle of stamens is visible, the second circle of stamens develops and appears to merge with the outer circle as a result of the development of basal tissue. A single carpel appears almost simultaneously with the last circle of stamens. The calyx forms a protective covering during the development of these inner organs. The petal primordia do not begin to develop rapidly until the microspores begin to develop in the anthers; then there is a rapid growth of the petals. The filaments supporting the anthers also develop rather early and separately until the tetrads are beginning to round into microspores. This sequence of development makes it very easy to detect the presence of the flower buds since a sharp needle breaking the calyx covering usually will reveal the stamens at some stage of development even when the flower primordium is very young. Fukui and Gotoh[32] also discuss developmental stages in the floral organs of different varieties of soybean.

Borthwick and Parker,[3] in what is perhaps the most pertinent anatomical discussion, relate the differentiation of meristems and the blossoming of Biloxi soybeans to floral induction and photoperiodism. Flower buds could not be identified by dissection until about a week after transfer to short days. The first evidence of flower bud formation was found in the axil of the 15th leaf which was a primordium near the tip of the main stem at the time of transfer to short days. Thus the region of most rapid morphological response to short-day treatment is an undifferentiated meristem in the terminal bud. The bud at the 15th node developed into a small inflorescence consisting of a short branch with reduced prophylls and two bracteal leaves, each allied with a single flower in the axil. The tip of the axis of this branch differentiated to give one additional leaf. Two short days were sufficient to induce this particular response. When the plants received more than two short days, additional flower buds developed at nodes above the 15th. Some plants which received only a few short days did not develop mature flowers. Plants which received 8 short days blossomed earlier than those receiving only 6 short days. Treatments of less than 8 short days did not suppress the addition of compound leaves in the terminal buds when the plants were returned to long days.

Nielsen[80] found that plants of Biloxi soybean which were given from 2 to 5 short days developed flower buds with easily recognized stamens. The sporocytes may begin to enlarge, but this was accompanied by a marked vacuolation of the cytoplasm and ultimate disintegration of the nuclei. Only a few sporocytes ever reached the metaphase stage of meiosis. Some plants which received 6 or more short days exhibited a similar degeneration of microsporocytes, but in others the sporocytes apparently underwent normal meiosis and four groups of chromosomes were formed. Degenerative changes sometimes occurred at this point before cleavage into microspores took place. In others, cleavage occurred followed by degeneration before the development of normal microspores. In only a few instances did apparently normal microspores form. Even plants receiving as many as 10 photoinductive cycles showed a high percentage of degenerated microspores. However, control plants continually exposed to short days developed normally.

My experience is that Biloxi soybean plants receiving from 2 to 8 short days and then returned to long days will develop flower buds, but rarely produce visible flowers. Dissection shows clearly identifiable stamens and pistils about 18 days after the short-day treatments. The buds seem to cease development at this stage. If the plants remain on long days in the greenhouse for too long a time many of the flower buds will abscise. It is desirable therefore to maintain the plants on long-day conditions only long enough after treatment to permit development of the buds.

Criteria for flowering response

Much of the work on soybeans in relation to photoperiodism and floral induction has been done with Biloxi soybean. In this plant the effectiveness of an inductive treatment is related to the number of nodes on the main axis which produce flower buds. A discussion of the quantitative response of Biloxi soybean is given in section 7. Some investigators have used the number of flowers produced, rather than the number of nodes with flowers, as a measure of the effectiveness of an inductive treatment. The accuracy of this measure is not always clear with the particular variety used. Van Schaik and Probst[109] discussed the mode of inheritance of inflorescence type, peduncle length, flower number per node, and percent flower shedding in 6 crosses of 4 varieties of soybeans. All of these factors were inherited quantitatively with dominance and complementary gene effects for long peduncles, high flower number, and high shedding. They point out that environmental factors have considerable influence. It is emphasized, therefore, that one should be extremely careful to obtain a pure strain of seed of a particular variety and indicate specifically the variety used. Usually a report on the seed source is desirable.

4 The Effect of Plant Age

Borthwick and Parker[4] found the effectiveness of the treatment of Biloxi soybeans with 4 short days increased with the age of the plant up to 6 weeks. When the older plants were treated, the first flower bud formed at a higher node.

Borthwick and Parker[7] found that the most effective leaf in inducing floral initiation is the one which has most recently attained its full size. The capacity of leaves to effect floral initiation increases until they attain full size after which the leaves gradually decline in effectiveness. A single leaf which has recently attained its full size is just as effective in causing floral initiation as are all of the leaves functioning simultaneously. It is the physiological age of the leaf and not its position on the plant which determines its effectiveness. For example, the third trifoliate leaf is more effective in inducing flower primordia in the axil of the first leaf than is the first leaf itself. Several workers[26,27,59] have reported that the auxin concentration in soybean leaves decreases as the leaves age. They postulate that this may be one of the factors responsible for the effect of leaf age on effectiveness in induction. Fisher[26] reports that commencement of flowering in two varieties of soybeans is related more closely to the ratio of mature to immature leaf areas than to leaf age. Continuous removal of all immature leaves starting when the 3rd, 4th, 5th or 6th trifoliate leaves were mature induced earlier flowering and at lower nodes. On the other hand, removal of mature leaves numbers 4 and 5, 5 and 6, or 4, 5 and 6, delayed flowering. In this case the first flowers appeared at higher nodes. These results are discussed later in section 18 in relation to a hypothesis involving auxin and a flower-forming substance.

5   Vernalization and Devernalization

Pal and Murty,[83] who included soybean in a study of the effect of vernalization on several Indian crops, found that low temperature treatment during germination had little effect on soybean. They also found that an initial period of darkness given immediately after sowing did not affect flowering. Lysenko considered soybean to belong to a group which he called thermophytes, a group which is supposed to undergo vernalization at relatively high temperatures. However, I have never found any evidence of vernalization in soybean. There are so many varieties of soybean that it would be unwise to deny the possibility of vernalization existing in some variety. Nevertheless, all of the varieties studied behave as short-day plants and the effects of environmental variables, including temperature, have been studied thoroughly. Since there have been no reports of anything equivalent to vernalization in any of the varieties studied, it seems unlikely that the phenomenon exists in the species.

7   Photoperiod Response

Varietal studies

Garner and Allard[38] pointed out that when Biloxi soybeans were exposed to daylengths of 8 to 10 hours they rapidly flowered, set fruit and soon died. On daylengths of 12 hours the plants grew vegetatively to a much greater size and produced flowers in greater abundance. In long days, the plants did not flower. They compared Peking (IV) soybean with Biloxi (VIII) soybean and concluded that different varieties of the same species might have different daylength responses when grown at different latitudes. In subsequent work[39,40] they included five varieties of soybean, which all responded as short-day plants. In 1930[42] they grew Mandarin (I), Peking (IV), Tokyo (VII), and Biloxi (VIII) soybeans under numerous environmental conditions. They did not examine the plants for the presence of flower buds, but merely reported on flowering. All varieties flowered if they were planted in a warm greenhouse in either winter or very early spring. However, if they were planted in the late spring as the days were lengthening, Biloxi soybean remained vegetative until early September. The other varieties flowered in July and August since their critical daylength for flowering is longer than that of Biloxi.

Borthwick and Parker[6] subjected 12 varieties of soybeans to daylengths varying from 8 to 24 hours. All 12 varieties flowered promptly on 8 to 12-hour daylengths. Five varieties remained vegetative on a 16-hour day. Seven varieties initiated some flower buds on a 24-hour day but only one, Agate (00), developed pods more than 5 cm long within the 50-day period of the experiment. All varieties were more vegetative on long days than on short days.

Parker and Borthwick[89] made a detailed study of the appearance of first flower buds, first flowers, the amount of vegetative growth, and the appearance and development of pods in the different varieties under different conditions. They indicate that varieties which are grown at different latitudes have differing daylength responses. Some varieties from northern latitudes are successful only in a 50-mile range of latitude, whereas the varieties grown in more southern latitudes are successful over a wider range.

Steinberg and Garner[107] found that low temperature delayed flowering in each of the varieties Mandarin, Peking and Biloxi soybean (which behaved as early, medium and late varieties). Temperature altered the critical daylength to only a limited degree and there were no marked contrasts in the effects on the three varieties. They concluded that the three varieties behaved as early, medium or late primarily because of differences in their critical daylengths.

Garner and Allard,[41,43] using the same three varieties of soybean, found that short periods of darkness during the daytime had no effect on the photoperiodic response. When plants were exposed to relatively short cycles of 30 seconds up to many hours in length, consisting of alternations of light and darkness, they responded as if they were on long days.

Biloxi soybeans

The Biloxi variety of soybean has been used almost exclusively in critical studies on the general problems of photoperiodism and induction of flowering. I have found the critical daylength of Biloxi soybean to be between $13\frac{1}{2}$ and 14 hours. Earlier varieties evidently have longer critical daylengths, as indicated by the work of Borthwick and Parker[6] discussed earlier. In Biloxi there is a direct relationship from the second to seventh day between the number of nodes producing flower primordia and the number of short days[47] (Fig. 3–2). One short day never produced flowers. Between 5 and 6 flowering nodes per plant were produced with 7 short days. In much subsequent work, 7 cycles have been used as an inductive treatment and the number of nodes producing flowers has been used as a measure of the effectiveness of such treatment. When plants receive appreciably more than 7 short days, the response becomes saturated and flower buds may be produced at every node of the main axis including the terminal bud. If the terminal bud flowers it may produce an inflorescence, in which case the growth of the axis ceases. The number of short days required to produce this saturation varies with the growing conditions.

When the light period of each of the 7 cycles remained constant and the length of the dark period was varied, flowering was produced only if the dark periods were longer than 10 hours. This was true with both 16-hour and 4-hour photoperiods. In a separate experiment plants were exposed to 7 cycles of treatment in which each cycle consisted of a 16-hour dark period and a photoperiod of variable length. Photoperiods up to 36 hours in duration were employed. In this experiment flowering occurred in response to photoperiods of 4 to 18 hours. The maximum flowering response was produced by photoperiods approximately 11 hours in length. No flowering was produced with photoperiods longer than 20 hours. In a subsequent experiment, plants were exposed to either 5 or 10-hour photoperiods in each cycle. The light during the photoperiods was varied from 50 to 800 f.c. At both photoperiod lengths flowering increased with increasing light intensity from 100 to 800 f.c. No flowering was produced when the light during the photoperiod was less than 100 f.c.

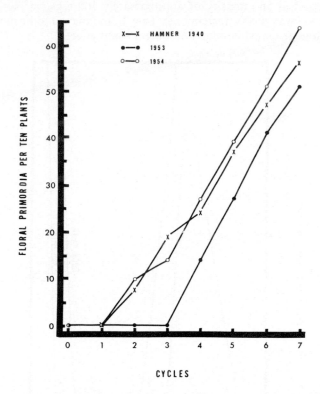

FIGURE 3–2. Effect of number of inductive cycles on number of nodes bearing flower buds (after Blaney and Hamner[2]).

8 Spectral Dependence

Relatively few investigations of the high intensity light reaction have been conducted with soybeans. The possibility that such a reaction occurs in Biloxi soybean was first shown by Borthwick and Parker in 1938.[5] They subjected plants to 8-hour photoperiods during each 24-hour cycle. Initiation of flower buds occurred only if the light during the photoperiod was above 100 f.c. Funke[33] exposed three varieties of soybean to natural daylight from 7 a.m. to 2 p.m. Throughout the remainder of the 24-hour cycles, boxes which contained the plants were covered with either colored glass or with a light-proof lid. Plants which were covered with blue glass flowered as early as those which received 17 hours of darkness. Thus in these experiments blue light elicited the same flowering responses as did darkness. However, blue light resembled white light in its control of vegetative growth. Further evidence of a high intensity light reaction is given in the discussion of endogenous rhythms (section 9).

Borthwick and Parker[5] found that when an 8-hour photoperiod of natural light was supplemented by 8 hours of incandescent light, flower initiation occurred only if the illuminance of the supplemental light was below 0.5 f.c. Gaertner and Braunroth[34] report that the appearance of flowering in soybean was delayed by several days when the plants were exposed to full moonlight. Withrow and Withrow[116] studied the effects of various wavelengths of supplementary radiation on the photoperiodic response of Mukden soybeans. The short natural daylengths of wintertime at Lafayette, Indiana were supplemented with red, yellow-green, or blue irradiations. All three irradiations were given throughout the night period at an intensity of approximately 100 ergs/cm^2/sec. A second intensity of blue was at 400 ergs/cm^2/sec. They found the red to be more effective than the yellow-green, while blue had only a slight effect.

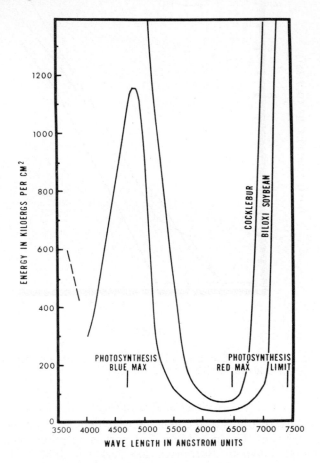

FIGURE 3–3. Composite action spectrum for suppression of floral initiation in soybean. Points give energy requirements at middle of a 14-hour dark period to prevent floral initiation (after Parker et al.[91]).

Not only is the flowering response of soybean (and other short-day plants) very sensitive to supplemental illumination used to lengthen the photoperiod, it is also very sensitive to very brief exposures to light during the middle of an otherwise inductive dark period. Biloxi soybean was the first plant in which the action spectrum of the light interruption effect was studied in detail.[90,91] Plants were defoliated to leave only the terminal leaflets of the third compound leaf, and were subjected to six short days (10L: 14D). Control plants, which received no light interruption treatments, averaged 3.2 flowering nodes per plant. The experimental plants received light treatments during the middle of the dark period. It was found that radiation from any part of the visible spectrum could inhibit flowering provided sufficient energy was supplied. Nevertheless, there were great differences in the effectiveness of the various wave-length bands. A composite action spectrum for suppression of floral initiation is shown in Figure 3–3.

9 Endogenous Rhythms

Early work

The first evidence than an endogenous rhythm participates in the photoperiodic response of Biloxi soybean was obtained in 1940 by Snyder,[106] who interspersed various numbers of short cycles of 3 minutes light and 3 hours of darkness between the main photoperiod and the main dark period. Control plants which received no short cycles flowered abundantly. The response of the plants treated with varying numbers of short cycles seemed to depend on the number and time of application of the short cycles. When the experimental treatments were inserted after the main dark period, there was a rhythmic fluctuation in the number of flowers initiated. There was one minimum of flowering with three or four such cycles, followed by a maximum with seven or eight cycles, and a second minimum with 12 cycles. With additional short cycles the plants tended to die. The minimum flowering values were thus obtained when the short cycle treatments were of 12 or 36 hours duration. Snyder obtained a similar rhythmic response when he used various lengths of continuous low intensity light following the main dark period of each cycle. When he inserted the same short cycles or low intensity light treatments after the main light period, instead of after the main dark period, there was no conclusive evidence of a rhythmical response. The reason for response differences based on whether the short cycles precede or follow the main light period is not apparent. The work of Snyder was not followed up immediately although Bünning did cite Snyders' work in papers in which he postulated that an endogenous rhythm was involved in the photoperiodic response.

Allard and Garner, in 1941,[1] tested the photoperiodic response of a number of plants, including Peking and Biloxi soybean, by exposing them to various ratios of light and dark. They found that the time of flowering of Biloxi soybeans depended on both the ratio of light to darkness and upon the length of the cycle. Also, when Peking soybean was given a light period of 18 hours or longer, no flowering resulted regardless of the length of the following dark period. Thus, while they did not show any rhythmic behavior, it seems probable that if their studies had been extended they would have made this discovery.

Wareing in 1953,[111] exposed Biloxi soybeans to photoperiods of 6, 9, 12, 15 and 18-hour cycles with associated dark periods of greatly varying length, for 10 cycles. If one examines the results carefully, one may conclude that they indicate a rhythmic response. However, the number of treatments used was insufficient to demonstrate a rhythm clearly. Wareing placed emphasis on the length of the light period which was associated with the various dark periods. When this was too long the plants failed to flower regardless of the length of the dark period, and he concluded that there were limiting lengths of both light and dark periods for flowering.

In 1954, Wareing[112] applied what he considered to be a critical test to Bünning's theory concerning the participation of an endogenous rhythm in the photoperiod response. He exposed Biloxi soybean plants to 48-hour cycles with either a 6-hour or a 9-hour photoperiod. He interrupted the long dark periods of each cycle with a 30-minute exposure to illumination from incandescent lamps of 100 f.c. intensity. He found that such interruptions inhibited flowering if given near the beginning or near the end of the long dark period. In those experiments involving a photoperiod of 9 hours, interruptions in the middle of the long dark period gave an indication of stimulation of flowering. In another experiment he used a main photoperiod of 9 hours and a total cycle length of 60 hours. He found that a light break was inhibitory during the early hours and near the end of the dark period, but had some promotive effect during the middle.

He used this evidence as a refutation of the Bünning theory. Since he obtained essentially the same results on 48-hour cycles as on 60-hour cycles, he concluded that Bünning's theory did not fit his results. Bünning[9] disputed Wareing's interpretation and insisted that the results could be explained on the basis of an endogenous rhythm and supported his contention with results of leaf movement experiments.

Length of cycle experiments

In experiments similar to those of Wareing,[111] Blaney and Hamner[2] exposed plants to various photoperiods and lengths of darkness, and found that cycle length was a primary factor in determining floral initiation. Maximum flowering occurred in response to photoperiods of 4 to 12 hours when the cycle length was 24 hours. Ten-hour photoperiods were the most promotive (Fig. 3–4). No

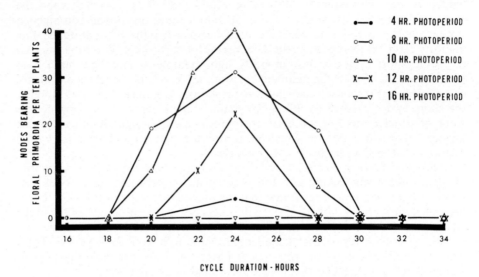

FIGURE 3–4. Flowering response of Biloxi soybean to cycles of various durations. The different curves give the response for treatments with different photoperiod lengths (after Blaney and Hamner[2]).

flowering occurred with a 16-hour photoperiod regardless of the length of the dark period. In contrast, when an 8-hour photoperiod was used and the length of the cycle was varied by varying the length of the dark period, a maximum of flowering resulted at cycle lengths of 24 and 48 hours. Minimum flowering was obtained at cycle lengths of 32 to 36 hours. Nanda and Hamner[77] found that when an 8-hour photoperiod initiated each cycle, variations in the length of the dark period produced a rhythmic flowering response. Maximum flowering responses were produced by cycle lengths of 24, 48, and 72 hours. No flowering was produced by cycle lengths of 32 hours, and only a minimum response was produced by cycle lengths of 56 hours. This rhythmic response to varying cycle length has been found in all subsequent experiments in Hamner's laboratory. Approximately 14 such experiments have been conducted and all yielded essentially identical results (Fig. 3–5).

Additional evidence for the participation of a circadian rhythm in the photoperiodic response of Biloxi soybean was found by Sirohi and Hamner,[104] who used 7 cycles of 48-hour (di-diurnal) treatment. One set of controls received seven consecutive 24-hour cycles (8L: 16D), another received seven consecutive

48-hour cycles (8L: 40D). The first set of controls produced an average of 43 flowering nodes per 10 plants and the second 42 flowers. In the experimental series a second photoperiod was introduced beginning at the 24th hour of the 48-hour cycle. The duration of this second photoperiod was varied from 0 to 14.75 hours. Photoperiods of 1 to 2 hours did not affect the flowering level attained by the controls. The flowering response increased rapidly as the second photoperiod was extended beyond 2 hours. The response was saturated as the photoperiod was lengthened from 6 hours to 10 hours. One should note that these latter treatments are equivalent to exposing the plants to 14 short days. As photoperiods lengthened from 10 to 12 hours there was a rapid decrease in flowering until, with photoperiods of 12½ hours, there was no response difference between the experimental plants and the controls. As the photoperiod was increased beyond 12½ hours, there was a rapid decrease in the flowering response to the point that no flowering occurred with photoperiods of 14 hours.

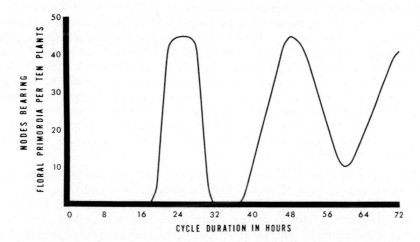

FIGURE 3–5. Summary response curve for Biloxi soybean in six experiments. Plants were exposed to seven cycles, each cycle consisting of eight hours of high-intensity light (1000–1500 f.c) and associated dark periods of various lengths. Total nodes flowering per ten plants are plotted against cycle length. The standard error for flowering response at cycle durations of 24, 48, 60 and 72 hours was 0.15, 0.17, 0.45 and 0.25 respectively (after Hamner and Takimoto[49]).

Long[70] had shown that soybeans do not flower regardless of the number of short days given if one or more long days intervene between successive short days. In the work outlined above, a similar inhibition is produced if the intervening day has a photoperiod of 14 hours or longer. If the intervening day has a photoperiod shorter than 12 hours, it may be stimulatory providing the light intensity is high. If the intervening day has a photoperiod of about 12 hours, it does not seem to produce a response much different from the controls. Such a noneffective intervening day is therefore called an innocuous treatment. Clearly, the di-diurnal cycle employed by Sirohi and Hamner can be divided into distinct segments. One can consider the first day of the 48-hour cycle as being an inductive short day (8L: 16D). The second 24-hour period consists of two 12-hour periods. High intensity light in the first 12 hours stimulates flowering and either low or high intensity light in the second 12 hours inhibits flowering. One may conclude from this that photoperiodic control of flowering in Biloxi soybean is under the control of an endogenous rhythm consisting of two alternating 12-

hour phases: a photophil followed by a photophobe phase. The critical day-length of soybean may be considered as being determined by the amount of inhibition produced by light given during the second 12-hour photophobe phase. One would presume that under natural days, plants receive a high stimulation toward flowering during the first 10 hours of the photoperiod, which then decreases with increasing lengths up to 12 hours. Days longer than 12 hours begin to produce an inhibitory effect which becomes sufficient to inhibit flowering completely when the day becomes about 14 hours in length.

In the experiments described above, the basic treatment periods were 48-hour cycles repeated 7 times. Coulter and Hamner[18] designed a similar set of experiments using 72-hour cycles, each initiated with an 8-hour photoperiod. The controls received 64 hours of continuous darkness in each cycle. In the experimental series, the 8-hour photoperiod was followed by a 16-hour dark period. At the 24th hour, plants were exposed to second photoperiods varying in length from 0 to 20 hours. The illumination during the experimental photoperiods was 1000 f.c. Since the experimental cycle length was 72 hours, the second photoperiods did not decrease the following dark period to less than a possible critical dark period, even when they were extended up to 20 hours. The amount of flowering increased as the second photoperiod was lengthened to about 10 hours. When this photoperiod was increased beyond 10 hours, flowering abruptly decreased. A 12-hour photoperiod appeared innocuous. In striking contrast to the results of Sirohi and Hamner, photoperiod lengths of 14 to 18 hours were also innocuous, and inhibition did not occur until photoperiods as long as 20 hours were used. Unfortunately for the discussion at hand, photoperiods longer than 24 hours were not used.

The results of Coulter and Hamner indicate that an endogenous rhythm is established in a tri-diurnal cycle which is initiated by a main photoperiod of 8 hours. High intensity light stimulated flowering from the 24th to the 36th hours of the cycle. However, this stimulation was not uniform. Flowering reached a maximum at photoperiods ending at approximately the 34th hour, then there was a rapid decrease in the stimulatory effect from the 34th to the 36th hour. In attempting to interpret the results of second photoperiods longer than this, one has difficulty establishing what is a main photoperiod and what is an interrupting photoperiod. If one assumes that an 8-hour main photoperiod can establish a basic endogenous rhythm, certainly an intervening photoperiod of from 10 to 12 hours could also establish a basic endogenous rhythm. One may then be dealing with two rhythms which interact with one another. This problem is taken up in the discussion below.

Light perturbation experiments

Sirohi and Hamner[104,105] and Carpenter and Hamner[10,11] exposed Biloxi soybean plants to 48-hour cycles initiated with an 8-hour photoperiod. They interrupted the 40-hour dark period of each cycle with illumination of approximately 1000 f.c. from fluorescent lamps. The interruptions varied from 30 minutes to 4 hours in duration. They found, as had Wareing, that light perturbations, regardless of the length used, inhibited flowering when given near the beginning or near the end of the dark period. Short perturbations given near the middle of the dark period were not inhibitory; when the perturbations were as long as 2 to 4 hours, flowering was stimulated. Coulter and Hamner[18] used a 72-hour cycle with a main photoperiod of 8 hours (see Fig. 3–6). The long dark period was interrupted at various points with 4 hours of illumination (1000 f.c.) from fluorescent lamps. The interruptions inhibited flowering near the beginning and near the end of the long dark period. Flowering was also inhibited by interruptions given near the 40th hour of the cycle. Flowering was stimulated when 4-hour interruptions were given from 24 to 36 hours and from 48 to 60 hours after the beginning of the cycle. In each tri-diurnal cycle there seemed to be 3 photophil phases and 3 photophobe phases. These phases

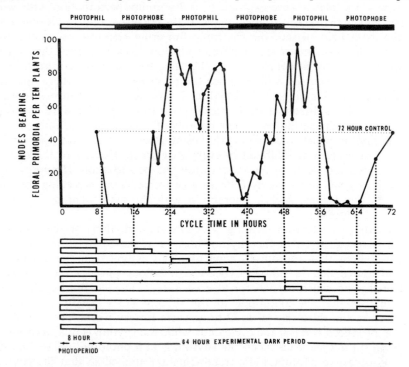

FIGURE 3–6. Four-hour high intensity light breaks applied during the experimental dark period of a 72-hour cycle. Responses shown are those resulting from 7 cycles of the designated treatment. Points are plotted to correspond with the beginning of the light break interval. The 72-hour control level indicated is that level of flowering produced by 7 tri–diurnal cycles in which no light interruptions were given during the 64-hour dark period. Below is a treatment diagram of selected treatments represented in a single cycle (after Coulter and Hamner[18]).

presumably correspond to the oscillations of a circadian rhythm.

It seems reasonable to conclude, therefore, that in both di-diurnal and tri-diurnal cycles, the plant goes through a photophil phase and a photophobe phase during each 24-hour segment of the cycle. Perturbations with white light given during a photophil phase stimulate flowering only when the intensity is high and the duration is about 2 hours or longer. In di-diurnal cycles, brief perturbations with white light inhibit flowering during the photophobe phases of the cycle, especially during the first photophobe phase. In tri-diurnal cycles, such perturbations reduce flowering in all three photophobe phases, particularly during the first and third photophobe phases.

Interaction of light and the endogenous rhythm

The third photophobe phase of a tri-diurnal cycle may be almost as sensitive as the first to a light perturbation which seems to conflict somewhat with the results obtained in the length-of-cycle experiments. From the length-of-cycle experiments, one might assume that an 8-hour photoperiod initiates an endo-genous circadian rhythm. The amplitude of the rhythm apparently decreases rapidly during the 64-hour dark period of a 72-hour cycle. Nanda and Hamner[79] combined length-of-cycle experiments with perturbation treatments. They initiated each cycle of treatment with an 8-hour photoperiod. After a period of darkness, the plants were exposed to a 30-minute perturbation with white light and a dark period of variable length. If the perturbation was given 4 hours after the main light period, the rhythmic flowering response associated with length of cycle was damped as compared to the controls. However, the maxima and minima occurred at approximately the same time as in the controls. When the perturbation occurred 8 hours after the main light period, there appeared to be a complete damping of the rhythm. No flowering resulted regardless of the length of the subsequent dark period. Perturbations that were separated from the main light period by longer periods of time seemed to interact with the basic rhythm which was presumably established by the main light period. However, flowering was inhibited in every case where the end of the cycle of treatment occurred within a few hours after the perturbation. It appears that perturbations given immediately following or immediately preceding the main light period have some special interaction with the main light period which causes floral inhibition.

In the extensive literature dealing with circadian rhythms or the biological c ock, it is recognized that the rhythm may be rephased by exposure of the organism to light at an appropriate time. One may assume from the experiments escribed above that in Biloxi soybeans, an 8-hour photoperiod initiates a circadian rhythm which persists for at least 3 days. The length-of-cycle experi-ments indicate that the amplitude of the rhythm fades rapidly, so that the oscillation on the third day of a 72-hour cycle is very weak. The amount of flowering produced is less if the cycle ends while the rhythm is in a photophobe phase than if the cycle ends when the rhythm is in a photophil phase. In other words, if successive photoperiodic treatments are applied so that the rhythms induced by each 8-hour photoperiod are in phase, then maximum flowering will result. On the other hand, if they are applied partly out of phase there will be a reduction in the amount of flowering.

The degree of inhibition by a light perturbation during a photophobe phase appears to depend on the amplitude of the oscillation at that particular time. Thus light is most effective in inhibiting flowering during the first photophobe phase. In the second photophobe phase, light does not produce as much in-hibition presumably because the rhythm has partially faded away. Thus we could account for the apparent interaction between the main light period and a perturbation given shortly thereafter. However, such an explanation does not provide an answer to the interaction between a perturbation and a subsequent light period. It is known that under free-running conditions, the circadian activity rhythms in animals and insects may be rephased by a light perturbation. Perturbations given in photoperiodic experiments might similarly rephase the endogenous rhythm and thus account for some of the observed results. That this may happen is strongly indicated in the experiments of Nanda and Hamner,[79] who found that while cycle lengths of 36 and 60 hours produced very little flowering, a brief perturbation given at the proper point during the long dark period of such cycles may greatly stimulate flowering. It would appear that these perturbations rephased the rhythm and thus caused what were other-wise unfavorable cycle lengths to become much more favorable for flowering. It should be noted that such a perturbation never increased the flowering res-ponse above the maximum level produced by favorable cycle lengths without perturbations. In other words, perturbations given during unfavorable cycle lengths could cause a phase shift sufficient to make that cycle length more nearly approach the ideal condition. Carpenter and Hamner[11] also found evidence of perturbations causing some rephasing of the basic endogenous rhythm. However, they found that even two 30-minute white light perturbations did not completely overcome the basic rhythm established by the main 8-hour photoperiod.

Coulter and Hamner[19] found that a 4-hour perturbation given in a 72-hour cycle was very inhibitory during the first photophobe phase and also during the third photophobe phase. Since 4-hour perturbations greatly stimulated flowering during the photophil phases, it would seem that this light interruption was sufficiently long to establish its own endogenous rhythm. If such rhythms were out of phase with the rhythm established by the main photoperiod, as they would be if the perturbations were given in the photophobe phases, one would expect antagonistic effects. If a 4-hour perturbation given during the third photophobe phase initiates its own rhythm, it would cause the following 8-hour photoperiod to fall in the photophobe phase. Thus the short light period might cause a great deal more inhibition in the third photophobe phase than in the second photophobe phase. In the latter case, the rhythm induced by the 4-hour perturbation might fade away nearly completely before the start of the following main photoperiod.

Shumate[103] investigated the effects of perturbations given during a tri-diurnal cycle and corroborated much of the work of Coulter and Hamner. Shumate used short perturbations of 3 or 30 minutes and investigated only the photophobe phases of the tri-diurnal cycle. He found that these brief perturbations were very inhibitory during the first photophobe phase, much less inhibitory during the second photophobe phase, and were slightly more inhibitory during the third photophobe phase than during the second. There appears to be an interaction between a brief perturbation given near the end of a very long dark period and the subsequent main photoperiod. It is possible that these brief perturbations induce a very weak oscillation of the rhythm which accounts for the interaction. Such a weak oscillation might not carry from the second photophobe phase to the end of the cycle, but could be effective near the end of the cycle.

Effects of red and far-red light

Perturbations during a long dark period discussed above were with white light. The effect of light quality during perturbations has received considerable attention. Perturbations with white light from fluorescent lamps have essentially the same effect as red light. A possible exception is when plants are exposed to perturbations during the photophil phases of long cycles. For example, 30-minute perturbations with white light during the photophil phase of a di-diurnal cycle may produce a slight inhibition, but red light produces no inhibition.

Studies of the effective action spectrum of perturbations on Biloxi soybean led to the discovery of phytochrome (see Section 8). There seems to be ample evidence that phytochrome is at least one of the pigments involved in absorbing the light which produces a perturbation effect. One of the tests to determine if phytochrome is physiologically involved in a particular response is to determine whether or not an effect produced by red light is reversed by a subsequent exposure to far-red light and vice versa. Downs[21] found that the inhibitory effect produced by red light given during the middle of the dark period of an otherwise effective short day (10L: 14D), was partially reversed by an immediately subsequent exposure to far-red. If the exposure to far-red was delayed by 45 minutes or more, the inhibitory effect of the red light was not reversed. Carpenter and Hamner[10] used di-diurnal cycles (8L: 40D) as a basic treatment and found that red or white light given for 3 minutes at the 16-hour point in the cycle inhibited flowering completely. The inhibition was not reversed by exposure to far-red at any subsequent point in the cycle. When red or white light was given at the 20-hour point in the cycle it did not inhibit flowering completely and this inhibition was partially overcome by immediate or subsequent exposure to far-red light. The reversal by far-red was obtained no matter how much time elapsed between the exposure to white light and subsequent exposure to far-red. In appropriate controls they found that the effects produced by 3 minutes of white, red or far-red were the same as produced by 30-minute exposures. Carpenter and Hamner also found that exposing Biloxi soybean plants to far-red irradiation at any time except near the very end of the long dark period of a 48-hour cycle produced some inhibition. There was no evidence of a rhythmic effect in this response.

Since there is a rhythmic response to perturbations with red or white light during a long dark period and no rhythm in response to far-red light, it is difficult to postulate just how phytochrome acts as the factor in determining the photoperiodic response. The rhythmic response obtained by perturbations must be associated with an endogenous rhythm established by the main photoperiod. If phytochrome is involved in the establishment of the basic endogenous rhythm then such establishment must occur during the high-intensity light period. Such a postulation would involve the assumption of an oscillation in the status of phytochrome during the continuous exposure to high-intensity light for it has been shown that the main light period has a maximum effectiveness dependent on its length. The effectiveness of the main light period increases with increasing length up to about 8 or 10 hours and then rapidly decreases to zero when the main light period is 12 hours long. With longer main light periods an inhibitory effect is produced. It is unfortunate that there has not been more work on the effects of light quality during the main light period of the photoperiodic cycle with Biloxi soybean.

Conclusions concerning control of photoperiodism

Under natural conditions the plant is exposed to a period of continuous light followed by a period of continuous darkness during each 24-hour day. Previously, researchers have speculated that short-day plants fail to flower when the days are long because the associated dark periods are shortened to such an extent that critical dark reactions cannot proceed to completion. This does not seem to be the case. Results such as those in Figure 3–4 indicate that Biloxi soybean fails to flower regardless of the length of the dark period if the photoperiods are 16 hours or longer. The findings of Sirohi and Hamner[104] indicate that in a 24-hour cycle high-intensity light periods longer than 12 hours actively inhibit flowering. Photoperiods of about 12 hours are innocuous in spite of the fact that they induce flowering under natural day. Therefore, under natural conditions, long days prevent flowering because the photoperiod extends beyond 12 hours and not because the extension of the photoperiod shortens the dark period to a critical level.

It seems, therefore, that during a 24-hour cycle, the plant goes through two alternating phases: (1) a photophil phase which is initiated at the start of the photoperiod; and (2) a photophobe phase which begins and reaches a maximum of oscillation followed by a decrease until again the inflection at the completion of the cycle occurs at about 24 hours. It appears that the curve of oscillation is not a perfect sine curve since the photoperiod produces its maximum effectiveness at lengths of 8 to 10 hours and maximum sensitivity of the photophobe phase occurs about 16 hours after the beginning of the cycle.

10 Fractional Induction

The reviewer found no evidence in the literature to indicate that fractional induction occurs in soybean.

11 Photoperiodic Inhibition

Schwabe[101] studied the inhibitory effect of long days on flowering in Biloxi soybean. Plants were exposed to 12 short days. Various numbers of long days were interspersed among the short days and the effect of long day treatments on flowering was compared to the controls. He determined that one long day annuls the effects of 2.2 short days. He concluded that an intervening long day acts on the short days following the long day treatment rather than destroys the promotive influence of previous short days. If Biloxi soybeans are grown prior to treatment exclusively on long days, two or more short days are required to induce flowering. Long[70] found that alternating short days with long days did not induce flowering regardless of the number of short days given. He also found that if two inductive treatments were separated by a period of long days, then each inductive treatment produced a number of flowering nodes corresponding to the effectiveness of that treatment. In other words, when two inductive treatments are separated by one or more long days, two successive short days are necessary to initiate any additional flowers. The subsequent initiation occurs quantitatively according to the number of succeeding short days and regardless of the number of intervening long days. Sirohi and Hamner[104] alternated short days with days of various photoperiod lengths and found that intervening days produced complete inhibition if the critical daylength was reached (i.e. 14 hours). This is in good agreement with the conclusion of Schwabe.[101] These intervening days inhibited to some degree if the intervening photoperiods were longer than $12\frac{1}{2}$ hours.

All of the recent work with Biloxi soybean in the reviewer's laboratory has indicated that long days fail to induce flowering because of an active inhibitory effect and that this inhibition is produced by exposing the plants to light during unfavorable phases of an endogenous circadian rhythm. For example, Coulter and Hamner[19] attempted to make a quantitative assay of the inhibition caused by exposing the plant to light during the most inhibitory phase of the rhythm. If Biloxi soybeans are exposed to an 8-hour photoperiod at the beginning of each tri-diurnal cycle and then are exposed to 30 minutes of light at the 16-hour point in each cycle, the plants must be exposed subsequently to favorable photoperiodic treatments to overcome the inhibition produced by the light break. Coulter and Hamner measured the degree of inhibition by varying the lengths of the photoperiod in the succeeding photophil phases of the tri-diurnal cycles to just overcome the inhibitory effect. In suitable controls, they also measured the stimulatory effect caused by the particular favorable photoperiods they used. From these rather complex experiments they concluded that 30 minutes of light given at the 16-hour point in a short day produced an inhibition equivalent to 80 flowers. They found that 2 hours of light given at the 16-hour point produced an inhibition equivalent to about 97 flowers. Since the control treatments without perturbations of any sort produced 39 flowers, it is apparent that a perturbation at the 16-hour point produced an inhibition of flowering that was about twice as much as the stimulation caused by the control. Thus one long day seems to inhibit twice as much as a short day stimulates.

Fratianne[28] conducted experiments with dodder, *Cuscuta campestris*, Yuncker. This parasite was allowed to grow on a number of photoperiodically sensitive plants including Biloxi soybean. The dodder flowered only on those host plants which were themselves flowering. The flowering of the host plant appeared to be unaffected by the parasitism of the dodder. When non-flowering dodder was introduced to soybean plants which were on non-inductive photoperiods, neither dodder nor soybean flowered; when the soybean plants were defoliated completely, the dodder on 7 of 9 host plants began to flower. This result indicated the possibility that under non-inductive photoperiods, the leaves of the host plant produced a substance which inhibited the flowering of dodder. In other experiments, soybean plants which had been linked together with bridges of living dodder were treated so that one member of each soybean pair was kept on inductive short photoperiods while the other was kept on non-inductive long photoperiods. No transmission of a flowering stimulus from the induced member of each pair through the dodder bridge to the non-induced member of the pair could be demonstrated. The results instead supported the concept that a flowering hormone-inhibitor is translocated from the non-induced soybean partner to the induced partner via the dodder bridge.

13 Effects of Temperature

There have been numerous reports indicating that low temperatures, particularly during the dark period, greatly reduce the response of soybeans to inductive photoperiods.[23,45,98,99,100,107,110] Steinberg and Garner[107] found that low temperatures delayed the development of flowers in early, medium, and late varieties of soybean, but that the critical daylengths were altered only to a limited degree. There was no marked contrast in the effects of temperature on the three varieties. Parker and Borthwick[85] found that initiation of flower primordia in Biloxi soybeans was influenced to a much greater extent by variations in temperature during the dark period than during the photoperiod. A temperature of 13°C during the dark period limited the amount of initiation that occurred. At 19°C the initiation was much more extensive. This increase in temperature during the dark period produced a greater effect on initiation than any other temperature variation of the same degree. Lowering the temperature during the dark period reduced the number of nodes formed, but this reduction in node formation was not enough to account for the differences in floral initiation.

Borthwick, Parker, and Heinze[8] studied the effects of localized low temperatures on the meristems and petioles. Plants were defoliated so that only the youngest fully-expanded trifoliate leaf was present on each plant. Fewer flower buds were produced in response to induction treatments if the terminal buds were cooled to 3°C. A similar decrease was produced by cooling the petioles. At 13°C the inhibiting effect of both treatments was not as pronounced as at 3°C, and only a slight growth of the terminals occurred during the induction treatment. Low temperature had a greater effect on the growth of the meristem than on the floral response of the meristem. Cooling the petioles seemed to inhibit the transport of the flower stimulus from the leaf to the bud. Parker and Borthwick[87] exposed individual leaves of Biloxi soybean to low temperatures during the dark period of a short-day treatment while maintaining the rest of the plant under long photoperiods at greenhouse temperatures. When the experimental leaf was held at 10°C or lower during the 5-day induction period, floral initiation was greatly inhibited. At 21°C to 32°C, initiation was equal to that of controls held at greenhouse temperatures, but at temperatures higher than 32°C the amount of initiation was again reduced. They concluded that low temperatures inhibit floral initiation by affecting the photoperiodic reactions occurring in the leaf blade during the dark period, rather than by affecting translocation of the floral stimulus from the leaf to the terminal meristem or by directly acting on the terminal meristem to prevent the differentiation and development of flower buds. Thrower[108] found that the translocation of ^{14}C-labelled assimilate within the plant ceased when the plant was held at 2 or 3°C. Cooling a short length of petiole to 1°C prevented translocation of labelled assimilates past the chilled section.

The relation between temperature and endogenous rhythms

Blaney and Hamner[2] found clear indications that some of the effects produced by low temperature treatment influence the endogenous rhythm and thereby influence the flowering response. For example, they found that 4 hours of low temperature given during the dark period of a short day (8L: 16D) reduced the flowering response. On the other hand, on a 28-hour cycle (8L: 20D), 4 hours of low temperature during the dark period stimulated flowering. At normal temperature, a 28-hour cycle is much less effective in inducing flowering than is a 24-hour cycle. Similarly, when plants were exposed to a 32-hour cycle (8L: 24D) at normal temperature, no flowering was produced. Lowering the temperature to 4°C during 12 hours of the long dark period stimulated flowering markedly. Similarly, introducing a period of low intensity light at 4°C immediately following or immediately preceding the 8-hour light period of a 32-hour cycle stimulated flowering markedly. At normal temperatures all of these 32-hour cycle treatments were completely inhibitory.

In the discussion of endogenous rhythms it was noted that at normal temperatures, a 16-hour photoperiod inhibits flowering regardless of the length of the dark period. Blaney and Hamner[2] found that lowering the temperature to 12°C during the 16-hour photoperiod of a 32-hour cycle produced more flowers than a regular 24-hour (8L: 16D) treatment at normal temperatures. It seems apparent therefore, that low temperature during a portion of the photoperiodic cycle affected the oscillations of the endogenous rhythms in such a manner that the optimum length of the cycle for maximum flowering was changed. Nanda and Hamner[76,78] studied the effects of temperature during the light or dark period on the oscillations of flowering which resulted by varying the length of the cycle of treatment. At 23°C maximum flowering was produced by 24, 48, and 72-hour cycles. At 10° to 12°C, the maximal response was obtained at cycle lengths of 36 and 60–66 hours. Lowering the temperature caused the rhythm to become about 12 hours out of phase with the rhythm at higher temperatures. The maximal flowering response was decreased at the lower temperature. Thus the amplitude of the oscillation was decreased in addition to the phase shift.

Coulter and Hamner[18] compared the effectiveness of photoperiods of different lengths in a 72-hour cycle. At 28°C, the maximum effectiveness of the photoperiods was reached after about 8 to 10 hours. Photoperiods longer than 18 hours were completely ineffective. In contrast, at 12°C, maximum effectiveness of the photoperiod was reached at about 18 hours and the photoperiod was still effective at lengths greater than 28 hours. In a similar fashion, they varied the temperature of the photoperiod of an intervening 48-hour cycle which was alternated with regular short-day donor cycles. Again they found that the maximum effectiveness of the intervening photoperiod was reached at much longer photoperiods at low temperature than at high temperature. Also the inhibitory effect of very long intervening photoperiods was much less at the lower temperature. Unfortunately, no one has yet made a study over a wide range of cycle lengths with photoperiods of high and low temperatures.

Many studies of the effect of temperature on endogenous rhythms indicate that a change in temperature produces a phase shift in the rhythm. For example, a circadian rhythm in leaf movement is obtained at both high and low temperature. The period of the leaf movement rhythm is approximately the same at both temperatures. If the temperature is shifted during a 'free-running' period, the oscillation of the rhythm undergoes a few transients during which the period of the rhythm is not circadian. After a few such oscillations, the rhythm again reaches the circadian frequency. It is not surprising, therefore, that peculiar effects of temperature shifts occur in the photoperiodic response. In all of the above mentioned experiments, the plants were shifted from one temperature to another during each cycle of treatment. In other words, the light period may be at normal temperature whereas the dark period would be at low temperature or low temperatures might be given during a portion of either the light period or the dark period. There is not enough information available concerning circadian rhythms to predict just what effect a particular temperature shift might have in relation to subsequent transient oscillations.

14 Effects of Mineral Nutrition

Mineral nutrient supply seems to have little effect on the initiation of flowers in soybeans. Most of the investigations[15,16,66,102,114] have dealt with the effect of nitrogen upon flowering and fruiting. Scully et al.[102] studied varieties of soybean which flowered on all durations of photoperiod. They found that the position of the first flower primordia did not vary with nitrogen treatment when the plants were grown on short photoperiods. However, on long photoperiods, certain varieties initiated flower primordia at higher nodes as the amount of nitrogen in the nutrients was increased. Most other investigations emphasize the fact that nitrogen supply may affect total yield but does not affect the initiation of flower buds.

15 Effects of Gas Composition

Parker and Borthwick[86] showed that the initiation of flower primordia in Biloxi soybean was influenced by controlling factors which affect photosynthesis during an induction treatment. If CO_2 was not supplied during the photoperiods of an inductive treatment, no initiation of primordia occurred. If plants received CO_2, supplied as natural air, during a portion of each photoperiod, flower primordia were produced in proportion to the duration of exposure of the plants to the CO_2. Increasing the CO_2 concentration in the air increased floral initiation when the plants were exposed to short days. Eaton,[23] in less precisely controlled experiments, obtained somewhat similar results. Langston and Leopold[65] found that floral initiation of Biloxi soybean was inhibited when plants were exposed to long dark periods which were maintained essentially free of CO_2.

17 Grafting Experiments

Kuijper and Wiersum[62] in 1936 and Kuijper and Schuurman[61] in 1938, working with soybean, obtained some of the first evidence for the transport of a flowering hormone. They found that if a flowering scion was grafted to a stock treated with long days, side branches on the stock produced flowers in spite of long-day treatment. Conversely, they found that a scion maintained on long day produced flowers when grafted to a short-day stock. They concluded that a substance causing floral initiation passed across the graft union and that the substance could be transported in either direction in the same stem although it was transported more easily in a basal direction. This paper came out at about the same time that similar papers appeared in Russia involving other plants. Borthwick and Parker[5] demonstrated that the stimulus causing floral initiation in soybean originates in the leaves and moves to the growing points. Floral initiation was obtained only through the application of appropriate photoperiods to the leaves. Ermolaeva[25] and Loehwing[69] apparently reached this same conclusion at about the same time. Borthwick and Parker[7] demonstrated that the first fully expanded trifoliate leaf was the most effective in producing the floral stimulus and that the stimulus could be translocated both upward and downward in the same stem. Heinze, Parker and Borthwick[50] performed numerous grafting experiments using Biloxi soybean as the receptor plant, maintaining the receptor in long day at all times. The donor components of the grafts were Agate, Batorawkå or Biloxi soybeans or various varieties of *Phaseolus vulgaris*. The floral stimulus passed readily across graft unions between Agate, Batorawka and Biloxi. A single Agate leaf grafted to an entire Biloxi plant caused floral initiation. When Biloxi and Agate plants were approach grafted, only 50 per cent of the receptor plants responded. Defoliation of the receptor several days after grafting increased the percentage of floral initiation. Biloxi leaves subjected to several short days before grafting failed to produce flower primordia on the receptors. Induced Biloxi leaves, therefore, did not seem to continue to supply the stimulus after being returned to long-day conditions. Approach grafts of Biloxi to Biloxi produced a response in only one receptor although firm graft unions were formed in many cases. Although they performed many successful leaf grafts and stem grafts of *Phaseolus* to Biloxi receptors, no flower primordia were induced in the receptors. The authors conclude that the flower stimulus probably moves with assimilates. Galston[37] performed similar experiments with the same results. In addition, he found that the floral stimulus did not pass from the donor leaf if the petiole was scalded nor did it pass a 1-mm. water gap between donor leaf and receptor petiole. Carr[12] exposed detached Biloxi soybean leaves to short days and then re-grafted them to vegetative plants. Such detached leaves, even though they were exposed to as many as 15 short days, failed to induce flowering in the receptor plant. Through the use of appropriate controls, Carr concluded that a leaf cannot be photoperiodically induced unless it is in organic connection with an actively growing shoot apex.

Kiyosawa and Kiyosawa[58] grafted early, midseason, and late varieties of soybean in various combinations. The scion with a half-developed leaf was removed at the first leaf stage and inserted into the internode of a stock. After the scion started to grow, 'the leaves of the scion were removed if necessary'. They observed the flowering response of both stock and scion. They concluded that late varieties produced flower inhibitor(s) in the conditions under which midseason varieties produced flowers. Early varieties seemed to produce sufficient flowering hormone to overcome the inhibiting action of late varieties. The results indicated that, under short days, midseason varieties produced equal or smaller amounts of flowering hormone than late varieties. They discuss the control of flowering in the various varieties on the basis of inhibitor formation versus flower hormone production without reaching a definite conclusion as to which determines differences between varieties.

18 *Effects of Growth Substances and Growth Retardants*

Soybean has been used rather extensively in studies attempting to relate auxin metabolism to the flowering response.[53] In 1937 Murneek[73] reported that he found no effect of growth promoting substances such as indoleacetic, indolepropionic, and phenylacetic acids on the initiation of flowers in Biloxi soybean. Galston in 1946[35,36] treated vegetative and photoinduced Peking soybeans with 2,3,5-triiodobenzoic acid (TIBA). Plants growing under long days were not induced to flower by TIBA; photo-induced plants showed a tenfold increase in the number of flower buds formed. He suggested that TIBA was an anti-auxin and that the increased flowering was produced by the antagonistic effect on auxin. Ishihara[55] also reported that TIBA increases the number of flower buds.

Leopold and Guernsey[67,68] studied the effect of naphthaleneacetic acid (NAA) on the flowering of induced Biloxi soybean plants. The seeds were soaked in NAA solution and subsequently exposed to either low or high temperatures. The low temperature treatment increased the numbers of flower primordia whereas the high temperature decreased the number of primordia. In another experiment, Biloxi soybeans were grown for two weeks under long days in the greenhouse and then placed in controlled temperature rooms under fluorescent lights at a temperature of 10° or 25°C. The tip of the youngest mature leaf of each plant was removed and the cut surface immersed in a solution of NAA during the treatment. The concentrations of NAA used were 0.1 to 1.0 ppm. After treatment the plants were transferred to long days in the greenhouse and dissected 7 weeks later. Those plants which had been given low temperature during the auxin treatment produced more flowers than either the controls or those treated with auxin at a higher temperature. Cooke[17] treated one set of Biloxi soybean plants with a short period of induction and maintained another set on long days as controls. After the induction treatment, both sets of plants were dried at 75°C and extracted overnight at 5°C in freshly distilled peroxide-free ether. When the plants were placed on short-day conditions, there was an initial increase in auxin concentration which continued for about 2 weeks following which there was a decrease. While the authors found changes in the auxin content related to the short-day treatment, they do not claim that the change is involved in the initiation of flowering. Fisher and Loomis[27] using Lincoln (III) and Ogden (VI) varieties of soybean, both of which have rather long critical daylengths, found that spraying 1 or 2-month old plants with nicotine sulphate at a concentration of 2,000 ppm caused the production of abundant and apparently normal macroscopic flowers under otherwise non-inductive treatments (18L: 6D). They considered the nicotine sulphate to be acting as an anti-auxin. They also applied TIBA at 10 ppm and found that this substance also acted as had nicotine sulphate. They claim that auxin inhibits flowering and that an anti-auxin can induce flowering by lowering the effective auxin content. They considered that aging similarly lowers the effective auxin content thus producing flowering in older plants even under long days. Fisher[26] found that a midseason variety, Lincoln (III), became indeterminate in its photoperiodic response with increased age and eventually flowered on 18-hour photoperiods. On the other hand, Ogden (VI), a late variety, did not flower on photoperiods longer than $14\frac{1}{2}$ hours. Spraying with nicotine sulphate induced earlier flowering, flowering at lower nodes, more flowers per node, and flowering at a lower ratio of mature to immature leaf areas for both varieties. For the Ogden variety only nicotine sulphate treated plants bloomed on a 16-hour day. Spraying with IAA tended to delay flowering. IAA did offset toxic effects of overdose of nicotine sulphate, suggesting that nicotine sulphate was antagonistic to IAA. Nicotine sulphate was more effective in inducing flowering if applied to immature leaves or to all leaves than when applied to mature leaves only. The results of the experiments, including defoliation experiments which have been previously mentioned, support the hypothesis that flowering is conditioned by a balance between auxin produced in young tissues and the flower-promoting substance produced in older leaves.

DeZeeuw and Leopold[20] found that a low concentration of NAA applied before an induction treatment had a pronounced promotive effect on floral initiation of Biloxi soybean. A smaller promotive effect was also obtained when NAA was applied after the induction period. These results seem to disagree with those obtained by some other workers. Kiyosawa and Wake[59] determined the auxin that diffused from leaves and stems of two varieties of soybean and obtained variable results. They found diurnal variations in auxin content which led to difficulty in comparing results of tests made after various photoperiods. Late and early flowering varieties gave no difference in auxin content between controls and short-day plants if they were measured after periods of darkness. Age of leaf was found to be a factor in determining auxin content. Kiyosawa[57] exposed early, midseason, and late varieties of soybean to short days, long days, or short days with light interruptions in the dark period. Auxin was assayed in both diffusable and extractable forms. He considered auxin as a possible inhibitor of flowering and concluded that the extent of change of auxin content does not seem to account for varietal differences in earliness of flowering. Hamner and Nanda[48] applied different concentrations of IAA to Biloxi soybeans by immersing the entire tops of the plants in the desired concentration at the end of the photoperiod of each of 7 short days. The IAA decreased flowering in proportion to the log of the concentration from 1 to 80 ppm. They also found[78] that while auxin application inhibited flowering, it did not affect the periodic oscillations of the endogenous rhythm but rather decreased the amplitude of the rhythmic response.

Klein and Leopold[60] found that maleic hydrazide inhibited to some degree the flower primordia in Biloxi soybean when the plants were exposed to short days. They concluded that the effect of maleic hydrazide was to inhibit growth and thus affect the development of flower primordia rather than the photoperiodic mechanism itself. Lang[63] reports that gibberellin did not affect flower formation in Biloxi soybean. Reports[30,31,113] of the effect of 2,4-dichlorophenoxyacetic acid (2,4-D) on Biloxi soybeans do not seem to have any particular bearing on this particular report since they are related primarily to weed control and crop production.

22 Chemical, Histochemical and Ultrastructural Changes at Induction

Several papers[24,52,73,74,84] report on studies of the effects of short-day treatment on chemical composition of soybeans. Emphasis was placed on the carbohydrate fractions and on nitrogen analyses. While the reports indicate that short-day treatments affect the chemical composition markedly, none of the reports claim that the observed changes are associated directly with floral initiation. Hibbard[51] studied changes in the activity of the enzymes catalase, peroxidase, invertase, amylase, and reductase. Short-day treatment at first depressed the activity of the enzymes. After 5 days, there was an increased activity in invertase and peroxidase; after 15 or 20 days, there was an increase in catalase activity. The amylase and reductase enzymes were affected little or not at all. The enzyme activity changes seemed to be correlated with the growth response rather than with the induction of flowering. Chailakhyan and Jarkovaja[14] found no changes in catalase and peroxidase activity during induction and also report that neither the carbohydrate content nor its relation to nitrogenous substances appeared to be responsible for induction of flowering. Garner et al.[44] found an increase in acidity in the sap of the youngest leaves of Biloxi soybean when the plants began to initiate flowers. There was a temporary rise in pH in the stem at the time of floral initiation. When Biloxi soybeans were transferred from natural daylengths to 10-hour days, there was a marked increase in pH up to the 5th day of the inductive treatment. Thereafter, there was a rapid decrease in pH as plants began to flower and fruit. These measurements were made on the young topmost leaves of the plants.

23 Inflorescence Differentiation

This topic was discussed in section 3.

REFERENCES
[1] Allard, H. A. and Garner, W. W. 1941. Responses of some plants to equal and unequal ratios of light and darkness in cycles ranging from one hour to 72-hours. *J. Agr. Res.* **63**, 305.

[2] Blaney, L. T. and Hamner, K. C. 1957. Interrelations among effects of temperature, photoperiod, and dark period on floral initiation of Biloxi soybean. *Bot. Gaz.* **119**, 10.

[3] Borthwick, H. A. and Parker, M. W. 1938. Influence of photoperiods upon the differentiation of meristems and the blossoming of Biloxi soybeans. *Bot. Gaz.* **99**, 825.

[4] Borthwick, H. A. and Parker, M. W. 1938. Effectiveness of photoperiodic treatments on plants of different ages. *Bot. Gaz.* **100**, 245.

[5] Borthwick, H. A. and Parker, M. W. 1938. Photoperiodic perception in Biloxi soybeans. *Bot. Gaz.* **100**, 374.

[6] Borthwick, H. A. and Parker, M. W. 1939. Photoperiodic responses of several varieties of soybeans. *Bot. Gaz.* **101**, 341.

[7] Borthwick, H. A. and Parker, M. W. 1940. Floral initiation in Biloxi soybeans as influenced by age and position of leaf receiving photoperiodic treatment. *Bot. Gaz.* **101**, 806.

[8] Borthwick, H. A., Parker, M. W. and Heinze, P. H. 1941. Influence of localized low temperature on Biloxi soybean during photoperiodic induction. *Bot. Gaz.* **102**, 792.

[9] Bünning, E. 1954. Die Beziehung einiger photoperiodische Phanomene bei *Soja* und *Xanthium* zur endogene Tagesrhythmik. *Ber. Deutsch. Bot. Ges.* **67**, 420.

[10] Carpenter, B. H. and Hamner, K. C. 1963. Effect of light quality on rhythmic flowering response of Biloxi soybean. *Plant Physiol.* **38**, 698.

[11] Carpenter, B. H. and Hamner, K. C. 1964. The effect of dual perturbations on the rhythmic flowering response of Biloxi soybean. *Plant Physiol.* **39**, 884.

[12] Carr, D. J. 1953. On the nature of photoperiodic induction. I. Photoperiodic treatments applied to detached leaves. *Physiol. Plantar.* **6**, 672.

[13] Cartter, J. L. and Hartwig, E. E. 1963. The management of soybeans. In *The Soybean*, 162. Ed. A. G. Norman. Academic Press, N.Y.

[14] Chailakhyan, M. Kh. and Jarkovaja, L. M. 1938. The effect of day length on the activity of oxidizing enzymes and carbohydrate content in leaves. *Trudy Inst. Fiziol. Timirjazev* **2**, no. 2: 95.

[15] Chailakhyan, M. Kh. 1944. Nitrogenous food as a factor increasing the rate of flowering and fruiting in plants. *C.R. (Dokl.) Acad. Sci. URSS* **43**, 75.

[16] Chailakhyan, M. Kh. 1945. Flowering in different plant species as a response to nitrogenous food. *C.R. (Dokl.) Acad. Sci. URSS* **47**, 146.

[17] Cooke, A. R. 1954. Changes in free auxin content during the photoinduction of short-day plants. *Plant Physiol.* **29**, 440.

[18] Coulter, M. W. and Hamner, K. C. 1964. Photoperiodic flowering response of Biloxi soybean in 72-hour cycles. *Plant Physiol.* **39**, 848.

[19] Coulter, M. W. and Hamner, K. C. 1965. Quantitative assay of photoperiodic floral inhibition and stimulation in Biloxi soybean. *Plant Physiol.* **40**, 873.

[20] DeZeeuw, D. and Leopold, A. C. 1956. The promotion of floral initiation by auxin. *Am. J. Bot.* **43**, 47.

[21] Downs, R. J. 1956. Photoreversibility of flower initiation. *Plant Physiol.* **31**, 279.

[22] Earley, E. B. and Cartter, J. L. 1945. Effect of temperature of the root environment on growth of soybean plants. *Am. Soc. Agr. J.* **37**, 727.

[23] Eaton, F. M. 1924. Assimilation-respiration balance as related to length of day reactions of soybeans. *Bot. Gaz.* **77**, 311.

[24] Eremenko, V. 1936. (Dynamics of carbohydrates and nitrogen substances in soybean in relation to photoperiodism.) *Zbirn. Prac. (Rob.) Agrofiziol.* **1**, 84.

[25] Ermolaeva, E. J. 1938. On the significance of leaves and buds in the photoperiodic response of plants. *Sovet. Bot.* **1**, 92.

[26] Fisher, J. E. 1955. Floral induction in soybeans. *Bot. Gaz.* **117**, 156.

[27] Fisher, J. E. and Loomis, W. E. 1954. Auxin-florigen balance in flowering of soybean. *Science* **119**, 71.

[28] Fratianne, D. G. 1965. The interrelationship between the flowering of dodder and the flowering of some long and short-day plants. *Am. J. Bot.* **52**, 556.

[29] Fred, E. B., Wilson, P. H. and Wyss, O. 1938. Light intensity and the nitrogen hunger period in the Manchu soybean. *Proc. Nat. Acad. Sci.* **24**, 46.

[30] Freiberg, S. R. and Clark, H. E. 1952. Effects of 2,4-dichlorophenoxyacetic acid upon the nitrogen metabolism and water relations of soybean plants grown at different nitrogen levels. *Bot. Gaz.* **113**, 322.

[31] Fribourg, H. A. and Johnson, I. J. 1955. Response of soybean strains to 2,4-D and 2,4,5-T. *Agron. J.* **47**, 171.

[32] Fukui, J. and Gotoh, T. 1962. (Varietal difference and the effect of day-length and temperature on the development of floral organs in the soybean. I. Developmental stages of floral organs of the soybean.) *Japan. J. Breeding* **12**, 17.

[33] Funke, G. L. 1943. Observations on the flowering periodicity. Extrait du *Recueil des Travaux botaniques neerlandais*, **40**, 393.

[34] Gaertner, T. von and Braunroth, E. 1935. Uber den Einfluss den Mondlichtes auf den Bluhthermin der Lang-und Kurztagspflanzen. *Beih. Bot. Zbl.* **53**, 554.

[35] Galston, A. 1946. The effects of a new auxin inhibitor on the flowering of Peking soybeans. *Am. J. Bot.* (*Suppl.*) **33**, 835.

[36] Galston, A. W. 1947. The effect of 2,3,5-triiodobenzoic acid on the growth and flowering of soybeans. *Am. J. Bot.* **34**, 356.

[37] Galston, A. W. 1949. Transmission of the floral stimulus in soybeans. *Bot. Gaz.* **110**, 495.

[38] Garner, W. W. and Allard, H. A. 1920. Flowering and fruiting of plants as controlled by the length of day. *Yearbook Agr. U.S. Dept. Agr.* 377.

[39] Garner, W. W. and Allard H. A. 1920. Effect of the relative length of day and night and other factors of the environment on growth and reproduction in plants. *J. Agr. Res.* **18**, 553.

[40] Garner, W. W. and Allard, H. A. 1923. Further studies in photoperiodism, the response of the plant to relative length of day and night. *J. Agr. Res.* **23**, 871.

[41] Garner, W. W. and Allard, H. A. 1929. Effect of short alternating periods of light and darkness on plant growth. *Science* **66**, 40.

[42] Garner, W. W. and Allard, H. A. 1930. Photoperiodic responses of soybeans in relation to temperature and other environmental factors. *J. Agr. Res.* **41**, 719.

[43] Garner, W. W. and Allard, H. A. 1931. Effect of abnormally long and short alternations of light and darkness on growth and development of plants. *J. Agr. Res.* **42**, 629.

[44] Garner, W. W., Bacon, C. W. and Allard, H. A. 1924. Photoperiodism in relation to hydrogen-ion concentrations of the cell sap and the carbohydrate content of the plant. *J. Agr. Res.* **27**, 119.

[45] Gilbert, B. E. 1926. The response of certain photoperiodic plants to differing temperature and humidity conditions. *Ann. Bot.* **40**, 315.

[46] Guard, A. T. 1931. Development of floral organs of the soybean. *Bot. Gaz.* **91**, 97.

[47] Hamner, K. C. 1940. Interrelation of light and darkness in photoperiodic induction. *Bot. Gaz.* **101**, 658.

[48] Hamner, K. C. and Nanda, K. K. 1956. A relationship between applications of indoleacetic acid and the high-intensity light reaction of photoperiodism. *Bot. Gaz.* **118**, 13.

[49] Hamner, K. C. and Takimoto, A. 1964. Circadian rhythms and plant photoperiodism. *Am. Naturalist.* **48**, 295.

[50] Heinze, P. H., Parker, M. W. and Borthwick, H. A. 1942. Floral initiation in Biloxi soybean as influenced by grafting. *Bot. Gaz.* **103**, 518.

[51] Hibbard, A. D. 1937. Photoperiodism and enzyme activity in the soybean plant. *Missouri Agr. Expt. Sta. Res. Bull.* 271.

[52] Hopkins, E. W. 1935. The effect of long and short-day and shading on nodule development and composition of the soybean. *Soil Sci.* **39**, 297.

[53] Howell, R. W. 1963. Physiology of the soybean. In *The Soybean*, 75. Ed. A. G. Norman. Academic Press, N.Y.

[54] Hunter, J. R. and Erickson, A. E. 1952. Relation of seed germination to soil moisture tension. *Agron. J.* **44**, 107.

[55] Ishihara, Aiya. 1956. The effect of 2,3,5-triiodobenzoic acid on the flower initiation of soybeans. *Crop Sci. Soc. Japan Proc.* **24**, 211.

[56] Johnson, H. W. and Bernard, R. L. 1963. Soybean genetics and breeding. In *The Soybean*, 1, Ed. A. G. Norman. Academic Press, N.Y.

[57] Kiyosawa, S. 1960. Effects of daylength treatments on auxin content and its diurnal variation in soybean. *Crop Sci. Soc. Japan Proc.* **29**, 163.

[58] Kiyosawa, S. and Kiyosawa, K. 1962. A study of varietal difference in flowering habits of soybean plants as followed by grafting experiments. *Plant & Cell Physiol.* **3**, 263.

[59] Kiyosawa, S. and Wake, M. 1958. On the relationship between photoperiodic response and auxin level in soybean. *Crop Sci. Soc. Japan Proc.* **27**, 363.

[60] Klein, W. H. and Leopold, A. C. 1953. The effects of maleic hydrazide on flower initiation. *Plant Physiol.* **28**, 293.

[61] Kuijper, J. and Schuurman, J. J. 1938. Experiments with soybeans and potatoes on the transport of a substance causing flowering. *Landbouwk. Tijdschr.* **50**, 583.

[62] Kuijper, J. and Wiersum, L. K. 1936. Occurrence and transport of a substance causing flowering in the Soy bean (*Glycine max* L.). *Proc. Roy. Acad. Sci., Amsterdam* **39**, 1114.

[63] Lang, A. 1957. The effects of gibberellin upon flower formation. *Proc. Natl. Acad. Sci.* **43**, 709.

[64] Langer, R. H. M. and Bussell, W. T. 1964. The effect of flower induction on the rate of leaf initiation. *Ann. Bot.* **28**, 163.

[65] Langston, R. and Leopold, A. C. 1954. The dark fixation of carbon dioxide as a factor in photoperiodism. *Plant Physiol.* **29**, 436.

[66] Lathwell, D. J. and Evans, C. E. 1951. Nitrogen uptake from solution by soybeans at successive stages of growth. *Agron. J.* **43**, 264.

[67] Leopold, A. C. and Guernsey, F. S. 1953. Modification of floral initiation with auxins and temperatures. *Am. J. Bot.* **40**, 603.

[68] Leopold, A. C. and Guernsey, F. S. 1953. Interaction of auxin and temperatures in floral initiation. *Science* **118**, 215.

[69] Loehwing, W. F. 1939. Foliar influences upon photoperiodic response. *Chron. Bot.* **4**, 497.

[70] Long, E. M. 1939. Photoperiodic induction as influenced by environmental factors. *Bot. Gaz.* **101**, 168.

[71] Morse, W. J. 1927. Soybeans, cultures and varieties. *U.S. Dept. Agr. Farmer's Bull.* 1520.

[72] Morse, W. J. 1950. In *Soybeans and Soybean Products*, 3. Ed. K. S. Markley. Interscience, N.Y.

[73] Murneek, A. E. 1937. Biochemical studies of photoperiodism in plants. *Missouri Univ. Agr. Expt. Sta. Res. Bull.* 268.

[74] Murneek, A. E. and Gomez, E. T. 1936. Influence of length of day (photoperiod) on development of the soybean plant, var. Biloxi. *Missour Univ. Agr. Expt. Sta. Res. Bull.* 242.

[75] Nagata, T. 1960. Interrelation of the effects of daylengths on the period to flowering, flowering period, and seed forming period, with special regards to the relative flowering period and the relative growing period of soybeans. *Japan. J. Breeding* **10**, 188.

[76] Nanda, K. K. and Hamner, K. C. 1958. Studies on the nature of the endogenous rhythm affecting photoperiodic response of Biloxi soybean. *Bot. Gaz.* **120**, 14.

[77] Nanda, K. K. and Hamner, K. C. 1959. Photoperiodic cycles of different lengths in relation to flowering in Biloxi soybean. *Planta* **53**, 45.

[78] Nanda, K. K. and Hamner, K. C. 1959. The effect of temperature, auxins, antiauxins and some other chemicals on the endogenous rhythm affecting photoperiodic response of Biloxi soybean (*Glycine max.* L.; Merr.). *Planta* **53**, 53.

[79] Nanda, K. K. and Hamner, K. C. 1961. Investigations on the effect of 'light break' on the nature of the endogenous rhythm in the flowering response of Biloxi Soybean (*Glycine max*, L.; Merr.). *Planta* **58**, 164.

[80] Nielsen, C. S. 1942. Effects of photoperiod on microsporogenesis in Biloxi soybean. *Bot. Gaz.* **104**, 99.

[81] Norman, A. G. (ed.) 1963. *The Soybean.* Academic Press, N.Y.

[82] Ohmura, T. and Howell, R. W. 1960. Inhibitory effect of water on oxygen consumption by plant materials. *Plant Physiol.* **35**, 184.

[83] Pal, B. P. and Murty, G. S. 1941. Studies in the vernalization of Indian crop plants. I. Preliminary experiments on gram, wheat, chilli, and soybeans. *Indian J. Genet. Pl. Breed.* **1**, 61.

[84] Parker, M. W. and Borthwick, H. A. 1939. Effect of photoperiod on development and metabolism of the Biloxi soybean. *Bot. Gaz.* **100**, 651.

[85] Parker, M. W. and Borthwick, H. A. 1939. Effect of variation in temperature during photoperiodic induction upon initiation of flower primordia in Biloxi soybeans. *Bot. Gaz.* **101**, 145.

[86] Parker, M. W. and Borthwick, H. A. 1940. Floral initiation in Biloxi soybeans as influenced by photosynthetic activity during the induction period. *Bot. Gaz.* **102**, 256.

[87] Parker, M. W. and Borthwick, H. A. 1943. Influence of temperature on photoperiodic reactions in leaf blades of Biloxi soybeans. *Bot. Gaz.* **104**, 612.

[88] Parker, M. W. and Borthwick, H. A. 1949. Growth and composition of Biloxi soybean grown in a controlled environment with radiation from different carbon-arc sources. *Plant Physiol.* **24**, 345.

[89] Parker, M. W. and Borthwick, H. A. 1951. Photoperiodic responses of soybean varieties. *Soybean Digest* **11**, 26.

[90] Parker, M. W., Hendricks, S. B., Borthwick, H. A. and Scully, N. J. 1945. Action spectrum for the photoperiodic control of floral initiation in Biloxi soybeans. *Science* **102**, 152.

[91] Parker, M. W., Hendricks, S. B., Borthwick, H. A. and Scully, N. J. 1946. Action spectrum for the photoperiodic control of floral initiation of short-day plants. *Bot. Gaz.* **108**, 1.

[92] Psarev, G. M. 1938. Effect of daylength upon growth of stem parenchyma cells in *Soya*. *C.R. (Dokl.) Acad. Sci. URSS* **20**, 731.

[93] Psarev, G. M. 1939. Yellowing and dying of leaves in *Soya* as related to daylength. *C.R. (Dolk.) Acad. Sci. URSS* **24**, 679.

[94] Psarev, G. M. 1940. Influence of daylength on stem growth in transverse direction. *C.R. (Dokl.) Acad. Sci. URSS* **28**, 537.

[95] Psarev, G. M. and Neuman, N. F. 1940. Effect of daylength on cambial growth. *C.R. (Dokl.) Acad. Sci. URSS* **29**, 497.

[96] Psarev, G. M. and Veselovskaja. 1941. Growth and development in the soybean. *C.R. (Dokl.) Acad. Sci. URSS* **30**, 844. (Abstract by R. O. Whyte. *Herbage Abst.* (*Suppl.*) **12**, 52.

[97] Ricker, P. L. and Morse, W. J. 1948. The correct botanical name for the soybean. *J. Am. Soc. Agron.* **40**, 190.

[98] Roberts, R. H. 1943. The role of night temperature in plant performance. *Science* **98**, 265.

[99] Rosenbaum, H. 1937. Short-day conditioned growth anomalies in soybeans. *Forschungsdienst.* **3**, 138.

[100] Rudorf, W. and Schroeck, O. 1941. Neuere Beobachtungen uber den Photoperiodismus. *Z. Pflanzenz.* **24**, 108.

[101] Schwabe, W. W. 1959. Studies of long-day inhibition in short-day plants. *J. Expt. Bot.* **10**, 317.

[102] Scully, N. J., Parker, M. W. and Borthwick, H. A. 1945. Relationship of photoperiod and nitrogen nutrition to initiation of flower primordia in soybean varieties. *Bot. Gaz.* **107**, 218.

[103] Shumate, W. H. 1965. Floral inhibition of Biloxi soybean during a 72-hour cycle. Ph.D. thesis. University of California, Los Angeles.

[104] Sirohi, G. S. and Hamner, K. C. 1962. Floral inhibition in relation to photoperiodism in Biloxi soybean. *Plant Physiol.* **37**, 785.

[105] Sirohi, G. S. and Hamner, K. C. Unpublished.

[106] Snyder, W. E. 1940. Effect of light and temperature on floral initiation in cocklebur and Biloxi soybean. *Bot. Gaz.* **102**, 302.

[107] Steinberg, R. A. and Garner, W. W. 1936. Response of certain plants to length of day and temperature under controlled conditions. *J. Agr. Res.* **52**, 943.

[108] Thrower, S. L. 1965. Translocation of labelled assimilates in the soybean. IV: Some effects of low temperature on translocation. *Aust. J. Biol. Sci.* **18**, 449.

[109] Van Schaik, P. H. and Probst, A. H. 1958. The inheritance of inflorescence type, peduncle length, flowers per node, and percent flower shedding in soybeans. *Agron. J.* **50**, 98.

[110] Van Schaik, P. H. and Probst, A. H. 1958. Effects of some environmental factors on flower production and reproductive efficiency in soybeans. *Agron. J.* **50**, 192.

[111] Wareing, P. F. 1953. A new photoperiodic phenomenon in short-day plants. *Nature* **171**, 614.

[112] Wareing, P. F. 1954. Experiments on the 'light break' effect in short-day plants. *Physiol. Plantar.* **7**, 157.

[113] Williams, J. H. 1953. Differential varietal response of root tissues to exogenous growth regulators in soybeans, oats and corn. *Agron. J.* **45**, 293.

[114] Withrow, A. P. 1945. The interrelationship of nitrogen supply and photoperiod on the flowering, growth and stem anatomy of certain long and short-day plants. *Butler Univ. Bot. Stud.* **7**, 40.

[115] Withrow, A. P. and Withrow, R. B. 1947. Plant growth with artificial sources of radiant energy. *Plant Physiol.* **22**, 494.

[116] Withrow, R. B. and Withrow, A. P. 1940. The effect of various wavebands of supplementary radiation on the photoperiodic response of certain plants. *Plant Physiol.* **15**, 609.

[117] World Agriculture Production and Trade Statistical Report. March 1967. U.S. Depart. Agr., Foreign Agricultural Service.

4

Pharbitis nil Chois.

By Atsushi Takimoto

1 History of Use

In 1922, Yoshii[55] sowed seeds of *Pharbitis nil* at different times under natural conditions in Tokyo and found that plants sown in spring required 107 days for the opening of the first flower while those sown in summer required less than 50 days. Subsequently,[56] he found that plants grown in 4 and 8-hour photoperiods flowered in 31–32 days, whereas those grown under summer day-lengths flowered in 90 days, and those under continuous illumination did not flower within 123 days. No further systematic work was done with this short-day plant until Nakayama and Imamura began, independently, to work with it.

Nakayama working with Yoshii, used the strain 'Shifukurin' (formerly named 'Violet Flower with White Margins'[31]) which is not so sensitive as 'Violet'. This strain was used in experiments at Beltsville.

Imamura obtained from Kihara the strain 'Violet', for which exposure to a single dark period is enough to induce a maximum flowering response, even with seedlings 3–4 days old. The sensitivity of the strain to photoperiod, and the ease of working with it, have led to its recent widespread use.

2 Growing Techniques and Growth Habit

Young seedlings of *Pharbitis nil* are fully sensitive to photoperiodic induction, and have been used in most experiments. When using young seedlings it is very important to obtain uniform germination, and this is done by selecting seeds uniform in size and color and treating them with concentrated sulfuric acid. The optimal duration of acid treatment depends on the water content of the seeds and on the temperature. With occasional stirring, the temperature of the acid usually rises to 32–35°C within the first 10–15 minutes of treatment, and uniform germination is obtained after a 30-minute treatment. If the temperature of the acid does not reach much above 20°C, 1 to 2 hours of treatment may be required. After acid treatment the seeds are thoroughly washed in running water overnight. The next morning they are placed on moist sand in petri dishes and kept at about 20°C. One day later, when the radicles have emerged, the germinating seeds are again selected for uniformity and planted about 1.5 cm deep in clay or plastic pots filled with soil. The pots are kept at 30–32°C for 20 to 30 hours, by which time all seedlings appear above ground. They are then transferred to a temperature of 20 to 25°C and exposed to long days or continuous illumination. Care should be taken that seed coats are removed from the cotyledons. In the earlier work, seedlings were grown in a glasshouse illuminated at night by incandescent lamps, and their flowering response varied with the season and with the time at which dark treatments began. In most recent work, therefore, seedlings have been grown entirely under artificial light at a constant temperature (20°C) before treatment. For reasonable growth and high photo-periodic sensitivity, cool white or daylight fluorescent light of 400 f.c. intensity is sufficient. Nakayama usually cultivates the seedlings in a glass bottle with Knop's solution. Water culture of this plant is very easy.

In some experiments adult plants may be more useful than seedlings, in which case they are better grown in a glasshouse. The optimum temperature for growth is 20–30°C and if the plants are exposed to low temperature (below 15°C) for long durations, they may flower even in continuous light (cf. Section 13).

In Kyoto (35°N), seeds should be sown early in May for the best growth of strain Violet in the field. The plants branch at the base, develop long vines, and produce many axillary flowers from July to September (500–800 flowers per plant under favorable conditions). At the latitude of Kyoto, where the day-length in midsummer is slightly shorter than the critical, the photoperiodic stimulus is not strong enough to produce terminal flowers. In late autumn, terminal flowers develop and growth ceases.

3 Inflorescence Structure and Criteria of Flowering Response

After a weak inductive stimulus, the shoot apex gives rise to floral primordia in the axils of a few successive nodes, but the terminal meristem of the shoot remains in the vegetative state. After strong induction by short days, the apex of the main axis stops the production of leaves and initiates a terminal flower. No further primordia can be formed on that particular axis.

FIGURE 4–1. *Pharbitis nil*, strain Violet. Left – plant in short days: Right – plant in long days.

The flowering response of *Pharbitis nil* may be measured by three criteria: (1) the percentage of plants flowering; (2) the percentage of plants with terminal flower buds; and (3) the average number of flower buds per plant.

The first sign of flower differentiation is obtained by examination of the shape of the first two leaf primordia of the bud. Because the bract primordia arise in closer succession than those of vegetative leaves, the two bracts enclosing flower buds are equally developed and more or less symmetrical, whereas the leaf primordia of vegetative buds are at different developmental stages and the bud is strikingly asymmetric. Flower buds are also less hairy than vegetative buds.

In most cases flowers occur singly in the leaf axils. In vigorous plants, however, side flowers may develop in the axils of one or both bracts of the primary flower, forming inflorescences with two or three flowers. In experiments with young seedlings, the only bract to have an axillary flower bud is that on the terminal flower. In our early experiments with seedlings, flower buds in the axils of bracts were not included in the 'number of flower buds'. Since 1962 axillary flower buds of the bracts of the terminal flowers have been included. The maximum number of flower buds initiated in seedlings may vary with plant age and nutritional conditions.

4 Effects of Plant Age

Young seedlings of *Pharbitis nil* are fully sensitive to short days, but those in the first stage of germination cannot respond to photoperiod. Marushige and Marushige[25,26] investigated the photoperiodic sensitivity of seedlings at different ages in relation to changes in growth pattern with age. The sprouted seeds were kept in darkness for various times and they were then exposed to a light period (250 f.c.) of various durations followed by a single dark period of 16 hours at 28°C, the optimum temperature for induction. The light period required to reach full photoperiodic sensitivity decreased with an increase in the duration of the initial dark period. When the seedlings were grown under continuous illumination from the start of germination, 64 to 72 hours of light period were required to get photoperiodic sensitivity, but in the seedlings grown in darkness for 48 or 72 hours only 8–16 hours of illumination were required. The appearance of photoperiodic sensitivity coincided with a change from loss to gain in the dry weight of the cotyledons, and with the differentiation of their mesophyll into palisade and spongy tissue. Growth of the hypocotyl ceased, and that of plumules became predominant at this stage.[25] These changes in growth patterns may have some connection with photoperiodic sensitivity.

When etiolated seedlings grown in darkness for two or three days were exposed to light for different durations the length of the light period required to ensure 100 per cent flowering following a 16-hour dark period was 32 hours. However, illumination continuously for 32 hours was not required. If the light period was separated into an initial 4-hour period and a terminal 8-hour period, with 20 hours of darkness between them, nearly 100 per cent flowering occurred.[26] The light intensity required to induce 100 per cent flowering was 10 f.c. in the first period, but more than 100 f.c. in the second. The light intensity required for the first light period was the same as the intensity required to cause hook opening, cotyledon expansion and inhibition of hypocotyl elongation. This suggests that such photomorphogenetic changes are closely related to the appearance of photoperiodic sensitivity. In the second light period, increase in photosynthetic activity and chlorophyll was observed to parallel that in photoperiodic sensitivity. This suggests that photosynthesis or photosynthate is one of the factors affecting the photoperiodic sensitivity of the seedlings.[26]

Flowering responses of seedlings and adult plants are somewhat different; the seedling produces a terminal flower more easily than the adult, but the former produces less flower buds than the latter in response to a given photoperiodic treatment. The critical dark period in adult plants is somewhat shorter (8–9 hours)[14] than in young seedlings (9–10 hours).[13]

Old plants initiate some flower buds even in long days. This response seems to be temperature dependent. When plants were kept at 31°C in the daytime and at 27°C at night (31/27°) no flower buds were observed below the 30th node; under the 27/23° and 23/19° regimes, however, the lowest nodes with flower buds were the 24th and 17th respectively.[59]

7 *Photoperiod Response*

The photoperiodic sensitivity of *Pharbitis nil*, like that of many plants, differs from strain to strain. Six strains were examined for their photoperiodic sensitivity and critical dark period:[13] (1) Tendan (abbreviated to T in Figs. 4–2 and 4–3), collected in a suburb of Peking in North China and probably a wild

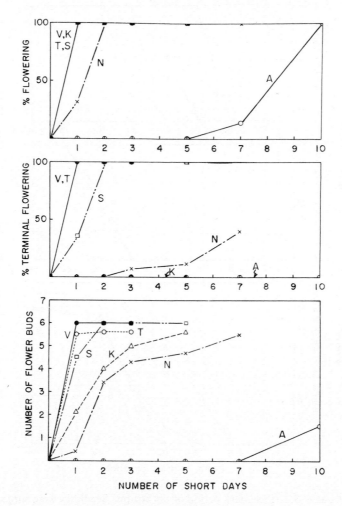

FIGURE 4–2. Flowering responses of six strains to different numbers of short days (8-hour light and 16-hour dark). Abbreviations are explained in the text (Imamura *et al.*[13]).

type; (2) Violet (V), a Japanese garden variety with large violet flowers, used extensively in work at Kyoto; (3) Shifukurin (S), a Japanese garden variety used by Nakayama and others to study photoperiodic response; (4) Kidachi, a dwarf mutant of a Japanese garden variety; (5) Nepal (N), a wild strain collected in Nepal; (6) Africa (A), collected in Guinea, West Africa.

Flowering responses of these six strains to different numbers of short photoperiods or to different daylengths are shown in Figures 4–2 and 4–3. The fewer short days required the shorter was the critical dark period. The relative photoperiodic sensitivity of the six strains was T > V > S > N > A. Kidachi was unusual in that it had the shortest critical dark period but produced no terminal flower even when the dark period was prolonged to 14 hours. All data presented below refer to strain Violet unless otherwise indicated.

The lower the temperature the longer is the single dark period required for induction and for maximal flowering (Fig. 4–4). With repeated short days,

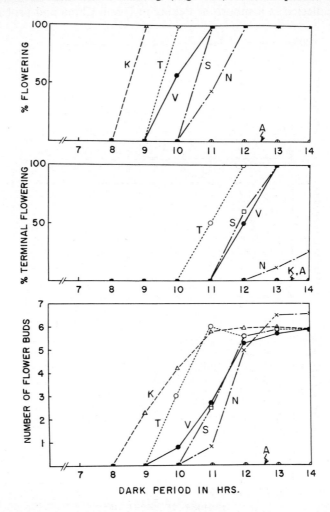

FIGURE 4–3. Critical dark period of six strains. Seedlings were subjected to 10 short days of various lengths (Imamura *et al.*[13]).

however, the critical dark period for floral induction (8–10 hours) is scarcely influenced by temperature. A brief irradiation at an appropriate point in the dark period inhibits flowering. The most sensitive period is about 8 hours after the beginning of the inductive dark period, irrespective of its length[45] or temperature[44] (Fig. 4–5). The dark process required for flower initiation is very sensitive to temperature (Fig. 4–4) but the timing process, which shows a maximum sensitivity to red light after 8 hours of darkness, is hardly influenced by temperature. Red light is also inhibitory during the last half of the 48-hour dark period at temperatures of 18 to 18.5°C, which will be discussed in Section 9.

Light sensitivity of the inductive dark process varies with time during the dark period. When a 16-hour dark period, which induces a maximum flowering response, was divided into 4 phases of 4 hours each, the first phase was least sensitive to light and was not inhibited by 10 f.c. of fluorescent light (Fig. 4–6). This implies that the first process taking place in the inductive dark period proceeds under light of 10 f.c. intensity as readily as in darkness. The third phase (8th to 12th hour) was most light sensitive and was inhibited even by 0.1 f.c. of light.

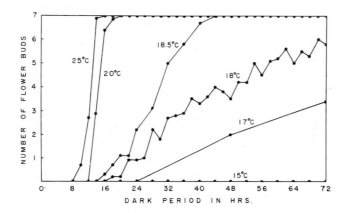

FIGURE 4–4. Flowering response after a single dark period of various durations at different temperatures. The plants were exposed to continuous illumination of 400 f.c. from cool white fluorescent lamps before the dark treatments (Takimoto and Hamner[44]).

Under natural conditions, the beginning and end of an inductive dark period cannot be clearly determined because of the progressive change in intensity during the evening and morning twilights. However, plants exposed to natural daylight in the evening and darkened as soon as the intensity had declined to 20, 10, 5, 1, 0.1, or 0 f.c. showed similar flowering responses, and plants darkened

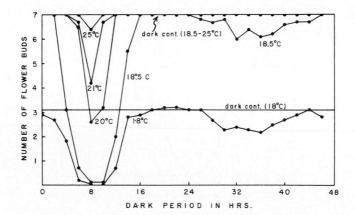

FIGURE 4–5. Flowering responses at different temperatures when plants were exposed to 5 minutes of red light (3300 ergs/cm²/sec) at different times in a 48-hour dark period. The plants were exposed to continuous illumination before dark treatment (Takimoto and Hamner[44]).

when the intensity was 50 f.c. initiated significantly more flower buds.[49] This shows that the first flower-inducing process of the dark period can proceed under natural daylight of 0–20 f.c. as readily as in darkness. Light-sensitivity of the last phase of the dark process may vary with the length of the dark period. In midsummer at Kyoto, natural night length is 9–10 hours, and the

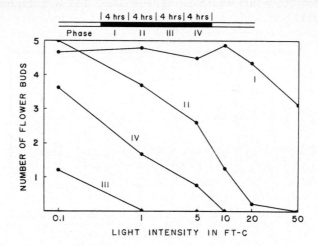

FIGURE 4–6. Light sensitivity of the dark process in the 1st, 2nd, 3rd and 4th phases of a 16-hour dark period. Each phase consisted of 4 hours duration. Plants were exposed to daylight fluorescent light of various intensities during the 1st, 2nd, 3rd, or 4th phase and kept in darkness during the remaining three phases (Takimoto and Ikeda[50]).

last phase of this night period corresponds to the third phase of the 16-hour dark period previously described, which is very sensitive to light. Only 0.1 f.c. of morning light was sufficient to inhibit the last phase of the dark process.[49]

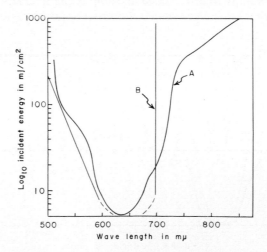

FIGURE 4–7. Action spectra for inhibition of flower initiation near middle of each of three 16-hour dark periods (A), and for repromotion of flowering following far-red irradiation at the beginning of each of three 16-hour dark periods (B) (Strain Shifukurin) (Nakayama *et al.*[29]).

8 Spectral Dependence

The action spectrum for inhibition of flowering in *Pharbitis* seedlings (strain Shifukurin) by a light interruption in the middle of inductive dark periods (about 8 hours after the beginning of the dark period) has been investigated by Nakayama *et al.*[29] They observed a maximum effectiveness in the red (Fig. 4–7, curve A) suggesting the participation of phytochrome in this reaction. The inhibitory effect of this red light was partially reversed by subsequent exposure to far-red, if the exposure time to red and far-red was 30 seconds.[7,48] However, if the exposure time to red and far-red was prolonged, or if 3 minutes of darkness were inserted between two 30-second irradiations, no reversibility was observed.[7] It was supposed that the reaction between P_{fr} and its substrate may proceed very rapidly, and that if the exposure time to red is prolonged, or the time of far-red irradiation was delayed, physiological processes have gone to completion before far-red irradiation which fails to repromote flowering.[7]

The action spectrum of light breaks at the beginning of the dark period was also studied by Nakayama *et al.*[29] (Fig. 4–8). Flowering was sharply inhibited

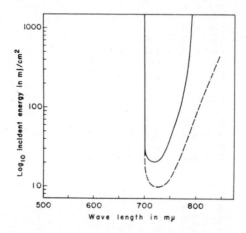

FIGURE 4–8. Action spectrum for floral initiation in *Pharbitis* seedlings (strain Shifukurin) irradiated at the start of three 16-hour dark periods. Two levels of reduced flowering are indicated by solid and broken lines (Nakayama *et al.*[29]).

at wave-lengths of 700–800 mμ (far-red light). Red light given after this far-red irradiation at the beginning of the dark period repromoted flowering.[28,29] The wavelength region longer than 700 mμ was completely ineffective for the reversion of the far-red effect but was somewhat effective for the light break (compare curves A and B in Fig. 4–7). Nakayama *et al.* considered that in the spectral region of 700–800 mμ, where the wing of the absorption curve of P_r lies under the absorption curve of P_{fr}, the only action indicated was a weak absorption by P_r.

Takimoto and Hamner,[48] working with strain Violet, found that the reversibility of the red and far-red effects at the 8-hour point was strongly affected by the length of the dark period. The flower inhibiting effect of 30 seconds of red light given at the 8-hour point was slightly reversed by subsequent exposure to far-red when the dark period was 16 hours. Increasing the red light exposure to 5 minutes completely inhibited flowering and subsequent exposure to far-red was without effect. When the dark period was 48 hours however, the effect of red was not reversed by subsequent exposure to far-red even when the exposure times were reduced to 30 seconds. Far-red light actually intensified the inhibitory effect of red light.

    The additional inhibition resulting from far-red treatment given after exposure to red light is completely reversed by subsequent red irradiation at any point during the 48-hour dark period, though the effect of red light is not reversed by subsequent exposure to far-red. This is clearly shown in Table 4–1.

TABLE 4–1

Flowering response of *Pharbitis* seedlings exposed to red and far-red light alternately at 0, 4, 8, or 12 hours after the beginning of a 48-hour dark period. Dark temperature was 20°C. R: 5 minutes of red light (3300 ergs/cm^2/sec). FR: 5 minutes of far-red light (6000 ergs/cm^2/sec) (Takimoto and Hamner[48]).

	Treatment	No. of flower buds
	Dark control	7.0
Beginning of dark period	FR	1.5
	FR + R	7.0
	FR + R + FR	1.0
	FR + R + FR + R	7.0
	FR + R + FR + R + FR	0.4
	FR + R + FR + R + FR + R	7.0
4-hour point	FR	2.8
	R	7.0
	R + FR	2.0
	R + FR + R	7.0
	R + FR + R + FR	0.9
	R + FR + R + FR + R	7.0
8-hour point	FR	5.0
	R	3.4
	R + FR	1.5
	R + FR + R	3.2
	R + FR + R + FR	0
	R + FR + R + FR + R	2.8
12-hour* point	FR	5.9
	R	6.2
	R + FR	1.7
	R + FR + R	6.5
	R + FR + R + FR	0.6
	R + FR + R + FR + R	6.3

* In this group, dark temperature was 19°C.

Plants given a 48-hour dark period were exposed to 5 minutes of red and far-red light alternately several times at the start, or at the 4th, 8th, or 12th hour of the dark period. If the interruptions were terminated with far-red light, the flowering response decreased with repeated irradiation irrespective of when the interruptions were applied (Table 4–1). If the interruptions were terminated with red light however, similar flowering responses were obtained regardless of the number of repetitions of red and far-red treatments. It is clear that phytochrome is in a reversible form at these points though the red effect is not reversed by far-red.

    The flower inhibiting effects of red and far-red are additive when they are given in that order (Table 4–1). The far-red effect is reversed by red light but the red effect is not reversed by far-red. These phenomena suggest that phytochrome is concerned in the far-red effect and that red radiant energy absorbed by some non-reversible pigment other than phytochrome is also effective for floral inhibition (red effect). The following facts support this assumption:

1. The flower inhibiting effect of red light given at the 8th to 10th hour of a 48-hour dark period is intensified by simultaneous or subsequent irradiation with far-red light.[47] This suggests that red and far-red radiant energies are absorbed by two different pigments and both are inhibitory to flowering.

2. When plants are exposed to red or far-red light at different times during a long dark period, flowering response to red light interruption shows a rhythmic response but that to far-red interruption does not. Red light interruption is most inhibitory when applied 8 hours after the beginning of the dark period and the second maximum inhibition occurs 24 hours later[44,45] (see Section 9). Far-red interruption, on the other hand, is most inhibitory at the beginning of the dark period and the inhibitory effect decreases almost linearly with delay of far-red exposure.[47] Thus, the flower inhibiting effects of red and far-red light are independent of each other.

3. The far-red energy required for saturation of its effect at the beginning of an inductive dark period is about 360 kiloergs/cm^2.[48] Once a saturating energy of far-red has been given, the amount of red energy required to completely nullify the far-red effect is about 80 kiloergs/cm^2. This level of red energy was sufficient to completely annul the effect of far-red, even when the energy in far-red was increased up to 3600 kiloergs/cm^2. It is clear that 360 kiloergs/cm^2 of far-red produce maximum conversion of P_{fr} to P_r and the 80 kiloergs/cm^2 of red energy completely reconvert the P_r to P_{fr}. The saturation energy of far-red at a given time remained constant throughout the inductive dark period. Such was the case even if the far-red irradiation was immediately preceded by red irradiation.[48] This means that the amount of far-red absorbing pigment and also the total amount of phytochrome remains relatively constant during the dark period. Phytochrome is probably mainly in the P_{fr} form at the end of the light period, and must therefore be predominantly in the P_{fr} form during the dark period. Nevertheless a red light interruption inhibits flowering when given during an inductive dark period and the amount of red light required for maximal inhibition was more than 1980 kiloergs/cm^2 at the 6-hour point, and more than 150 kiloergs/cm^2 at the 10-hour point. As previously mentioned maximum conversion of P_r to P_{fr} occurs with only 80 kiloergs/cm^2 of red light. These phenomena strongly support the assumption mentioned above, i.e. flowering is inhibited by some non-reversible pigment that absorbs red radiant energy.

4. When red light is given at the 8th hour of a dark period, the flower inhibiting effect of this red light is partially overcome by increasing the duration of the following dark period up to at least 72 hours, and the red interruption is assumed to slow down the subsequent dark process necessary for flowering (Fig. 4–9). Flower inhibition caused by far-red irradiation on the other hand, is not overcome by increasing the dark period beyond 12–16 hours, and it is supposed that far-red light completely stops the dark process required for flowering after a certain time.[47] It is therefore suggested that some non-reversible pigment which absorbs red energy is concerned with the slowing of the dark process by red light, and that the reversible pigment phytochrome is concerned with the stopping of the dark process by far-red.[47,48]

Far-red light given at the beginning of the dark period slightly promoted flowering when the dark period was short (10–13 hours) and the light intensity in the main light period was kept high.[7,51] Far-red light given after red was also slightly promotive at the 8-hour point, if the dark period was kept relatively short.[48] Under these conditions, far-red light could promote the dark process during the first 8–13 hours, but even in such cases the flower promoting dark process stopped after a certain duration of time.[48,51]

The spectral dependence of light required to reverse the far-red effect and that required to give a light break effect could be different if they are mediated by different pigments. Action spectra for these two reactions shown in Figure 4–7 are somewhat different, but Nakayama et al. considered that phytochrome controlled both of these reactions. Takimoto[42] found that if the relative intensity of red (600–700 mμ), green (500–600 mμ), blue (400–500 mμ), and white (400–700 mμ) light was 12 : 30 : 1,000 : 30, each region of the spectrum exerted the same effect for both light break and reversal of the far-red effect. This suggests that the same pigment controls these two reactions. However, other evidence described above, suggests that some non-reversible pigment absorbing red light is involved in the light break effect, and phytochrome in the reversal of the far-red effect. Either some non-reversible pigment other than phytochrome is involved in the photoperiodic response, with a spectral absorbance similar to phytochrome P_r, or some phytochrome P_r may be converted by red irradiation to a form which is inhibitory to flowering when produced during the light sensitive phase of an inductive dark period, but which is not converted to P_r by far-red irradiation.

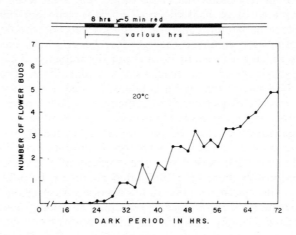

FIGURE 4–9. Flowering response to a single dark period of various durations, interrupted with 5 minutes of red light (3300 ergs/cm^2/sec) 8 hours after the beginning of the dark period. The plants were exposed to continuous illumination before dark treatment, and the dark-period temperature was 20°C (Takimoto and Hamner[44]).

The effects of blue light are complex. When given for short periods at high intensity the effect is similar to red light. For example, when 15 minutes of blue light at high intensity was given at different times in a 24-hour dark period, it was most inhibitory at the 8th hour, and the response was very similar to red.[42] Also high-intensity blue reverses the flower inhibiting effect of far-red given at the beginning of the dark period.[42] When long periods of blue light were given before a long dark period, however, the effect was similar to that obtained with far-red light, flowering was inhibited and this effect was red reversible.[42] These results might be interpreted as the action of phytochrome and/or the non-reversible pigment mentioned above. So far, there is no evidence which suggests the participation of the so-called high-energy reaction (B-FR pigment system) in photoperiodic response of *Pharbitis nil*.

9 Endogenous Rhythms

Two endogenous circadian rhythms are involved in the photoperiodic responses of *Pharbitis nil.*

1. When plants were subjected to an 8-hour dark period followed by either 8 or 12 hours of light preceding a main dark period of various lengths, the flowering responses increased stepwise with increasing length of the dark period (Fig. 4–10). When the flowering response is plotted in relation to the time of

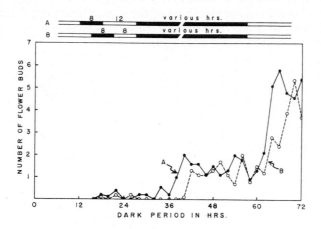

FIGURE 4–10. Flowering response at 18°C, after a single dark period of various durations preceded by different light conditions. Light conditions preceding the main dark period are shown diagrammatically (Takimoto and Hamner[44]).

initiation of the light period preceding the experimental dark period, it is seen that the peaks in the curves coincide. Sharp increases in flowering are observed between 48 and 54, and between 70 and 76 hours after the initiation of the light period in both groups. These results suggest that the light-on signal of the preceding light period initiated an endogenous rhythm which affected the photoperiodic response (light-on rhythm). A theoretical curve of this rhythm is shown in Figure 4–11, curve a. No endogenous rhythm was evident when plants were subjected to continuous illumination prior to exposure to the long dark period (Fig. 4–4) and this response represents an hourglass type of timing (curve b in Fig. 4–11). An integration of the two curves a and b is shown in curve c which represents the expected flowering response when plants are exposed to 8 hours of darkness followed by either 8 or 12 hours of light preceding a main dark period of various lengths. Curve c is similar to the actual experimental curves which were shown in Figure 4–10.

2. When plants were subjected to a long dark period of different lengths and exposed to 5 minutes of red light at different times, maximum inhibition of flowering was seen about 8 hours after the beginning of the dark period, irrespective of the length of the dark period or of temperature (Figs. 4–5 and 4–12 to 14). All of these curves showed a second dip 30 to 40 hours after the onset of darkness, i.e. about 24 hours after the first maximal depression of flowering at the 8-hour point, providing evidence for the activities of a circadian rhythm. This was so even when plants were exposed to continuous illumination before the inductive dark period (Figs. 4–5, 4–12, and curve A in Fig. 4–13). This suggests that the onset of darkness may induce a second endogenous rhythm (light-off rhythm) which results in high sensitivity to red light 8 hours after the

onset of darkness and a second weaker pulsation of sensitivity to red light about
24 hours later.

The effect of a red interruption on the flowering response depends on whether
plants have been exposed to continuous illumination or given a light-dark cycle
prior to the main dark period (compare curves A and B in Figs. 4.13 and 4.14).
The initial dip in the curve extended further into the dark period when the dark
period was preceded by an 8-hour dark and 8-hour light period. A similar effect
was seen on the second dip in the curve. This suggests that the light-on rhythm,
which may be initiated at the beginning of the 8-hour light period, influences the
time of effectiveness of the red light interruption. Details on these phenomena
were discussed by Takimoto and Hamner.[44]

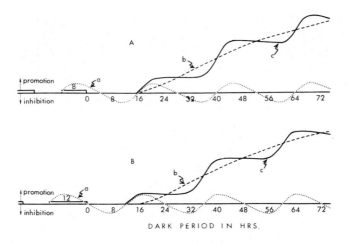

FIGURE 4–11. Theoretical curves for flowering responses to a single dark
period of various lengths. For details see text (Takimoto and Hamner[44]).

One might expect that the light-off rhythm would also be shown as a stepwise
increase in the flowering response with increasing length of the dark period,
but such was not the case. A stepwise response to increasing duration of dark
treatment was only shown when plants were pretreated with a light-dark regime
and not when pretreated with continuous illumination. The only evidence for
the participation of the light-off rhythm after pretreatment with continuous
light was obtained by interrupting the long dark period at various times with
red light. A possible explanation of this difference in response follows:

One component of time measurement during the dark period shows an hourglass type of response (Fig. 4–4). This hourglass component is very sensitive to
temperature and a red light interruption during an inhibitory phase of the dark
period slows it down, resulting in flower inhibition. For example, at 20°C, a
dark period of about 16 hours is enough to obtain a maximum flowering
response (Fig. 4–4). If the plant is exposed to 5 minutes of red light after 8
hours of darkness, the flowering response increases slowly with increasing
duration of the subsequent dark period, and even a 72-hour dark period is not
sufficient to induce maximal flowering (Fig. 4–9). The red light interruption
slows down the hourglass component in a similar manner to lowering the
temperature (compare curves in Figs. 4–4 and 4–9), and results in flower inhibition. When the dark period is terminated with continuous light, the hourglass component of the timing mechanism apparently stops at the end of the
dark period, and in this case the effect of the light-off rhythm would not be

evident because the flowering response is determined solely by the length of the dark period.

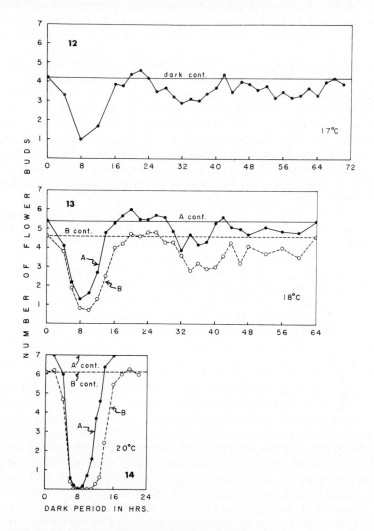

FIGURES 4–12 to 14. Flowering responses when plants were exposed to 5 minutes of red light (3300 ergs/cm²/sec) at different times in a 72- (Fig. 4–12), 64- (Fig. 4–13), and 24- (Fig. 4–14) hour dark period. Plants in Fig. 4–12 and those of group A in Figs. 4–13 and 4–14 were exposed to continuous illumination before dark treatment (solid line). Plants of group B in Figs. 4–13 and 4–14 were exposed to an 8-hour dark followed by an 8-hour light period before the main dark period (broken line). The dark temperatures are shown in each figure (Takimoto and Hamner[45]).

The oscillation of the light-off rhythm is rapidly damped after one cycle (cf. Figs. 4–12 and 4–13). This damping may be more apparent than real however, since the curves show only the response to red light interruption, which is controlled by the light-off rhythm. We could assume, for example, that red light given at either the 8-hour or 32-hour point slows down the hourglass component to the same extent. However, the inhibition produced by red light at the 32-hour point is slight because the plants have already been exposed to the action of the hourglass component for 32 hours of darkness before the interruption.

Since even a brief period of illumination gives the plant both light-on and light-off signals, the question arises whether the intensity of the light and the duration of the photoperiod affect the amplitude or effectiveness of the two rhythms produced. Furthermore, if light is given during the dark period how much is required to interfere with or damp a previously induced rhythm?

If two red light interruptions (5 minutes each) were given one might expect the first to reset the timing mechanism which may control the effect of the second. The effect of the second interruption is, however, mainly controlled by the persistence of the light-off rhythm started at the beginning of the dark period and so depends on the time interval from the beginning of the dark period, rather than from the first interruption.[46] After the first red interruption, the effect of the second was inhibitory when given in the inhibitory phase of the light-off rhythm (6th to 12th hour) and stimulatory when given in the stimulatory phase (16th to 24th hour). The net effect of a double red light interruption thus depends mainly on the timing of the second interruption.[46]

Even when two hours of white light (400 f.c.) was given 8 hours after the beginning of a long dark period, the light-off rhythm initiated at the beginning of the initial dark period still persisted, so that red light interruptions applied 12 to 20 hours after the beginning of the dark period (4–10 hours after the end of the 2-hour light period) promoted flowering.[44,46] Exposure to at least 4 hours of light was necessary to interfere with a preinduced rhythm and establish a new one. The initiation of an endogenous rhythm may be influenced more by the duration of illumination than by the total amount of light received. As little as 7 f.c. of light was effective in initiating a new rhythm when given for 4 hours, while 400 f.c. for 2 hours was not effective.[43] As this amount of light is less than that required for ordinary photosynthesis, the photosynthate supply may have little effect on the initiation of an endogenous rhythm.

As has been mentioned above, there are at least three kinds of timing mechanisms in the photoperiodic response of *Pharbitis nil*. The first, which is very sensitive to temperature, is similar to an hourglass in that increasing the duration of the dark period results in a linear increase in the flowering response. The second, the light-on rhythm, is an endogenous circadian rhythm which starts at the beginning of the light period. The third, the light-off rhythm, is also endogenous and circadian, starting at the beginning of the dark period, and has a red-sensitive phase with a maximum 8 hours after the onset of darkness. How is the critical dark period determined? It is little affected by temperature, unlike the first type of timing mechanism, the hourglass response. The timing mechanism determining the critical dark period may therefore be either one or both of these circadian rhythms. If the light-on rhythm determines the critical dark period, flowering response should be controlled by the length of the light-dark cycles rather than the length of the dark period. Experimental results in which plants were subjected to seven light-dark cycles of different lengths, separated from preceding continuous illumination by an 8-hour dark period, showed that irrespective of the length of the light period (6–12 hours), 10 hours of darkness, but not 8 hours, were sufficient for floral initiation.[41] This suggests that the critical dark period is determined by the light-off rhythm, and when the most light sensitive phase is reached (the 8-hour point) the hourglass component of the timing mechanism is able to begin. This hourglass component is considered to be a process required for synthesis of the floral hormone. Because of the high sensitivity of the hourglass component to temperature, the photoperiodic response is also very sensitive to night temperature, though the critical dark period is hardly affected by temperature.

11 *Photoperiodic Inhibition*

In seedlings with two cotyledons, a dark treatment given to one cotyledon is more effective in inducing flowering when the other cotyledon is cut off than when the other is exposed to light. The same holds for an adult plant, a long-day leaf having an unfavorable effect on the flowering response. There are four possible explanations of this phenomenon: (1) The stimulus transmitted from the induced leaf may be diluted by the photosynthate of the illuminated leaf; (2) The illuminated leaf functions as a sink for the stimulus; (3) The transmission of the stimulus from the induced leaf to the bud is disturbed by the presence of the illuminated leaf; (4) The illuminated leaf may have an active inhibitory function.

Imamura[12] exposed one cotyledon to different intensities and colors of light, covering the other cotyledon with a light-proof bag. No significant differences between the intensities or colors of light were observed, suggesting that the photosynthate produced in the illuminated leaf has no significant influence on floral inhibition. This eliminates the first possibility mentioned above.

Even if the illuminated cotyledon was removed at the end of a 16-hour dark treatment given to the other cotyledon, the flower inhibiting effect of the former was not reduced.[12] The translocation of the floral stimulus from cotyledon to bud is not yet completed at the end of the 16-hour dark period (cf. Section 16). This phenomenon therefore eliminates the second and the third possibilities mentioned above.

It is most probable that the illuminated leaf has an active inhibitory function, but the details of the mechanism of the inhibition are unknown.

13 *Effects of Temperature*

High or low temperature given during the light period preceding an inductive dark period has no significant effect on the flowering response of *Pharbitis* seedlings grown under continuous illumination.[11] However, as will be shown later, the temperature in the light period has a marked effect on flowering when

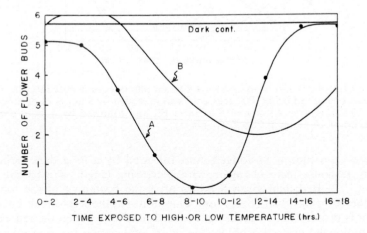

Fig. 4–15. Flowering responses when plants were exposed to low temperature of 1°C (A) or high temperature of 36°C (B) for two hours at various times in an 18-hour dark period. Control plants were subjected to 18 hours of darkness at 27.5°C (A) or 25°C (B). Curve A: after Ikeda,[11] Curve B: after Nakayama.[28]

the light period is preceded by a non-inductive dark period of about 8 hours and followed by an inductive dark period. If plants are exposed to high temperature (34°C) after the inductive dark period, flowering is reduced to some extent, but low temperature (10°C) has less effect.[11]

The effect of temperature during the inductive dark period has been shown in Fig. 4–4. The flower-promoting dark process is very sensitive to temperature. The optimum night temperature is 25–30°C, and temperatures above 32°C are inhibitory.[11,28] Flowering is reduced by short exposures to extremely high or low temperature during the inductive dark period. Maximum inhibition by low temperature treatment (0–10°C) occurred in the middle of an 18-hour dark period, but that by high temperature (36°C), 2–4 hours later (Fig. 4–15).

If plants were exposed to low temperature for 8 hours or more during the first part of an inductive dark period, flowering was strikingly reduced even when a long dark period at normal temperatures was given subsequently. The flower inhibition caused by the low temperature was slightly overcome by a subsequent long dark period at normal temperature. The flower-promoting dark process may be slowed down or stopped after exposure to low temperature.[11]

Interruption of the dark period by red light is most inhibitory at the 8th hour of the dark period irrespective of the length of the dark period.[45] At this time, the flower inhibiting effect of red light is saturated by a few minutes' irradiation.[48]

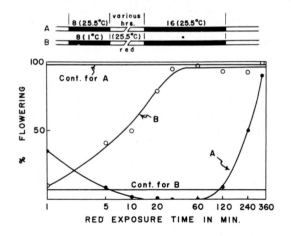

FIGURE 4–16. Flowering responses when plants were exposed to various durations of red light (1000 ergs/cm²/sec) preceded by 8 hours of darkness at 25.5°C (Curve A) or at 1°C (Curve B), and followed by a main dark period of 16 hours at 25.5°C (Ikeda[11]).

If the exposure time is prolonged, and followed by a long dark period, the flowering response increases again with increasing length of exposure to red radiation.[11,48] Red light given 8 hours after the beginning of the long dark period therefore has dual effects, one is inhibitory (the light-break effect) and the other is promotive (the main light period reaction). When the red exposure time is prolonged up to 4–8 hours, the main light period reaction takes place, which makes the subsequent dark period inductive, and the flower inhibiting effect of red light is cancelled. The temperature during this light period has a marked effect on flower promotion.[11] When the temperature is lowered during this light period, the flower promoting effect of light is greatly suppressed. As mentioned above, flowering was not affected when low temperature was given during the light period preceding an inductive dark period to seedlings grown under continuous illumination. These phenomena suggest that low temperature during the light period does not positively inhibit flowering, but may suppress the main light period reaction which must take place before an inductive dark period can be effective. In other words once the main light period reaction is completed, subsequent low temperature in light is without effect; after a dark period of about 8 hours a second main light period reaction may be necessary at normal temperature in order to make the subsequent dark period effective.

As shown above, low temperature (1°C) given during the first 8 hours of a long dark period at normal temperatures, is very inhibitory to flowering. However, if red irradiation is given after 8 hours of darkness at low temperature, followed by a long dark period at normal temperatures, flowering increases with increasing duration of red irradiation. Only 5 minutes of red irradiation are needed for this repromotion of flowering, although at normal temperature such a short exposure to red light at the 8th hour was very inhibitory (Fig. 4–16). This suggests that the process which takes place during the first 8 hours of the dark period is suppressed by lowering the temperature to 1°C. The effect (or products) of the main light period may be nullified during the 8 hours of the dark period, even at low temperature, and red light given after this dark period may be used for the main light period reaction, resulting in flower promotion. When red light is given after 8 hours of darkness at low temperature, there is no inhibitory light-break effect, and only the main light period effect is evident, resulting in flower promotion.

When *Pharbitis* plants are exposed to low temperature either continuously (10–15°C) or alternating with normal temperature (5–10°C for 16–20 hours and 20–25°C for 8–4 hours daily) for long durations, flower initiation takes place even under continuous illumination.[21,22,32,52] Flower initiation at low temperature is not influenced by photoperiod, intensity, or quality of light, but is significantly influenced by the culture medium.[19,20,21,40] When seedlings are cultured on modified White's medium containing 5 per cent sucrose and kept at 15°C for 30 days, they easily initiate floral primordia under continuous illumination. However, if sucrose is withheld, the flowering at low temperature is prevented. Glucose, fructose, mannose, lactose, and raffinose were as effective as sucrose in promoting floral initiation at low temperature but xylose, galactose, mannitol and soluble starch were not.[19,21]

Under constant temperature conditions, the optimal temperature for flower initiation under continuous illumination was 15°C, but when the plants were exposed to alternating low and normal (25°C) temperatures, the optimal low temperature was 5–10°C.[21,22] Some growth is required under low-temperature treatment in order to initiate flower buds. Plants kept continuously at 10°C or 5°C grew poorly and did not differentiate flower buds even after 30 days. Plants kept at 15°C continuously, or under alternating temperature conditions in which plants were kept at 5 or 10°C for part of the time, showed greater growth and flower buds were differentiated in 30 days. These small flower buds were visible at the end of effective low temperature treatment suggesting that the effect of low temperature is direct and not inductive.

Pharbitis plants must be exposed to low temperature for at least 25–30 days in order to obtain 100 per cent flowering. High temperature given after this period of low temperature does not significantly affect the flowering response. When plants are exposed to low temperature for only 10–20 days however, the flowering response is suppressed by subsequent exposure to high temperature.[21] Such phenomena are very similar to devernalization.

16 Translocation of the Floral Stimulus

The floral stimulus produced in the leaf is transmitted to the bud where the differentiation of floral primordia takes place. Buds can respond to the floral stimulus produced in leaves even when separated from them by long stems or graft unions.[15,16,39] Removal of the buds on the induced part of the plants, and removal of the leaves on the non-induced part, increases the transmission of the floral stimulus.[15] The photoperiodic stimulus moves only through living cells, and not through vessels.[17]

The velocity of transmission of the floral stimulus in *Pharbitis nil* has been estimated in three ways:

1. Maximum flowering response was obtained when seedlings were subjected to a 14-hour dark period, but the response was reduced if the cotyledons were removed before the 18th hour of the dark period. Zeevaart[58] considered that the floral stimulus took about 4 hours to travel from the cotyledons to the bud. The length of the petioles in Zeevaart's experiment was 14 mm, giving a velocity of 3.5 mm per hour. This estimate assumed that the stimulus had only to move across the petiole, whereas some of the stimulus would have to traverse the cotyledons, as pointed out by Evans and Wardlaw.[6]

2. Imamura and Takimoto[15,16] obtained a velocity of 2–3.8 mm per hour using another method. They used two-branched plants, with the donor leaf on one branch and the receptor bud on the other. It was later discovered however, that the floral stimulus was greatly attenuated on passing through the stem from one branch to the other.[18] It is not possible to estimate the transmission velocity in such a system because a single dark period given to one branch is not quite sufficient for the induction of flowering in the other. In Imamura and Takimoto's experiments, 5 short days were given to the donor leaf, but the velocity was calculated assuming that the stimulus produced by the first short day was able to cause flowering in the receptor bud. Estimated in this way the velocity is far too low, as flowering was probably not induced until the stimulus from the second or third short day arrived in the receptor bud.

3. Recently Takeba and Takimoto[39] obtained a higher velocity using plants with a long single stem. Preliminary experiments showed that the floral stimulus was scarcely attenuated by passing through a single stem longer than 100 cm. Plants having stems 50–150 cm long were decapitated just above the youngest fully expanded leaf, and all leaves except for the upper three donor leaves were removed. These plants were divided into two groups. In the experimental group, all axillary buds were removed except for one receptor bud at the base of the stem, and in the control group all buds were removed except for the one in the axil of the lowest donor leaf. When these plants were subjected to a 14-hour dark period, and all leaves and stems were cut off just above the receptor buds at the end of the dark period, no flower buds were initiated in either group. However, many plants whose donor leaves and stems were removed two hours later (16 hours after the start of the dark period) initiated flower buds irrespective of the length of the stem between the donor leaves and the receptor bud. The tallest plant had a stem 102 cm long between the lowest donor leaf and the receptor bud at the base, and initiated two flower buds. Sufficient floral stimulus to initiate flowering had evidently moved 102 cm over a period of 16 hours. As there was no flowering in the axil of the lowest donor leaf in control plants from which donor leaves were removed after a 14-hour dark period, the flowering stimulus must have moved through 102 cm of stem within two hours, yielding a velocity of more than 51 cm per hour. The flowering response of the receptor bud was, however, little influenced by the length of stem through which the stimulus had to move, suggesting a much more rapid rate of movement.

Zeevaart's experiment mentioned above and a similar experiment with adult plants[39] clearly showed that after the production of the floral stimulus in the leaf, 4 to 6 hours were required for transmission to the leaf axil, whereas the stimulus may travel in the stem at a velocity of more than 50 cm per hour. These results suggest that about 4–6 hours are required for the stimulus to change into a transmissible form in the leaves, or to move from cell to cell before arriving in the phloem, after which movement is very rapid.

17 Grafting Experiments

The transmission of floral stimulus across the graft union occurs easily when short-day treatment is given to the donor after the graft union has been completed.[16] However, if flowering plants which have been exposed to fully inductive short days are grafted to vegetative ones (approach grafting) and kept under long-day conditions, the receptors can scarcely initiate floral primordia (Imamura and Takimoto, unpublished). The floral stimulus produced in leaves may dissipate rapidly.

Varietal differences in photoperiodic sensitivity may be caused by differences in either the production of the floral stimulus in the leaves or the response of the shoot apex to the stimulus. These possibilities were examined by grafting two different strains and giving short-day treatments to either partner.[13] In one experiment the most sensitive strain Tendan was grafted to the most insensitive strain Africa (cf. Section 7). One fully expanded leaf was left intact on the donor plant and one bud on the receptor plant; all other leaves and buds were removed. The donor leaf was enclosed by a light-proof bag and given inductive dark treatments. When Tendan was used as the donor, more flower buds were produced on the receptor (either Africa or Tendan) than when Africa was used as the donor leaf. The bud of Tendan initiated more flower buds than Africa, regardless of the variety of donor leaf. The difference in photoperiodic sensitivity of these two strains is thus attributable to differences in both the leaf and the bud.

18 Effects of Growth Substances and Growth Retardants

1. Auxin: Flower initiation of *Pharbitis nil* is inhibited by IAA applied just before or during the inductive dark period.[28,36] IAA given to the cotyledons was more effective than that given to plumules, suggesting that IAA inhibits some parts of the dark process taking place in the leaves rather than the morphogenetic reaction in the shoot apex. The antiauxin TIBA also has an inhibiting effect on flowering if given at high concentrations (100 mg/1)[28]. No significant changes in the auxin level in the leaf after the inductive dark period were found.[36]

2. Gibberellins: Ogawa[33,35] reported that many kinds of gibberellins and gibberellin-like substances increased the flowering response of *Pharbitis* when applied before, during, or immediately after a slightly inductive dark period. Maximum promotion was obtained when application was before the inductive dark period. Application to cotyledons and to the shoot apex had similar effects, though the former type of treatment was slightly more effective than the latter. All of the gibberellins and gibberellin-like substances which promoted flowering were also more or less effective in causing shoot elongation. In *Pharbitis* the acceleration of growth by gibberellin is mainly caused by an increase in cell number and only slightly by cell elongation, i.e. gibberellins increase the mitotic activity in the shoot apex.[37] The floral stimulus seems to be in need of an actively growing bud in order to exert its action.[57] Therefore, it is possible that gibberellins may promote flower initiation by increasing the

mitotic activity in the apical meristem, rendering it more responsive to the floral stimulus.

3. Kinetin: Kinetin applied to cotyledons before or during the first part of an inductive dark period promotes flowering, but that applied to the plumule does not.[34] The inhibitory effect of the far-red at the beginning of the inductive dark period was greatly reduced by subsequent application of kinetin but not of gibberellins.[31,34] The inhibition caused by red light interruption in the middle of a 16-hour dark period was also overcome by kinetin application but less strikingly. The inhibiting effect of IAA applied before an inductive dark period was also greatly reduced by subsequent application of kinetin.[31,34]

4. Growth retardants: Growth retardants which have been studied extensively are Amo-1618, CCC, Phosfon D, and B995. These retardants inhibit flowering when applied immediately before or during the inductive dark period.[61] The order of effectiveness in suppressing flower formation is Phosfon D > Amo-1618 > CCC > B995. The order of effectiveness for reducing internode growth is somewhat different: Amo-1618 > Phosfon D > B995 > CCC.[61] It is clear that the effects of the four retardants on flower formation and stem growth were not strictly correlated.

Most of the retardants are active only when applied via the root, but B995 is active even when applied to the plumules. Furthermore it inhibits flowering even when applied at the end of the long night.[60,61] B995 appears to exert its flower inhibiting effect in the shoot apex rather than in the cotyledons.

The effects of growth retardants are overcome by applications of gibberellins. Zeevaart[59] reported that the minimal amount of gibberellin necessary to overcome flower inhibition by CCC was 100 times less than that required to overcome inhibition of internode growth. Similar results were also reported with B995.[60]

Anatomical observation revealed that suppression of growth was due to decreased mitotic activity in the apex.[59] Gibberellin could completely overcome this effect. Since actively growing buds are essential for expression of the floral stimulus in *Pharbitis*, growth retardants may inhibit flowering by decreasing the activity of the apex.

Under long-day conditions, CCC caused formation of flower buds at a lower node than in untreated plants.[59] Similar results were obtained with abscisin II[5] which is known to accelerate abscission, induce dormancy in woody plants, counteract auxin in *Avena* coleoptile growth, and counteract gibberellin in barley endosperm hydrolysis. The flower-promoting effect of CCC in long days could be prevented by gibberellin application.

19 Effects of Metabolic Inhibitors

Effects on floral initiation of 5-fluorouracil (5-FU), an inhibitor of both DNA and RNA synthesis, and 5-fluorodeoxyuridine (5-FDU), an inhibitor of DNA synthesis, were studied extensively by Zeevaart.[57] These inhibitors inhibited flowering when applied during or within 40 hours after the end of an inductive dark period (16 hours). Application to the bud was more effective than that to cotyledons, suggesting that these substances inhibit the reaction taking place in the bud, not the production of stimulus in the cotyledons. 5-FDU applied to the plumule was about one thousand times more effective than 5-FU in suppressing floral initiation, and the inhibition caused by 5-FU and 5-FDU was fully reversed by precursors of DNA such as thymidine, thymidylic acid, and deoxyuridine, if these substances were applied to the plumule before or simultaneously with the inhibitors. It is concluded that both 5-FU and 5-FDU inhibit flowering by causing a deficiency of thymidylic acid which results in suppression of DNA multiplication.

The microscopic observation of the shoot apex showed that 5-FDU inhibited cell division in the apex for longer than 24 hours but less than 48 hours.[57] This suggests that 5-FDU inhibits DNA multiplication for only 24–48 hours. Applications of 5-FDU inhibited flowering completely if made up to 40 hours after the beginning of the dark period and this effect became negligible when applied later than 50 hours after the beginning of the dark period. Since the floral stimulus is considered to arrive at the shoot apex shortly after the inductive 16-hour dark period (cf. Section 16), this means that 5-FDU inhibits flowering when applied shortly before or after the arrival of the floral stimulus in the apex. In other words, the floral stimulus must find multiplying DNA at the apex to cause the formation of flower buds. Probably the genes for flowering must be in the process of multiplication in order to become activated by the floral stimulus.[57]

From the floral genes the appropriate molecules of messenger RNA must be transcribed. The newly formed m-RNA may direct the synthesis of specific protein through which the new metabolic function and floral structure are mediated. Such an assumption is supported by the experiment of Galun et al.[8] They found that actinomycin D, an inhibitor of m-RNA synthesis, inhibited flowering when applied to the plumule just before or after an inductive dark period (16 hours). Deoxyguanosine applied before the application of actinomycin D reversed the effect of the latter.

Nucleic acid base analogs, 8-azaguanine and thiouracil, also inhibited flower initiation when applied during the inductive dark period.[23] The inhibition was reversed by simultaneous application of the corresponding metabolites, guanine and uracil, respectively. The effect of 8-azaguanine on floral initiation was slight, but vegetative growth was not affected at all, so the effect was specific to flowering. On the other hand, thiouracil inhibited both flowering and plumule growth.

Bonner et al.[2] found that an inhibitor of steroid biosynthesis, SK&F 7997, inhibited flowering without affecting vegetative growth when applied to the cotyledons before the inductive dark period. Application to the plumule was without effect. The chemical did not change the critical dark period, in other words, it did not affect time measurement in this plant. Thus, it was supposed that the effect was concerned with florigen synthesis, and that floral hormone may be a steroid. A wide variety of steroid precursors have been tested for ability to overcome this inhibition without any success. The steroid composition of the plumule was also examined after photoinduction or after the application of the inhibitor. No significant differences between the induced and vegetative plants were observed.

Recently Sachs[38] reported that old seedlings with fully expanded cotyledons or with fully expanded true leaves were scarcely influenced by SK&F 7997, though the young seedlings were affected in the same way as reported by Bonner et al. In another approach along this line, Zeevaart (unpublished) gave ^{14}C-mevalonic acid to cotyledons before an inductive dark period, and extracted the plumules with methanol about 20 hours later, when most of the floral hormone had moved from the cotyledons to the plumules. No qualitative nor quantitative differences in labelled compounds were observed in his experiment. Bennett et al.[1] on the other hand, carried out a similar experiment in which they used (−)-kaurene-17-^{14}C, a gibberellin precursor, instead of ^{14}C-mevalonic acid, and found two or more labelled compounds in the plumule of the induced plants which were either absent or present in lower concentration in the noninduced seedlings. These substances were found in the neutral fraction, they were not gibberellic acids, and their nature is still unknown, but they may be involved in some steps of floral induction.

Nakayama et al.[27,30] applied some inhibitors of respiration to cotyledons during the inductive dark period. Malonic acid (10^{-3}M) was inactive. Cyanide (2×10^{-4}M) and azide (4×10^{-4}M) inhibited flowering particularly when applied during the second half of the inductive 16-hour dark period; they did not inhibit flowering when applied during the light period. These results show that the inductive dark process may involve respiratory systems, but any energy-requiring process involves respiration, and these results may not give any information on the specific processes of floral induction.

Ethionine (5×10^{-3}M) completely inhibited flowering, and also vegetative growth.[23] Vegetative inhibition was partially eliminated by simultaneous application of methionine, but floral inhibition was not. Methionine at 10^{-2}M inhibited flowering without any influence on the vegetative development. The other amino acids examined were not so effective as methionine. It is interesting that ethionine at 5×10^{-4}M when applied just before the inductive dark period, stimulated flowering and this stimulation was completely reversed by simultaneous application of 10^{-3}M methionine, which by itself did not suppress floral induction.[23]

21 Induction of Excised Apices

Butenko and Chailakhyan[3] reported successful flower formation from isolated buds under long-day conditions. However the isolated buds were 4–5 mm long. They cultured the buds on White's medium containing various substances: (1) controls, no addition; (2) GA_3 0.1 mg/1; (3) enzymatic casein hydrolyzate 500 mg/1; (4) mixture of RNA nucleosides (adenosine, guanosine, cytidine, uridine) 0.5 mg of each per liter and casein hydrolyzate 500 mg/1; (5) as (4) with uridine replaced by thymidine.

In short days all plants except those given GA_3 flowered. Budding began earliest (after 30 days) in the control plants.

In long days all plants remained for a long period in the vegetative state. However, five months after the isolated buds were planted, the plants in the tubes containing the nucleoside mixture with casein hydrolyzate began to bud and to flower. In the case where uridine was replaced by thymidine there was a slight delay in flowering. Other plants were still in the vegetative state at the end of the experiment.

They considered that flowering of short-day plants is closely correlated with enhancement of the metabolism of proteins and nucleic acids. This enhancement occurs in short-day conditions, but can also be produced experimentally in long-day conditions by treatment of the plants with a mixture of nucleosides and amino acids.

22 Chemical, Histochemical and Ultrastructural Changes at Induction

The production of a specific RNA in leaves after photoperiodic induction was reported by Yoshida et al.[54] They examined the base compositions of the RNA in nuclear, mitochondrial, microsomal, and supernatant fractions (centrifugal fractions) of induced and non-induced cotyledons. No significant changes in the base compositions were observed after one or three inductive dark periods (16 hours). However, if the seedlings were supplied with ^{32}P for one hour immediately after an inductive 16-hour dark period and the cotyledons were then extracted for messenger RNA, the base ratio (A + U/G + C) of the messenger RNA measured by the radioactivity of each nucleotide differed significantly from that obtained from the seedlings exposed to long days. The seedlings subjected to a 16-hour dark period interrupted by a brief light break in the middle did not show such changes. They proposed the following reaction sequence in leaves: Photoperiodic derepression of specific gene DNA → Transcription to m-RNA → Synthesis of enzyme protein directed by the RNA → Synthesis of floral hormone by the aid of the enzyme.

The electrophoretic pattern of extracts obtained from reproductive shoot apices differed from that obtained from vegetative ones.[24] The extracts were obtained 6 days after the start of the short-day treatment, when the flower primordia had already differentiated. This change may not be a primary reaction of photoinduction but this shows that the initiation of floral primordia is associated with the appearance of a specific pattern of proteins.

Ultrastructural and histochemical changes in the shoot apex upon induction have been observed. The level of cytoplasmic RNA, the number of ribosomes, and the activity of dictyosomes in the central zone increased within 24 hours after the end of an inductive 16-hour dark period.[9,10] A correlation existed between the RNA concentrations and total protein staining (in both the peripheral and central zone), although a detectable increase in total protein lagged behind increased RNA concentrations.[9] Starch digestion in the central zone, rib meristem, and young pith also started within 24 hours after the end of the inductive dark period.[10]

An increase in the number of dictyosomes and the appearance of multiple layers of endoplasmic reticulum were observed after morphological changes were observed in the apex.[10]

Gifford[9] stained the shoot apex for sulfhydryl groups and reported an increased amount of -SS- coupling upon induction. Unfortunately the time required to show such a change after induction was not described in his report.

23 Inflorescence Differentiation

Short photoperiods favor the development of floral primordia even after floral induction.[4] When plants given relatively few short-day cycles are transferred to long-day conditions, many flower buds fail to develop and eventually die, especially at high temperatures. If all other buds are removed however, a flower bud initiated by a single dark period may continue development, anthese, and produce normal seeds even under continuous illumination (Yoshikawa, unpublished).

The early stages of floral differentiation were investigated by Wada (unpublished). When the 4-day-old seedlings were subjected to an inductive dark period, the second axillary bud (the most sensitive bud) showed the first signs of flower initiation 4 days after dark treatment. Bracteal leaves were initiated during the first 3 days, but in the primordial stage were not distinguishable from foliage leaves. The time interval between initiation of successive leaf primordia is however, strikingly shortened during the first three days after photoperiodic induction.

The differentiation of the flower bud is strongly affected by gamma-ray irradiation.[53] Gamma-rays from a ^{60}Co source, at a dose rate of 44γ per minute applied for 10 or 20 minutes, modified floral differentiation without affecting vegetative growth. Gamma-irradiation was only effective when applied to the plumule, and was without effect when applied to the cotyledons or cotyledonary petioles. Furthermore, only floral primordia at a very early stage of development were affected by gamma-irradiation, giving various types of malformed buds with structures intermediate between leaf and flower buds (Wada, unpublished). X-rays have a similar, but less marked, effect.

REFERENCES

[1] Bennett, R. D., Ko, S. T. and Heftmann, E. (1966). Effect of photoperiodic floral induction on the metabolism of a gibberellin precursor, (−)-kaurene, in *Pharbitis nil. Plant Physiol.* **41**, 1360.

[2] Bonner, J., Heftmann, E. and Zeevaart, J. A. D. (1963). Suppression of floral induction by inhibitors of steroid biosynthesis. *Plant Physiol.* **38**, 81.

[3] Butenko, R. G. and Chailakhyan, M. Kh. (1961). Effect of nucleic acid metabolites on growth and flowering of morning glory (*Pharbitis nil* Chios.). *Dokl. Akad. Nauk SSSR* **141**, 1239.

[4] Eguchi, T. (1937). Effects of the day-length upon the time of differentiation of flower bud and the subsequent development to flowering. *Proc. Imp. Acad.* **13**, 332.

[5] El-Antably, H. M. M. and Wareing, P. F. (1966). Stimulation of flowering in certain short-day plants by abscisin. *Nature* **210**, 328.

[6] Evans, L. T. and Wardlaw, I. F. (1964). Inflorescence initiation in *Lolium temulentum* L. IV. Translocation of the floral stimulus in relation to that of assimilates. *Aust. J. Biol. Sci.* **17**, 1.

[7] Fredericq, H. (1964). Conditions determining effects of far-red and red irradiations on flowering response of *Pharbitis nil*. *Plant Physiol.* **39**, 812.

[8] Galun, E., Gressel, J. and Keynan, A. (1964). Suppression of floral induction by actinomycin D an inhibitor of 'messenger' RNA synthesis. *Life Sci.* **3**, 911

[9] Gifford, E. M. Jr. (1963). Developmental studies of vegetative and floral meristems. In *Meristems and Differentiation*. Brookhaven Symp. Biol. No. 16, 126.

[10] Healey, P. L. and Jensen, W. A. (1965). Changes in ultrastructure and histochemistry accompanying floral induction in the shoot apex of *Pharbitis*. *Amer. J. Bot.* **52**, 622.

[11] Ikeda, K. (1965). Über den Einfluss der Temperatur auf die Blütenbildung von *Pharbitis nil* Chois., einer Kurztagpflanze. *Bull. Fac. Agr. Mie Univ.* **31**, 1.

[12] Imamura, S. (1960). The nature of inhibition of flowering by the leaves illuminated continuously during the inductive dark treatment of other leaves in short day plants. *Recent Advances in Botany* 1287. Univ. of Toronto Press, Toronto.

[13] Imamura, S., Muramatsu, M., Kitajo, S. I. and Takimoto, A. (1966). Varietal difference in photoperiodic behavior of *Pharbitis nil* Chois. *Bot. Mag. Tokyo* **79**, 714.

[14] Imamura, S. and Takimoto, A. (1955). Photoperiodic responses in Japanese morning glory, *Pharbitis nil* Chois., a sensitive short day plant. *Bot. Mag. Tokyo* **68**, 235.

[15] Imamura, S. and Takimoto, A. (1955). Transmission rate of photoperiodic stimulus in *Pharbitis nil*. *ibid*. **68**, 260.

[16] Imamura, S. and Takimoto, A. (1956). Transmission rate of the photoperiodic stimulus across the graft union in *Pharbitis nil* Chois. *ibid*. **69**, 23.

[17] Imamura, S. and Takimoto, A. (1957). Effect of ringing and incision given to the stem on the transmission of photoperiodic stimulus in *Pharbitis nil*. *ibid*. **70**, 13.

[18] Imamura, S. and Takimoto, A. (1957). Decrement of photoperiodic stimulus in transmission in *Pharbitis nil*. *ibid*. **70**, 53.

[19] Kimura, K. (1963). Floral initiation in *Pharbitis nil* subjected to continuous illumination at relatively low temperatures. II. Effect of some factors in culture medium on floral initiation. *Bot. Mag. Tokyo*. **76**, 351.

[20] Kimura, K. (1964). Ditto III. Effect of intensity and quality of light. *ibid*. **77**, 115.

[21] Kimura, K. (1966). Floral initiation of *Pharbitis nil* at low temperatures. *Ber. Ohara Inst. landwirtsch. Biol.* **13**, 39.

[22] Kimura, K. and Takimoto, A. (1963). Floral initiation in *Pharbitis nil* subjected to continuous illumination at relatively low temperatures. I. Effect of various temperatures. *Bot. Mag. Tokyo* **76**, 67.

[23] Marushige, K. and Marushige, Y. (1962). Effects of 8-azaguanine, thiouracil and ethionine on floral initiation and vegetative development in seedlings of *Pharbitis nil* Chois. *Bot. Mag. Tokyo* **75**, 270.

[24] Marushige, K. and Marushige, Y. (1962). An electrophoretic study of tissue extracts from leaf and flower in *Pharbitis nil* Chois. *Plant & Cell Physiol.* **3**, 319.

[25] Marushige, K. and Marushige, Y. (1963). Photoperiodic sensitivity of *Pharbitis nil* seedlings of different ages in special reference to growth patterns. *Bot. Mag. Tokyo* **76**, 92.

[26] Marushige, K. and Marushige, Y. (1966). Effects of light on the appearance of photoperiodic sensitivity of etiolated *Pharbitis nil* seedlings. *ibid*. **79**, 397.

[27] Nakayama, S. (1955). The effects of certain metabolic inhibitors on the dark reaction during photoperiodic treatment. *Bot. Mag. Tokyo* **68**, 61.

[28] Nakayama, S. (1958). Studies on the dark process in the photoperiodic response of *Pharbitis* seedlings. *Sci. Rep. Tohoku Univ. S4, Biol.* **24**, 137.

[29] Nakayama, S., Borthwick, H. A. and Hendricks, S. B. (1960). Failure of photo-reversible control of flowering in *Pharbitis nil*. *Bot. Gaz.* **121**, 237.

[30] Nakayama, S., Fukamizu, O., and Sei, I. (1957). Experimental researches on photo-periodism (6). Photoperiodic responses of *Pharbitis* seedlings for the metabolic inhibitors. *Mem. Fac. Lib. Educ. Miyazaki Univ.* **1**, 97.

[31] Nakayama, S., Tobita, H. and Okumura, F. S. (1962). Antagonism of kinetin and far-red light or β-indoleacetic acid in the flowering of *Pharbitis* seedlings. *Phyton* **19**, 43.

[32] Ogawa, Y. (1960). Über die Auslösung der Blütenbildung von *Pharbitis nil* durch niedere Temperatur. *Bot. Mag. Tokyo* **73**, 334.

[33] Ogawa, Y. (1961). Über die Wirkung des Gibberellins auf die Blütenbildung von *Pharbitis nil* Chois. *Plant & Cell Physiol.* **2**, 311.

[34] Ogawa, Y. (1961). Über die Wirkung von Kinetin auf die Blütenbildung von *Pharbitis nil* Chois. *ibid.* **2**, 343.

[35] Ogawa, Y. (1962). Weitere Untersuchungen über die Wirkung von gibberellin-ähnlichen Substanzen auf die Blütenbildung von *Pharbitis nil.* *ibid.* **3**, 5.

[36] Ogawa, Y. (1962). Über die photoperiodische Empfindlichkeit der Keimpflanzen von *Pharbitis nil* Chois. mit besondere Berücksichtigung auf dem Wuchsstoff-gehalt der Kotyledonen. *Bot. Mag. Tokyo* **75**, 92.

[37] Okuda, M. (1964). Physiological observation of the gibberellin effects on the development and growth of plants. *Contr. Biol. Lab. Kyoto Univ.* **18**, 1.

[38] Sachs, R. M. (1966). Inhibition of flower initiation in *Pharbitis nil* by an inhibitor of steroid biosynthesis is dependent on seedling age. *Plant Physiol.* **41**, 1392.

[39] Takeba, G. and Takimoto, A. (1966). Translocation of the floral stimulus in *Pharbitis nil.* *Bot. Mag. Tokyo* **79**, 811.

[40] Takimoto, A. (1960). Effect of sucrose on flower initiation of *Pharbitis nil* in aseptic culture. *Plant & Cell Physiol.* **1**, 241.

[41] Takimoto, A. (1966). Timing mechanism determining the critical dark period in *Pharbitis nil.* *Bot. Mag. Tokyo* **79**, 474.

[42] Takimoto, A. (1967). Spectral dependence of different light reactions associated with photoperiodic response in *Pharbitis nil.* *ibid.* **80**, 213.

[43] Takimoto, A. (1967). Studies on the light affecting the initiation of endogenous rhythms concerned with photoperiodic responses in *Pharbitis nil.* *ibid.* **80**, 241.

[44] Takimoto, A. and Hamner, K. C. (1964). Effect of temperature and pre-conditioning on photoperiodic response of *Pharbitis nil.* *Plant Physiol.* **39**, 1024.

[45] Takimoto, A. and Hamner, K. C. (1965). Studies on red light interruption in relation to timing mechanisms involved in the photoperiodic response of *Pharbitis nil.* *ibid.* **40**, 852.

[46] Takimoto, A. and Hamner, K. C. (1965). Effect of double red light interruptions on the photoperiodic response of *Pharbitis nil.* *ibid.* **40**, 855.

[47] Takimoto, A. and Hamner, K. C. (1965). Effect of far-red light and its interaction with red light in the photoperiodic response of *Pharbitis nil.* *ibid.* **40**, 859.

[48] Takimoto, A. and Hamner, K. C. (1965). Kinetic studies on pigment systems concerned with the photoperiodic response in *Pharbitis nil.* *ibid.* **40**, 865.

[49] Takimoto, A. and Ikeda, K. (1960). Studies on the light controlling flower initiation of *Pharbitis nil.* VI. Effect of natural twilight. *Bot. Mag. Tokyo* **73**, 175.

[50] Takimoto, A. and Ikeda, K. (1960). Ditto VIII. Light-sensitivity of the inductive dark process. *ibid.* **73**, 468.

[51] Takimoto, A. and Naito, K. (1962). Ditto IX. Further studies on the effect of far-red preceding the inductive dark period. *Bot. Mag. Tokyo* **75**, 205.

[52] Takimoto, A., Tashima, Y. and Imamura, S. (1960). Effect of temperature on flower initiation of *Pharbitis nil* cultured in vitro. *Bot. Mag. Tokyo* **73**, 377.

[53] Wada, K. (1962). Inhibition of flower initiation of *Pharbitis nil* by gamma-irradiation (Preliminary report). *Bot. Mag. Tokyo* **75**, 483.

[54] Yoshida, K., Umemura, K., Yoshinaga, K. and Oota, Y. (1967). Specific RNA from photoperiodically induced cotyledons of *Pharbitis nil.* *Plant & Cell Physiol.* **8**, 97.

[55] Yoshii, Y. (1925). Über die Reifungsvorgänge des Pharbitis-Samens. *J. Fac. Sci. Univ. Tokyo* **III-1**, 1.

[56] Yoshii, Y. (1927). Some preliminary studies on the influence upon plants of the relative length of day and night. *Sci. Rep. Tohoku Univ. 4th Ser.* **2**, 143.

[57] Zeevaart, J. A. D. (1962). DNA multiplication as a requirement for expression of floral stimulus in *Pharbitis nil.* *Plant Physiol.* **37**, 296.

[58] Zeevaart, J. A. D. (1962). Physiology of flowering. *Science* **137**, 723.

[59] Zeevaart, J. A. D. (1964). Effects of the growth retardant CCC on floral initiation and growth in *Pharbitis nil.* *Plant Physiol.* **39**, 402.

[60] Zeevaart, J. A. D. (1966). Inhibition of stem growth and flower formation in *Pharbitis nil* with N,N-dimethylaminosuccinamic acid (B995). *Planta* **71**, 68.

[61] Zeevaart, J. A. D. (1967). The relation of growth regulators to flowering: Growth retardants. In *Physiology of flowering in Pharbitis nil*, 112. Ed. S. Imamura. Jap. Soc. Plant Physiol. Tokyo.

5

Perilla

By Jan A. D. Zeevaart

1 History of Use

Perilla, a representative of the mint family, is an erect herb native from the Himalaya regions to China and Japan.[5] The red-leaved strains are sometimes grown as border plants for the colored foliage; the leaves are used extensively in Japan to make pickles.[114] The green-leaved varieties are highly valued for the oil produced in the seeds which is used as a drying oil in paints and varnishes. The oil content averages 38 per cent, and is mainly of linoleic and linolenic acid composition.[130] Areas of commercial seed production are: Manchuria, the Soviet Union, China, and Japan.[4]

Since around 1930 *Perilla* has also been a favorite plant for studies on flowering, and a great deal of our present knowledge of the flowering process has been gathered in work with this plant.

In 1931 Garner and Allard[73] published results indicating that *Perilla* responds to alternations of light and darkness as a typical SDP. A later bulletin[3] by the same workers contained more extensive data on the flowering response of *Perilla*. The seeds used in these experiments were collected from wild plants growing along the upper Potomac river, or they were obtained from introductions by the Division of Drug and Related Plants, U.S. Department of Agriculture. The collection contained both red- and green-leaved varieties. In 1936 and 1937 seven different strains were grown in daylengths from 10 to $14\frac{1}{2}$ hours, and in natural daylength at Arlington Experiment Farm near Washington D.C. (39° N.L.). Flowering occurred rapidly in photoperiods up to 14 hr, but increasing the daylength from 14 to $14\frac{1}{2}$ hours delayed flowering in certain strains by nearly 2 months. In the natural daylength (which becomes less than 14 hours in early August in the Washington area) flowering did not take place until late September. Allard and Garner[3] concluded '... the critical length of day is such that in the latitude of Washington the strains in question barely flower in time to escape frost'.

Despite the fact that *Perilla* was known in the U.S.A. as a typical SDP quite early, very few studies[77,83,121,122] on flowering with *Perilla* have been made in this country.

Research on flowering in the Soviet Union also started in the early 1930's. The first observations on earlier flowering due to SD treatment were made by Lubimenko and Sčeglova[102] in Leningrad in 1933 and 1934, and by Botvinovsky[14] in Zhitomir, the Ukraine, in 1932. Ever since this early work, *Perilla* has remained the favorite SDP of Russian investigators.

Investigations on flowering in *Perilla* by Chailakhyan and his co-workers at the K. A. Timiriazev Institute of Plant Physiology, Academy of Sciences of the U.S.S.R., Moscow, have continued up to the present time in numerous contributions.

Moshkov, working in Leningrad, also contributed several significant papers on flowering in *Perilla*.

Some highly original experiments with *Perilla* were performed by Lona in Milano, and later in Parma, Italy. He found that photoperiodic induction in *Perilla* is strictly localized.[88,93] Lona was also the first to show that a detached

Perilla leaf without any bud can be induced.[90] Unfortunately, Lona's work was published in Italian in rather obscure journals; it was generally descriptive, and contained few experimental results in the form of graphs or tables. For these reasons, Lona's work initially received little attention, but his ideas have since been supported.[153] A summary of Lona's work with *Perilla* has been published in English.[93]

Wellensiek[145-147] and several of his students at Wageningen have worked on flowering in *Perilla*, as have Mathon at Poitiers, and Stroun at Geneva. In recent years the Belgian-French school has described in detail the growing point of *Perilla*, and the changes which are associated with floral initiation.[7,8,115]

Taxonomy

The confusing nomenclature of *Perilla* was briefly discussed by de Zeeuw.[150] The Russian workers[56,109] call the red-leaved or ornamental variety *P. nankinensis* (Lour.) Decne., and the green-leaved or oil variety *P. ocymoides* L. The same nomenclature was used by Funke.[70] Lona called the red-leaved material with which he experimented *P. ocymoides* (L.), var. *nankinensis* (Lour.) Voss. Both Garner and Allard,[73] and Jacobs and Raghavan[77] described their material as *P. frutescens* (L.) Britt. It is clear from the descriptions, however, that the former authors worked with a red variety, the latter with a green one. Japanese workers[136] used *P. frutescens* Britt., var. *crispa*, this apparently being a red-leaved strain.

At Doorenbos' suggestion, de Zeeuw[150] proposed to follow Nakai's nomenclature[114] and to use *P. crispa* (Thunb.) Tanaka for the red-leaved material; the green variety is then called *P. crispa* var. *ocymoides*. This proposal has been adopted by some authors.[12,66,74,132,146,153] In case a different nomenclature is followed, it would be most useful to physiologists if the leaf color of the material under study were indicated. Additional complications are, however, that photoperiodic responses may vary considerably among various strains.[72,73]

Since it was impossible to determine which *Perilla* had been used in each study, the species names quoted in this chapter are those used by the authors in their papers.

2 Growing Techniques and Growth Habit

Perilla plants can be grown both from seeds and from cuttings. Root formation on cuttings as affected by the vegetative or flowering state of the mother plant, has been the topic of an extensive investigation by Selim.[132]

Plant material raised from seeds is quite uniform, but it is essential that one has a batch of seeds with a high percentage of germination. It was my experience that seed samples obtained from seed companies often did not fulfill this requirement, and I have therefore adopted the practice of growing my own seed supply. Plants at least 50 cm tall are given SD treatment for approximately 1 month. After that they can be kept in either SD or LD. As soon as seeds start to mature (*ca.* 6 weeks after the beginning of SD treatment) the plants are shaken every other day over a large sheet of paper, so that the seeds can be collected easily. Half a dozen plants will yield several thousand seeds. Freshly harvested seeds germinate very poorly, but after storage at room temperature for a few months, germination practically reaches the 100 per cent level. At that point the seeds are transferred to a screw-cap jar and stored at 0 to 2°C. One lot of seeds stored under these conditions for 5 years, is still completely viable.

Germination is quick and uniform if seeds are planted in soil. Vermiculite and sand have given less satisfactory results. About one week after emergence, the seedlings are transplanted into soil in 340 ml plastic beakers. Once the plants have produced 3 to 4 leaf pairs, they are transplanted into quart (950 ml) containers, using a mixture of fine gravel and vermiculite. Watering is done daily with half-strength Hoagland nutrient solution containing sequestered iron.

Plants can be kept vegetative in the greenhouse by supplementing daylight with light from incandescent bulbs, or from fluorescent tubes. We have used a photoperiod of 20 hours, or even continuous light. It is important to realize that under conditions of continuous low intensity light, flower formation will ultimately also occur in LD.[150]

With the appearance of the 4th leaf pair maximal photoperiodic sensitivity has been reached,[153] and flower buds become visible 18 to 20 days after the shift to SD with an 8-hour photoperiod and a dark period temperature around 20°C.

Red spider infestations are the only pests we have encountered on *Perilla*, particularly on old plants. For example, plants grown for seed production should be watched closely, and sprayed if necessary.

Perilla belongs to the *Labiatae*, and consequently it has decussate leaves. Seedlings of the red *Perilla* emerge with green cotyledons, but the true leaves are dark wine-purple with a bronze lustre due to the presence of anthocyanin. As the plants are shifted to SD, the anthocyanin fades from the leaves and at the fruiting stage the leaves are practically green. Ermolaeva and Sčeglova[67] studied this phenomenon and concluded that there is no direct connection between flowering and decrease in anthocyanin content, although the latter is a good indicator to determine the developmental stage of the plant.

FIGURE 5–1. *Perilla crispa*. Plant on left growing vegetatively in LD. Plant on right fruiting after 5 weeks in SD.

Detached leaves of *Perilla* can be grown in vials with nutrient solution[42,153] and should be kept in the shade during the first days following the removal from the plants. Roots are produced quickly at the base of the petiole, but no shoots are regenerated. Blades of detached leaves thicken and become brittle. In our experiments detached leaves could be kept in excellent condition for several months.

Perilla is an ideal plant for grafting experiments and the grafting technique has been employed by many workers to demonstrate the transmission of floral stimulus from donor to receptor. Cleft-grafting is easiest to perform and was used routinely in my experiments with leaf grafts.[153] It is essential that the internode in which a leaf or shoot will be grafted, is still elongating and not woody. All operations are carried out with new razor blades. The petiole or the basal part of the scion is cut wedge-shaped, inserted into the cleft internode and bound tightly with raffia. The scion should be kept in an atmosphere with high humidity for about one week. In my experiments this was done simply by enclosing the scions in polyethylene bags. Due to the high humidity fungal infections may occur; these can be prevented by soaking leaves or shoots to be grafted in a $\frac{1}{2}$ per cent aqueous suspension of the fungicide tetramethyl-thiuram disulfide for a few minutes.

On the receptor stock only one leaf pair is retained at the base. The secondary buds on the node below the graft union are allowed to develop as receptor shoots. All other buds are removed from the receptor.

3 Inflorescence Structure and Criteria of Flowering Response

The inflorescence of *Perilla* superficially resembles a compact raceme, and is often described as such. It is, however, a verticillaster, characteristic of the *Labiatae*.

Vegetative plants show strong apical dominance, but in SD axillary shoots develop and flower (Fig. 5–1).

The flowers of *Perilla* are inconspicuous; the corolla is pinkish in the red-leaved strains, white in the green-leaved ones.

Several criteria have been used to measure the flowering response in *Perilla*: (1) the percentage of plants in a given treatment with flower buds;[68,153] (2) number of days from the start of the experiment to appearance of flower buds;[56,153] (3) number of days from the start of the experiment to flowering;[56] (4) length of the inflorescence;[136] (5) in grafting experiments the total number of flower buds produced on the receptor shoots was used as a quantitative measurement.[153]

Criterion (2) is undoubtedly the most convenient one, and has been used by most investigators. The light-green inflorescence forms a sharp contrast with the dark-red leaves, and can be recognized at an early stage.

Reversibility

If *P. crispa* is exposed to 1 month of SD treatment, the plants produce seeds and the life cycle ends with death. However, if the plants receive a suboptimal induction of 10 to 20 SD, they exhibit the so-called 'reaction of reversibility'.[14,70,102] This means that the terminal inflorescence produces some flowers and fruits, and then reverts to vegetative growth. The first signs are enlarged bracts, and via a series of intermediary stages new vegetative shoots with large leaves are formed. The main axis elongates considerably in the process with the result that the uppermost fruits are shifted far from each other (Fig. 5–2). The shift from SD to LD can, in addition to reversion, also cause other morphological abnormalities.[118]

The phenomenon of reversion was described in several early papers,[14,22,102,109,142,] and more recently again by Jacobs and Raghavan.[77] Vakulin[142] ascribed reversion to environmental factors other than daylength. This does not seem to be a valid explanation, however, since sowings were made in the natural day of Odessa (46° NL) in spring. Several strains did not flower until late summer, but a few flowered in June and then reverted to vegetative growth. These latter strains most likely had a high critical daylength and were induced to flower early in the season, and then reverted to vegetative growth due to the longer days in June.

Receptor shoots of grafted plants[70,153] as a rule exhibit reversibility, particularly if defoliation is discontinued after appearance of flower buds.

Reversion to vegetative growth in *Perilla* is due to the fact that the shoot apex splits off axillary flower buds, but never forms a terminal flower bud.[77,115]

The physiological basis of reversion will be discussed in section 17.

FIGURE 5–2. *Perilla crispa* exposed to 20 SD and subsequently grown in LD for 2 months. Following the formation of fruits on the main axis, complete reversion to vegetative growth has taken place. Beginning of reversion is also visible on some axillary branches.

4 Effects of Plant Age

Shortly after germination *Perilla* seedlings are insensitive or at least much less sensitive to SD treatment than at later stages of ontogenesis.[89,125,156] According to Moshkov,[106] *P. ocymoides* seedlings had to be at least 15 days old to respond with flower formation to 7 SD, and *P. nankinensis* was totally insensitive to SD during the first 20 days after emergence.

Wellensiek (unpublished data quoted by Zeevaart[153]) found that photoperiodic sensitivity increased up to a certain limit with increasing age. *P. crispa* was sown at weekly intervals in LD and transferred to SD when a series of plants of the following ages was available: 12, 19, 26 . . . 75, 82, 89 days. It took

51 days in the youngest seedlings for flower buds to become visible. This number decreased gradually with increasing age until it became a constant 24 days for plants which were 75 days or older when shifted to SD.

The physiological basis for the insensitivity of young *Perilla* plants to induction was further investigated by Zeevaart.[153] Grafting was employed to test the capacity of leaves on different nodes to function as donors for LD stocks, thus excluding possible differences in sensitivity of the growing points in seedlings of different ages. Leaves on the 2nd or 3rd node (counted above the cotyledons in acropetal direction) did not induce flowering when grafted on LD stocks unless they had been exposed to 46 SD. On the other hand, leaves from higher nodes successfully functioned as donor after receiving 26 SD. Since the latter leaves expanded during induction, whereas the 2nd leaf pair was already fully mature at the beginning of induction, the possibility was considered that expanding leaves need fewer inductive cycles than fully mature ones. But again it was established that a 2nd leaf pair required about twice as many SD as a leaf located on a higher internode, even though it expanded during induction.[153] Thus, differences in photoperiodic sensitivity encountered between different leaf pairs appeared to be due to their position on the stem rather than to their physiological age. Further support for this idea was obtained in the following experiment.[153] In two groups of plants, sown with a 4-week interval in LD, the 5th and 2nd leaf pair had just fully expanded, respectively. Leaves from these two different nodes were reduced to an area of 25 cm^2 and grafted onto LD stocks. After a graft union had been established, the donor leaves were induced by daily darkening with light-tight bags. The results summarized in Table 5.1

TABLE 5–1

Flowering response of LD stocks onto which 25 cm^2 of a 2nd or 5th leaf pair had been grafted. Donor leaves exposed to various numbers of SD, starting 10 days after grafting (after Zeevaart[153]).

Number of SD	% plants with flower buds		Days until appearance of flower buds	
	2nd leaf	5th leaf	2nd leaf	5th leaf
0	0	0	~	~
14	0	100	~	31
21	25	100	78	23
28	100	100	43	22
35	100	100	38	22

show that leaves from the 2nd node required approximately twice as many SD to become induced as those from the 5th node. Since the leaf area and physiological age were kept identical, it is clear that the difference in sensitivity was due to their position on the plant. Unlike in *Xanthium*, physiological age appears to be a rather unimportant factor in determining photoperiodic sensitivity of *Perilla* leaves, because fully expanded leaves require no more SD for induction than those which are expanding during induction.[153]

These observations explain why young *Perilla* seedlings require so many more SD for floral initiation than do older plants. The first two leaf pairs are quite insensitive to induction, but sensitivity increases in every new leaf pair produced, until it becomes constant in the 4th or 5th leaf pair. Thus, the physiological basis for juvenility in *Perilla* is the inability to produce floral stimulus at optimal rates.

No experiments have been performed with *Perilla* showing that the growing-points of juvenile plants are capable of initiating flower buds upon receipt of the floral stimulus, as they are in *Bryophyllum* (p. 439).

5 Vernalization

Perilla has no chilling requirement for flowering. Yarovization of *Perilla* in the Russian literature means any treatment, usually high temperature, which will promote flowering. If seeds were kept at 25°C for 10 days with water added equal to 40 per cent of the weight of air-dry seeds, subsequent flowering was hastened by as much as 19 days.[149] After a similar treatment given for 14 days, flowering was 26 days earlier than in the controls.[120]

7 Photoperiod Response

When big plants of *P. crispa* are transferred to a SD treatment consisting of 8 hours light and 16 hours darkness (8: 16 hr), flower buds become macroscopically visible after approximately 20 days. Wellensiek[145] reported that under these conditions the first microscopical signs of floral differentiation were observed after 10 SD, and flower primordia could be distinguished after 14 SD.

Number of inductive cycles

In an experiment performed with *P. crispa*[154] under controlled conditions (8 hours light at 23°C, 16 hours darkness at 19°C) some plants produced flower buds after exposure to 7 or 8 SD, but 9 or more SD were required to induce flowering in all plants. Although relatively few inductive cycles cause the formation of some flower buds, prolonged SD treatment results in more abundant flowering until saturation is reached after approximately 4 weeks in SD.[153]

In close agreement with the data for *P. crispa* are those obtained by other workers: Funke[70] found that 7 SD induced flowering in *P. ocymoides*, but not in *P. nankinensis*. Schwabe[131] obtained 100 per cent flowering in *P. ocymoides* with 9 SD, and Jacobs and Raghavan[77] found that *P. frutescens* required 9 or more SD for flowering.

According to Lona[89,93] young plants of *P. ocymoides* var. *nankinensis* needed 10 to 14 inductive cycles, but in plants 16 weeks old 3 to 5 cycles of 12 : 12 hours sufficed for flower formation. In old plants with adequate reserve material it was possible to induce flowering with a single dark period exceeding 130 hours,[89] or even in continuous darkness.[36,89]

Critical light and dark period

In Moshkov's experiments[106] with *P. ocymoides* the lower limit of the light period which permitted flower formation in a 24-hour cycle was 3 hours, and the upper limit was 16 hours. Thus, the critical dark period in this material was 8 hours. Moshkov[106] further observed that flower formation also took place in 3:9-hour and 4:8-hour cycles which combined the minimal lengths of the light and dark periods determined in 24-hour cycles.

The critical daylength of *Perilla* has been determined by several workers, probably all working with red-leaved strains. The following are the longest photoperiods in 24-hour cycles under which still 100 per cent flower formation was obtained. Allard and Garner[3] for *P. frutescens*: 14½ hours; Bouillenne[15] for *P. nankinensis*: 14 hours; Mathon and Stroun[103] for *P. nankinensis*: 14 hours; Takimoto and Ikeda[136] for *P. frutescens* var. *crispa*: 14 hours. Thus, there is excellent agreement that the critical daylength of the red-leaved *Perilla* is around 14 hours.

On the other hand, the critical daylength of seven different strains of *P. ocymoides* grown under fluorescent light varied from 16 to 20 hours.[72] This agrees with Moshkov's value of 16 hours for the critical photoperiod in *P. ocymoides*. Funke[70] also observed that in natural daylength *P. ocymoides* flowered a full month earlier than *P. nankinensis*. These data would indicate that the critical daylength of green-leaved *Perilla* is at least 2 hours longer than that of red-leaved material. This would also explain why green-leaved *Perilla* can be grown successfully for seed production as far North as Japan, Manchuria, and the Ukraine.

Light preceding the dark period

Bouslova and Lubimenko[16] found that high intensity light given during the short photoperiod was more favorable to flowering in *P. ocymoides* than weak light.

In Samygin's work[127] a photoperiod of 13 hours was subdivided into a period of sunlight and a period of weak incandescent light (7 f.c.). His results indicated that weak light for more than 6 hours preceding the long night delayed flower formation considerably, whereas weak light given after the dark period did not.

Chailakhyan and Rupcheva[60] used a different approach to reduce the light energy given during a basic light period of 11 hours. Short periods of 10, 20, or 40 minutes were alternated with longer dark periods of 45, 90, or 180 minutes, respectively. As a result the plants were exposed to a total of 2 hours basic light and an uninterrupted dark period of 13 hours. Control plants in 11:*13*-hour cycles produced flower buds after 22 days, and those in 2:*22*-hour cycles after 26 days. In the different treatments with interrupted illumination, flower buds were visible after 27 to 32 days. In other words, the plants responded basically as if exposed to the sum of the interrupted illuminations (2 hr).

As a whole, these data show that the light requirement of the short photoperiod can be satisfied in *Perilla* by 2 to 5 hours of high intensity light. To obtain an optimal flowering response, long periods of weak light should not be given immediately before the dark period.

Low intensity light during long photoperiods

Perilla is able to initiate flower buds under photoperiods which are normally considered to be LD, provided the light intensity is very low.[80,150] The flowering response under these conditions of weak light is very slow, however. Under continuous illumination at an intensity of 300 $\mu W/cm^2$ ϕ flower buds appeared after 70 days.[150] Flowering of several *Perilla* strains in continuous weak light was also reported by Gaillochet et al.[72] The same workers also found that the critical daylength of *P. nankinensis* increased from 14 to 16 hours as the light intensity was decreased from 6000 to 2300 ergs. cm^{-2} . sec^{-1}.

These observations probably explain why old *Perilla* plants sometimes produce flower buds on the basal parts of the stem during winter when prevailing light conditions are poor.[144]

Threshold light intensity

Takimoto and Ikeda[136] exposed *P. frutescens* var. *crispa* to a main light period of 12 hours and determined the intensity of supplementary fluorescent light given during the first or last 3 hours of the 12-hour dark period which was effective in preventing flowering. An intensity of 20 f.c. did not entirely suppress flower formation when given during the first 3 hours of the dark period, but none of the plants irradiated for 3 hours at the end of the night with 1 f.c. produced flower buds. Thus, *Perilla* is more sensitive to light towards the end of the inductive dark period than at the beginning.

Light-break effects

The effects of light breaks given during the long night have not been studied extensively in *Perilla*. Carr[19] stated that the interruption of a 14-hour night with 40 f.c. for 30 minutes fully suppressed flowering. The results published by Skvortzov[134] and Taravet[137] indicate that light breaks inhibit flowering most effectively if given near the middle of the dark period.

Interruption of the light period by darkness

Interruption of the long natural day with a period of darkness from 10 a.m. until 3 p.m., thus dividing a long photoperiod into two short light periods separated by a short dark period, did not induce flowering.[73] This experiment established that the long uninterrupted night, rather than the short photoperiod is crucial for photoperiodic induction of *Perilla*. This conclusion was further confirmed by Chailakhyan and Rupcheva[59] who interrupted a basic light period of 10 hours in the middle with 2 or 4 hours darkness; this resulted in normal flowering as the corresponding dark periods of 12 and 10 hours were longer than the critical night length. Interrupting the main light period in the same experiment with 6 hours darkness prevented flower formation, since the plants now received only short nights, one of 6 and one of 8 hours.

8 Spectral Dependence

Although there are several reports on the effects of different spectral regions on growth and flowering in *Perilla*, insufficient evidence is available to indicate the participation of either a high-energy reaction or phytochrome in the photo-reactions controlling flower formation.

Moshkov[111] grew *Perilla* in a 14-hour photoperiod in the following spectral regions: violet-blue and yellow-green, both obtained from mercury lamps, and red (with a high admixture of far-red) from incandescent lamps. The plants remained compact in violet-blue, and elongated strongly in yellow-green. Growth was poor in red, probably due to the far-red admixture. Flowering occurred only in violet-blue.

Van der Veen and Meijer[143] mentioned that *Perilla* had shorter internodes in red light than in blue. No data on flowering were reported.

In Mathon and Stroun's experiments[103] *P. nankinensis* produced flower buds in continuous green light of relatively high intensity. *P. ocymoides* forma *viridis* grown in continuous green light at an intensity of 1300 ergs . cm^{-2} . sec^{-1} produced flower buds after 84 days whereas it took 140 days for flower buds to appear in plants grown in continuous white light at an intensity of 980 ergs . cm^{-2} . sec^{-1}. Apparently, a long photoperiod consisting of green light does not have a long-day effect, i.e. it does not inhibit flower formation. In this respect *Perilla* resembles the related SDP *Salvia occidentalis*, in which spectral dependence of flower formation has been studied much more extensively.[104]

On the other hand, if green light was given during short photoperiods, it was much less effective in causing flower formation in *P. nankinensis* than was white, red or blue irradiation.[135]

No detailed, quantitative analysis has been made of the effectiveness of different spectral regions in inhibiting flower initiation in *Perilla* when given as nightbreaks, or as supplementary illumination.

Funke[69,70] exposed *Perilla* to full daylight from 8 a.m. till 4 p.m. For the rest of the day he covered the plants with black cases, or with white, red or blue glass, transmitting approximately equal amounts of energy. White, red and blue supplementary light were equally effective in delaying flowering in *Perilla*.

Kleshnin[78] exposed *Perilla* to a 10-hour main light period and found that supplementary illumination given during the remaining 14 hours at an intensity of at least 50 ergs . cm^{-2} . sec^{-1} inhibited flower formation irrespective of spectral composition.

Moshkov[112] claimed that far-red irradiation of wavelengths from 1000 to 2500 nm given during a 10-hour night prevented flowering. This report, however, is hard to reconcile with our present knowledge of action spectra for preventing flower formation in other SDP. It is possible that flower inhibition was actually caused by high temperature (section 13).

Interruption of the dark period with white light (400–800 nm) much more effectively inhibited flowering than interruption with ultraviolet (253–390 nm).[113]

Low dosages (1–3 kr) of γ-rays given to *Perilla* promoted flower bud formation slightly in SD, but 30 kr inhibited flower formation completely.[129] This inhibitory effect was localized in the meristems, because receptor shoots shielded with lead flowered normally when the donor leaves were radiated with 30 kr.

9 Endogenous Rhythms

Rhythmic changes in photoperiodic sensitivity can be demonstrated either by light interruptions of long dark periods, or by exposing plants to light-dark cycles deviating from the natural 24-hour one.

The first approach was followed by Carr[19] with *P. ocymoides*. Plants were grown on 48-hour cycles with 8 or 10-hour light periods, and lightbreaks were given at different times during the long night. Flowering was most strongly inhibited by light interruptions near the beginning or end of the dark period. These two maxima for flower inhibition were approximately 24 hours apart and located at 18 and 42 hours from the beginning of the light period. A light break given near the middle of the dark period had a flower-promoting effect. These data could be interpreted according to Bünning's theory of photoperiodism that in SDP light promotes flowering when given during the photophile phase, but inhibits it when given during the skotophile phase. However, the results also fit the alternative explanation that lightbreaks act only in conjunction with preceding or subsequent photoperiods. Whatever the correct interpretation may be, this experiment clearly established that the flowering response of *Perilla* to nightbreaks of a long dark period varies, with minima 24 hours apart.

The second approach, exposure to cycles of various lengths was pioneered by Garner and Allard.[73] *P. frutescens* was grown in the natural daylength and darkened on alternate days, thus exposing plants to 15:33-hour cycles. Flowering was somewhat delayed under these conditions as compared to that in plants kept in 10:14-hour cycles. The same workers also grew *Perilla* in alternations of equal periods of light and darkness ranging from 12:12 hours to 15:15 seconds. Mazda lamps of 1000 W were used as light source in these experiments. The 12:12-hour cycle was the only one in which flower formation occurred. Although the total amount of energy received by the plants in each treatment was the same, cycle length had an enormous effect on vegetative growth. As the length of the cycle decreased, growth was retarded and the plants exhibited more severe symptoms of malnutrition. However, dry weight accumulation was better in 15:15-second cycles than in 1:1-minute ones.

Rupcheva[124] exposed *P. nankinensis* to cycles of 24, 48, 72, or 96 hours duration, in each case with 2, 4, 8, 16, or 24 hours of light. As shown in Table 5–2, the critical dark period increased with increasing length of the photoperiod, e.g. flower formation was induced if a 16-hour light period was combined with dark periods of 32 hours or longer. However, there was an upper limit to the light period beyond which flowering no longer took place: 24 hours light alternating with 72 hours darkness failed to induce flowering. Rupcheva's data suggest that flowering of *Perilla* is determined only by the lengths of the light and dark periods. No rhythmic changes in the response became apparent. The possibility of a diurnal rhythm in the flowering response of *Perilla* is not ruled out, however, by this experiment. For example, the cycles studied were all multiples of 24 hours. Possible minima in the flowering response in cycles of 36 and 60 hours as observed in soybean (p. 72) would have been missed completely in Rupcheva's experiment.

TABLE 5–2

Days until appearance of flower buds in *Perilla nankinensis* when grown in cycles of different durations. All plants received 21 cycles and were then returned to non-inductive conditions (after Rupcheva[124]).

Photoperiod hr	Cycle length in hr			
	24	48	72	96
2	20	22	38	—
4	20	22	29	52
8	20	23	28	28
16	~	88	57	42
24	~	~	~	~

The time of the 24-hour cycle at which *P. ocymoides* plants were exposed to a short photoperiod of artificial light had no effect on the flowering response.[125] The diurnal pattern of leaf movement was similar in SD and LD, the downward movement starting early during the long night in the former condition, and towards the end of the light period in the latter.

10 Fractional Induction

As discussed in section 7, several inductive cycles are required for photoperiodic induction of *Perilla*. The question is whether or not the effects of inductive cycles separated by non-inductive ones can be summated. The first evidence in the affirmative was presented by Garner and Allard[73] who exposed *P. frutescens* to alternate SD (10:14 hr) and LD (natural daylength prevailing during summer in Washington D.C.). Plants which received alternating SD and LD flowered after 55 days, while controls flowered in response to the decreasing natural daylength after 84 days. Clearly, alternating 1 SD and 1 LD for a long period of time hastened flowering significantly, but it should be realized that the natural daylength, supposedly acting as LD, decreased actually to SD towards the end of the experiment.

Samygin[128] exposed *Perilla* to alternations of 1 SD and 1 LD, or 1 SD and 2 LD for almost 5 months. Flower formation was about 2 months later than in SD controls, but earlier than in LD controls which responded to the decreasing natural daylength. Summation was not affected by the light intensity (sunlight or 7 f.c. incandescent light) given during the non-inductive photoperiods.

Schwabe[131] did not observe any flower formation in *P. ocymoides* when he alternated SD (8:16 hr) and LD (16:8 hr) 12 times. Schwabe's material remained vegetative following exposure to 6 SD, but 9 SD were sufficient to cause a 100 per cent flowering response. Intercalating 3 LD in the middle of 12 SD completely inhibited floral initiation, but 2 LD did not.

Schwabe[131] also investigated the question whether intercalated LD inhibit the effect of the SD which precede or those which follow it. To this end he intercalated a 'neutral' dark period of 24 hours prior to, or following the LD. A dark period following the LD, and thus preceding the SD, allowed photoperiodic induction to proceed, while the same dark period was without effect if given following the SD. Schwabe[131] concluded therefore that intercalated LD prevent the succeeding SD from being inductive.

Wellensiek[146,147] interrupted SD treatment of *P. crispa* after 0, 2, 4, 6 ... 18 days with either 2 days of CL, or with 2 SD at 5°C. Low temperature treatment delayed flower formation by approximately 2 days, indicating that it merely stopped photoperiodic induction. On the other hand, 2 days of continuous light (CL) delayed appearance of flower buds by as much as 6 to 7 days, indicating that the effect of this treatment was not merely passive, but was an active inhibition of induction. CL given for 2 days at low temperature did not inhibit flower formation. The flower-inhibiting effect of 2 days of CL was most pronounced when given after 6 to 8 SD. In the closely related SDP *Salvia occidentalis* maximal inhibition caused by 2 days of CL was observed when given after 10 SD, whereas at least 11 SD were required for floral initiation in this species.[11] Although the minimal number of SD required for floral initiation was not determined in Wellensiek's experiments, it would appear that in *Perilla* too, intercalated CL is most inhibitory to flowering when given just before the threshold of photoperiodic induction has been reached. This suggests that CL acts on the processes leading towards the induced state rather than on production of the floral stimulus.

The inhibitory effect of intercalated CL can be accumulated only to a limited extent. Wellensiek[147] observed that maximal flower inhibition was reached in *Perilla* after 3 days of CL, and the same was established in *Salvia*.[11]

Light breaks given during inductive nights also had an inhibitory effect on flower formation, although this effect was quantitatively smaller than that due to CL.[147]

Irradiation with different spectral regions for 2 days inhibited flower initiation irrespective of wavelength, and no red/far-red antagonism was observed.[147] However, the experimental set-up with continuous exposure to light would not have allowed the detection of phytochrome involvement in flower inhibition. Since both forms of phytochrome are known to absorb throughout the visible region of the spectrum, and a small fraction of the pigment present as P_{fr} is sufficient to exert biological control, *in casu* inhibition of flowering, Wellensiek's results obtained by exposure for 48 hours are not surprising. It would seem that involvement of phytochrome as the receptor for light inhibition could be established or ruled out, definitely, only by determining the action spectrum for interruption of long dark periods by different spectral regions, and by establishing whether or not far-red reversibility is evident.

Since studies on fractional induction are closely connected with those on flower inhibition, further evidence will be discussed in the next section.

11 Photoperiodic Inhibition

The flower-inhibiting effect of CL intercalated during SD treatment, discussed in the preceding section, was further studied by Bhargava.[11,12] He was particularly concerned with the question whether inhibition is strictly localized in the leaf, or can be transmitted to the shoot apex. This was examined by applying differential photoperiodic treatments to different leaf pairs on the same plant. The experimental approach is diagrammatically represented in Figure 5-3. Partially defoliated *Perilla* plants retained 3 leaf pairs of which the lower and upper pair were continuously kept in SD whereas the middle pair received 2 days of CL following 10 SD. This treatment delayed appearance of flower buds by an average of 4.6 days. If the middle leaf pair was removed immediately following 2 days of CL, flower formation was inhibited somewhat less. Bhargava concluded from these and similar, more extensive experiments with the SDP *Salvia occidentalis* that a flower inhibitor is produced in CL which is transported to the shoot apex where it interferes with the action of the flower hormone.

Flower initiation would thus be determined by the balance between flower-inhibiting and flower-promoting substances.

In *Perilla*, the flower-inhibiting effect of 2 days CL was relatively small, indicating that only part of the SD induction was nullified. In *Salvia*, on the other hand, the intercalation of 3 days CL, following 10 SD, delayed flower bud appearance by at least 10 days. This suggests that the inductive effect of the previous 10 SD was completely nullified. Further evidence to support this conclusion was obtained by alternating 10 SD with 3 days of CL several times.[11] No summation of induction was obtained. Thus, the inhibition by intercalated LD is quantitatively much stronger in *Salvia* than in *Perilla*, although both species need approximately the same minimal number of inductive cycles for flower initiation.

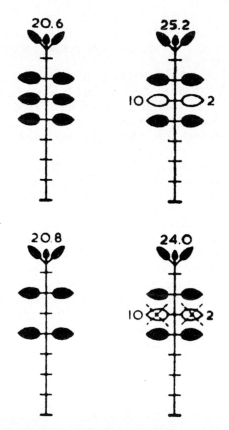

FIGURE 5–3. The effect of differential photoperiodic treatments applied to different leaf pairs on the same plant. The figures on the left of the leaf pair indicate the number of SD cycles preceding 2 days of CL (figures on the right). Crosses mean that leaf pair was cut off immediately following 2 days of CL. Numbers above plants are days until appearance of flower buds (from Bhargava[12]).

Intercalated non-inductive cycles inhibited induction[12] even when a leaf pair kept in SD all the time was located between the shoot apex and the leaf pair which was exposed to long days. This strongly suggests that the flower inhibitor, unlike the flower hormone, is not translocated with the assimilates (c.f. section 16).

It should be stressed that the LD inhibition as studied by Wellensiek and Bhargava, while undoubtedly interesting and deserving further study, is demonstrable only after some preparatory step of induction has taken place. The inhibitor appears to be released in maximal amounts only from those leaves which had received a SD treatment just short of the minimum required for floral initiation. The inhibitory effect of CL did not further increase after 2 to 3 days. Furthermore, CL preceding SD treatment did not exert any flower-inhibiting effect.[11,146,147] This is a strong argument against any hypothesis which postulates the accumulation of a flower inhibitor in plants grown under non-inductive daylength, and its disappearance under inductive conditions as the sole requirement for flower formation.

Interesting as Bhargava's data[11,12] are, it is clear that the inhibitor he studied is produced only under special experimental conditions, but does not play a role when SDP are grown continuously in LD and are then shifted to SD. Processes leading towards the build-up of the induced state can take place in *Perilla* only in dark periods exceeding a certain minimal length, and long photoperiods prevent these processes from proceeding. Wellensiek[146] suggested that light is generally inhibitory to flowering in *Perilla* and that this inhibition can be removed only by long dark periods. However, inhibition in this context can also be considered as absence of the induced state, and should be clearly distinguished from the active inhibition encountered when a non-inductive daylength is intercalated during SD treatment.

13 Effects of Temperature

The optimal temperature for the dark phase of photoinduction has not been determined accurately in *Perilla*. Rapid flower formation takes place at 20 to 25°C, but the flowering response decreases both at lower and higher temperature. Moshkov[112] showed that *Perilla* exposed to different temperatures during the 10 hr dark period produced flower buds after 17 days at 20–22°C, but only after 37 days at 30–35°C, and not at all at 5–10°C.

TABLE 5–3

The effect of differential temperature treatments given during the light or dark parts of 16:8-hr cycles for 8 weeks. After-treatment in SD at 20°C (after Wellensiek[147]).

16-hr light period at	8-hr dark period at	Days until flower buds appeared from beginning of SD
20°C	20°C	20
5°C	5°C	13
5°C	20°C	−2*
20°C	5°C	21

* Flower buds appeared during LD treatment.

Chailakhyan and Zhdanova[63] found that the inhibitory effect of low temperature could also be observed when given only during part of the dark period.

Wellensiek[145] gave differential temperature treatments during the light (8 hr) and dark (16 hr) phases of inductive cycles. A dark period at 5°C completely prevented floral initiation, whereas the same low temperature given during the light period delayed, but did not prevent flowering. This shows that the crucial processes of photoinduction take place during the dark period and that they are of a biochemical nature.

Of further interest are the effects of differential temperature treatments given during the light and dark periods of LD treatment.[147] As shown in Table 5–3, prolonged exposure of *Perilla* to LD with cold photoperiods and warm nights, ultimately resulted in flower formation. Thus, a light period given at low temperature is relatively ineffective in preventing floral induction, and the critical dark period is shortened accordingly.

14 Effects of Mineral Nutrition

The effect of mineral nutrition on floral initiation in *Perilla* has been studied extensively. Chailakhyan[30] found that *P. nankinensis* produced flower buds earlier with normal or increased nitrogen supply and classified this SDP therefore among the nitropositive plants. Appearance of flower buds was also slightly promoted by submerging SD-treated leaves daily for 1 or 2 hours in solutions of ammonium- or potassium nitrate.[29]

El Hinnawy[66] noticed that flower bud appearance was delayed by a few days in *Perilla* plants grown in nutrient solutions lacking nitrogen or phosphorus. Deficiencies of other elements had little or no effect on floral initiation. High nitrogen levels which promoted flower formation in SD, did not induce flowering in LD.

It appears from these results that the effects of minerals on flower formation in *Perilla*, if noticeable at all, are indirect through their effects on vegetative growth.

15 Effects of Gas Composition

Carbon dioxide

According to Odumanova[119] photoperiodic induction does not take place in *P. ocymoides* under conditions which exclude photosynthesis. In her experiments all leaves except one were removed. The remaining leaf was subjected to 14 SD in normal air or in an atmosphere lacking CO_2. Plants which were exposed to SD in the absence of CO_2 remained strictly vegetative while the controls induced in air with CO_2 flowered normally. Odumanova[119] concluded therefore that in order to be induced, a *Perilla* leaf subjected to SD should be able to carry out photosynthesis. This conclusion is at variance with Fredericq's results[68] obtained with *P. crispa*. Plants kept in air without CO_2 during the 9-hour photoperiods of 24 SD dropped their leaves, but 69 per cent of the plants became nevertheless reproductive. If a 3 per cent sucrose solution was fed through the stem while CO_2 was being withheld, the plants remained healthy and 92 per cent flowered. Since sucrose could fully substitute for CO_2, Fredericq[68] concluded that photosynthesis is not specifically involved in photoperiodic induction of *Perilla*.

Important differences between Fredericq's and Odumanova's experiments were that in the latter case only the leaves subjected to SD were kept in an atmosphere lacking CO_2 throughout the experimental period of 14 days; Frédéricq on the other hand withheld CO_2 from the entire plants, but only during the light periods. It is of further interest to note that with the same experimental set-up which allowed flowering in *Perilla*, Fredericq[68] was able to confirm earlier observations that the presence of CO_2 in the atmosphere is essential for photoperiodic induction of the SDP *Kalanchoë* (Ch. 9).

Oxygen

Zhdanova[159] reported that the effectiveness of 14-hr dark periods in inducing flower formation in *P. ocymoides* was greatly reduced by a nitrogen atmosphere given during part of the long night. More detailed results on this topic were reported by Chailakhyan and Konstantinova.[55,56] Their data, summarized in Table 5–4, illustrate that anaerobiosis (0.6–0.8 per cent O_2 remained) was particularly inhibitory to flowering during the last hours of an otherwise inductive night. Similar results were also obtained when only the leaves, instead of whole plants were kept in a nitrogen atmosphere at night. These data suggest that oxidative reactions during the latter part of the long night play a decisive role in photoperiodic induction of *Perilla*.

TABLE 5-4

Effect of anaerobiosis during part of the long night on flowering in *Perilla* (after Chailakhyan and Konstantinova[56]).

| | | | Days until | |
Species	Number of SD	N$_2$ atmosphere during 14-hr night	Appearance of flower buds	Flowering
P. nankinensis	15 SD	None	15	43
		First 5 hr	19	47
		Last 5 hr	~	~
P. ocymoides	14 SD	None	17	41
		First 6 hr	21	48
		Last 6 hr	~	~

Narcotics

Zhdanova,[159] in her 1950 paper dealing with the flower-inhibiting effect of nitrogen atmosphere, also mentioned briefly some results with *Perilla* plants kept in an atmosphere containing the following narcotics: Phenylurethane (3 mg/1), monoiodoacetic acid (2 mg/1), diethyl ether (0.1 ml/1), and ethylene (0.15 or 0.3 ml/1). Flower formation was inhibited completely, but the plants remained in satisfactory condition. The incidental report on the flower-inhibiting effect of ethylene is of particular interest, since this effect has recently been rediscovered with *Xanthium* (Ch. 2).

16 Translocation of the Floral Stimulus

This section will be confined to movement of the flowering hormone, but in so far as they bear on this problem, data from grafting experiments will also be included. Special problems which can be approached experimentally only by grafting, will be discussed in the next section.

Donor-receptor relationships

Evidence for a floral stimulus in *Perilla* was first presented by Russian workers. When leaf blades were subjected to short photoperiods, the axillary shoots flowered earlier than those in the axils of leaves kept in natural daylength.[101] These and similar experiments performed with other species, firmly established that the leaf is the receptive organ in photoperiodism. It should be pointed out in this connection, however, that the stem of *Perilla* plants, stripped of all leaves and buds except the terminal apex, will respond to SD with flower formation just as rapidly as intact plants do.[132,153] Thus, *Perilla* stems can perceive the daylength and produce floral stimulus. In this respect *Perilla* differs from *Xanthium* or *Pharbitis* since neither plant will initiate floral primordia in SD when totally defoliated. Consequently, to study movement of the stimulus out of a *Perilla* leaf, the SD treatment should be applied to the leaf blades only (see e.g. illustrations in Chailakhyan[44]).

Involvement of a transmissible stimulus in the flowering of *Perilla* was also demonstrated by localized induction of the basal or apical part of the plant,[22,24,50] and subsequent appearance of flower buds on shoots kept in unfavourable day-length. In grafting experiments (section 17) the situation is quite similar, except that the inductive treatment of the donor is discontinued at grafting.

To ensure a successful transmission of floral stimulus, it is important to observe the following rules: (1) the donor partner must be de-budded;[22,24,61,110,153] (2) mature leaves should be removed from the receptor,[22,23,24,110,153] but the presence of the very young leaves is favorable for flower formation.[110] There are several reports,[61,70,110,153] however, which indicate that flower formation on non-defoliated receptors can occur, albeit much delayed (Tables 5–5, 5–6).

TABLE 5–5

Basipetal and acropetal movement of the floral stimulus from an induced interstock in double-grafted plants as affected by presence ($+$) or absence ($-$) of one pair of LD leaves on stocks or scions.

Numbers are days to appearance of flower buds (after Zeevaart[153]).

	> 100	> 100	40	40
Scion	+	+	−	−
Stock	53	46	48	40
	+	−	+	−

TABLE 5–6

Acropetal movement of floral stimulus from a donor stock as affected by various leaf areas left on the receptor scion (after Zeevaart[153]).

Area of LD leaf pair	Number of days to appearance of flower buds
0	40
2 × 15 cm²	47
2 × 40 cm²	77
Intact	> 90

At what time during induction does production of floral stimulus begin?

Perilla requires around 10 SD before any flowering will occur (section 7), whereas one single dark period suffices in *Xanthium* and *Pharbitis*. The reasons for these differences between species are not obvious. It could be that *Perilla* produces floral stimulus at lower rates, or perhaps the growing points are relatively insensitive to the hormone. It is reasonably certain that a minimal amount of floral stimulus has to reach the bud before floral initiation can start (section 17), but it is not clear at what time during SD treatment production of floral stimulus actually starts in *Perilla*. This point was considered in a paper by Zhdanova.[158] She removed the youngest and oldest leaves from *P. ocymoides* plants raised in LD and subjected the remaining 8 leaves to 2 SD. In the first treatment all leaves were given 2 SD simultaneously; after that they were immediately removed. No flowering took place. In the other treatment, each leaf in turn received 2 SD, starting with the uppermost leaf and proceeding towards the base. Again the leaves were removed at the end of SD exposure. After this treatment all plants flowered. If reproducible, these results would mean that: (1) production and export of floral stimulus from leaves to buds starts on the very first days of induction; (2) the floral stimulus is more effective in causing flowering if reaching the growing points in small amounts from each leaf consecutively for a long time, than in larger quantities from all leaves simultaneously for a short period.

Characteristics of floral stimulus movement

Depending upon the position of donor and receptor with respect to one another, the floral stimulus can move in the stem both upwards and downwards.[6,24,153] This is clear in the experiment of Table 5.5 in which a piece of stem, with an induced leaf pair attached, was grafted as interstock, while both stock and scion functioned as receptors. Transmission of the flowering condition took place in either direction, but acropetal movement in particular was strongly inhibited by the presence of mature leaves on the scion.

Removal of a ring of bark from the stem between donor and receptor prevented transfer of the stimulus,[24,153] and also blocked completely the translocation of labeled assimilates.[50] Selim[133] reported that ringing the stem did not interfere with movement of the floral stimulus. However, a very thin strand of bark is sufficient for transfer.[153] Since Selim[133] reported extensive callus formation on the wounded surface, his positive results should come as no surprise.

Lateral transport across the stem can also take place, as proven by experiments in which the stem was girdled half-way,[24,153] and flower buds appeared above or below the incision. For lateral transport across the stem, see also Fig. 5–4e.

Local treatments of stem portions between donor and receptor with narcotics such as ether or chloroform,[28] with low temperature,[28] or with steam[153] all interrupted transmission of the stimulus. These data not only indicate that the presence of living tissue is an absolute requirement for the successful transmission of the floral stimulus, but they also suggest that the tissue plays an active role in the transfer.

Lubimenko and Bouslova[101] reported that severing the midrib at the base of the leaf blade hindered movement of the stimulus out of the leaf. This could not be confirmed in more extensive experiments by Chailakhyan,[25] and it would appear therefore that the stimulus can move through the mesophyll.

By splitting *Perilla* stems and main roots lengthwise except for a small piece of either stem or root, the floral stimulus could be forced from the donor half with leaves across stem,[26] or stem and root tissue[27] to the receptor buds. From the delay in the appearance of the flower buds on the receptor as compared to that on the donor, and the distance traveled by the stimulus, Chailakhyan[27] estimated the velocities of movement across the stem and root at 1.9–2.0 cm/day, and 0.4–0.5 cm/day, respectively. These values are quite low, but conditions were undoubtedly not optimal, since the stimulus was supplied by a single leaf and had to move first down, and then up the split stem. Much higher velocities are indicated by the finding[153] that flower buds appeared simultaneously on shoots directly below a grafted leaf, or positioned two nodes lower (a distance of 15 to 20 cm).

Inhibitory effect of non-induced leaves

The flower-inhibiting effect of mature leaves on the receptor was mentioned earlier in this section. The following facts have emerged concerning this inhibition:

1. As is obvious from the data in Table 5.5, the inhibition is much stronger when the stimulus has to move upward than in the case of downward transport. This was also observed in Chailakhyan's experiments (see illustrations in Chailakhyan[44,50]) with receptor shoots on one node and leaf pairs positioned

above and below this node. With the upper leaf pair in SD, and the lower one in LD, flower buds appeared after 28 days. When the day-length treatments were reversed (i.e. the receptor shoots were located above the SD leaves, but below the LD leaves) it took 56 days for flower buds to appear.

2. The inhibition is most pronounced if the leaves in LD are positioned between the site of photoperiodic perception and the receptor bud. Chailakhyan[32,50] subjected one leaf to SD, and maintained another leaf in LD: the latter was positioned on the node above, at the same node, or on the node below the SD leaf. Flower buds on the terminal shoot appeared after 72, 53, and 38 days, respectively.

Splitting off the upper SD leaf by a longitudinal cut down the stem to its node or lower, increases the flower-inhibiting effect of the lower LD leaf. Conversely, when a piece of stem with an upper LD leaf is split off, the flower-promoting effect of the lower SD leaf is considerably increased.[33] Thus, severing the vascular connection between the upper leaf and the shoot tip reduces the influence this leaf exerts on development of the growing point.

3. The inhibition by mature leaves on the receptor increases with increasing leaf area retained on the receptor (Table 5–6).

4. The inhibition is reduced by keeping the LD leaves in low intensity light,[34] or in total darkness.[110]

5. The inhibitory action of a LD leaf located more acropetally than a SD leaf could be simulated by cutting off the blade and introducing a 3 per cent sucrose solution *via* the petiole and leaf scar.[34] In the intact combination flower buds appeared after 51 days on the terminal shoot; removal of the LD leaf reduced this to 24 days, whereas replacing the LD leaf by a sugar solution resulted in appearance of flower buds after 49 days.

One unifying hypothesis can explain all these observations, viz. that the floral stimulus is translocated with the assimilates in the phloem. The uppermost leaves would play a dominant role in supplying organic substances to the terminal shoots and – depending upon their photoperiodic regime – in determining vegetative or reproductive development. In decapitated plants the main flow of assimilates would be downward, which would explain the data in Table 5–5, and also the dominant role of the uppermost leaf pair in Chailakhyan's experiment discussed above.

This hypothesis has been supported by the results of experiments by Chailakhyan and Butenko,[50] in which $C^{14}O_2$ was fed to a leaf on a *Perilla* plant, and the distribution of labeled assimilates was determined later by autoradiography of the entire plant. A comparison was made between the effectiveness of a SD leaf in causing flowering when located in various positions, and the ability of this leaf to transport assimilates to the receptor shoot. The results in Fig. 5–4f–k show first of all that translocation patterns were not affected by the photoperiodic regime of the leaf exposed to $C^{14}O_2$. Movement of assimilates into the stem apex took place mainly from the upper leaf. As the SD leaf was positioned closer to the terminal shoot, flower buds appeared earlier, and more label accumulated in the buds.

Another example of the excellent correlation between translocation of assimilates, and movement of flower stimulus, is illustrated in Fig. 5–4a–e. If two opposite leaves on the stem were exposed to different daylengths, the axillary shoot of the LD leaf remained vegetative, whereas the shoot in the axil of the SD leaf flowered. The SD leaf induced flowering in the opposite shoot only if its own axillary shoot and the opposite leaf were removed (Fig. 5–4e). It is clear from the movement of labeled assimilates that the axillary shoots receive their assimilates exclusively from their supporting leaves. Induction of flowering in the opposite shoot (Fig. 5–4e) was correlated with a large amount of labeled assimilates reaching that bud from the opposite leaf.

The interpretation of these results is clear: non-induced leaves do not produce specific flower-inhibiting substances, but whenever such leaves happen to be in close proximity to the receptor buds, they are the chief suppliers of organic substances. Thus, they prevent the products of SD leaves from reaching shoots in significant amounts.

One-sided flowering, as observed by Lona[93] when only one leaf of a pair was induced, can be explained by assuming that movement of the stimulus in longitudinal direction takes place predominantly through the section of the stem adjacent to the donor leaf, thus keeping the vegetotropic and anthotropic streams more or less separated.

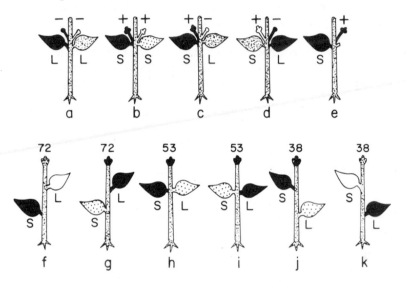

FIGURE 5–4. Correlation between movement of the floral stimulus and of C^{14}- labeled assimilates from leaves to buds in *Perilla*. L: Leaf in LD. S: Leaf in SD. *Upper row*: Axillary shoots as receptors. + = Flower buds; − = Vegetative. *Lower row*: Terminal apex as receptor. Numbers are days until appearance of flower buds. The leaves in black were exposed to $C^{14}O_2$. The degree of shading shows the relative amounts of C^{14}-assimilates in the plants after 24 hr (after Chailakhyan and Butenko[50]).

All observations discussed so far support the view that transmission of the floral stimulus is very closely or perhaps inseparably connected with translocation of assimilates from donor leaves to receptor shoots. This makes one wonder whether the floral stimulus is really one single substance produced in SD leaves and absent under LD conditions, or a specific combination of metabolites produced by leaves in the favorable daylength.

The estimated velocity for floral stimulus movement in the stem of 2 cm/day (see above) would seem to be much below the values measured for velocities of assimilate translocation. However, as discussed before,[153] this cannot be considered as a serious objection against the idea of the floral stimulus moving in the phloem with the assimilates. Chailakhyan's velocities[27] were not determined under optimal conditions. Moreover, velocities for phloem translocation and the floral stimulus would have to be determined under identical conditions in the same plant. It should be kept in mind that the velocities of movement of the floral stimulus will tend to be underestimated, since a threshold value will have to accumulate in the apex before flower initiation can proceed.

Flower inhibition by non-induced leaf tissue was also observed when one half of a leaf blade was exposed to SD and the other half to LD or darkness.[31] The greatest inhibition was exerted when the basal half was kept in LD, i.e. between the induced half and the receptor bud. Darkness applied to the basal half had little effect. Lona[87] obtained similar results and further showed by grafting that the basal half did not become induced by SD treatment of the apical half (also section 17).

17 Grafting Experiments

Perilla is a very suitable plant for demonstrating the transmission of the floral stimulus in grafting experiments and has therefore been used for that purpose by several investigators. The first report was by Chailakhyan[22] in 1936; however, in that particular experiment, the donor stock was given SD *after* grafting, so that the set-up was the same as when the basal part of an intact plant is subjected to SD. In the next year Chailakhyan[61] published results of a grafting experiment in which SD induction was completed *before* grafting was performed. This showed that the leaves on the donor stock could transmit the floral stimulus to the receptor even though they were no longer kept in a photoperiod favorable for flowering.

Various types of donor-receptor graft combinations have all been found to transfer the floral stimulus in *Perilla*; a shoot,[24,110,153] a single leaf,[13,42] or part of a leaf blade[153] can all function as donors. In double grafts it was even possible to graft one scion simultaneously onto 2 different stocks, or 2 scions onto one stock. For successful or optimal transmission it is usually necessary that the donors are de-budded and the receptors defoliated.

The results of grafting experiments, like those performed on localized induction, have indicated that depending on the position of donor and receptor relative to one another, the floral stimulus can move both upward and downward in the stem. In the case of double grafts with one induced and one non-induced stock or scion, movement of the stimulus appeared to be almost exclusively unilateral in the stem sector above or below the induced donor.[153]

Since the general characteristics of florigen movement have been discussed in the previous section, the present discussion will center around some topics studied by means of grafting.

Duration of graft contact

The minimal duration of graft contact between donor and receptor necessary to transmit the floral stimulus was first investigated by Moshkov.[108] Different groups of receptor shoots grafted on donor stocks were removed and rooted in sand after 1, 2, 3, 4, ... 15 days. Flower buds were produced only if the receptors had remained in contact with the donors for more than 10 days. Moshkov concluded that a tissue union, which was established after 9 to 12 days, was necessary for transmission of the stimulus.

Zeevaart[153] reinvestigated this problem by the use of leaf grafts. With optimally induced leaves, the donors had to remain on the receptor for at least 6 days to cause some flowering; a contact period of 10 days was sufficient for a 100 per cent flowering response. In later experiments[154] performed under continuous light of approximately 2500 f.c. at 23°C, this period has been shortened further as follows: Removal of donor leaves (27 SD) after 4, 5, or 6 days resulted in flower formation in 10, 70 and 100 per cent of the receptor shoots, respectively.

Anatomical studies[153] of graft unions made at different times were incon-clusive, although it was clear that xylem connections and possibly also phloem unions had been established between donor and receptor after 8 days, at the most.

In transport studies with C^{14}-sucrose the minimal duration of contact neces-sary to transmit both the floral stimulus and C^{14}-label was 6 to 7 days.[153] It was therefore concluded that phloem continuity between donor and receptor is required for transfer of the stimulus. The analogies between transmission of the floral stimulus and a phloem-restricted virus, as opposed to a parenchyma virus, also favor this interpretation.[153]

It was observed in these experiments[153] that the longer the graft contact between donor and receptor, the more flower buds were initiated. This suggests that at least over a certain range a quantitative relationship exists between the amount of stimulus received in the shoot apex, and the number of flower buds produced. These data furthermore argue against the idea that photoperiodic induction is merely the removal of an inhibition, demonstrating that something limiting floral initiation moves from the donor leaf to the receptor bud.

Induction of detached leaves

Perilla is the only photoperiodically sensitive plant in which it has been possible to demonstrate unequivocally that leaves in the absence of any buds or roots can be photoinduced. Since *Perilla* leaves never regenerate shoots, proof for the successful induction of detached leaves could be obtained only by grafting onto LD receptors.

Lona[90] published a short note on the induction of excised *Perilla* leaves, stating that leaves with or without a piece of stem could be induced. Carr[20] questioned this experiment by suggesting that axillary buds might have been present in Lona's cuttings, overlooking the fact that most of the leaves were cut through the petioles.[90] This problem was then reinvestigated independently by several workers[13,42,152] who all confirmed Lona's report. Bocchi et al.[13] carefully debudded *Perilla* plants and found that leaves subjected to 20, 25, or 30 SD on the plants were as effective as donor as those induced on plants with buds. Chailakhyan[42] used detached leaves and found that they were induced by 32 SD, even if the roots had been removed regularly from the petioles. Zeevaart also found that detached leaves, and leaves on cuttings with or without axillary buds, functioned equally well as donors after being exposed to 39 SD. In further experiments,[153] the possibility that roots produced on the cuttings play a role in induction was ruled out by cutting off the basal piece of stem every other day, thus preventing the initiation of roots during the entire in-ductive period of 31 SD. Induction of flowering by SD in *Perilla* plants deprived of roots had been reported earlier by Chailakhyan.[38]

All workers obtained negative results when detached leaves were grafted which had been kept permanently in LD. These data, then, show that photoperiodic induction in *Perilla* takes place exclusively in the leaf and is not dependent upon any correlation with other organs.

Stability and reversibility

Suboptimal induction of *Perilla* will result in flower formation, but the plants will ultimately revert to vegetative growth (section 3). Chailakhyan's inter-pretation[22] of reversion in *Perilla* was that floral stimulus accumulated during SD treatment and became exhausted in subsequent LD, so that vegetative growth could resume. Moshkov[109] on the other hand expressed the view that in short photoperiods the leaves of *Perilla* acquire an irreversible state which enables them to produce the floral stimulus under non-inductive conditions. This was supported by the finding[108] that 14 days after the last inductive cycle, the leaves could still transfer the floral stimulus to a non-induced scion. In another experiment, Moshkov[109] defoliated the donor stock at the time of grafting and found that this failed to induce flowering in the receptor. He concluded therefore that the flower hormone is not accumulated in the stem. With an optimally induced donor stock, defoliated at grafting, it has been possible, however, to induce flowering in receptor scions.[153] This does not necessarily have to be considered as evidence for accumulation of the floral stimulus in the stem. Since the stem perceives daylength just as well as do the leaves (section 16), it is possible that induced stems produce enough hormone to induce flowering in the receptor.

The problem of permanent versus reversible induction was further investigated by the use of leaf grafts.[153] Leaf blades, trimmed to an area of 30 cm^2 were grafted onto LD receptor stocks. A minimum of 14 SD was necessary to cause flowering on the receptors, whereas an optimal response was obtained if donor leaves had been in SD for one month or longer (Fig. 5–5).

FIGURE 5–5. SD leaf (area 30 cm^2) grafted onto stock in LD. Receptor shoots flowering 37 days after grafting.

The question asked in these experiments was whether the ability of an induced leaf to supply floral stimulus is preserved or gradually lost after transfer to LD conditions. This was done by grafting induced leaves onto a group of vegetative stocks. After a certain time these leaves were removed from the stocks, and re-grafted onto a second group of LD stocks. This procedure was repeated at regular intervals until the leaves became senescent. The results of these experiments[151,153] showed decisively that induced leaves continue to supply floral stimulus under LD conditions. In the most extensive experiment[153] leaves were grafted successively onto 7 different groups of stocks. Even in the final grafting, performed 97 days after the first one, there was no indication of a decrease in flowering response of the receptors. Likewise, leaves on induced, de-budded plants, or induced and subsequently detached leaves all retained the ability to transmit the floral stimulus when kept in LD for various periods of time. It is highly unlikely that SD leaves accumulated such large amounts of floral stimulus that no significant decrease would have occurred after more than 3 months. Therefore, it was concluded that *Perilla* leaves, once induced, possess the ability to produce the floral stimulus for the rest of their life span.

Flowering receptor shoots, on the other hand, did not function as donors for LD stocks on which they were grafted. This indicates that the floral stimulus neither accumulates, nor is being perpetuated in the receptor shoots. Thus, the phenomenon of indirect induction described for *Xanthium*,[87,93,153] does not take place in *Perilla*.

The following terminology was used[153] to describe induction of flowering in *Perilla*:

1. The *induced state*, also called photoperiodic impression,[93] is acquired in SD, is irreversible, and strictly localized.

2. The *floral stimulus* is produced in leaves having acquired the induced state, and is transmitted to receptor buds.

A striking example of the strict localization of induction was presented by Lona.[88] Induction of the apical half of a leaf did not render the basal part effective as a donor in grafting experiments. Since the induced and non-induced leaves, or parts of leaves, have different physiological properties and can be present on the same plant without affecting one another, such a plant behaves as a physiological chimera.

Attempts to destroy the induced state with continuous light of high intensity, high temperature, auxin, 2,4-dinitrophenol, or sodium azide met with no success.[153] Exposure to the favorable daylength changes the leaf metabolism from the vegetative to the induced state, but the biochemical basis for this interesting phenomenon remains to be elucidated.

As described in section 3, suboptimally induced *Perilla* plants revert to vegetative growth. This is possible because the terminal shoot apex does not differentiate into a flower primordium (section 23). Young leaves and bracts developing at the top of the stem after the end of SD treatment are non-induced and will gradually take over control of the growing point from the more basipetal, induced leaves.[109] Thus, due to the localization of induction in the SD treated leaves, *Perilla* can revert to vegetative growth.

So far, a coherent picture of the permanency of the induced state in *Perilla* has been presented. Some data, however, would seem to be at variance with the viewpoint presented above. Zhdanova[157] exposed *P. nankinensis* to 32 SD. After transfer to LD, intact plants flowered and matured normally. However, if all flowering shoots were systematically removed, new vegetative shoots appeared after 40 days. This was taken as evidence that the amount of floral stimulus supplied by the leaves to the growing points had sharply diminished.[22,157] In a similar approach, Lam and Leopold[83] confirmed that debudding promoted reversion to vegetative growth. These workers further found that reverted leaves could be re-induced by a second SD treatment. They suggested that Zeevaart's findings of an irreversible induced state would hold true only for optimally induced leaves. The fact of the matter, however, is that sub-optimally induced leaves had been shown to retain their induced state.[153] It is regrettable that Lam and Leopold[83] failed to test their so-called reverted leaves in grafting experiments, or at least they did not report any results of such experiments.

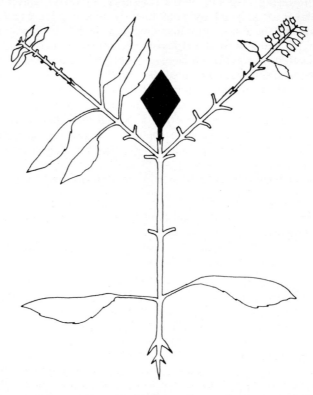

FIGURE 5–6. Permanency of the induced state in the leaf of *Perilla* as illustrated in double-grafting experiment. Donor leaf in black (exposed to 15 or 28 SD). A vegetative tip grafted on the first receptor branch flowered if the latter was defoliated (right), but not if 2 leaf pairs were retained (left). Shoot tips grafted 48 days after the donor leaf had been grafted.

In my own experiments[154] with induced and subsequently de-budded plants, appearance of vegetative shoots had also been observed. However, when the induced leaves were grafted onto LD stocks, they always caused flowering. This was also the case with suboptimally induced leaves (14 or 15 SD) kept in LD for more than two months, conditions which according to Lam and Leopold[83] should have led to complete disappearance of the induced state. Results of grafting experiments show therefore that the ability of induced leaves to cause flowering on receptors does not decline during LD after-treatment. Thus, there seems to be something peculiar about the shoots that are forced out by repeated de-budding: despite the presence of induced leaves, they grow vegetatively. As the plant ages, the stem becomes more woody, and it is conceivable that anatomical connections between induced leaves and newly appearing buds from swellings in the leaf axils are not adequate for transfer of the floral stimulus. In any event, the difference in flowering response between normal axillary buds and regenerated adventitious buds remains to be explained.

One might perhaps object to the use of grafting technique for testing the ability of a leaf for transfer of the floral stimulus. However, this would seem to introduce fewer variables than continuous de-budding of induced plants. With grafting, treatments of the donor leaves are varied, but the receptor stocks are strictly standardized. In addition, the ability of a grafted leaf to supply floral stimulus following LD treatment was not only tested as usual,[153] by re-grafting it, but also by grafting new receptor tips on the original receptor shoots (Fig. 5–6). Induced leaves did not lose the capacity to transmit floral stimulus to newly grafted receptor shoots, provided no LD leaves were located between the donor and receptor bud.[154] This experiment also demonstrates that the LD leaves on the indirectly induced shoots did not function as donor, but prevented transmission of the floral stimulus (also section 16).

In summary, although reversion to vegetative growth of de-budded plants remains to be explained, it cannot be taken as a serious objection against the idea that the induced state of *Perilla* leaves is of a permanent nature.

Tissue contact with other species

Various attempts have been made to transfer the floral stimulus from *Perilla* to other species or, conversely, to induce flower formation in *Perilla* by grafting with another species. All such efforts have met with complete failure.

Chailakhyan[35] and Lona[91] grew parasitic *Orobanche ramosa* on *Perilla* plants in SD and LD. *Orobanche* flowered perfectly on vegetative host plants in LD, suggesting that the parasite is autonomous for production of the floral stimulus.

Harada[74] tried to use *Cuscuta gronovii* as a bridge between induced and non-induced *Perilla* plants, but the receptors remained vegetative. It seems likely, however, that *Cuscuta* received assimilates from the donor as well as from the receptor. So, presumably very little or no organic material moved from induced plants via *Cuscuta* to non-induced plants.

Efforts to induce flowering in *Perilla* by grafting with *Chrysanthemum* or soybean,[117] and with *Xanthium* or *Salvia*[153] failed, possibly because tissue union was not established in these intergeneric grafts, or was perhaps limited to xylem union.

18 *Effects of Growth Substances and Growth Retardants*

Applied auxins

Leaf treatments with 2,4-D or NAA of *Perilla* in SD slightly delayed flowering.[37] Applications of IAA or NAA to the tips of plants in either LD or SD did not affect flower formation, but stem growth was inhibited, particularly by NAA.[53] When NAA and GA_3 were applied simultaneously, the auxin suppressed the extra stem growth caused by GA_3 alone.

Preliminary reports indicate that indole-butyric acid[95] can promote stem elongation in *Perilla*, and that indole-propionic acid[97] can quantitatively promote flowering.

Spraying of *Perilla* plants with a 0.002 per cent solution of eosin[98] before or during SD treatment reduced the number of SD needed for flower formation from more than 10 to 7 or 8. This was interpreted to be due to a reduction in the level of endogenous auxin.

Daily sprayings with NAA solutions of induced leaves grafted onto LD stocks did not diminish their effectiveness in transmitting the floral stimulus.[153]

Endogenous auxins

The first auxin determinations in *Perilla* were made by Chailakhyan and Zhdan-ova[62] using the *Avena* curvature test. They found more auxin in apices from plants in LD than in SD, but no auxin could be detected in mature leaves. Using the geotropic reaction of detached *Perilla* leaves as a measure for auxin content, Zhdanova[155] concluded that leaves in SD contain less auxin than those in LD. Selim[132] used adventitious root formation as a criterion for auxin content, and found that root formation and flowering are mutually antagonistic processes. His data tend to support a suggestion made earlier by Turezkaya[141] that at the stage of floral initiation, auxins accumulate in the flower buds, thus leaving an insufficient amount for root initiation. If correct, this would mean that SD causes a redistribution of auxin rather than a decrease in the total level.

Root formation on the petioles of induced and detached leaves was poor in SD, but many roots were produced on the petioles of leaves induced on the plant and subsequently detached and kept in LD.[153]

Haupt[75] found that auxin transport in *P. ocymoides* and *P. crispa* is strictly polar in both vegetative and flowering plants.

Harada[74] harvested shoot apices of *P. crispa* which also included the young surrounding leaves not exceeding 1.5 cm in length. Methanol extracts were chromatographed on paper and the various zones assayed in the *Avena* mesocotyl test which responds to both auxins and gibberellins. It was found that the level of growth substances was higher in LD apices than in those exposed to 14 SD, but no qualitative differences were found.

Michalski[105] extracted whole plants of *P. ocymoides*, except the root system, and subjected the extracts to chromatography or electrophoresis. Assays were carried out with the *Avena* coleoptile straight growth test. A high level of growth-promoting substances was detected in plants kept in LD, but after transfer to SD growth-inhibiting substances became more prominent. The level of inhibitors was particularly high just before appearance of flower buds. It was suggested therefore than an increase of inhibitors over growth-promoting substances is decisive for floral initiation in *Perilla*. However, the relationship between level of inhibitors and flower formation need not necessarily be one of cause and effect.

Using Rf-values, UV fluorescence and various color reagents, Michalski[105] concluded that the following growth substances were present in his *Perilla* extracts: Indole-3-acetic acid, indole-3-acetonitrile, ethyl indole-3-acetate, indole-3-aldehyde, and other not fully identified indole derivatives.

Applied gibberellins

Several workers[10,41,43-46,54,76,92,94,97,100,123,148] have established that application of GA_3 to *Perilla* increases stem growth in both SD and LD conditions, but it does not cause flower formation in LD. However, flowering under suboptimal inductive conditions is considerably accelerated by GA_3. Lona[94] observed that treatment with GA_3 promoted expression of the floral stimulus in plants induced with 15 SD. Subsequently, however, it also hastened reversion to the vegetative stage, perhaps through an increased growth rate.

Wellensiek[148] also observed that appearance of flower buds was accelerated by GA_3 treatment of suboptimally induced plants, but the number of flower buds per plant was markedly reduced.

In Razumov's experiments[123] the minimal number of SD cycles necessary for flowering decreased from 12 to 9 following a single spray with 0.01 per cent GA_3.

Chailakhyan[43] investigated differences in the GA response when applications were made to different organs and found that tip applications gave more stem growth than treatment of a mature leaf, but neither caused any flowering in LD. It would seem therefore that GA_3 acts directly in the growing points and does not undergo any transformation in the leaves.

The effectiveness of gibberellins 1 to 9 was tested on *Perilla* seedlings grown in 18-hour photoperiods.[100] No flower formation was observed, but there was a marked difference among the 9 GA's in causing extra stem growth. The order of effectiveness was as follows:

$$A_5 > A_1 > A_7 > A_9 > A_3 > A_4 > A_2 > A_8 \geqslant A_6 = \text{Control.}$$

The interaction of GA_3 with several chemicals was also studied. NAA[53] and cinnamic acid[54] markedly reduced the growth promotion caused by GA_3. Vitamins B_1 or C applied simultaneously with GA_3 had a synergistic effect on stem growth.[53] These growth responses were observed in *Perilla* grown both in SD and in LD. No flower buds were formed in LD, and none of the chemicals applied alone or in combination with others had any striking effect on flower formation in SD.

Endogenous gibberellins

Extracts of GA-like substances have been prepared from *P. nankinensis* by Chailakhyan and coworkers.[45,57,58] Plants were grown in LD and SD and after flowers appeared in the favorable daylength, leaves for extraction were taken from the mid regions of the plants. Corn seedlings or rosette plants of *Rudbeckia bicolor* in SD were used as bioassay plants. Extracts from LD leaves caused more elongation in corn leaf sheaths than those prepared from SD leaves. With *Rudbeckia* the LD leaf extracts caused bolting and formation of flower buds, whereas plants treated with SD *Perilla* extracts did not produce flower buds at all. It is clear from these data that the amount of extractable GA-like substances is higher in *Perilla* plants grown in LD than in those grown in SD. This would be in agreement with Chailakhyan's general hypothesis of flowering[43–46] which postulates that florigen is a complex of two groups of substances, the gibberellins and anthesins. In a caulescent plant such as *Perilla* which does not respond to GA treatment with flower formation, endogenous gibberellins would be non-limiting for flowering, although more gibberellin would be produced in LD than in SD. Anthesins, however, would be produced in SD, but not at all in LD.

Growth retardants

Lona[96] reported that treatment of *P. ocymoides* grown in the natural day with Phosfon D caused earlier flowering. It is not clear, however, if this response was due to a change in the critical daylength or to a requirement for fewer long nights.

Deltour and Jacqmard[65] found that stem length and leaf area of *P. nankinensis* grown in LD were strongly reduced by Phosfon D applied via the roots, but the rate of leaf formation was not affected. Applied GA_3 completely overcame the growth inhibition caused by the growth retardant.

An interesting observation is that the diterpenoid atractyligenin, which is structurally related to GA, had a growth-retarding effect on *Perilla* plants,[97] but this finding does not seem to have been pursued further.

Maleic hydrazide (MH) applied to *Perilla* during SD treatment is reported both to delay[54] and to accelerate[82] flowering.

Kozlova et al.[81] sprayed 0.01, 0.1 and 0.25 per cent solutions of MH on *P. ocymoides* grown in 16-hour photoperiods. The lowest concentration slightly stimulated growth, but the others were inhibitory. Sections of shoot apices prepared 56 days after treatment showed that inflorescences had been produced whereas control plants had remained vegetative. These workers assumed that the readiness to flower is determined by the ratio of old to young leaves. Since MH seemed to decrease the activity of young leaves, possibly by accelerating their maturation, earlier flower formation would be expected. This conclusion is further supported by the finding[144] that removal of the young, still expanding leaves and all axillary shoots, resulted in flower formation in *P. ocymoides* grown in LD.

Cytokinins

In intact *Perilla* plants, kinetin had an effect[99] similar to that of eosin (see auxins, this section), i.e. it reduced the number of SD required for flower formation. In control plants 10 SD were not sufficient for flower formation, but daily spraying with 10^{-4} M kinetin caused 100 per cent flowering.

Application of a 0.1 per cent kinetin solution to the stem tips of *Perilla* plants exposed to 12 SD promoted flower formation; stem height was reduced.[54]

Miscellaneous chemicals

The following chemicals promoted flower formation and flowering in *Perilla* plants subjected to 14 SD: Vitamin C, thiamine, nicotinic acid,[40] adenine, adenosine, guanosine, cytosine, and uridine.[54] None of these chemicals caused flowering in plants kept in LD.

Cinnamic acid[54] inhibited both flowering and stem growth.

2,3,5-triiodobenzoic acid (TIBA) had no effect on flowering.[140]

19 Metabolic Inhibitors

Experiments on the effect of cyanide on floral induction of *P. nankinensis* were conducted by Aksenova.[2] Only one leaf pair was retained per plant and the leaves were treated with cyanide vapors by placing them in beakers over KCN solutions. When the leaves were exposed to cyanide during the first half of a long night, this had little or no effect on flowering. However, treating the leaves during the second half of the long night led to complete suppression of induction. This finding is in good agreement with the effect of low temperature (section 13) and of anaerobiosis (section 15) given during part of the long dark period. As a whole, these data suggest that the crucial dark processes of induction are absolutely dependent upon energy provided by the respiratory processes.

Treatment of induced leaves with 2,4-dinitrophenol or sodium azide did not diminish their effectiveness as donors for LD receptors.[153]

The flower-inhibiting effect of an atmosphere containing various narcotics was mentioned in section 15.

Extensive experiments were performed on the effects of 5-fluorouracil, 2-thiouracil and ethionine on photoperiodic induction of *Perilla* leaves.[154] Since treatment of leaves on intact plants caused severe malformations in the shoots, the following approach was followed. Large plants were debudded and defoliated except for 1 or 2 mature leaf pairs. The remaining leaf pairs were treated daily with antimetabolites by spraying, or dipping the leaves into solutions. After exposure to 14 to 18 SD, 30 cm^2 of the treated leaves were grafted onto LD stocks to test their capacity in producing floral stimulus. By this method treatment of the leaves during SD treatment and expression of the floral stimulus were separated in time and space, avoiding possible effects of the inhibitors on floral initiation. The leaves survived daily treatments with inhibitors in concentrations as high as 5×10^{-3}M, although loss of pigment was often noticeable. The results of this approach were clear-cut. It was found in all experiments that leaves treated with antimetabolites induced flowering in receptor buds just as readily as untreated leaves. Although it is always hazardous to infer too much from data obtained with inhibitors, it would seem from these results that nucleic acid and protein synthesis are not directly involved in induction of *Perilla* leaves.

An inhibitor of steroid biosynthesis, tris-(2-diethylaminoethyl) phosphate trihydrochloride was tested on *Perilla* leaves in a similar manner, but again induction remained unaffected, as apparent from the flowering response on the receptor shoots.[154]

20 Florigenic Extracts

Until now, there are no reports of successful attempts at preparing an extract from induced *Perilla* plants which would cause flowering in plants kept under non-inductive daylength. Lincoln[86] reported that an extract prepared from flowering *Xanthium* caused a significant flowering response in green *Perilla*, but no further details have been published.

The existence of a floral stimulus in *Perilla* is so obvious from physiological experiments (sections 16 and 17), that many experiments to obtain active extracts must have met with failure and have therefore remained unpublished, as indicated by a statement of Chailakhyan,[34] 'Despite numerous attempts, we have not yet succeeded in isolating the hormones of flowering, nor in demonstrating the possibility of their transportation through non-living media'.

One may wonder then, why the flower hormone has remained so elusive? First of all, there is no good clue what kind of compound to search for. Secondly, physiological experiments suggest that the material is quite stable in *Perilla*, but this need not necessarily be so once it is outside the living cell. Thirdly, there appears to be a continuous flow of floral stimulus from induced leaves, but the actual amount present at a given moment, when a leaf is harvested for extraction, may be quite low in comparison with the amount needed to induce flower formation in an apex. Finally, of course, there is the problem of application, penetration and movement of the material to the bud. With so many obstacles in the way it is perhaps not too surprising after all that an interesting and challenging problem has remained unsolved for over 30 years.

21 Induction of Excised Apices

The technique of culturing stem apices to study growth and development of excised *Perilla* tips under the influence of the chemical and physical environment has been explored by Chailakhyan and coworkers,[18,44-46,51,52] and by Raghavan and Jacobs.[121,122]

Terminal buds 3 to 4 mm long were taken from the main or upper lateral shoots of *P. nankinensis* grown in LD. Upon sterilization with 0.1 per cent mercuric chloride for 3 minutes,[18] they were planted on a basic nutrient medium, to which various substances had been added. Of all media tested, *Perilla* tips grew best on Gautheret's medium.[18]

Growth and development of the tips proceeded as follows:[51,52] Growth of the young leaves resumed 2 to 3 days after planting. Calluses formed on the submerged part of the stem, and shoot growth began after 7 to 10 days. Roots appeared 15 to 20 days after planting. Under SD the plantlets formed flower buds in all treatments after 25 to 35 days, except in the presence of kinetin which strongly retarded growth. Flower primordia appeared mainly on the axillary shoots of lower leaves. A second period of flowering took place on the upper part of the shoots 2 months later, due to induction of the developing leaves. In continuous darkness only one etiolated internode was produced, but shoot tips formed flower buds in all treatments after 25 to 30 days.

In LD conditions (natural daylight supplemented with fluorescent and incandescent light to a photoperiod of 16 hours) growth was more vigorous. Explants on the basal medium remained strictly vegetative. On the other hand, tips on media containing 1 mg/l kinetin or adenine, produced flower buds in the lower axillary shoots at the same time as those grown in SD or total darkness, but no more flower buds appeared later on. Flower formation in LD-grown tips at an early stage was attributed to the fact that young excised tips are strongly dependent on the substances present in the medium whereas older plants with roots and leaves manufacture their own organic substances and respond as intact plants to the photoperiod.

In further experiments[46,52] various nucleic acid metabolites were added to the medium. Adenosine, guanosine, cytosine or a mixture of the 4 RNA nucleosides caused flower formation under LD conditions. However, flower buds developed only into flowers on media containing kinetin (1 mg/l), adenosine (2 mg/l), or a mixture of the 4 RNA nucleosides (0.5 mg/l of each), particularly if the latter was supplemented with 400 mg/l casein hydrolysate. Chailakhyan et al.[46,52] concluded that these metabolites act directly on the metabolism of the shoot meristems since they can exert their effect only at an early age when no roots or mature leaves have formed. As the authors[52] point out correctly, these results do not resolve the question as to what the relationship is between the nucleic acid derivatives in the medium, and the flowering stimulus which moves from SD leaves to the growing points in intact plants. It is speculated that these substances may increase nucleic acid and protein synthesis which seems to be associated with the change from the vegetative to the flowering condition in SDP.

Quite different results with excised apices were reported by Raghavan and Jacobs.[121,122] These workers cultured 8 to 10 mm long tips of P. frutescens (green variety), including 3 pairs of leaf primordia, on White's medium. No roots were produced and there is no sign of shoot elongation in the photographs published by these authors. When cultured in SD, the tips initiated flower buds in 31 days and flowered in 82 days. In LD the shoot apices also underwent the early stage of inflorescence differentiation, although it took an average of 81 days. The structures produced in LD were described as 'superficially resembling Selaginella cones'. When maintained continuously in LD, development was arrested at the stage prior to formation of sporogenous cells. If the tips were cultured in LD with 2 pairs of mature leaves either attached to them, or detached and implanted with the apices in the medium, no reproductive development took place at all. Adding IAA to the medium inhibited the early stage of initiation as well as actual flowering.[121]

Raghavan and Jacobs[122] concluded from these observations that the first stage of floral differentiation is not induced by a floral stimulus, but will occur automatically after the flower-inhibiting effect of mature leaves in LD has been removed (for arguments opposing this view see section 17). At the present stage of our knowledge it is not clear how floral initiation of apices cultured in vitro can be related to the events occurring in the intact plant (see also above). For example, it is puzzling why in Raghavan and Jacobs' experiments[122] not only LD leaves, but even leaves in SD implanted in the agar with the cultured apices exerted a flower-inhibiting effect.

22 Chemical, Histochemical, and Ultrastructural Changes at Induction

Metabolic changes

Several differences in the metabolism between vegetative and induced Perilla plants have been observed.

The content of chlorophyll, carotene and xanthophyll[48] was always higher in SD leaves than in LD ones. On the other hand the anthocyanin content decreased sharply in induced leaves[67] (also section 3).

Novitsky[116] found that in an inductive photoperiod the flow of labeled assimilates from leaves was temporarily less than from comparable leaves in LD. This was interpreted to mean that more products of photosynthesis were needed for specific reactions associated with induction of the leaves. In the early part of a short photoperiod, less radioactivity was incorporated into amino acids than under LD conditions.

Tsybul'ko[138,139] also reported that more assimilates accumulated in leaves kept in SD than in LD. Translocation of products of photosynthesis from *Perilla* leaves occurred mostly during the long night.

Chailakhyan[39] found little loss of starch from SD leaves; the protein content of these leaves was higher than of those in a LD regime.

The respiration pattern of *Perilla* leaves changed rapidly under influence of the shift from LD to SD.[47] In the inductive daylength the respiration remained rather constant throughout the day and night. In LD respiration showed a diurnal variation, exceeding that of SD leaves only during part of the light period. A higher respiratory activity in SD than in LD was also reported by Deleuze.[64]

Keeping *Perilla* leaves in a nitrogen atmosphere (section 15) for 6 hr reduced the evolution of CO_2, and increased the respiratory quotient.[79]

Peroxidase[1,49] activity was higher in SD than in LD whereas the activity of copper-containing oxidases, including polyphenol-oxidase and ascorbic acid oxidase, decreased in SD as compared to LD.

There is no evidence at present that any of these differences is directly connected with floral induction of *Perilla*.

Structure of the shoot apex and early events during induction

Ontogenetic development of the shoot apex of *P. nankinensis* in the period from germination to floral initiation has been described by Nougarède et al.[115] The present discussion will be mainly restricted to those changes which occur during the transition from the vegetative to the reproductive phase.

The following zones were distinguished in a vegetative *Perilla* shoot apex (Fig. 5–7):

1. The *central zone* with relatively large cells which have a low affinity for RNA stains. The frequency of mitosis is low in this zone.

2. On the flanks of the apex is the so-called *peripheral zone* which splits off leaf primordia. This zone surrounds the base of the apex and is approximately ring-shaped. The cells in the peripheral zone are smaller than in the central zone; they also have a higher RNA content. The number of ribosomes per unit area of cytoplasm is higher than in cells of the central zone.

3. The *pith-rib meristem* consisting of vacuolated cells with a low RNA content as evident from affinity for stains. The cells in this zone divide in the transverse direction, thus producing the underlying pith cells. The pith-rib meristem was found to be more active in LD than in SD (Table 5–7), but applied GA_3 had no effect on its activity.[10]

At the transition from the vegetative to the reproductive stage, the following histological and histochemical changes were observed in the apex.[115] Mitotic activity (Table 5–7) as well as RNA content of the central cells increased, so that the central and peripheral zones appeared quite similar, thus forming a superficial meristematic mantle. At this stage the meristem was called prefloral by Nougarède et al.[115] The increased mitotic activity resulted in an increased size and modified shape of the apex.[77,115] At the subcellular level there was a marked increase in the number of ribosomes in the cytoplasm of central cells (Table 5–7).

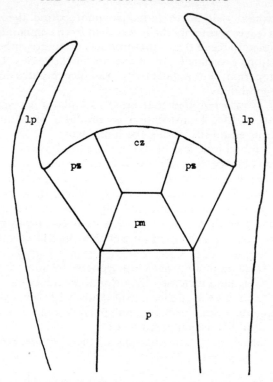

FIGURE 5–7. Schematic representation of the zonation in the vegetative
shoot apex of *Perilla* according to Nougarède *et al.*[115] cz = central zone;
pz = peripheral zone; pm = pith-rib meristem; p = pith; lp = leaf
primordium.

TABLE 5–7

Mitotic activities and numbers of cytoplasmic ribosomes in various zones of
the shoot apex of *P. nankinensis* at different stages of development. Percentages
of labeled nuclei after 6 hr treatments with ^{3}H-thymidine (after Bernier,[7] and
Lance-Nougarède et Bronchart[84]).

		% of labeled nuclei			Number of cytoplasmic ribosomes per $5\mu^2$	
Daylength	State of meristem	Peripheral zone	Central zone	Pithrib meristem	Peripheral zone	Central zone
SD	Vegetative	14.0	7.3	3.1	5115	3290
	Prefloral	17.5	14.8	–*	6377	6728
	Floral	18.1	7.5	–*	3865	3011
LD	Young, 18 days	18.3	9.7	4.8		
	Old, 50 days (Intermediate phase)	11.1	3.3	4.8	4565	4020

* Disappeared

The increased activity of central cells was only transient and returned to that of the vegetative apex during the floral stage, when the floral primordia were actually differentiated (Table 5–7).

In plants grown continuously in LD the mitotic activity of the shoot apex slowed down considerably (Table 5.7) which was accompanied by increased length of the plastochron. The typical zonation of young plants disappeared as plants grew older. Such meristems were called intermediate.[8,115] They never developed beyond this stage in LD. In *Perilla* the intermediate stage is not associated with an increased sensitivity to inductive treatment as is the case in some other species.[8]

It is of further interest that GA_3 applications which do not induce flower formation in *Perilla* (Section 18) have no effect on the central zone, but do increase mitotic activity of the peripheral zone (accelerated leaf formation) and of the subapical pith[10] (extra stem elongation).

Phosfon D inhibited leaf growth and stem elongation. At the cellular level this growth retardant reduced the number of mitoses in the subapical pith.[65]

It would appear from these data that activation of the central zone is an essential step towards flowering, although the *Perilla* apex itself never differentiates into a terminal flower bud.[77,115]

23 Inflorescence Differentiation

Jacobs and Raghavan[77] described floral differentiation in *P. frutescens* in relation to the number of SD received by the plants. After 7 SD they observed a slight broadening of the apex which was accompanied by an increase in the number of mitotic figures. Two days later thickenings appeared on the flanks of the apex which were the beginnings of floral primordia. After 11 SD these primordia, located in the axils of bracts, began to differentiate. The calyx and corolla lobes were visible after 13 to 15 SD. Microsporangia and ovules differentiated after about 17 to 19, and 19 to 21 SD, respectively.

Following the transfer from LD to SD the number of leaf pair primordia initiated per day increased from 0.12 to 0.40 in *P. frutescens*[77], and in good agreement with this from 0.16 to 0.40 in *P. nankinensis*.[85]

Under LD conditions the terminal apex varied in height from 20 to 33μ. Upon the shift to SD, the height started to increase after the 5th day and ultimately reached a value of 70 to 80μ.[77] Despite this marked elongation, the shoot apex of induced *Perilla* plants has never been observed to differentiate into a terminal flower bud.[77,115] Thus, after a limited number of inductive cycles, reversion to vegetative growth remains possible (sections 3 and 17). At the time of reversion, the apex shows histochemical characteristics which are quite similar to those of the prefloral apex[17] (section 22).

If the plants are kept permanently in SD, the apical cells become vacuolated; ultimately the apex degenerates and dies.[115]

Conclusion

Exposure of *Perilla* to long dark periods results in the formation of a transmissible flower-inducing stimulus as is evident from localized SD treatment of leaves and from grafting experiments. The ability to produce this stimulus, the so-called induced state, is permanently retained in induced leaves whereas the stimulus itself appears to decay. The simplest working hypothesis is that the floral stimulus is a single substance produced in induced leaves, and absent in non-induced ones.

Movement of the floral stimulus in *Perilla* is very closely correlated with translocation of assimilates. Non-induced leaves inhibit flower formation, particularly those positioned between donor leaf and receptor bud. Available data indicate that this inhibition is due to interference with transmission of the stimulus rather than to production of specific flower-inhibiting substances in LD leaves.

There is evidence that intercalating non-inductive cycles between inductive ones results in the formation of a transmissible inhibitor which interferes with the action of the floral stimulus in the apex. Since this inhibition becomes apparent only in leaves which have received a SD treatment insufficient for flower formation, it is unlikely that this plays a role in plants grown continuously in LD.

Arrival of the floral stimulus in the shoot apex affects specifically the cells of the central zone: their mitotic activity, RNA content, and number of ribosomes all increase. Although the terminal shoot apex enlarges considerably, it is never transformed into a flower bud, thus leaving open the possibility of reversion to vegetative growth on return to non-inductive daylengths.

REFERENCES

[1] Aksenova, N. P. (1963). The effect of daylength on oxidase activity in plants. *Fiziol. Rast.* **10**, 166.

[2] Aksenova, N. P. (1966). The effect of cyanide on the development of *Rudbeckia* and *Perilla* under various daylength conditions. *Fiziol. Rast.* **13**, 265.

[3] Allard, H. A. and Garner, W. W. (1940). Further observations on the response of various species to length of day. *U.S.D.A. Techn. Bull.* No. 727.

[4] Anonymous (1963). The market for drying oils. *Rep. Trop. Prod. Inst.* **5**, 1.

[5] Bailey, L. H. (1963). *The Standard Cyclopedia of Horticulture.* Vol. III, 2553. The Macmillan Co., N.Y.

[6] Bărbat, I. and Ochesanu, C. (1965). The nature of the photoperiodical induction. The presence of a flowering-hormon or a flowering-inhibitor. *Naturwiss.* **52**, 458.

[7] Bernier, G. (1966). Evolution of nucleic acid metabolism during the ontogenetic development of apical meristems. In *Differentiation of apical meristems and some problems of ecological regulation of development of plants.* (Praha-Nitra 1964). Czechoslovak Acad. Sci. 115.

[8] Bernier, G. (1966). The morphogenetic role of the apical meristem in higher plants. In *Les phytohormones et l'organogenèse. Congrès et Colloques de l'Université de Liège* **38**, 151.

[9] Bernier, G., Bronchart, R. and Jacqmard, A. (1964). Action of gibberellic acid on the mitotic activity of the different zones of the shoot apex of *Rudbeckia bicolor* and *Perilla nankinensis. Planta* **61**, 236.

[10] Bernier, G., Bronchart, R., Jacqmard, A. et Sylvestre, G. (1967). Acide gibbérellique et morphogénèse caulinaire. *Bull. Soc. roy. Bot. Belg.* **100**, 51.

[11] Bhargava, S. C. (1964). Photoperiodism, floral induction and floral inhibition in *Salvia occidentalis. Meded. Landbouwhogesch. Wageningen* **64** (12), 1.

[12] Bhargava, S. C. (1965). A transmissible flower bud inhibitor in *Perilla crispa. Proc. Kon. Nederl. Akad. Wetensch. Amsterdam Ser. C* **68**, 63.

[13] Bocchi, A., Lona, F. and Sachs, R. M. (1956). Photoperiodic induction of disbudded *Perilla* plants. *Plant Physiol.* **31**, 480.

[14] Botvinovsky, V. V. (1934). On the photoperiodic reaction in *Perilla ocymoides. Bot. Zhur. SSSR* **19**, 5.

[15] Bouillenne, R. (1963). Recherche de la photopériode critique chez diverses espèces de jours longs et de jours courts cultivée en milieu conditionné. *Bull. Acad. roy. Belg., Class Sci.* **49**, 337.

[16] Bouslova, E. D. et Lubimenko, V. N. (1937). Influence de l'induction lumineuse sur le développement de *Perilla ocymoides.* I. *C.R. (Dokl.) Acad. Sci. URSS* **14**, 143.

[17] Bronchart, R., Bernier, G. et Schumacker, R. (1967). In press.[8]

[18] Butenko, R. G. (1960). Application of a method for cultivation of isolated terminal buds to study the process of growth and organogenesis of plants. *Fiziol. Rast.* **7**, 715.

[19] Carr, D. J. (1952). The photoperiodic behaviour of short-day plants. *Physiol. Plant.* **5**, 70.

[20] Carr, D. J. (1953). On the nature of photoperiodic induction. I. Photoperiodic treatments applied to detached leaves. *Physiol. Plant.* **6**, 672.

[21] Chailakhyan, M. Kh. (1936). On the hormonal theory of plant development. *C.R. (Dokl.) Acad. Sci. URSS* **12**, 443.

[22] Chailakhyan, M. Kh. (1936). New facts in support of the hormonal theory of plant development. *Ibid.* **13**, 79.

[23] Chailakhyan, M. Kh. (1937). Concerning the hormonal nature of plant developmental processes. *Ibid.* **16**, 227.

[24] Chailakhyan, M. Kh. (1938). Motion of blossom hormone in girdled and grafted plants. *Ibid.* **18**, 607.

[25] Chailakhyan, M. Kh. (1940). Translocation of flowering hormones across various plant organs. I. Across the leaf. *Ibid.* **27**, 160.

[26] Chailakhyan, M. Kh. (1940). Translocation of flowering hormones across various plant organs. II. Translocation across the stem. *Ibid.* **27**, 255.

[27] Chailakhyan, M. Kh. (1940). Translocation of flowering hormones across various plant organs. III. Across the root. *Ibid.* **27**, 373.

[28] Chailakhyan, M. Kh. (1941). Translocation of flowering hormones in the plant as affected by temperature and narcotics. *Ibid.* **31**, 949.

[29] Chailakhyan, M. Kh. (1944). Contribution to the analysis of the theory of flowering of plants. *Ibid.* **44**, 348.

[30] Chailakhyan, M. Kh. (1945). Flowering in different plant species as a response to nitrogenous food. *Ibid.* **47**, 146.

[31] Chailakhyan, M. Kh. (1945). Photoperiodism of individual parts of the leaf, its halves. *Ibid.* **47**, 220.

[32] Chailakhyan, M. Kh (1946). Photoperiodic response of plants when their individual leaves are subjected to different daylengths. *Ibid.* **54**, 735.

[33] Chailakhyan, M. Kh. (1947). Influence of leaves exposed to different daylength upon development of shoots. *Ibid.* **54**, 837.

[34] Chailakhyan, M. Kh. (1947). On the nature of the inhibitory effect of leaves upon flowering. *Ibid.* **55**, 69.

[35] Chailakhyan, M. Kh. (1947). Development of different species of broomrape as connected with growth and development of their hosts. *Ibid.* **55**, 869.

[36] Chailakhyan, M. Kh. (1948). Photoperiodism and the capacity of plants to flower. *Dokl. Akad. Nauk. SSSR* **59**, 1003.

[37] Chailakhyan, M. Kh. (1948). On the inner factors of the ripeness-to-flower condition in plants. *Ibid.* **60**, 1269.

[38] Chailakhyan, M. Kh. (1950). The part played by roots in the photoperiodic reaction of plants. *Ibid.* **72**, 201.

[39] Chailakhyan, M. Kh. (1955). The effect of daylength on the nature of carbohydrate-protein metabolism in the leaves of plants. *Ibid.* **100**, 373.

[40] Chailakhyan, M. Kh. (1956). The effect of vitamins on the growth and development of plants. *Ibid.* **111**, 894.

[41] Chailakhyan, M. Kh. (1957). The influence of gibberellin on plant growth and flowering. *Ibid.* **117**, 1077.

[42] Chailakhyan, M. Kh. (1958). Photoperiodic sensitivity of excised plant leaves. *Ibid.* **118**, 197.

[43] Chailakhyan, M. Kh. (1958). Hormonale Faktoren des Pflanzenblühens. *Biol. Zbl.* **77**, 641. Also: *Fiziol. Rast.* **5**, 541.

[44] Chailakhyan, M. Kh. (1961). Principles of ontogenesis and physiology of flowering in higher plants. *Can. J. Bot.* **39**, 1817.

[45] Chailakhyan, M. Kh. (1961). Effect of gibberellins and derivatives of nucleic acid metabolism on plant growth and flowering. In *Plant growth regulation* (4th intern. Conf. on Plant Growth Regul., Yonkers, N.Y. 1959) 531. Iowa State Univ. Press, Ames.

[46] Chailakhyan, M. Kh. (1964). Florigen, gibberellins and anthesins. In *Régulateurs naturels de la croissance végétale* (5th intern. Conf. on Plant Growth Regulators, Gif-sur-Yvette, France, 1963) 589. CNRS, Paris.

[47] Chailakhyan, M. Kh. and Aksenova, N.P. (1959). The connection between photoperiodism and respiration in plants. *Fiziol. Rast.* **6**, 699.

[48] Chailakhyan, M. Kh. and Bavrina, T. V. (1957). Effect of daylength on pigment content of plant leaves. *Fiziol. Rast.* **4**, 312.

[49] Chailakhyan, M. Kh. and Boyarkin, A. N. (1955). The effect of daylength on the activity of the oxidizing enzymes in plants. *Dokl. Akad. Nauk SSSR* **105**, 592.

[50] Chailakhyan, M. Kh. and Butenko, R. G. (1957). Translocation of assimilates from leaves to shoots during different photoperiodic regimes of plants. *Fiziol. Rast.* **4**, 450.

[51] Chailakhyan, M. Kh. and Butenko, R. G. (1959). The effect of adenine and kinetin on the differentiation of flower buds in *Perilla* stem tips. *Dokl. Akad. Nauk SSSR* **129**, 224.

[52] Chailakhyan, M. Kh., Butenko, R. G. and Lyubarskaya, I.I (1961). Effect of derivatives of nucleic acid metabolism on the growth and flowering of *Perilla nankinensis*. *Fiziol. Rast.* **8**, 101.

[53] Chailakhyan, M. Kh. and Khlopenkova, L. P. (1959). The effect of auxins and vitamins on growth and development of plants treated with gibberellin. *Dokl. Akad. Nauk SSSR* **129**, 454.

[54] Chailakhyan, M. Kh. and Khlopenkova, L. P. (1961). Effect of growth substances and nucleic acid derivatives on growth and flowering of photoperiodically induced plants. *Ibid.* **141**, 1497.

[55] Chailakhyan, M. Kh. and Konstantinova, T. N. (1960). The effect of anaerobiosis on plant photoperiodism. *Ibid.* **135**, 1539.

[56] Chailakhyan, M. Kh. and Konstantinova, T. N. (1962). Effect of aeration conditions on the photoperiodic reactions in plants. *Fiziol. Rast.* **9**, 693.

[57] Chailakhyan, M. Kh. and Lozhnikova, V. N. (1959). Effect of gibberellin-like substances extracted from the leaves of various plants on the growth and development of *Rudbeckia*. *Dokl. Akad. Nauk SSSR* **128**, 1309.

[58] Chailakhyan, M. Kh. and Lozhnikova, V. N. (1960). Gibberellin-like substances in higher plants and their effect on growth and flowering. *Fiziol. Rast.* **7**, 521.

[59] Chailakhyan, M. Kh. and Rupcheva, I. A. (1948). On the significance of interruption of the light period by darkness in the photoperiodic reactions of plants. *Dokl. Akad. Nauk SSSR* **60**, 1441.

[60] Chailakhyan, M. Kh. and Rupcheva, I. A. (1948). The effect of interrupted illumination on the generative development of plants. *Ibid.* **61**, 565.

[61] Chailakhyan, M. Kh. and Yarkovaya, L. M. (1937). New facts in support of the hormonal theory of plant development. II. *C.R. (Dokl.) Acad. Sci. URSS* **15**, 215.

[62] Chailakhyan, M. Kh. and Zhdanova, L. P. (1938). Hormones of growth in formation processes. I. Photoperiodism and creation of growth hormones. *Ibid.* **19**, 107.

[63] Chailakhyan, M. Kh. and Zhdanova, L. P. (1948). Influence of temperature on the photoperiodism of plants. *Dokl. Akad. Nauk SSSR* **62**, 549.

[64] Deleuze, G. G. (1966). L'activité respiratoire de *Perilla nankinensis* (S.D.P.) en fonction des conditions lumineuses (durée, intensité). *Photochem. Photobiol.* **5**, 461.

[65] Deltour, R. et Jacqmard, A. (1967). Influence du Phosfon-D sur le fonctionnement du bourgeon terminal de *Perilla nankinensis*. *Bull. Soc. roy. Bot. Belg.* **100**, 141.

[66] El Hinnawy, E. I. (1956). Some aspects of mineral nutrition and flowering. *Meded. Landbouwhogeschool Wageningen* **56** (9), 1.

[67] Ermolaeva, E. J. and Sčeglova, O. A. (1948). Anthocyanin and plant development. *Dokl. Akad. Nauk SSSR* **60**, 901.

[68] Fredericq, H. (1962). Le rôle du gaz carbonique de l'air pendant les jours courts des cycles inductifs chez *Kalanchoë blossfeldiana* et *Perilla crispa*. *Bull. de la Soc. roy. Bot. Belg.* **94**, 45.

[69] Funke, G. L. (1939). Proeven over photoperiodiciteit bij verschillend gekleurd licht. *Biol. Jaarboek Natuurw. Genootsch. Dodoneae (Gent)* **6**, 351.

[70] Funke, G. L. (1943). Observations on the flowering photoperiodicity. *Rec. trav. bot. Néerl.* **40**, 392.

[71] Gaillochet, J., Grossin, F. et Mathon, C. C. (1961). Effets des lumières blanche et verte sur *Perilla ocymoides* L., forma *viridis*. *Bull. Soc. bot. France* **108**, 268.

[72] Gaillochet, J., Mathon, C. C. et Stroun, M. (1962). Nouveau type de réaction et changement du type de réaction au photopériodisme chez le *Perilla ocimoides* L. *C.R. Acad. Sci. Paris* **255**, 2501.

[73] Garner, W. W. and Allard, H. A. (1931). Effect of abnormally long and short alternations of light and darkness on growth and development of plants. *J. Agr. Res.* **42**, 629.

[74] Harada, H. (1962). Etude des substances naturelles de croissance en relation avec la floraison. – Isolement d'une substance de montaison. *Rev. gén. Bot.* **69**, 201.

[75] Haupt, W. (1956). Gibt es Beziehungen zwischen Polarität und Blütenbildung? *Ber. deutsch. Bot. Ges.* **69**, 61.

[76] Hořavka, B., Krekule, J. and Seidlová, F. (1962). An anatomical study of the effect of gibberellic acid on differentiation of the shoot apex in the species *Perilla ocimoides* L. in short and long days. *Biol. Plant., Prague* **4**, 239.

[77] Jacobs, W. P. and Raghavan, V. (1962). Studies on the floral histogenesis and physiology of *Perilla* – I. Quantative analysis of flowering in *P. frutescens* (L.) Britt. *Phytomorphology* **12**, 144.

[78] Kleshnin, A. F. (1943). On the role of spectral composition of light in photoperiodic reaction. *C.R. (Dokl.) Acad. Sci. URSS* **40**, 208.

[79] Konstantinova, T. N. (1963). Effect of anaerobiosis on plant respiration in connection with photoperiodism. *Fiziol. Rast.* **10**, 480.

[80] Kornilov, A. A. (1949). The flowering of *Perilla* under continuous illumination. *Dokl. Akad. Nauk SSSR* **64**, 401.

[81] Kozlova, N. A., Ermolaeva, E. Y. and Batska, P. (1960). Effect of maleic hydrazide on flower formation in *Perilla ocymoides* under long-day conditions. *Ibid.* **130**, 231.

[82] Krajewska, E. (1960). The influence of indolylacetic acid (IAA) and of maleic hydrazide (MH) on the time at which flower buds develop in *Perilla ocymoides* L. *Naturwiss.* **47**, 213.

[83] Lam, S. L. and Leopold, A. C. (1961). Reversion and reinduction of flowering in *Perilla. Amer. J. Bot.* **48**, 306.

[84] Lance-Nougarède, A. et Bronchart, R. (1965). Métabolisme des acides nucléiques dans le méristème apical du *Perilla nankinensis* au cours des diverses phases du développement. *C.R. Acad. Sci. Paris* **260**, 3140.

[85] Langer, R. H. M. and Bussell, W. T. (1964). The effect of flower induction on the rate of leaf initiation. *Ann. Bot. N.S.* **28**, 163.

[86] Lincoln, R. G. (1964). Paper presented in the Symp. on Flower Induction at the 10th Intern. Bot. Congress, Edinburgh.

[87] Lona, F. (1946). Sui fenomeni di induzione, postefetto e localizzazione fotoperiodica. L'induzione antogena indiretta delle foglie primordiali di *Xanthium italicum* Moretti. *Nuovo Giorn. bot. ital.*, *N.S.* **53**, 548.

[88] Lona, F. (1947). 'Chimere funzionali' come conseguenza della localizzazione e autonomia del carattere fisiologico delle foglie in rapporto coi processi di sviluppo della pianta. *Lavori di Botanica*, 277. Vol pubbl. in occasione del 70° genetliaco del Prof. G. Gola. Rosenberg & Sellier, Turin.

[89] Lona, F. (1949). La fioritura delle brevidiurne a notte continua. *Nuovo Giorn. bot. ital.*, *N.S.* **56**, 479.

[90] Lona, F. (1949). L'induzione fotoperiodica di foglie staccate. *Boll. Soc. ital. Biol. sperim.* **25**, 761.

[91] Lona, F. (1953). Fioritura di *Orobanche* e *Cuscuta* su ospiti vegetativi. *L'Ateneo Parmense* **24**, 1.

[92] Lona, F. (1956). Osservazioni orientative cuia l'effetto dell'acido gibberellico sullo sviluppo riproduttivo di alcune longidiurne e brevidiurne. *L'Ateneo Parmense* **27**, 867.

[93] Lona, F. (1959). Results of twelve years of work on the photoperiodic responses of *Perilla ocymoides*. *Proc. Kon. Nederl. Akad. Wetensch. Amsterdam Ser. C.* **62**, 204.

[94] Lona, F. (1959). Brief accounts on the physiological activities of gibberellic acid and other substances in relation to photothermal conditions. In *Colloque intern. s'.r le photo-thermopériodism.* Parma, 1957. *U.I.S.B. Sér. B*, No. 34, 141.

[95] Lona, F. (1962). Ontogenetical sites of gibberellin-like manifestations. In *Eigenschaften und Wirkungen der Gibberelline*, 73. Ed. R. Knapp. Symp. der Oberhessischen Gesellschaft für Natur- und Heilkunde, Naturw. Abt., Giessen, 1960. Springer-Verlag, Berlin.

[96] Lona, F. (1963). Inibitori dell'accrescimento, età fisiologica e fioritura nella brevidiurna *Perilla ocymoides*. *L'Ateneo Parmense* **34**, 386.

[97] Lona, F. (1964). The action of Morphogenins, especially gibberellins, before, during and after flowering. Paper presented in the Symp. on Flower Induction at the 10th Intern. Bot. Congress, Edinburgh.

[98] Lona, F., e Bocchi, A. (1955). Verminderung der photoperiodischen Notwendigkeiten von *Perilla ocymoides* Lour. var. *nankinensis* Voss. durch Hypoauxinisation mittles Eosin. *Beitr. Biol. Pfl.* **31**, 333.

[99] Lona, F., e Bocchi, A. (1957). Effetti morfogenetici ed organo-genetici provocati dalla Cinetina (kinetin) su piante erbacee in condizioni esterne controllate. *Nuovo Giorn. bot. ital.*, *N.S.* **64**, 236.

[100] Lona, F. e Fioretti, L. (1962). Accrescimento e fioritura di piante brevidiurne e longidiurne in relazione alle diversa attivita delle gibberelline (A_1–A_9). *Ann. di Bot. (Rome)* **27**, 313.

[101] Lubimenko, V. N. et Bouslova, E. D. (1937). Contribution à la théorie du photopériodisme. II. *C.R. (Dokl.) Acad. Sci. URSS* **14**, 149.

[102] Lubimenko, V. N. and Sčeglova, O. A. (1934). New experimental data on photoperiodic induction. *Trudy Bot. Inst. Akad. Nauk SSSR Ser.* **4**, No. 1, 109.

[103] Mathon, C. C. et Stroun, M. (1961). Mise à fleur de *Perilla nankinensis* Voss., plante de jour court typique, en jour continue. *C.R. Soc. biol.* **155**, 1387.

[104] Meijer, G. (1959). The spectral dependence of flowering and elongation. *Acta bot. Néerl.* **8**, 189.

[105] Michalski, L. (1966). Investigations on the influence of the length of light period on the level of growth regulators in short- and long-day plants. In *II Symp. on Plant Growth Regulators*, Torun, Poland, 1963. 46.

[106] Moshkov, B. S. (1939). Minimum intervals of darkness and light to induce flowering in short day plants. *C.R. (Dokl.) Acad. Sci. URSS* **22**, 456.

[107] Moshkov, B. S. (1939). Photoperiodic response of plants as determined by their ontogenesis. *Ibid.* **22**, 460.

[108] Moshkov, B. S. (1939). Transfer of photoperiodic reaction from leaves to growing points. *Ibid.* **24**, 489.

[109] Moshkov, B. S. (1941). On the photoperiodic after-effect. *Ibid.* **31**, 699.

[110] Moshkov, B. S. (1941). Elimination of leaves in grafting. *C.R. (Dokl.) Acad. Sci. URSS* **31**, 161.

[111] Moshkov, B. S. (1950). The significance of different parts of the spectrum of the physiological range of radiation in growth and development of some plants. *Dokl. Akad. Nauk. SSSR* **71**, 171.

[112] Moshkov, B. S. (1950). The effect of infrared radiation on the dark processes in the short-day plant *Perilla*. (Energoperiodism). *Ibid.* **71**, 391.

[113] Moshkov, B. S. and Mihajlov, A. P. (1964). The effect of ultra-violet radiation on the dark phase of the actinorhythmic reaction of plants. *Ibid.* **158**, 990.

[114] Nakai, T. (1928). Notulae ad Plantas Japoniae and Koreae. *Bot. Mag. Tokyo* **42**, 451.

[115] Nougarède, A., Bronchart, R., Bernier, G. et Rondet, P. (1964). Comportement du méristème apical du *Perilla nankinensis* (Lour). Decne. en relation avec les conditions photopériodiques. *Rev. Gén. Bot.* **71**, 205.

[116] Novitsky, Y. I. (1957). Photosynthesis and flow of assimilates in *Perilla* and lettuce grown in different photoperiods. *Fiziol. Rast.* **4**, 243.

[117] Obsil, K. (1939). Zur Frage der Blühhormone. *Planta* **29**, 468.

[118] Ochesanu, C. und Bărbat. I. (1967). Morphologische Veränderungen bei *Perilla ocymoides* durch photoperiodische Behandlungen. *Planta* **75**, 172.

[119] Odumanova, G. A. (1959). Concerning the relationship between photosynthesis and photoperiodism in plants. *Dokl. Akad. Nauk SSSR* **124**, 50.

[120] Pogorleckii, B. K. (1953). Vernalization of *Perilla* in the dark. *Agrobiologija* **3**, 153.

[121] Raghavan, V. (1961). Studies on the floral histogenesis and physiology of *Perilla*. III. Effects of indoleacetic acid on the flowering of apical buds and explants in culture. *Amer. J. Bot.* **48**, 870.

[122] Raghavan, V. and Jacobs, W. P. (1961). Studies on the floral histogenesis and physiology of *Perilla*. II. Floral induction in cultured apical buds of *P. frutescens*. *Amer. J. Bot.* **48**, 751.

[123] Razumov, V. I. (1960). Hastening of flowering in short-day plants by gibberellin treatment. *Fiziol. Rast.* **7**, 354.

[124] Rupcheva, I. A. (1948). The significance of the length and the ratio of light and dark periods in the photoperiodic response of plants. *Dokl. Akad. Nauk SSSR* **61**, 741.

[125] Rylska, T. (1958). The influence of the length of light period on the photoperiodic reaction of the short-day plant *Perilla ocymoides* L. *Acta Soc. Bot. Polon.* **27**, 649.

[126] Rylska, T. and Wislocka, M. (1956). Photoperiod investigations on *Perilla ocymoides* L. *Acta Agrobot.* **4**, 13.

[127] Samygin, G. A. (1948). The effect of strong and weak light applied before or after the dark period on development of *Perilla* and *Rudbeckia*. *Dokl. Akad. Nauk SSSR* **60**, 1265.

[128] Samygin, G. A. (1948). The effect of light intensity in photoperiods unfavourable to the development of *Rudbeckia* and *Perilla*. *Ibid.* **60**, 1433.

[129] Savin, V. N. (1964). The effect of ionizing radiation on the photoperiodic reaction of *Perilla* plants. *Ibid.* **159**, 676.

[130] Schery, R. W. (1952). *Plants for Man*, 332. Prentice-Hall, N.Y.

[131] Schwabe, W. W. (1959). Studies of long-day inhibition in short-day plants. *J. expt. Bot.* **10**, 317.

[132] Selim, H. H. A. (1956). The effect of flowering on adventitious root-formation. *Meded. Landbouwhogeschool Wageningen* **56** (6), 1.
[133] Selim, H. H. A. (1957). Translocation of the floral stimulus in two-branched plants of *Perilla*. *Proc. Kon. Nederl. Akad. Wetensch. Amsterdam Ser. C.* **60**, 67.
[134] Skvortzov, S. S. (1947). Photoperiodic reaction in *Perilla* as affected by light impacts. *Dokl. Akad. Nauk. SSSR* **55**, 773.
[135] Stroun, M., Mathon, C. C., Sandmeier, M., Chodat, F. et Giroud, A. (1961). Long-day effect as a function of interrelations between light quality, duration of photoperiod, and development phases in *Perilla nankinensis* Voss. In *Progress in Photobiology*, 384. Eds. B. C. Christensen and B. Buchmann. Proc. 3rd internat. Photobiol. Congr., Copenhagen, 1960. Elsevier, Amsterdam.
[136] Takimoto, A. and Ikeda, K. (1961). Effect of twilight on photoperiodic induction in some short day plants. *Plant & Cell Physiol.* **2**, 213.
[137] Taravet, A. (1947). Action de la répartition de la lumière au cours du cycle nychéméral de 24 heurs sur la réaction photopériodiques des plantes. *C.R. Acad. Sci. Paris* **224**, 1373.
[138] Tsybul'ko, V. S. (1962). Diurnal variations in the assimilation products in the leaves of long-day and short-day plants. *Fiziol. Rast.* **9**, 567.
[139] Tsybul'ko, V. S. (1965). Variation in the content of assimilation products and plant photoperiodism. *Fiziol. Rast.* **12**, 622.
[140] Tumanov, I. I. and Lizandr, A. A. (1946). On the physiological action of triiodo-benzoic acid upon plants. *Bot. Zhur. SSSR* **31**, 13.
[141] Turezkaya, R. (1941). Ueber den Einfluss des Alters der Mutterpflanze auf die Bewurzelung des Stecklings. *C.R. (Dokl.) Acad. Sci. URSS* **33**, 78.
[142] Vakulin, D. J. (1937). Reaction of reversibility in *Perilla ocymoides* L. under natural conditions. *Ibid.* **15**, 263.
[143] Veen, R. van der and Meijer, G. (1959). *Light and Plant Growth*. Philips' Technical Library, Eindhoven.
[144] Volodarskij, N. I. (1961). On the problem of flowering of short-day plants in continuous illumination. *Dokl. Akad. Nauk SSSR* **138**, 473.
[145] Wellensiek, S. J. (1952). Photoperiodism and temperature in *Perilla*. *Proc. Kon. Nederl. Akad. Wetensch. Amsterdam Ser. C* **55**, 701.
[146] Wellensiek, S. J. (1958). Photoperiodical reactions of *Perilla crispa*. *Ibid.* **61**, 552.
[147] Wellensiek, S. J. (1959). The inhibitory action of light on the floral induction of *Perilla crispa*. *Ibid.* **62**, 195.
[148] Wellensiek, S. J. (1962). Gibberellin and Flowering. In *Eigenschaften und Wirkungen der Gibberelline*, 60. Ed. R. Knapp. Symp. der Oberhess. Ges. für Natur- und Heilkunde, Naturw. Abt., Giessen, 1960. Springer Verlag, Berlin.
[149] Zakharov, B. S. (1937). The problem of yarovization of *Perilla*. *C.R. (Dokl.) Acad. Sci. URSS* **15**, 369.
[150] Zeeuw, D. de (1954). De invloed van het blad op de bloei. *Meded. Landbouwhogeschool Wageningen* **54** (1), 1.
[151] Zeevaart, J. A. D. (1957). Studies on flowering by means of grafting. I. Photoperiodic induction as an irreversible phenomenon in *Perilla*. *Proc. Kon. Nederl. Akad. Wetensch. Amsterdam Ser. C* **60**, 324.
[152] Zeevaart, J. A. D. (1957). Ibid II. Photoperiodic treatments of detached *Perilla* and *Xanthium* leaves. *Ibid. C* **60**, 332.
[153] Zeevaart, J. A. D. (1958). Flower formation as studied by grafting. *Meded. Landbouwhogeschool Wageningen* **58** (3), 1.
[154] Zeevaart, J. A. D. Unpublished data.
[155] Zhdanova, L. P. (1945). Geotropic reaction of leaves and content of growth hormone in plants. *C.R. (Dokl.) Acad. Sci. URSS* **49**, 62.
[156] Zhdanova, L. P. (1947). Photoperiodic reaction of short and long-day plants in relation to their age. *Dokl. Akad. Nauk SSSR* **58**, 485.
[157] Zhdanova, L. P. (1948). Analysing the change of fruiting branches to a vegetative condition due to alternation in photoperiodic conditions. *Ibid.* **60**, 1421.
[158] Zhdanova, L. P. (1948). On the rate of export of flower hormone in photoperiodic induction. *Ibid.* **61**, 553.
[159] Zhdanova, L. P. (1950). Significance of the gaseous regime for the passage of the light stage in plants. *Ibid.* **70**, 715.

6

Chenopodium rubrum L. and related species.

By Bruce G. Cumming

1 History of Use

The genus *Chenopodium* possesses considerable genotypic and phenotypic variation both within and between its species. The species show wide variations in ecological distribution – some are common as weeds, others have been used on a small scale for food and as medicinal herbs.

A number of *Chenopodium* species, particularly *C. amaranticolor* and *C. album*, have been used for some time in physiological and morphological studies of flowering and related subjects. Using seeds taken from specimens in the herbarium of the Plant Research Institute, Canada Department of Agriculture, Ottawa, precocious flowering in short day lengths and extreme sensitivity to photoperiod was found in some previously uninvestigated species.[13] This led to the realization that certain species, particularly *C. rubrum*, could be germinated and maintained for flowering experiments in Petri dishes.[5] This represented a further step in the line of succession of the so-called belly plants – Went's[47] translation of C. Schroter's term 'Bauchpflanzen' meaning plants visible only while one is crawling on one's belly. A large number of selections of *Chenopodium* species, representative of different latitudinal origin and differing in photoperiodic response, have since been isolated and studied.[6,7,9,10]

The specimens of *C. rubrum* collected by Calder and Kukkonen[2] in the Yukon, represented a very valuable addition to the collection, because they can be induced to flower by exposure to a single dark period as soon as the cotyledons have emerged from the testa after germination.[6,7] Further, they can be induced to flower quite rapidly even in long days and this ability contrasts markedly with the obligatory short-day requirement for flowering of selections from further south – providing evidence of latitudinal selection for genetic changes in photoperiodic control.[7]

C. rubrum is irregularly but widely distributed in Asia Minor, Central Asia, Europe, and North America. Part of the value and ability of this species to survive satisfactorily in Petri dishes, even at very high moisture levels, can be attributed to its natural habitats. These include very wet saline areas – where plants may germinate and grow in standing water (e.g. at the edge of saline sloughs, lakes and pools, in North America).

2 Growing Techniques and Growth Habit

C. rubrum is an annual herb, normally producing a single primary stem which elongates from germination onwards. Higher order lateral shoots are produced in the axils of leaves. The leaves are coarsely and irregularly toothed and are spirally arranged on the stem. The inflorescence is variable, often dense, simple to much branched, leafy or leafless, the glomerules are usually crowded (Fig. 6–10).

Seeds, especially when first harvested from plants, may exhibit some degree of dormancy. To obtain earliest complete germination, specific requirements for light and/or temperature must be satisfied – especially if uniform germination and growth are desired. Only then can uniform seedling growth be obtained for photoperiodic treatment(s) in the earliest cotyledonary stage. Details other than those mentioned here are included in other references.[5,7,8,10,11,14] Wherever possible in the following discussion the origin of the plant material has been included – it would help considerably if such a practice were adopted more widely when reporting on responses of specific populations or genotypes.

Treatment of parental plants from which seeds are harvested

Seeds taken from plants grown in long days may be smaller and have more critical requirements for germination than seeds from plants grown in short days. Lona[34] first observed this effect in *C. amaranticolor* and suggested that it was due to formation of thicker seed integuments in long days.

C. *rubrum* is both self- and cross-fertile, and plants should be grown in isolation to preserve the identity of a genotype. Isolated or bagged single plants will set seed; brushing the stamens and stigma is generally unnecessary. For greater seed production from a single plant that can be prevented from flowering precociously, vegetative propagation in non-inductive photoperiods is recommended; the clone can then be transferred to inductive photoperiods for seed production.

Treatment of seeds before planting

Abrading or cutting the surface of seeds can hasten germination. Periods as short as 1 to 5 minutes in concentrated sulphuric acid can increase germination at 30°C in light. There is less likelihood of damaging the embryo if 50 to 70 per cent acid is used for periods of 4 to 30 minutes followed by washing the seeds in sterile water (examine the seeds for effects on the testa before deciding on the appropriate timing). Wetting agents may also hasten imbibition of water by seeds.[27] With or without prior treatment in a wetting agent, immersion for 12 to 24 hours in running tap water or in sterile water that is aerated or agitated, can also improve imbibition. Such treatments may substitute for light and/or temperature alternation requirements and provide faster germination.

Sterilization of seeds is necessary only if contamination by micro-organisms is prevalent and/or must be avoided. Seeds can be soaked for 10 minutes in a 1:1 solution of absolute ethanol and 20 volumes hydrogen peroxide, before planting in sterile conditions. Alternatively, seeds can be surface sterilized by soaking for 20 to 30 minutes in either a filtered saturated solution of calcium hypochlorite or a 1–2 per cent solution of Javex.

Dusting seeds with fungicide or using sterilants during or after germination may adversely affect growth.

Conditions for germination

A very convenient and economical method that provides satisfactory semi-sterile conditions for germination, subsequent growth and floral initiation, is to place seeds in small Petri dishes (6 × 1.5 cm, or 9 × 2 cm) on 7 layers of No. 2 Whatman filter paper moistened with water. Before planting the seeds, add sufficient water to immerse the filter paper in each dish, then autoclave and pour off excess liquid before sowing the seeds. As many as 150 seedlings can be grown in a 6 cm Petri dish (Fig. 6–1d). When comparing different populations, plants can be grown to maturity in Felsen quadrant 10 cm × 2 cm Petri dishes with as many as 50 seedlings in each quadrant. Stimulation of germination may be obtained using a 0.1 to 0.2 per cent solution of potassium nitrate or 0.034 per cent hydrogen peroxide. An additional effect of potassium nitrate or of nutrients can be to stimulate precocious growth of seedlings and this may alter photoperiodic sensitivity. Other substances can be added in solution to the filter paper and washed off as required.

Germination of *C. rubrum* is stimulated by light, particularly at high temperature.[5,8] Maximum stimulation of germination is obtained in light of high red to far-red spectral energy ratio.[8] Thus fluorescent light is more stimulatory than incandescent and also results in less hypocotyl elongation so that plants do not normally grow tall enough to touch the Petri dish lid. Since there is less infra-red radiation in fluorescent than incandescent light, temperature control is easier.

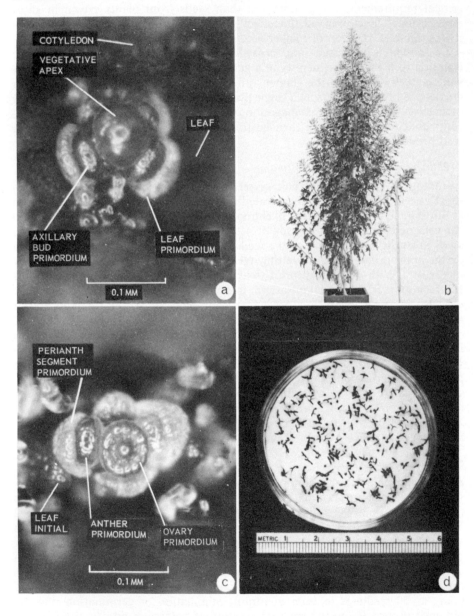

FIGURE 6–1. Transition of apical primordium of *C. rubrum* from (a), vegetative to (c), floral state; (b), vegetative plant of *C. rubrum* (49° 58′N) grown in continuous light for 250 days; (d) five-day old seedlings of *C. rubrum* (60° 47′N). Seedlings at this stage were readily induced to flower by a single dark period interrupting continuous light (Cumming[5,7,14]).

Seeds of *C. rubrum* may not germinate uniformly at constant temperature, but complete germination without any light requirement can be obtained if the temperature is alternated between a low of 10°C and a high of at least 20°C. Complete germination (cotyledons expanded), from untreated seeds, can be obtained in 2 1/2 to 3 1/2 days in alternating temperatures of 32.5°/10°C under low intensity fluorescent light of 100 to 600 f.c.[14] Germination is faster if imbibition is started at the higher temperature. A convenient schedule is 32.5°C (12 hr)–10° (12 hr)–32.5° (12 hr)–10° (12 hr)–32.5° (24 hr) – the last 24 hours at 32.5°C being to stimulate rapid erection of the hypocotyl and expansion of the cotyledons. When different photoperiods are imposed at alternating temperatures it may be preferable for the dark period to coincide with the lower temperature, because the light requirement for germination increases with temperature and a high temperature during darkness can be inhibitory to floral induction. Dark periods can be imposed by means other than darkened germinators. Petri dishes can be wrapped in aluminium foil or in black cloth or can be placed in 35 mm motion picture filter cans.[7] When dark periods differ by more than 12 hours in a single experiment, the germination period for half the total number of dishes can be started 12 hours before the other – so that each successive 24 hours of dark-period increments can be applied within a 12-hour period each day.[11]

Maintenance of germinated seedlings

To avoid contamination of seedlings in Petri dishes, water lost by evaporation should be replaced by boiled water using a plastic-plunger syringe. Application of nutrient solution to seeds before germination may be inhibitory, but there is no inhibition if nutrient solution is added to the medium after radicle extension has started.

Half or full-strength Hoagland's No. 1 solution[26] provides satisfactory growth; 5 or 10 p.p.m. iron should be added in a chelated form.[7] Proprietary soluble fertilizers can also be used.[14] Solutions should be boiled before use. The filter paper can be rinsed periodically with fresh solution. If fungal contamination is a problem, a trace of Captan 50W (N-trichloromercapto-4-cyclohexene-1,2-dicarboximide) can be added to the nutrient solution just after it has been boiled.[7,14]

C. rubrum has also been grown in water culture using half-strength Knop's solution.[43]

For spectrographic work, seeds of *C. rubrum* have been planted in plastic boxes with a 2:1 mixture of heat-sterilized soil and sphagnum in shallow furrows which corresponded with given wavelengths on the spectrograph.[29,30]

To obtain completely aseptic germination and continued growth, an agar culture medium developed by Miller[38] has been very satisfactory for germination and subsequent growth of *C. rubrum* *in vitro* and for production of callus from different tissues.[12]

To study the effects of kinetin and uracil on flowering, Narusako and Nakayama[39] have grown *C. rubrum* *in vitro* on White's medium[48] with 0.8 per cent agar and 5 per cent sucrose.

3 Inflorescence Structure and Criteria of Flowering Response

Floral initiation or later stages in flowering of seedlings can be determined very readily using a binocular dissecting microscope. With practice and care the time of initiation can be determined to within one day.[7] An apical vegetative primordium is visible as an undifferentiated spherical dome of cells which can produce leaves and axillary bud primordia (spiral phyllotaxy). Note, in Figure

6–1a, the youngest leaf initial (primordium) produced from the (upper left) side of the vegetative apex. Floral initiation can first be observed as an increase in size of the dome of cells, followed by the formation of a peripheral ridge of tissue on the dome that encircles an inner area with the apical protuberance (Fig. 6–1c). The latter eventually forms the stigma surmounting the monocarpic ovary, while the peripheral ridge grows up to surround the ovary but not the stigma.[7] Precocious axillary bud growth may also be visible at the apex within three days after induction but this is less characteristic when seedlings are induced at the earliest possible age. Four perianth members and four anthers are normally formed per floret, and they are derived respectively from axillary bud and leaf initials. However, these floral parts may be reduced or absent when there is precocious flowering or when nutrients are lacking. Thus, the flowers may be either hermaphrodite or female. The florets may occur singly or grouped together as glomerules, depending on time of flowering, size of plant, prevailing daylength and nutrition; the inflorescence becomes a spiked panicle if plants are sufficiently large.

Gifford and Tepper[19] observed that *C. album*, when subjected to inductive photoperiods, showed a decrease in plastochronic interval (that is, an increased rate of formation of leaf primordia) and a change in leaf morphology at the apex; there was also a small but noticeable increase in the length of the embryonic internodes. Thomas,[44] also working with *C. album*, was the first to observe that both the rate of leaf initiation and the growth of axillary meristems substantially increased after floral induction. Such changes are also evident in *C. rubrum*.

Flower induction can be assessed by four main methods:

(*a*) By measuring the increase in length of shoot apex,[43] early inflorescence length,[32] or the diameter of the apex.[28] This method provides a precise measurement at an early stage of floral induction but may provide misleading information. Some treatments that do not result in macroscopic floral initiation may cause induction-like swelling of the apex, while other treatments (for example, sugar application) that are fully inductive may partially inhibit both the growth of plants and the increase in size of the apex.

(*b*) By observing the time to floral initiation. This method of analysis provides a good compromise in evaluating both the quantitative and qualitative character of flowering over a period of time. It is most applicable when the time to flowering varies considerably according to genotype and treatment.

(*c*) By observing the percentage of plants sampled that show floral initiation within a given time. This method is most applicable to experiments of relatively short duration which involve treatments that can result in flowering ranging between 0 and 100 per cent.

(*d*) By assigning numbers on a linear scale according to the stage of induction of the apex, for example, 0 representing vegetative and 9 a suitably advanced stage of inflorescence development.[29,30] Thus, apices of plants in different treatments can be assessed when optimally-induced control plants reach stage 9. In this way a null method can be employed (stage 9 showing lack of inhibition), while inhibition of induction is also assessed. This method can indicate very precise differences between treatments (section 8) but is unsuitable when different treatments result in floral initiation that is spread over a protracted period of time.

4 *Effects of Plant Age*

When considering the effects of plant age it should be realized that some genotypes will eventually flower even in continuous light while others will not (Fig.

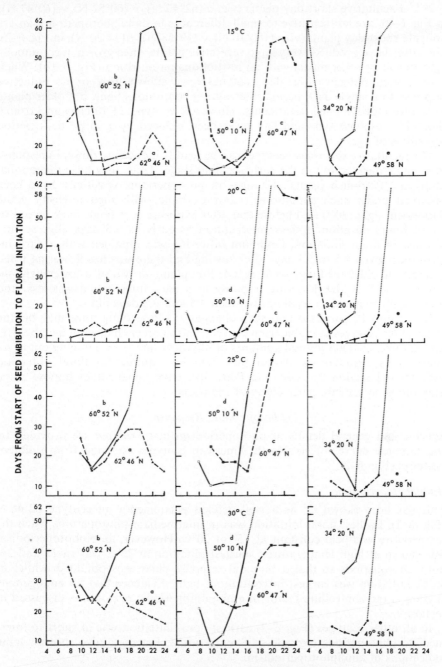

HOURS DAILY PHOTOPERIOD FROM START OF SEED IMBIBITION: 250 FT-C FLUORESCENT

FIGURE 6–2. Photoperiodic response curves for days from seed imbibition to floral initiation in six selections of *C. rubrum* grown at 15°, 20°, 25°, 30°C, in fluorescent light of 250 f.c. intensity. Extension of response curves by dotted line indicates plants were still vegetative in respective photoperiods at 62 days. Missing values at photoperiods < 10 hours indicate that plants died while vegetative (Cumming[10]).

6–2).[10] Facultative short-day plants (viz. *a* (62°46′N), *b* (60°52′N), *c* (60°47′N), in Fig. 6–2), are less sensitive to small differences in daily photoperiod than are obligate short-day plants (viz. *d* (50°10′N), *e* (49°58′N), *f* (34°20′N), in Fig. 6–2). The latter have produced very large vegetative plants when grown in continuous light in soil or other media with no restrictions on nutrition (Fig. 6–1b). When young, such obligate short-day ecotypes have shown little or no inductive response to a single dark period interrupting continuous light, but older plants have responded to such treatments. However, ecotype 34°20′N is an extreme short-day response type and has never been induced by a single dark period regardless of age.

The facultative short-day ecotypes can be readily induced to flower in response to a single dark period in the early seedling stage. Thus, they have exceptional utility as 'Petri-dish plants'. Changes in photoperiodic sensitivity have been observed under such conditions.[11] For example, with high intensity white fluorescent light (3000 f.c.) before and after exposure to a single dark period of 10–14 hours duration, a dark interruption as early as 3.5 days after sowing resulted in floral initiation. Optimum flowering was obtained with a dark interruption given 4.5 to 5.5 days after sowing and there was less flowering when younger or older seedlings were tested. For plants grown at a lower light intensity (600 f.c.), the flowering response to a dark interruption was less, and was largely confined to seedlings between 4.5 and 6.5 days old.

It can only be surmised that such changes at the seedling stage may be due to declining reserves available from the seed and to other changes in metabolism, for example, changes in total amounts of phytochrome,[25] or damping out of an endogenous circadian oscillation that may be required for floral induction (ref. 11 and section 9). Also, the Petri dish environment does impose some limitations on growth, particularly of the roots.

7 Photoperiodic Response

Specific and general details of photoperiodism in *C. rubrum* are provided by the response curves of six North American ecotypes collected from different latitudes (Fig. 6–2).[10]

Ambiphotoperiodism

This has been shown[7,11] as a well defined phenomenon in ecotype 62°46′N (Fig. 6–2). Earliest floral initiation was in intermediate photoperiods when the temperature was held constant at 15° or 20°C. However, ambiphotoperiodism was shown at high temperatures: earliest initiation at 25°C was in 12 and 24-hour photoperiods so that a bimodal response curve was obtained while, at 30°C, initiation was earliest in continuous light. Evidence that an endogenous rhythm is the controlling factor in ambiphotoperiodic response is discussed in section 9.

In all other ecotypes (Fig. 6–2) earliest floral initiation was in short to intermediate photoperiods regardless of temperature, but these also showed some indications of ambiphotoperiodism.

Sensitivity to photoperiod

The most extreme short-day response was shown by the most southern collections. Sensitivity of flowering response to small differences in daily photoperiod was in the order 39°20′N > 49°58′N > 50°10′N > 60°47′N > 60°52′N > 62°46′N.

The ability to flower in a wide range of photoperiods, including extremely long ones, stimulation of floral initiation by one or a few photoperiodic cycles, the rate of stem elongation, the rate of leaf production and the amount of lateral shoot formation were, in general, in the order $62°46'N > 60°52'N > 60°47'N > 50°10'N > 49°58'N > 39°20'N$. Other characteristics correlated with latitude of origin were the size of leaves of similar age and the amount of red pigmentation of leaves and stems, which was greater in plants of more southern origin.

High energy light processes

The occurrence of both first (pre-dark) and second (post-dark) high intensity light processes in the photoperiodic control of flowering induction has been shown by numerous experiments.[11]

Regardless of temperature there was more flowering with high rather than low intensity light preceding and/or following dark periods of different length. Differences attributable to light intensity (600 or 3000 f.c.) were most pronounced when very long dark periods were imposed.[11] The light intensity preceding the dark periods (first high-intensity light process) had a greater effect on flowering than the light period that followed darkness (second high intensity light process).

The effect of light at a range of intensities (incandescent light from 1 to 1000 f.c.) substituted for the last 12 hours of darkness of a 48-hour inductive dark period was examined.[12] A 48-hour dark period resulted in 70 per cent flowering, whereas light of low intensity (1 to 7.5 f.c.) inserted from the 36th to 48th hour completely inhibited flowering. With higher intensities (75–1000 f.c.) there was a low but consistent level of flowering. The differential effects of low versus higher intensity light terminating the dark period may be partly explicable if light of all intensities influenced phytochrome similarly by establishing an intermediate level of P_{fr}, while only the higher intensity light (75 to 1000 f.c.) resulted in significant photosynthesis.

In experiments of Kadman-Zahavi[28] seedlings of *C. rubrum* (49°58'N) were grown on either agar (0.75 per cent) or washed sand, with 2 per cent sucrose. The object of the experiment was to analyze the primary effects of light on flowering, using short exposures in low intensity light to avoid possible complications between photosynthetic and phytochrome controlled reactions. There was no induction either in total darkness or in a daily regime of 3 minutes red light in every hour. In contrast, there was 100 per cent induction in a daily regime of 6 minutes red light in every 30 minutes for 6 hours only and flowering was over 50 per cent with a single daily illumination of 12 minutes. These experiments suggest that, provided sucrose is available, some floral induction can occur without the high intensity light process as such, if phytochrome – P_{fr} is present at a high level (established by red radiation) during part but not all of each 24-hour period.

8 Spectral Dependence

Critical length of dark period

A decisive factor in the stimulation of flowering of *C. rubrum* in normal daily light/dark cycles, at moderate temperatures, is for the dark period to exceed a certain critical length. Flowering also depends partly on the light quality terminating the photoperiod. This was shown[7] when seedlings were exposed to different daily photoperiods which were terminated by light of varying spectral composition (Fig. 6–3). It was found that longer photoperiods were required for optimal floral initiation when the R/FR ratio was lowered for the last 30 minutes (Fig. 6–3) of the daily photoperiods. Low R/FR ratios were inhibitory when terminating daily suboptimal photoperiods, but stimulatory when terminating supra-optimal photoperiods. These results are evidence on the one hand of a requirement for phytochrome-P_{fr} during at least the initial part of each dark period of an inductive cycle, while on the other hand, they indicate that some minimum period of darkness is also required. These dual aspects are explicable if transition from light to darkness results in reversion of P_{fr} to P_r[7,14,29,30] and also sets the phase of an endogenous circadian rhythm[11,14]

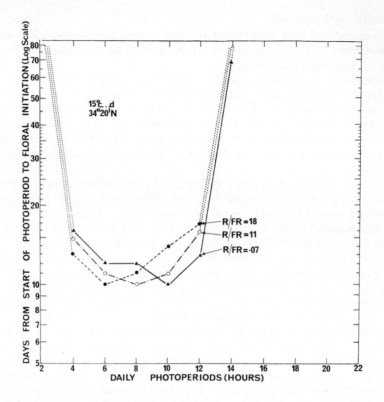

FIGURE 6–3. Response curves of *C. rubrum* (34° 20′N) at 15°C. Main light period, red to far-red (R/FR) spectral energy ratio of 10.3, cool white fluorescent light of 300 f.c. intensity. Terminal 30 minute R/FR ratio of 18, 11 or 0.07. Dotted line: plants remained vegetative (Cumming[7]).

(see section 9). Further evidence of a requirement for P_{fr} was shown in an experiment in which the illumination throughout each photoperiod differed in R/FR ratio (Table 6–1). In two ecotypes (62°46′N, 60°47′N) a low level of P_{fr} maintained by constant light of low R/FR ratio, resulted in earlier floral initiation than did photoperiods of similar R/FR ratio but with a daily dark period. Thus, darkness was not essential for early flowering of these short-day plants and the results suggest a promotive role of P_{fr} throughout a large part of the long photoperiod of low R/FR ratio. This reasoning is based on the assumption that, with photoperiods of any particular R/FR ratio, dark periods of greatest length would result in the most reversion or loss of P_{fr}, and therefore the lowest level of P_{fr} on a time-concentration basis.

The reaction of ecotypes of moderate sensitivity contrasted with those of greater sensitivity. For example, 50°10′N (Table 6–1) required longer dark periods for optimal initiation. The striking feature about this selection was its response in 16-hour photoperiods: flowering was much earlier when the R/FR ratio was decreased. With light of the lowest R/FR ratio 16-hour photoperiods were optimal and initiation was slightly earlier than in the optimal 8-hour photoperiods of higher R/FR ratios. In an ecotype of high sensitivity (49°58′N, Fig. 6.2), maintaining a low level of P_{fr} with far-red light for 70 minutes during the dark period of inductive cycles inhibited flowering,[29] suggesting that P_{fr} must be at a level lower than that maintained by far-red radiation during at least part of the inductive dark period(s). This was corroborated by the fact that several minutes of red radiation, given near the middle of a 16-hour dark period, was inhibitory to flowering, but flowering was re-promoted if red was followed immediately by several minutes of far-red radiation.

TABLE 6–1

Days from start of 8, 16, and 24-hr photoperiods to floral initiation, with red to far-red ratios of 18, 11, and 0.07, respectively, throughout photoperiod. Constant 15°C. Experiment terminated after 100 days* (Cumming[7]).

C. rubrum ecotype	R/FR ratio	Daily photoperiod		
		8 hr	16 hr	24 hr
62° 46′N	18	11	12	51
	11	16	13	40
	0.07	D	39	16
60° 47′N	18	8	17	78
	11	12	13	NF
	0.07	D	19	17
50° 10′N	18	9	62	NF
	11	10	32	84
	0.07	D	8	NF

* NF = no floral initiation. D = dead within 65 days, no floral initiation.

The foregoing results suggest that the differences in flower induction of ecotypes of C. rubrum may be partly explicable if plants with high sensitivity to photoperiod, requiring longer or more inductive dark periods (e.g. 50°N, 49°N, 34°N), have a lower or more restricted requirement for P_{fr}[7] (also section 9). With this in mind, the effects of interrupting dark periods with different spectral irradiations can be discussed more critically.

Level of P_{fr} during darkness

The effects of irradiations in the middle of daily 16-hour inductive dark periods[29,30] have provided estimates of the rates of dark reversion of P_{fr} to P_r in ecotype 49°58′N. The experimental method was based on the assumption that equal induction of flowering in plants, irradiated near the middle of a long night, indicated equality of P_{fr} levels, provided the periods of exposure were short. In one such experiment (Fig. 6–4) different parts of the spectrum in the region of 670–795 nm were tested for repromotion of flowering, following a red irradiation sufficient to keep the control plants completely vegetative. Repromotion of flowering had the lowest energy requirement at about 730–740 nm. With increased radiation time the apparent maximum for repromotion shifted to longer wavelengths (shown by dashed line in Fig. 6–4). For example, the maximum with 0.6 minutes radiation was at 730 nm but with 10 minutes radiation the maximum was at 760 nm. At each wavelength the mean inflorescence stage increased to a maximum and then decreased with increase in far-red exposure.

Flowering in C. rubrum (49°58′N) was suppressed by maintenance of 1–2 per cent of the phytochrome as P_{fr} for an adequate time.[29] For example, when

plants were irradiated in the middle of a 16-hour night with different wavelengths, flowering was lessened as the time of irradiation was increased. Plants
given 738 nm for 4 minutes developed to stage 8.9; those given 16 minutes
developed to stage 8.0; those given 64 minutes developed to stage 0.6. It was
concluded that 16 minutes irradiation at 738 nm increased the P_{fr} level from a
very low (unknown) percentage to the photo-steady state value near 1 per cent.
Exposure at 738 nm for 64 minutes completely inhibited flowering so that a
level of about 1 per cent P_{fr} maintained for 1 hour prevented flowering. Irradiations of 64 minutes at wavelengths beyond 740 nm did not appreciably suppress
flowering.

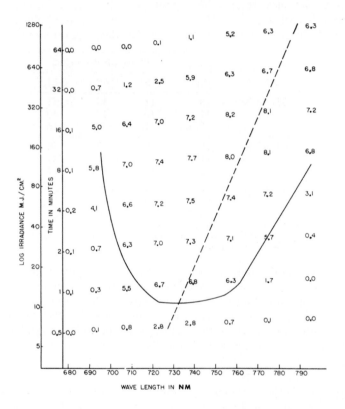

FIGURE 6–4. Effects of irradiation in region 670–795 nm on flowering stage
of *C. rubrum* (49° 58′N) previously exposed to red radiation sufficient for
complete inhibition of flowering. Solid curve gives interpolated position
of reversion from stage 0 to stage 6. Dashed line connects positions of
apparent maximum flowering responses attained for each time of
irradiation (Kasperbauer et al.[29]).

The main thesis of a low percentage of P_{fr} being able to inhibit flowering was
supported in another way. Referring to Figure 6–4, plants were first exposed to
red radiation, potentially stopping flowering by converting phytochrome primarily to P_{fr}. At 738 nm, for example, the absorbancy of P_{fr} was about 250 times
that of P_r; radiation of 738 nm would rapidly reduce the P_{fr} level and in fact
flowering stage 2.8 was potentiated after an exposure of only 0.5 minutes. A
maximum stage of 7.7 was attained after 8 minutes at 738 nm (producing photo-
steady state of ca. 1 per cent P_{fr}). Continued irradiation in 738 nm for 64 minutes
(maintaining ca. 1 per cent P_{fr}) reduced flowering to stage 1.1.

Further results (Table 6–2)[29] showed that similar stages of flowering were obtained after equal periods of treatment (from 10 to 70 minutes) whether P_{fr} was maintained near 2 per cent by continued far-red irradiation, or at about 80 per cent by continued red irradiation, or at 80 per cent P_{fr} by 5 minutes red radiation, followed by darkness that allowed P_{fr} to decay with time until a final 4 minutes far-red established about 2 per cent P_{fr} before the rest of the dark period. The results showed that response was time, not irradiation, dependent, provided that P_{fr} was maintained at 1–2 per cent of total phytochrome. Such a level may have saturated the reaction in which P_{fr} acted, perhaps due to substrate limitation.[29]

TABLE 6–2

Flowering responses of *C. rubrum* (49° 58′N) seedlings to various irradiations of broad band red (R)* and broad band far-red (FR)**, started 0.5 hr before the middle of 16-hour dark periods (Kasperbauer *et al*[29]).

Total duration (min.)	Continuous far-red	R until final 4 min FR	5 min R, dark, final 4 min FR	5 min R, then FR
	(1)	(2)	(3)	(4)
10	8.3	7.9	8.2	8.0
20	7.5	7.3	7.2	7.3
30	6.8	6.5	6.7	6.3
40	5.9	5.4	5.5	5.7
50	3.0	2.7	3.1	2.9
60	1.0	1.2	1.1	0.9
70	0.3	0.3	0.4	0.3

* R = 0.60 mw/cm²   ** FR = 0.75 mw/cm²

Calculations have been made of the rate of dark reversion of P_{fr} based on data of *C. rubrum* (49°58′N).[30] The rates probably do not apply to some other selections differing in photoperiodic response.[7,11,14] In ecotype 49°58′N, the average dark reversion rate, $P_{fr} \rightarrow P_r$, was calculated to be about 1 per cent of the total phytochrome per minute. A short exposure to red radiation, producing about 80 per cent P_{fr}, required about 80 minutes to revert to 2 per cent P_{fr}. P_{fr} was effective throughout the 80 minutes as an inhibitor of flowering.

In view of more recent findings on phytochrome physiology[3,23,45] indicating that far-red irradiation may result in less destruction of P_{fr} as compared with that resulting from red irradiation, it should be borne in mind that results obtained from red and far-red interruptions of inductive dark periods may be subject to some re-interpretation. Furthermore the postulation of the existence of two forms of P_{fr}, one of which is affected markedly by quantum flux density (the other being relatively resistant to irreversible destruction),[45] also bears upon this question and some presently controversial aspects of 'high energy' phenomena in plants.

9 Endogenous Rhythms

Effects of different spectral irradiations during light and darkness

The qualifications noted in the last paragraph (section 8) may apply to any critical interpretation of Konitz's[32] experiments with *Chenopodium amaranticolor*. The significance of these results has tended to remain open to question. Flowering was assayed by measuring changes in apex length (inflorescence development) in response to inductive 24-hour cycles consisting of 14-hour dark periods, alternated with 10-hour daily photoperiods (white fluorescent), that were interrupted by red or far-red radiation during light or darkness. An

important point to note is that the energy levels per unit time were equivalent
for both red and far-red radiation, but the total energy of a particular irradiation
was varied by altering its duration. Unfortunately, this approach may have
confounded low energy phytochrome effects with high energy phenomena.
Without further experimentation it does not seem possible to assess some of the
critical questions raised. Attempts to confirm Konitz's results in *C. amaranticolor* were unsuccessful,[31] but lack of confirmation may have been due to differences in light sources and/or genotypic differences in the plant material.

The objective of Konitz's experiments was to ascertain whether there were
any distinctive changes in response to red and far-red irradiations when these
were given during the skotophile phase (dark period) as compared with the
photophile phase (light period).

When applied during the dark period, 15 minutes of red light inhibited inflorescence development; for complete inhibition more energy (longer duration)
was required at the beginning and towards the end of the dark period than in
the middle. Relatively short periods of irradiation with far-red had no inhibitory
influence during darkness (prolonged periods of far-red alone were not tested).
Far-red reversed the inhibitory effect of short but not prolonged red irradiations,
but when the interval between red and far-red irradiation was increased beyond
60 minutes reversibility by far-red was less pronounced.

When applied during the light period, 3.5 hours of far-red radiation inhibited inflorescence development. To obtain equivalent inhibition of inflorescence development higher total irradiances were required at the beginning and
at the end of the photophile phase than in the middle. The total far-red energy
that was required in the light period for complete inhibition of inflorescence
development was about ten times that of the red radiation required for complete
inhibition during the dark period (i.e. 3.5 hours versus 15 minutes red). Red
radiation interpolated in the light period did not inhibit inflorescence development but it did reverse the effect of far-red.

The question has been asked why white light during the rest of the light period
did not also reverse the far-red effect. The answer may lie in the fact that the
actual red radiation in the white light source was less than that in the red source,
although the white light possessed considerable energy in other parts of the
spectrum. Thus, low and high energy effects of different spectral regions may
have been confounded according to the duration of the different light treatments.

The simplest interpretation of the foregoing results, based partly on findings
from *C. rubrum* that are also discussed here, would be that a high level of P_{fr}
is required for at least a certain period of the photophile phase (particularly at
the mid-point) of inductive cycles.

Phytochrome action during darkness

In two experiments (Fig. 6–5) a dark period of 72 hours was interrupted once,
or preceded with various mixtures of narrow band red and far-red radiation
for either 1 or 2 minutes.[14] The total energy of any radiation mixture was the
same for a given treatment duration (intensity 0.47 mw/cm^2). This type of
experiment assayed for the approximate phytochrome–P_{fr} level at a particular
time by a null-response method depending on determining the percentage of
red: far-red radiation resulting in the same level of flowering as the dark control.
Simultaneous irradiation with red and far-red sources provided intermediate
levels of P_{fr} depending on the intensities of the two sources. The levels for a
phytochrome solution *in vitro* are shown in Fig. 6–6[14] and although these cannot
be applied directly to an *in vivo* situation, due to chlorophyll absorption, they
serve as a guide to the P_{fr} levels attained. The results in Figure 6–5c suggest

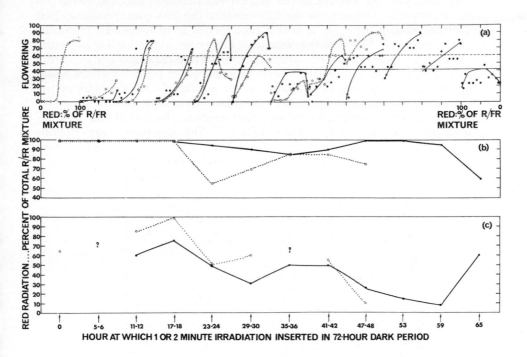

FIGURE 6–5. Flowering of *C. rubrum* (60° 47'N) in response to 1-minute (*solid circle, solid line*) or 2-minute (*open circle, broken line*) exposures of narrow band red and far-red radiation mixtures at one of the indicated times in a 72-hour dark period. Seedlings at start of dark period were aged 4 days (*solid line*) and 4½ days (*broken line*). In (a) horizontal lines are dark controls. In (b) curves are drawn through the percentage red radiation resulting in maximum flowering. In (c) curves are drawn through the percentage red radiation at each time that resulted in the same percentage flowering as the dark controls (after Cumming et al.[14]).

that there was a pronounced decrease in the P_{fr} fraction of phytochrome from the 17th to the 23rd hour of darkness and from the 41st to 47th hour. The times when these pronounced decreases ended were approximately 24 hours apart and corresponded to the approximate times of maximum stimulation of flowering by red radiation shown in Figure 6–5a (approximation because interruptions were based on 6-hr intervals). Since these red-stimulatory periods corresponded with the 1st and 2nd photophile phases of the dark period it is reasonable to speculate that they may also represent the times of maximum availability and utilization of substrate by P_{fr} and consequent reversion or loss of P_{fr}. Estimating from Figure 6–6, at the 17th hour (Fig. 6–5c) about 60 per cent of the phytochrome was P_{fr}, at the 41st hour about 40 per cent, and by the 53rd hour less than 30 per cent.

The indications (Fig. 6–5c) of an increase in endogenous P_{fr} level at about the 35th and again at the 65th hours of darkness that were independent of external irradiation raise a question that requires further investigation. These times coincide with the skotophile phases of the endogenous rhythm. Although the apparent increases were not outside the limits of possible experimental error, the results could be indicative of phytochrome changes other than just reversion of P_{fr} to P_r in darkness.

The failure of any mixture of red and far-red radiation imposed at the 5th hour of darkness to allow flowering equivalent to the dark control suggests that any disturbance of the P_{fr} level at that time tended to be inhibitory. However, it was the higher R/FR ratios that were least inhibitory, indicating a requirement for P_{fr}. It was also evident from other experiments that the reversibility criterion for P_{fr} action could not be satisfactorily applied at the 6th hour of a 12-hour or a 48 hour dark period. For example, in the middle of a 12-hour dark period the complete inhibition by 2 minutes red radiation was only partially reversible by far-red radiation, while a less pronounced inhibition by far-red radiation was almost completely reversible by red radiation.[14] Although these results provide

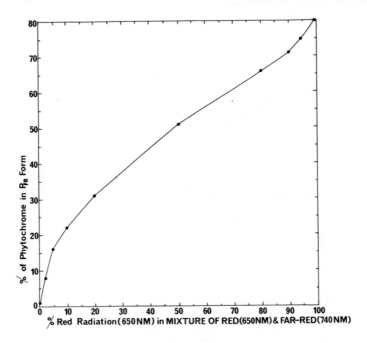

FIGURE 6–6. Phytochrome conversion *in vitro* after irradiation with mixtures of red and far-red radiation on a quantal basis after infinite time (data from Cumming *et al.*[14]).

no sure basis for comment, the simplest interpretation would be that P_{fr} may have a very rapid, and therefore non-reversible, action during this period and/or that the null-balance of P_{fr}/P_r required at this time was more critical than that achieved by the actual irradiations. An alternative explanation would be that an initial interruption with red radiation at this time of darkness results in a destruction of phytochrome-P_{fr} that does not occur when red radiation is preceded by far-red; studies of a different nature have indicated this possibility.[45]

Absence of P_{fr} for various durations from the start of a 48-hr period also affected flowering (Fig. 6–7). Without prior far-red, red radiation at the 3rd to 9th hour, and the 39th to 42nd hour, inhibited flowering. These inhibitory periods were very short compared with the periods of stimulation or non-inhibition. When P_{fr} was very low during the first 12 hours, as a result of initial far-red irradiation, flowering was reduced essentially to zero. Re-establishment of P_{fr} by red irradiation during the first twelve hours of darkness did not stimulate flowering. After this time P_{fr} became stimulatory. Very low P_{fr} until the 20th hour of darkness resulted in about 65 per cent flowering, which was less than that obtained with red radiation without previous far-red. The period of enhancement of flowering above zero, resulting from re-establishment of P_{fr} (after initial far-red), extended from the 15th to the 27th hour – a period corresponding to the interval for enhancing flowering by red radiation. From the 30th hour onwards of the 48–hour dark period, red radiation following initial far-red did not lead to flowering.

The foregoing results have important implications concerning both P_{fr} action and postulated oscillation in substrate for P_{fr} action. First, flowering after a

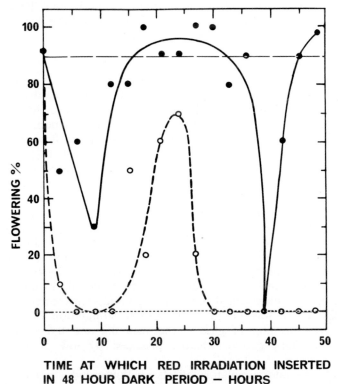

TIME AT WHICH RED IRRADIATION INSERTED IN 48 HOUR DARK PERIOD – HOURS

FIGURE 6–7. Flowering of *C. rubrum* (60° 47′N) in response to a single interruption by 5 minutes of red irradiation given at various times during a 48-hour dark period, either with (*open circle, broken line*) or without (*solid circle, solid line*) 7 minutes of intense far-red irradiation preceding darkness; controls were darkness preceded by white fluorescent light (*long dash*) or 7 minutes intense far-red irradiation (*short dash*) (after Cumming *et al.*[14]).

normally inductive long dark period was completely suppressed by irradiation with far-red at the zero hour, indicating that P_{fr} was required for flowering and did not then appear in darkness in this form by *de novo* synthesis – at least to an extent sufficient to stimulate flowering. Removal of P_{fr} was detectably detrimental to induction at least as late as the 65th hour of a 72-hour dark period (Fig. 6–5a). Second, with initial far-red radiation, followed after various intervals by red radiation, one crucial period when P_{fr} was needed for flowering was seen to be from the 15th to 27th hours of a 48-hour dark period, maximum promotion being near the 24th hour (Fig. 6–7). This can be explained by assuming that despite the effect of far-red radiation in reducing P_{fr} to an extent that potentially suppressed flowering, a rhythmic supply of substrate became available after the 12th hour but was not utilizable for stimulation of flowering after the 30th hour. Third, the similarity of the phasing of the rhythm, with and without initial far-red, strongly implicates the cessation of the high energy light period as setting the phase of the rhythm rather than any change in P_{fr} level. This was corroborated by experiments showing that advancing or retarding the termination of the light period by 6 hours did not change the flowering response; the significant time for phasing was the beginning of darkness when the preceding conditions were continuous light.[14] Fourth, a red irradiation within the 12th to 30th hour (Fig. 6–5a, 6–7) and the 41st to 59th hour (Fig. 6–5a) enhanced flowering above the dark controls. Accordingly, some P_r must have been converted to P_{fr} by red radiation in this period. The P_r must have become available either by *de novo* synthesis or by reversion of P_{fr} to P_r.

Glucose and sucrose effects on circadian rhythm

Although the identity of the substrate involved in P_{fr} action is unknown, more recent findings have implicated sugar(s) in the direct line of control of rhythmic flowering responses. For example, feeding glucose or sucrose either in the light period before darkness,[12] or during the whole of the dark period can enhance and sustain flowering (Fig. 6–8).[11] The rhythmic display of flowering in control plants was much less pronounced with low intensity (600 f.c.) than high intensity (3000 f.c.) light preceding darkness. However, the degree of enhancement of flowering by sugars was more apparent when the light intensity before the dark period was 600 f.c. rather than 3000 f.c. – that is, when the energy supplied by photosynthesis was more limiting;[11] the enhancement by glucose was as much as 90–100 per cent. Significant differences in the effects of glucose and sucrose have been observed. While glucose sustained the rhythmic display of flower induction, sucrose, of equal molarity, sustained a high level of flowering but considerably reduced the amplitude of the oscillations by enhancing flower induction at the normal minima (except at the beginning of darkness – presumably before the sucrose had been taken up and translocated to its area of effectiveness). There was progressively greater stimulation of flowering the higher the concentration of glucose (between 0.2 and 0.6 molar) supplied throughout the dark period, whether preceded by low or high intensity light.[11]

Both inhibitory and stimulatory effects on flower induction have been obtained from glucose application, depending on the time when it was applied during darkness.[11] Glucose caused some inhibition of flowering when applied for only the initial skotophile phase of darkness (0 to 9 hours), but there was no comparable effect of sucrose even though its equivalent molarity (0.6M) represented a higher percentage concentration. Specifically, glucose availability during the 0 to 9th hour of darkness did not significantly influence the first maximum for flowering (9th to 20th hour) but it did reduce the 2nd and 3rd maxima (35th to 55th hour and 65th to 85th hour, respectively). Glucose was stimulatory when applied from the 10th to 19th hour of darkness (first photophile phase), the stimulation being most evident in the position of the 3rd maximum. When glucose was applied from the 24th to 33rd hour of darkness (second skotophile phase) stimulation was evident in the following (second) maximum, after low light, but the 3rd maximum was not enhanced. These results indicate that the non-stimulatory or inhibitory effects of glucose were not expressed in the maximum following application, but in subsequent maxima. Corroborative evidence of these alternately inhibitory and stimulatory effects was evident from the repeated inhibition or lack of stimulation of floral induction that was obtained when glucose was applied in successive skotophile phases of a long inductive (72-hr) dark period; also by the considerable stimulation of induction that resulted from glucose application during the photophile phases.[11] These effects are an obvious parallel with those resulting from red light interruption of darkness (Fig. 6–5, 6–7). The results suggest that for optimal induction there was a stricter requirement or limitation on substrate utilization and/or availability for P_{fr} action during the skotophile than during the photophile phases.

At the 53rd hour of a 72-hour dark period, the proportion of red radiation required to provide flowering equivalent to the dark control was between 10

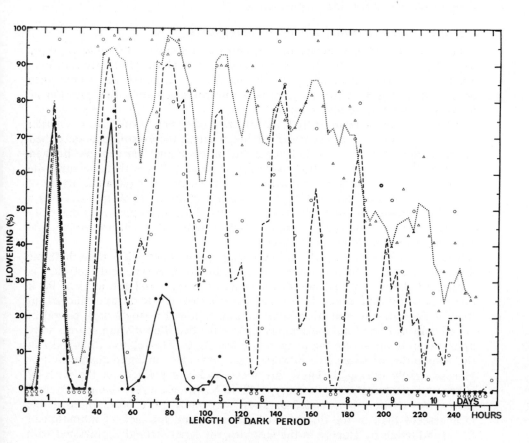

FIGURE 6–8. Percentage flowering of *C. rubrum* (60° 47′N) as affected by the length of a single dark period interrupting continuous cool white fluorescent light, and by glucose or sucrose supplied throughout darkness. *Solid circle, solid line*, Hoagland's solution; *open circle, dashed line*, plus 0.6 M glucose; *open triangle, dotted line* plus 0.6 M sucrose (Cumming[11]).

and 20 per cent (Fig. 6–5c) which should indicate a level of P_{fr} between 20 and 30 per cent – representing a considerable decline from the 12th hour of darkness and strongly indicating reversion of P_{fr} to P_r. As became clearly evident when dark periods were increased beyond 100 hours (Fig. 6–8), substrate was also declining and consequently the amplitude of the oscillations damped out. The glucose and sucrose feeding experiments strongly indicate the importance of sugar metabolism in sustaining rhythmic flower induction. While it is clear that sugars can have direct significance as an energy source, the inhibitory and non-stimulatory effects of glucose on flower induction, depending on its time of application, suggest some direct involvement of glucose in the oscillatory

mechanism controlling flower induction. The weight of evidence of a requirement for some P_{fr} availability during darkness, and the suppressive effect on
induction of its removal even at the 65th hour of a 72-hour dark period (Fig.
6–5a) suggest that some P_{fr} may remain even during 11 days of darkness, since
the oscillation, even though reduced, continued till then. By the end of 11 days
there was considerable growth of the primary apex of seedlings still in darkness,
that were fed either glucose or sucrose, and there was visible floral initiation on
some of the plants provided with sucrose.

Inherited differences in rhythmic flowering responses

Differences in rhythmic flowering responses of different latitudinal ecotypes
have clearly indicated that both the frequency and phase of the rhythm may
differ according to genotype.[11,12] The results are of particular significance
because they suggest a further approach towards elucidating the question of
phytochrome-substrate interactions.

It was concluded above (p. 167) that the rate of reversion of P_{fr} in C. rubrum
(49°58′N) was about 1 per cent per minute, whereas the experiments described
in this section (e.g. Fig. 6–5) indicate a rate of less than 1 per cent per hour in
60°47′N. A tentative suggestion made for 49°58′N[29,30] was that the substrate
supply could be limiting for P_{fr} action, as shown by the equivalent action of
about 1 per cent of the total phytochrome maintained for 80 minutes and a
single established level of 80 per cent P_{fr}. Thus, different populations may vary
greatly in the level and rate of supply of substrate for phytochrome action, and
accordingly in their flowering response.[14]

The results in Figure 6–9[11] strongly support the contention that rhythmic
flowering responses differ considerably according to genotype and that there is
a critical balance required between available substrate and the level of P_{fr} if
flower induction is to occur. Either incandescent (low R/FR ratio) or fluorescent
(high R/FR ratio) illumination preceded and followed a single dark period of
varied duration; the total incident energies of the two illumination sources were
approximately the same; the temperature was 25°C. The relative differences in
the amplitudes of successive maxima, that depended on light quality and/or
glucose supply during darkness, are most readily explained on the basis of
substrate/P_{fr} interactions. In ecotype 62°46′N, for example, damping out of
the control rhythm in extended darkness was much more pronounced in the
incandescent than in the fluorescent light series and the lack of inhibition of
flower induction by glucose in the incandescent series strongly contrasted with
the glucose inhibition in the fluorescent series. These differences are most
readily explicable if incandescent light, by establishing a lower P_{fr} level also
resulted in less availability or utilization of substrate (glucose or other sugars).
The faster damping out of flowering in the incandescent series also suggests
that extended darkness resulted in a suboptimal P_{fr} level.

The pronounced stimulation of flower induction in 60°47′N and 50°10′N
contrasted strongly with the inhibition observed in 62°46′N (fluorescent series).
In both 60°47′N and 50°10′N the relative differences in the amplitudes of the
successive maxima that depended on light quality are explicable on the basis of
substrate/P_{fr} interactions. Ecotype 50°10′N showed evidence of a more critical
interaction between substrate and P_{fr}, for attainment of flower induction, than
either 62°46′N or 60°47′N. Ecotype 50°10′N has also been demonstrated[7] as
more sensitive than either 60°47′N or 62°46′N to changes both in the length of
the daily photoperiod (Fig. 6–2) and the red to far-red spectral energy ratio of
either the entire daily photoperiod (Table 6–1) or the terminal part of each
photoperiod;[7] it is also less readily induced by a single dark period.[7]

Indications of an effect on phasing as a function of substrate/P_{fr} balance were shown in ecotype 62°46′N (fluorescent series), the curve for 0.4M glucose being the reciprocal of the control, except in darkness of short duration. If substrate availability or utilization was greatest in the photophile phases, then a supra-

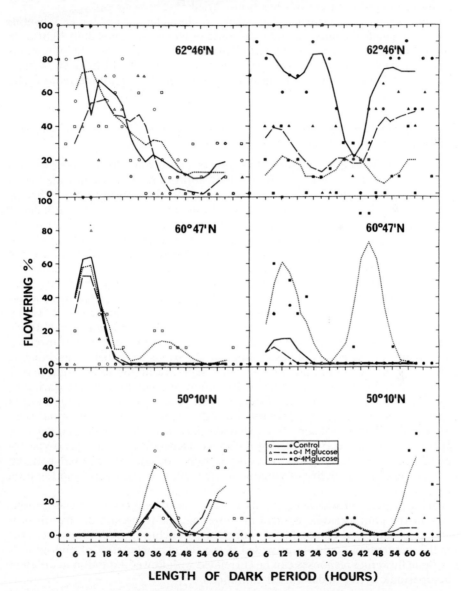

FIGURE 6–9. Percentage flowering of *C. rubrum*, ecotypes 62° 46′N, 60° 47′N, 50° 10′N, at constant 25°C. Either incandescent or fluorescent light preceding and following single dark period; 0 to 0.4 M glucose supplied throughout darkness (Cumming[11]).

optimal concentration of glucose could be most inhibitory during such phases and be reflected by a change in phase of the oscillation. In ecotype 60°47′N, when 0.4M glucose was available during darkness (Fig. 6–8), the phase of the second maximum in the incandescent series (at 39th hour of darkness) was more advanced than that in the fluorescent series (at 45th hour of darkness) although the phases of the first maximum were equivalent (*ca.* 12th hour).

Support for the above conclusions has also been obtained in preliminary experiments in which only the red/far-red ratio of the light immediately preceding prolonged dark periods has been varied.[12]

There is increasing evidence that inherited characteristics of the endogenous clock do regulate the photoperiodic response of plants in normal daily light/dark cycles. For example, the unusual periodicity in ecotype 62°46′N with indications of three different frequencies (i.e. periodicity of *ca.* 3–4 hr, 12 hr, and 24 hr)[11] can be correlated with its ambiperiodic response in daily photoperiodic cycles (Fig. 6–2).

Interpretation of rhythmic flowering responses. A working hypothesis of substrate availability and phytochrome action

Experimental findings of rhythmic flowering responses and phytochrome control in *C. rubrum* led to the postulation[14] that floral induction is controlled by a product of the enzymatic action of the far-red absorbing form of phytochrome (P_{fr}) on a single but unknown substrate. In acting, P_{fr} reverts to the inactive form P_r, or is changed from the P_{fr} form in some other way. The available substrate, if not utilized by P_{fr} action, may soon be depleted by other reactions. The substrate for P_{fr} action is low during the skotophile but high during the photophile phase. The significant time for phasing is the beginning of darkness. The initial substrate supply appears to be derived from the preceding light period but some time in the region of the 9th to 12th hour of darkness a significant rhythmic change of substrate starts up. The dependence of flowering on the time that darkness is interrupted by light is directly related to a rhythmic change in the optimum P_{fr} level required for the processes leading to flowering. To account for the effects of sugars applied at various times before and during darkness, it has also been postulated[11] that sugar formation in the light period is involved in providing substrate for P_{fr} action or mediation during darkness. Phytochrome-P_{fr} acts as a type of master gate, pacemaker, or valve, and exerts some control over sugar availability and utilization. Damping out of an oscillation and failure to flower after extended dark periods is a consequence of depletion of sugar reserves during darkness. Depending on the genotype involved, and the environmental conditions, some balance is required between the endogenous availability of glucose or other sugar derivative(s) and the level of phytochrome-P_{fr}.

On the question of whether a significant role can be assigned to an endogenous clock in the photoperiodic control of flowering, the foregoing discussion provides considerable evidence for an affirmative conclusion. Additional support for this contention could be provided if specific characteristics of endogenous rhythmic flowering responses can be correlated with flower induction in different photoperiodic cycles under varied conditions.

Another question that merits further attention is whether the time-dependent changes in sensitivity to photoinduction (p. 162) are indicative of changes in oscillatory properties that may control flower induction. If lack of flower induction in *C. rubrum*, after a prolonged period in constant conditions, is indicative of damping out of an oscillation controlling flowering, then a suitable perturbation such as a single short dark period, may elicit not only flower induction but also its rhythmic display in a subsequent prolonged dark period. Preliminary experiments[12] suggest that this is so and provide a further indication that the endogenous clock can be a basic timekeeper in photoperiodism.

Effects of ethanol and the possible significance of membrane changes

Inhibition of floral initiation has been obtained by applying dilute solutions of ethyl alcohol or ethanol vapour to seedlings of *C. rubrum* (60°47′N) during a long inductive dark period. Concentrations as low as 0.01 per cent were inhibitory when applied during the first 9 hours of darkness or during the 24th to 33rd hour. However, 0.2M sucrose added with the ethanol at that time resulted in a flowering level equal to that from sucrose alone. Glucose was less effective in overcoming alcohol inhibition.

11 Photoperiodic Inhibition

Long days can have a negating effect on the flowering of short-day plants, not only by preventing flowering (when continuously applied) but also when interspersed in a run of inductive short days. Earlier work of Lona[35,36,37] on *Chenopodium amaranticolor* should be mentioned here: flowering occurred in long days when plants were defoliated and supplied with sugar (defoliated plants flowered in short days without sugar feeding). Although Lona interpreted these results as evidence for anti-florigenic substances produced in long days, Lang[33] has pointed out that these results could be explained by assuming that, in the presence of adequate substrates, stem tissue of *C. amaranticolor* can produce small amounts of florigen even in long days, but, in intact plants, these are prevented (by the solute stream coming from the mature leaves) from reaching the apex. Schwabe[41] has studied this effect in *C. amaranticolor* from the viewpoint that each photoperiodic cycle should be considered in relation to other possible inhibitory as well as promotive conditions. These comments have even greater validity now, in view of the findings on endogenous circadian rhythms, particularly the fact that most endogenous rhythms are not phased to exactly 24 hours. Thus a photoinductive short day may result in rephasing that is then changed by a subsequent long day.

In Schwabe's experiments, plants were given a range of continuous short-day inductive cycles to provide a calibration curve for degree of flowering according to number of inductive cycles. Other plants were given a certain number of short days which were separated by different numbers of symmetrically intercalated long days. Long days interposed between the short days reduced the level of flowering as compared with that occurring after an equivalent number of uninterrupted short days. Interpolation of 24 hours darkness after each long day reduced flowering more than its interpolation after each short day.

It is difficult to interpret these results more fully without further information as to the effects of light in rephasing any endogenous rhythm that may have been influencing the level of flowering.

13 Effects of Temperature

The photoperiodic responses of different latitudinal ecotypes of *C. rubrum* in a range of constant temperatures are shown in Figure 6–2.

The responses of different ecotypes to changes in red/far-red spectral energy ratios terminating daily photoperiods, suggested that the rate of dark reversion or loss of P_{fr} is greater at higher temperatures.[7] Thus, in the ambiphotoperiodic response of *C. rubrum* (62°46′N) (Fig. 6–2), if dark reversion was faster at 30°C than at lower temperatures, and/or if there was a requirement for a higher level of P_{fr} with increase in temperature, then even short periods of darkness could result in sub-optimal P_{fr}. This interpretation has been supported by the fact that initiation was later in long photoperiods that had a low rather than high terminal R/FR ratio.[7]

14 Effects of Mineral Nutrition

When seeds of *C. rubrum* were provided with 0.2 per cent potassium nitrate from the start of imbibition, germination and growth were stimulated, but the inductive effects of a single dark period were generally reduced. Such effects may have been mediated through the carbohydrate:nitrogen ratio but no critical conclusions could be drawn.[12]

Mineral nutrition effects on induction have been approached more directly in *Chenopodium foetidum* – a day-neutral species.[10] In this species, there is greater phenotypic plasticity in response to nutrition because there are not the over-riding effects of extreme photoperiodic sensitivity that tend to be decisive in *C. rubrum*.

C. foetidum can flower as a very small seedling in all daily photoperiods, whether short or long, producing only 2 to 4 primary leaves when nutrition is strictly limited, but, with adequate nutrition, extremely large plants can be produced. In sand culture experiments, flowering was progressively delayed and the primary stem leaf number was greater with increase in concentration between 0.1 and full strength Hoagland's solution.[4]

17 Grafting Experiments

Leaf and stem (wedge) grafting and stem approach grafting have been made between *C. rubrum* 60° 47'N and 34° 20'N on a limited scale. Some floral induction was obtained on defoliated stocks of 34° 20'N, in non-inductive long daylengths, when grafted with induced leafy stem scions of 60° 47'N.

18 Effects of Growth Substances and Growth Retardants

Abscisin stimulation of flowering in non-inductive photoperiods

Seedlings of *C. rubrum* (origin uncertain, probably 49° 58'N) were grown in Petri dishes in continuous light at 20°C, and supplied with half-strength Hoagland's solution. After four weeks, the seedlings were transferred to filter paper in small crystallization dishes and supplied with an aqueous solution of abscisin (4 p.p.m.) for 7 days; control seedlings were supplied only with water.[15,16] All seedlings were then transferred to the original conditions. Although growth was slow, about 50 per cent of the abscisin-treated seedlings had flowered after 6 weeks, while the water-treated controls remained completely vegetative. This experiment was repeated and confirmed.

In further experiments, with larger plants of *C. rubrum* grown in pots in the greenhouse, abscisin was either sprayed on the leaves, fed through a lip of tissue cut in the stem, or applied to the roots of plants grown in sand. None of these treatments caused floral induction.

Kinetin and uracil

Seeds of *C. rubrum* (49° 58'N) were germinated and grown at 25°C aseptically *in vitro* on modified White's medium adjusted to pH 5 and including 5 per cent sucrose and 0·8 per cent agar.[39] Different concentrations of either kinetin (0-15 mg/1) or uracil (0–150 mg/1) were added to the medium after germination to avoid inhibitory effects on germination. In short days, floral induction occurred within 10 days without any significant effect of kinetin concentration. In long days, there was some flowering within 39 days with 5 to 15 mg/l kinetin although the control plants were completely vegetative; stimulation was as high as 50 per cent after 44 days with 10 mg/l kinetin.

With uracil added, floral induction occurred after 12 days in short days without any significant effect of uracil concentration. In long days there was stimulation of flowering within 27 days with 50 and 75 mg/l uracil and the subsequent level of induction was 40 per cent and 52 per cent respectively within 42 days; none of the other uracil concentrations stimulated flowering.

Effects of CCC and GA₃

Effects of CCC and GA$_3$

C. rubrum (60° 47'N) was grown in Knop's nutrient solution. The growth retardant CCC was added to the nutrient solution while GA$_3$ was applied to the apical bud during four daily photo-inductive cycles interrupting non-inductive continuous low intensity light.[42] CCC concentrations of 2.10^{-3} and 10^{-3} M delayed flowering but did not inhibit it completely. GA$_3$ also delayed flowering even when applied at low concentrations of 0.1–0.05 mg/l. When plants were treated simultaneously with 2.10^{-3} M CCC and low concentrations of GA$_3$ (e.g. 0.05 mg/l) inhibitory effects normally obtained from their separate application were not apparent and flowering was equal to that of the controls.

In other experiments CCC and GA$_3$ were applied at different times with respect to the 4-day inductive treatments. There was no apparent difference in sensitivity to CCC whether plants received it during the 4 days or only the latter 2 days of the inductive cycles, or 2 or 4 days later. However, GA$_3$ inhibited flowering more strongly when applied during the whole 4 days of induction rather than in only the last 2 days, or after induction.

As CCC is considered to interfere with biosynthesis of GA$_3$, it might be expected that endogenous gibberellins may be lowered in response to CCC. The endogenous levels of gibberellins in shoot apices of induced and non-induced plants have been assayed by thin layer chromatography. Preliminary experiments have shown that considerable changes in the amount and the Rf of gibberellin-like substances can occur in the apex.

19 Effects of Metabolic Inhibitors

If synthesis of nucleic acids is involved in floral induction, then the application of analogues of components or precursors of nucleic acids during photoperiodic induction may inhibit floral induction by disturbing nucleic acid synthesis.

Teltscherová *et al.*[43] have studied the effects of 10^{-5} to 10^{-2} M 6-azauracil and 2-thiouracil applied to *C rubrum* (60° 47'N) at different times before, during, or at the end of photoinductive cycles. After germination, seedlings were maintained in continuous low intensity fluorescent light at 21°C. A water culture method with half-strength Knop's solution was used; the metabolic inhibitors were added separately in Knop's solution for designated periods.

Floral initiation was completely blocked by 10^{-4}M 6-azauracil and 2-thiouracil. Inhibition could still be observed at concentrations ten times lower; similar results were obtained when the analogues were applied to the apical buds of seedlings. Inhibition was significantly greater when the analogues were applied either four days before or during the inductive cycles than four days after. The analogues affected vegetative growth, mainly by suppressing apical dominance, but there were also malformations and chlorosis of young leaves. The potential effects of 6-azauracil and 2-thiouracil on floral induction and vegetative growth were reversible by the nucleic acid metabolites uracil and uridine, suggesting that metabolic inhibitors influenced the metabolism of RNA. The greater effectiveness of treatments given before and at the beginning of induction is subject to two interpretations[43]: either, the analogues may have interfered with inductive processes taking place in the leaves, that is, with the formation or translocation of the floral stimulus; or, the analogues may have brought about changes in the apical meristem negating the response to stimulation coming from the leaves. The second alternative was favored[43] in view of the inhibitory effects on induction that resulted from the application of analogues in low concentration to the apex. The difficulty of distinguishing between effects on growth *per se* (which can influence the visible expression of floral induction), as compared with specific effects on floral induction, was evident from the fact that no concentration could be found that affected floral induction without influencing the growth of vegetative parts of the plant. However, in more recent work[42] 2-thiouracil at a concentration of 10^{-5}M or lower, primarily affected development (floral initiation) while the effects on vegetative growth were negligible.

Other preliminary work[40] has involved the application of a large number of anti-metabolites and other inhibitors to seedlings in various concentrations and at various times prior to and after an inductive dark period. The following compounds, when added as a 0.027 ml drop to cotyledons at the beginning of a 13-hour dark period reduced the percentage flowering of plants; hydroxyproline (10^{-2}M) reduced the percentage flowering from 90 per cent (controls) to 50 per cent, with no effect on dry weight or plant appearance; 6-azauridine (10^{-4} to 10^{-2}M) reduced flowering to between 60 per cent and 10 per cent with no effect on dry weight or plant appearance; DL-para-fluorophenylalanine ($2 - 5 \times 10^{-2}$M) resulted in 40 to 70 per cent inhibition of flowering, there was no chlorosis or necrosis but growth was inhibited; puromycin (10^{-4} and 10^{-5}M) inhibited flowering but growth was also slightly inhibited. The effects obtained according to time of application were too variable to draw definite conclusions.

Some effects of actinomycin D and 2-thiouracil on floral induction in *Chenopodium amaranticolor*[46] complement the foregoing results with *C. rubrum*. *C. amaranticolor* plants were grown in long days and then exposed to one or more 16-hour dark periods when plants were 40–50 days old. Solutions of either actinomycin D or 2-thiouracil, at a concentration of 500 µg/ml or less, were applied to plants by means of a micro-syringe introduced into a slit that was cut vertically in the stem immediately below the apical bud. Inhibition was measured by suppression of apex elongation following one inductive dark period. The lowest concentrations giving full inhibition were *ca.* 20 µg actinomycin D per plant and *ca.* 30 µg 2-thiouracil per plant. Suppression of apex elongation was correlated with suppression of floral development at a later stage.

Although both actinomycin D and 2-thiouracil inhibited floral initiation when applied before the end of an inductive dark period, their effects differed if application was delayed beyond the end of inductive darkness. The resistance of induced plants to actinomycin D rose rapidly after an inductive dark period, whereas 2-thiouracil influenced floral development whether applied before, during or as late as 10 days after an inductive dark period.

20 Florigenic Extracts

A substance 'E' not considered to be specifically an auxin or gibberellin but capable of stimulating germination, growth, and flowering of various test objects, was isolated by Harada[22] from a number of species, including *C. rubrum* (49° 58′N). The amount of substance E that was extracted from a given weight of apical tissues, from plants grown in non-inductive 17-hour photoperiods, stimulated oat mesocotyl elongation more than the comparable extract from plants grown in inductive 10-hour photoperiods. It is an open question whether substance E was anything other than a gibberellin.

21 Induction of Excised Apices

de Fossard[17,18] has been culturing stem tips of *C. rubrum* (34° 20′N), a qualitative short-day plant (Fig. 6–2) as a technique to study flower initiation *in vitro* without the complexities imposed by stems and roots. One major purpose of these studies is to investigate the feasibility of using stem tip cultures as a bioassay for florigen. The reasoning behind this approach is that attempts to isolate florigen may fail either because of chemical difficulties (e.g. extremely small quantities of florigen, instability during extraction) or because of difficulties associated with the biological assay for florigen.

de Fossard began with a complex medium based on the major elements of Knop's solution, the minor elements of Torrey's medium, and the growth factors of the medium devised by Murashige and Skoog. Callus alone was obtained when stem tips were placed on this medium but organized growth was obtained when IAA was omitted; flowers were initiated in a few cultures when growth factors were excluded.

22 Chemical, Histochemical, and Ultrastructural Changes at Induction

When ^{32}P-labelled RNA, isolated from induced buds of C. amaranticolor, was treated with ribonuclease or alkali, a ^{32}P-labelled component was detected which was not present in non-induced buds.[46] It should be noted, however, that this determination was made after 12 short-day inductive cycles, by which time differentiation would have been well advanced so that changes in RNA not specifically related to induction per se might also have occurred. Both actinomycin D and 2-thiouracil applied to plants before the end of the inductive dark period appeared to inhibit the production of this ^{32}P-labelled component. Lability of this component to alkali suggested that it was RNA, while its resistance to ribonuclease indicated it was not single-stranded RNA, suggesting that this component represented DNA-RNA hybrids. Messenger RNA production may be an early step in floral differentiation and the existence of DNA-RNA hybrids following induction may reflect the production of new floral messenger RNA's in the induced buds. Watson and Matthews[46] reasoned that failure of actinomycin D to inhibit floral differentiation when applied after inductive darkness could have resulted from its inability to bind to the DNA-RNA segment controlling differentiation; or, alternatively, inductive darkness may have allowed or induced synthesis of new messenger RNA, or new protein, which initiated an irreversible event locking the cell into floral differentiation. Binding of actinomycin D to DNA before induction could prevent synthesis of m-RNA and hence inhibit initiation.

A histochemical study of flower induction of C. album[19,20,21] merits discussion here because there have been no comparable investigations on C. rubrum.

All plants were past the early seedling stage when studied for changes occurring during the transition of an apex from the vegetative to floral stage, brought about by transferring plants from long to short days. Upon photoinduction, cell division increased throughout the apex and the histological zonation characteristic of the vegetative apex was gradually replaced by an outer uniformly stained mantle of 3 or 4 cell layers which enclosed a core of potential pith. The nucleoli of cells on the sides of the shoot apex and in the upper corpus enlarged, approaching the size of those in the tunica. The cells of the apex became more uniform, vacuoles were smaller and fewer in number in the tunica. With increase in the number of photoinductive cycles experienced by the plant, starch grains tended to disappear from the apex although persisting in leaf primordia and in the rib meristem, but after seven short days starch grains reappeared in the apex of the terminal flower of the inflorescence.

Mercuric bromophenol blue did not reveal any difference in protein in the various zones of the vegetative apex but the protein concentration of the apex became much greater after four short days; the increase was most apparent in the cytoplasm. After six short days there was a decrease in protein content.

The Feulgen reaction demonstrated the presence of large, lighter-staining nuclei in cells of the tunica near the summit of vegetative apices. After two short days the zone of lighter-staining nuclei became more extensive, indicative of increased mitosis; these cells reached maximum mitotic activity during the fourth inductive day.

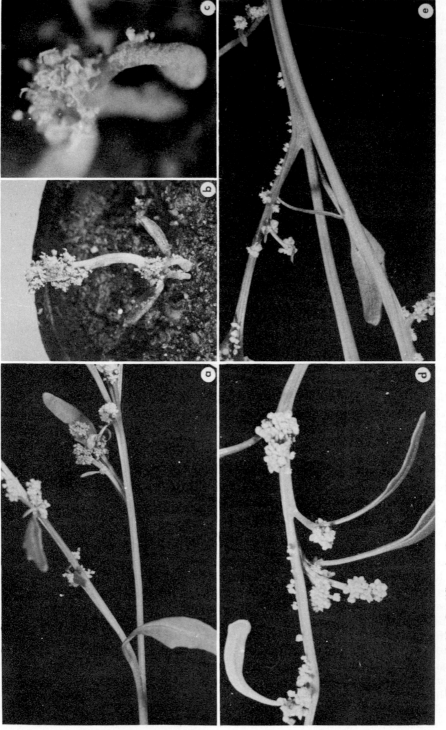

FIGURE 6–10. Cauliflory in *C. rubrum* (62° 46′N). (a). undamaged stems with inflorescence formation only in axils of leaves; (b). adventitious floret formation on cotyledon (plant grown from X-irradiated seed); (c). magnified view of (b); (d). and (e). adventitious floret formation on internode surface arising from area where surface cells were removed.

Histone

The staining reaction for histone (basic fast green) matched that of the Feulgen reaction (DNA) during the early stages of induction. However, from the fifth short day onwards there was a marked decrease in histone staining but no detectable change in DNA staining. This work still requires confirmation and elaboration.

RNA

This was distributed rather uniformly in cells of the vegetative apex; leaf buttresses and leaf primordia were somewhat higher in RNA concentration than the axial cells of the shoot apex. After two short days there was a definite increase in RNA concentration of cells in the apex, and this became more pronounced in all cells with progressive increase of photoinduction. [32]P autoradiography also indicated that the rate of nucleic acid synthesis increased in shoot apices of plants subjected to inductive photoperiods.

23 Inflorescence Differentiation

When plants of *C. rubrum* are induced in the early cotyledonary stage there is virtually no inflorescence to differentiate, except one or a few florets (Fig. 6–1). On larger plants the first flowers, which are generally formed in clusters (glomerules), are initiated on the primary and lateral shoot apices as spiked panicles (Fig. 6–10). More flower clusters are progressively differentiated basipetally as a result of the growth of lateral shoots at the lower nodes. In barely-inductive photoperiods the inflorescence panicles are much sparser and single florets may be borne on short panicles, or single aborted florets may be borne at scattered locations on the stem with oversize bract-like perianth members (moderate proliferation).

Cauliflory

An unusual occurrence of cauliflory has been obtained in *C. rubrum* (62° 46′N). Normally, in *C. rubrum*, inflorescences are only initiated from nodes subtended by a leaf (Fig. 6–10a). It was found in *C. rubrum* (62° 46′N) that when a young stem was damaged by rupturing the epidermis (presumably impeding translocation in that area) callus formation in the areas of damage was frequently followed by adventitious floret formation on the internodes in some of the damaged areas (Fig. 6–10d).[12] In another experiment a seedling of *C. rubrum* (62° 46′N) grown from seed subjected to X-irradiation (dosage 15 kR) produced adventitious florets on the cotyledon surface (Fig. 6–10b, c).[12]

These results are mentioned because out of the many plants of different ecotypes of *C. rubrum* that have been grown, this type of cauliflory has only been observed in ecotype 62° 46′N, and it is this genotype which will flower most readily in the widest range of photoperiods and temperatures (Fig. 6–2). The question arises whether this cauliflory is indicative of a high level of florigen present in the tissues. Such florigen might be capable of bringing about re-differentiation of tissue in a far more determinate fashion than normally occurs.

Occurrence of this phenomenon suggests that 62° 46′N may provide very useful material for *in vitro* investigations of floral induction in tissues other than organized apical primordia, such as stem segments or undifferentiated callus.

REFERENCES

[1] Butler, W. L. (1960). Some photochemical properties of phytochrome. In *Proc. 3rd Int. Cong. Photobiol.*, 569. Eds. B. C. Christensen and B. Buchmanns. Elsevier, Amsterdam.

[2] Calder, J. A. and Kukkonen, I. (1960). Personal Communication. Plant Research Institute, Ottawa.

[3] Clarkson, D. T. and Hillman, W. S. (1967). Stability of phytochrome concentration in dicotyledonous tissues under continuous far-red light. *Planta* **75**, 286.

[4] Cohen, A. S. and Cumming, B. G. Unpublished Results. Department of Botany, The University of Western Ontario, London, Canada.

[5] Cumming, B. G. (1959). Extreme sensitivity of germination and photoperiodic reaction in the genus *Chenopodium* (Tourn.) L. *Nature* **184**, 1044.

[6] Cumming, B. G. (1961). Photoperiodic response in the genus *Chenopodium* as related to geographical distribution. *Plant Physiol. Suppl.* **36**, li.

[7] Cumming, B. G. (1963). Evidence of a requirement for phytochrome-P_{fr} in the floral initiation of *Chenopodium rubrum. Can. J. Bot.* **41**, 901.

[8] Cumming, B. G. (1963). The dependence of germination on photoperiod, light quality, and temperature, in *Chenopodium* spp. *Can. J. Bot.* **41**, 1211.

[9] Cumming, B. G. (1963). Environment and the genus *Chenopodium*. In *Research Problems in Biology*, 19. Investigations for Students. Series 4, Anchor Books, Doubleday, N.Y.

[10] Cumming, B. G. (1967). Early-flowering plants. In *Methods in Developmental Biology*, 277. Eds. F. Wilt and N. Wessells. Thomas Y. Crowell Co., N.Y.

[11] Cumming, B. G. (1967). Circadian rhythmic flowering responses in *Chenopodium rubrum* L.: effects of glucose and sucrose. *Can. J. Bot.* **45**, 1105.

[12] Cumming, B. G. Unpublished results.

[13] Cumming, B. G. and Frankton, C. (1965). Response of some North American species of the genus *Chenopodium* (Tourn.) L. to daylength. *Res. Rept. Canada Agric. Nat. Weed Committee, Eastern Section*, 95.

[14] Cumming, B. G. ,Hendricks, S. B. and Borthwick, H. A. (1965). Rhythmic flowering responses and phytochrome changes in a selection of *Chenopodium rubrum. Can. J. Bot.* **43**, 825.

[15] El-Antably, H. M. M. and Wareing, P. F. (1966). Stimulation of flowering in certain short-day plants by abscisin. *Nature* **210**, 328.

[16] El-Antably, H. M. M., Wareing, P. F. and Hillman, J. (1967). Some physiological responses to D, L Abscisin (Dormin). *Planta* **73**, 74.

[17] de Fossard, R. A. (1967). Flower initiation in axenic cultures of stem tips of *Chenopodium rubrum* L. *Austral. J. Sci.* **29**, 427.

[18] de Fossard, R. A. (1967). Personal Communication. Department of Botany, University of New England, Armidale, Australia.

[19] Gifford, E. M. and Tepper, H. B. (1961). Ontogeny of the inflorescence in *Chenopodium album. Amer. J. Bot.* **48**, 657.

[20] Gifford, E. M. and Tepper, H. B. (1962). Histochemical and autoradiographic studies of floral induction in *Chenopodium album. Amer. J. Bot.* **49**, 706.

[21] Gifford, E. M. and Tepper, H. B. (1962). Ontogenetic and histochemical changes in the vegetative shoot tip of *Chenopodium album. Amer. J. Bot.* **49**, 902.

[22] Harada, H. (1962). Étude des substances naturelles de croissance en relation avec la floraison. Isolement d'une substance de montaison. *Rév. Gen. Botan.* **69**, 201.

[23] Hartmann, K. M. (1966). A general hypothesis to interpret high energy phenomena of photomorphogenesis on the basis of phytochrome. *Photochem. Photobiol.* **5**, 349.

[24] Herron, J. W. (1952). Study of seed production, seed identification, and seed germination of *Chenopodium* species. *Cornell Univ., Agric. Expt. Sta., Ithaca, N.Y.*, 1.

[25] Hillman, W. S. (1967). The physiology of phytochrome. *Ann. Rev. Plant Physiol.* **18**, 301–324.

[26] Hoagland, D. R. and Arnon, D. I. (1939). The water culture method for growing plants without soil. *Circ. Calif. Agr. Expt. Sta.* **327**, 1.

[27] Hollis, C. A. (1965). Personal communication. Duquesne University, Pittsburgh, Pennsylvania, U.S.A.

[28] Kadman-Zahavi, A. (1961). The growth of plants under very low light intensities. *Proc. 4th Congress of Scient. Societies*, 153. Rehovoth, April, 1961. Botan. Soc. Israel.

[29] Kasperbauer, M. J., Borthwick, H. A. and Hendricks, S. B. (1963). Inhibition of flowering of *Chenopodium rubrum* by prolonged far-red radiation. *Bot. Gaz.* **124**, 444.

[30] Kasperbauer, M. J., Borthwick, H. A. and Hendricks, S. B. (1964). Reversion of phytochrome 730 (P_{fr}) to P_{660} (P_r) assayed by flowering in *Chenopodium rubrum. Bot. Gaz.* **125**, 75.

31 Kofranek, A. M. and Sachs, R. M. (1964). Effect of far-red illumination during the photoperiod on floral initiation of *Chenopodium amaranticolor*. *Amer. J. Bot.* **51**, 520.

32 Könitz, W. (1958). Blühhemmung bei Kurztagpflanzen durch Hellrot- und Dunkelrotlicht in der photo- und skotophilen Phase. *Planta* **51**, 1.

33 Lang, A. (1965). Physiology of flower initiation. In *Encycl. Plant Physiol.* XV/I, 1380. Ed. W. Ruhland. Springer-Verlag, Berlin.

34 Lona, F. (1947). L'influenza delle condizioni esterne durante l'embriogenesi in *Chenopodium amaranticolor* Coste et Reyn. Sulle qualita germinative dei semi e sul vigore delle plantule che ne derivano. *Lavori di botanica*, 324. G. Gola Jubilee Vol. Padova, Italy.

35 Lona, F. (1948). La fioritura della brevidiurna *Chenopodium amaranticolor* Coste et Rein, coltivata in soluzione nutritizia con saccarosio, in assenza di stimolo fotoperiodico euflorigeno. *Nuova Giorn. Botan. Ital.* **55**, 559.

36 Lona, F. (1949). La fioritura delle brevidiurne a notte continua. *Nuova Giorn. Botan. Ital. N.S.* **56**, 479.

37 Lona, F. (1950). Il significato dei glucidi e del fattore nutiflorigeno nel meccanismo di fioritura delle piante erbacee ed in particolare delle brevidiurne. *Rendic. Ist. Lombardo Sci. e. Lette.*, *Cl. di Sci.* **83** (Ser. III, 14). 1.

38 Miller, C. O. (1965). Evidence for the natural occurrence of zeatin and derivatives: compounds from maize which promote cell division. *Proc. Nat. Acad. Sci. U.S.* **54**, 1052.

39 Narusako, H. and Nakayama, S. (1966). Flowering of Chenopodium rubrum cultured *in vitro*. *Chemical Regulation of Plants* **1**, 73 (In Japanese).

40 Ross, C. (1966). Personal communication (unpublished results). Colorado State University, Fort Collins, Colorado, U.S.A.

41 Schwabe, W. W. (1959). Studies of long-day inhibition in short-day plants. *J. Expt Botany* **10**, 317.

42 Teltscherová, L., Seidlová, F. and Krekule, J. (1966). Personal communication. Institute of Experimental Botany, Czechoslovak Academy of Sciences, Prague.

43 Teltscherová, L., Seidlová, F. and Krekule, J. (1967). Effect of some pyrimidine analogues on flowering of long-day and short-day plants. *Biologia Plantarum* **9**, 234.

44 Thomas, R. G. (1961). Correlation between growth and flowering. I. Initiation of leaf and bud primordia. *Ann. Bot. N.S.* **25**, 138.

45 Wagner, E. and Mohr, H. (1966). Kinetic studies to interpret high energy phenomena of morphogenesis on the basis of phytochrome. *Photochem. Photobiol.* **5**, 397.

46 Watson, J. D. and Matthews, R. E. F. (1966). Effect of actinomycin D and 2-thiouracil on floral induction and nucleic acid synthesis in the bud in *Chenopodium amaranticolor*. *Austral. J. Biol. Sci.* **19**, 967.

47 Went, F. W. (1957). *The experimental control of plant growth*. Chronica Botanica Co., Waltham, Mass.

48 White, P. R. (1943). *A handbook of plant tissue culture*. The Jaques Catell Press, Inc., Tempe, Arizona.

7

Lemna perpusilla Torr., Strain 6746

By William S. Hillman

1 History of Use

The Lemnaceae have attracted interest for the study of flowering at least since the work of Saeger[36], but only since Kandeler[18] in 1955 reported photoperiodic control in a strain of *Lemna gibba* has successful experimental work been done. At present, strains of two species of *Lemna*, *L. gibba* and *L. perpusilla* are fairly widely studied. Except for some similarities in the effects of medium composition, the responses of these two species seem very unlike. *L. gibba*, for instance, shows a long-day response, and *L. perpusilla* a short-day. For this reason and because of the writer's greater familiarity with the plant, only *L. perpusilla* will be considered here, although work with *L. gibba* will be cited under certain headings. For recent work on flowering in species of *Wolffia*, another genus of the family, see references 24 and 25, and for accounts of early observations on Lemnaceae flowering, references 10, 11, 18, 23, 36.

The first report of *L. perpusilla* flowering under experimental conditions was made in 1957 by Landolt[23], who found that his strain (collection-number) 6746 flowered in aging cultures under almost all conditions. The year afterwards, this writer confirmed Landolt's observations concerning old cultures, but also found that 6746 flowered rapidly in fresh medium as a short day plant[4]. Landolt originally observed highly significant differences in the flowering responses of various clones of *L. perpusilla* collected by him, both with respect to photoperiodic and other factors; unpublished work by the writer confirms the fact of these differences. Hence, it is of the utmost importance to note that this chapter deals only with *L. perpusilla* 6746, the only strain that has been at all widely studied. As for similarity in the responses of several other strains (notably Landolt's 7001), it is unwise to assume that there will necessarily be any.

An additional complication in the recent literature is that some of the work ostensibly done with *L. perpusilla* 6746 may well have been done with another plant, perhaps *L. paucicostata*, a similar species often included in *L. perpusilla*. Puzzled by Oda's[28] failure to observe any effects of EDTA on *L. perpusilla* 6746, Umemura and Oota[38] compared a strain they denoted *Lemna* I, supposedly *L. perpusilla* 6746 obtained originally from this writer, with *Lemna* II, said by the source from which they obtained it to have come from Oda's laboratory as *L. perpusilla* 6746. On the basis of various studies Umemura and Oota concluded that *Lemna* I was *L. perpusilla* 6746 and *Lemna* II was *L. paucicostata*. However, McClure[26] has since examined the flavonoid compounds of several materials, including: 6746 obtained directly from Landolt, 6746 obtained at times several years apart from this writer, and *Lemna* I and II obtained from Umemura. With this diagnostic procedure, which is almost certainly more definitive than any other, McClure concludes that, contrary to the conclusion of Umemura and Oota, all except *Lemna* I are identical, and that *Lemna* I, not *Lemna* II, is *L. paucicostata*. Hence strain or species difference has clearly not been demonstrated as the reason for the discrepancy between Oda's[28] and Hillman's[12,15] results. It is unfortunate that no other party to this confusion has yet examined material obtained directly from Oda. The moral of the story so far seems only to be that one *Lemna* looks much like another, and the same care is required to avoid confusing strains as is commonly exercised with microbes. It is noteworthy that an important observation reported by Oda on his strain, whatever it may be, was easily confirmed in undoubted 6746 in this laboratory (Section 8).

2 Growing Techniques and Growth Habit

All experiments in the literature have been conducted axenically in liquid medium. The medium most frequently used is Hutner's,[17] which has a high level of trace elements and ethylenediaminetetraacetic acid (EDTA). Appendix A summarizes the composition and a suggested formulation of this medium; for a discussion of other media see Section 14.

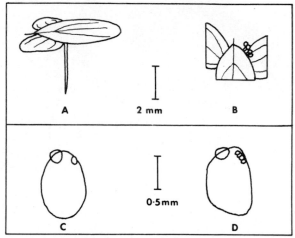

FIGURE 7-1. Diagrammatic sketches of *L. perpusilla* 6746. *A*, side view of a typical 3-frond colony used for starting cultures. *B*, a similar colony in which the mother frond has a fully developed flower, showing the two protruding stamens. *C*, a young vegetative frond, showing two frond primordia. *D*, a young flowering frond with anther primordia to the right and a frond primordium to the left (adapted from Hillman[5]).

At Brookhaven, stock cultures are currently maintained at 23–26°C under continuous cool white fluorescent light of 200–250 f.c. intensity growing on one-half strength Hutner's medium supplemented with 1 per cent sucrose. To ensure that microbial contaminations are easily detected, the medium is often further supplemented with 600 mg/liter of tryptone or casein hydrolysate and 100 mg/liter of yeast extract. These addenda have little or no effect on growth under the conditions described. Media are sterilized by autoclaving at 15 lb/sq inch for 10–15 min. Each 125 ml Erlenmeyer flask containing 50 ml of medium is inoculated with a single 3-frond colony: after a week, 60–100 fronds are present and rapid growth continues for at least another week. Experimental cultures are generally started with 3-frond colonies (Figs. 7–1 and 7–2) from stock cultures 10–16 days old and are grown either in Erlenmeyer flasks or in 20 × 130 mm culture tubes with 15 ml of medium.

The use of sucrose in the medium makes it possible to conduct experiments in relatively dim light, and little work has been done in the absence of sucrose. Although liquid media have been used exclusively in experiments, growth is excellent on media hardened with 1 per cent agar, which are extremely convenient for shipping cultures.

The growth habit of *Lemna perpusilla* 6746 is typical of its genus.[11] Each plant body or frond produces new daughter fronds from meristematic areas within two

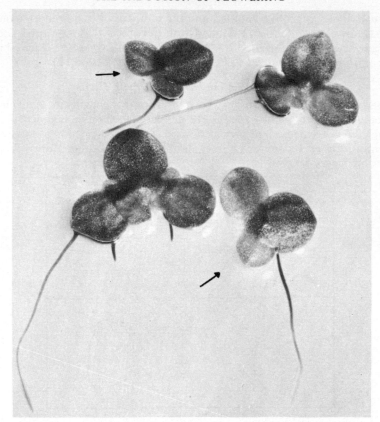

FIGURE 7-2. *L. perpusilla* 6746 seen from above. Arrows indicate 3-frond colonies of the kind used for starting cultures. Magnification about 9X.

pockets, one on each side of its narrower end very near the point at which the root arises, the node. This end of the frond is usually designated as proximal since in an attached daughter frond it is the portion closest to the older mother frond; the wider end is denoted distal. Each daughter frond becomes a mother in its turn, usually while still attached to its own mother. Such groups of attached fronds are called colonies (Figs. 7–1 and 7–2).

The degree to which mature fronds remain together as colonies is strongly affected by many factors, among them temperature, light intensity, and carbohydrate supply. One should also note that young fronds may be substantially developed before becoming visible by projecting beyond the mother pocket. Hence, a typical 3-frond colony consisting of one mother (generation 0) and two visible daughters (generation I) generally contains in addition several other fronds of generation I, several of generation II, and several of generation III, as well as primordia of further generations, a little like those oriental dolls that contain one within the other, a succession of smaller dolls. Use of the term generation and the fact that frond multiplication is essentially exponential under many conditions should not, however, lead to the erroneous notion that growth in *Lemna* cultures is precisely analogous to that in bacterial or algal cultures.

Under the conditions generally used, each mother frond produces 17–20 daughters and then dies.[30] Daughter fronds are produced alternately from side to side, developing earlier in one pocket than in the other. Clones of the same species may differ as to which pocket is plus, producing the first daughter. This characteristic tends to remain constant in a given clone except that shifts in handedness often occur spontaneously in offspring of senescent mother fronds.[30] There is no evidence of any physiological differences between left and right handed members of a clone. When flowering occurs, the inflorescence appears in the minus pocket.

3 Inflorescence Structure and Criteria of Flowering Response

There is some question in the literature as to whether *Lemna* produces an inflorescence composed of one pistillate and two staminate flowers or a single flower containing one pistil and two stamens. Whichever it is, it is enclosed in a sack-like organ that ruptures at maturity and may be regarded as a spathe, if the taxonomic proximity to the Araceae is taken into account. With rare exceptions, each frond produces a single flower in its lifetime and this, as noted, arises in the

FIGURE 7-3. A young frond of *L. perpusilla* 6746, magnified 88X, showing a vegetative primordium at V and floral (anther) primordia at F.

minus pocket. If a flower occurs in a pocket, it always seems to occur before the meristematic area in question produces daughter fronds, but daughter fronds may occur in a given pocket after flowering.[11]

Flowering is evaluated by examining a number of fronds under a dissecting microscope and either scoring various stages in floral development according to some scale of values[3,18] or simply counting the number of fronds bearing evidence of floral initiation.[5] The first method, employing relatively few fronds often selected to represent a particular succession of vegetative generations, was developed by Kandeler[18] for his work with *L. gibba*. It has also been used with *L. perpusilla*, but the latter method seems less susceptible to subjective variations; as adopted in this laboratory it is carried out as follows:[5]

All plants in a culture are placed in a Petri dish, separated into colonies of three fronds or fewer, and arranged in an orderly spiral to facilitate counting. All fronds, no matter how small, that project visibly beyond their mothers are counted. They are then examined under a dissecting microscope, the contents of the pockets being ejected or exposed by pressing or tearing with slightly flattened needles. Vegetative frond primordia appear in the pockets as almost circular transparent flat discs, while flower development, even in very small fronds, is distinguishable by the presence of anther primordia resembling groups of two or four appressed spheres (Figs. 7–1 and 7–3). In most of the younger fronds the pocket tissues are sufficiently transparent so that the anther primordia, if present, are visible without dissection, and look like air bubbles; dissection is then necessary only to confirm the apparent absence of flowering. Cases of ambiguity in which it is difficult to identify the contents of a pocket as either vegetative or floral are uncommon, occurring mainly in fronds too small to be included in the initial counts and these are not dissected. The number of fronds with floral primordia is then divided by the total number of fronds counted and multiplied by 100, giving a value of flowering percentage (FL%). In general, all values are determined from cultures containing at least 50 fronds, usually 70–100. If a culture contains more than 100 fronds, only 100 are dissected. Four or five cultures are generally evaluated for each treatment. If an experiment cannot be evaluated immediately the cultures may be stored for at least two weeks at refrigerator temperatures (about 4°C) without affecting the values obtained.

4 Effects of Plant Age

Since the vegetative growth of *Lemna* is unlike that of most other plants, the question of age has meaning only with respect to an individual frond in its growth from primordium to maturity. Thus, one may ask at what age or size a frond loses the possibility of being induced to flower by appropriate conditions. An estimate of this critical size for photoperiodic induction was made by exposing cultures to a single long night and then replacing them on interrupted nights. Some cultures were dissected immediately after the long night; all visible fronds were counted and then all unborn fronds were dissected, measured and counted down to primordia with lengths of 40–80 microns. Replicate cultures were followed and dissected for several days thereafter until fronds bearing flowers began to appear. By comparing the number of fronds preceding the flowering fronds with the number of unborn fronds present at the end of the long night, it was evident that induction took place only in fronds less than 80 microns long at the time of the long night.[5]

The lower limit of frond size for induction is unknown, nor is it clear whether each young frond directly perceives the photoperiodic conditions or whether a flowering stimulus moves from older to younger fronds. Certainly any change brought about in older fronds by photoperiodic conditions is not permanent; individual frond isolations have shown that once mother fronds have produced flowering fronds, they can again produce vegetative offspring, as can the flowering fronds themselves, if the cultures are replaced in conditions unfavorable to flowering.[5,11]

5 Vernalisation

No inductive effects of low temperature are known in *L. perpusilla* 6746. As a subtropical species, it apparently does not tolerate temperatures below about 14°C[23].

7 Photoperiod Response

When grown in Hutner's medium with red or white light on daily light-dark schedules of 24 hours total duration, *L. perpusilla* 6746 flowers as a typical short day plant.[4] With sucrose present to supply carbohydrates flowering is maximal with 15 minutes to 10 hours of light per day (night length of $23\frac{3}{4}$–14 hours) and no flowering takes place with 16 or more hours of light per day (night length 8 hours or shorter).[5,35] The exact shortest day length at which flowering is entirely suppressed varies slightly in the literature but is roughly 14 hours. As already noted, a single short day cycle causes some flowering, at least when a night length of 14 hours is used. Interpretations of experiments dealing with a single long night are complicated by the fact that, contrary to early impressions,[5] the precise conditions used after an inductive cycle have a profound effect on flowering (see Section 11).

The threshold intensities of light involved in the photoperiodic response of *L. perpusilla* 6746 are not known, but they must be very low. Three daily two-minute exposures, 8 hours apart, to a red source (standard red or cool white fluorescent light screened through red Plexiglass) emitting 1.2 ergs/cm^2/sec at 660 nm prevents flowering entirely, as does continuous exposure to 100th the intensity of the same source (Hillman, unpublished). Undoubtedly even lower total energies would be effective.

Light-breaks prevent the effects of long nights. When given within 15 minutes in the middle of a 14-hour night, a total energy of as little as 1.5 kiloergs/cm^2 inhibits significantly while 15 kiloergs inhibits completely.[5] The time during the dark period at which a light-break is maximally effective is reported to be at the seventh hour for 14-hour dark periods[5] and at the ninth hour for both 14 and 17-hour dark periods.[35] This discrepancy in the literature may be due to the use of different experimental prodcedures, particularly with respect to light quality during the main photoperiod. Another discrepancy in the literature concerns flowering under very dim light. Umemura and Oota[38] report that no flowering occurs at very low intensities (5 f.c.) but this result is at variance with observations of flowering with as little as 15 minutes of red light per day noted above, as well as with the fact that under 8-hour days 10 f.c. of white light allows fully as much flowering as 100 f.c.[31]

8 Spectral Dependence

Initial attempts to demonstrate a role of phytochrome by reversing the effects of red light-breaks with far-red proved unsuccessful since far-red alone was highly inhibitory as a light break.[5] Subsequently, Purves[35] showed that far-red given at the start of an inductive dark period inhibited flowering and that this inhibition was reversible by red thereby indicating the activity of phytochrome.

Further interest in the effects of light quality was stimulated by the report by Oda[28] that although a short day response was evident under red or white light, blue or far-red permitted daylength-indifference, since flowering occurred even under continuous blue or far-red light. Though in certain other respects Oda's results differed from previous reports, the observations on blue light were confirmed.[15] Blue light is not simply photoperiodically inactive, since addition of a small amount of red light to long day schedules otherwise composed of blue renders the entire schedule active as a long day schedule. A particularly clear instance of this blue-red synergism is to be found by combining a 10-hour main light period with a 1-hour light break in the middle of the dark period (Table 7–1). If both photoperiod and light break are red or white no flowering occurs.

TABLE 7–1

Flowering under combinations of red or blue main photoperiods with red or blue light breaks*

Color of 10-hr main photoperiod	Color of 1-hr light break at hr 6½ of dark period	Flowering percentage on day 9
Red	Red	0
Blue	Blue	39
Red	Blue	0
Blue	Red	0

*Plants grown in one-half strength Hutner's medium with 1 per cent sucrose at *ca.* 26°C. Red light (cuts off below 540 nm) total energy about 35 μW/cm² and blue light (cuts off above 540 nm) about 75 μW/cm² (adapted from Table VI of Hillman[15]).

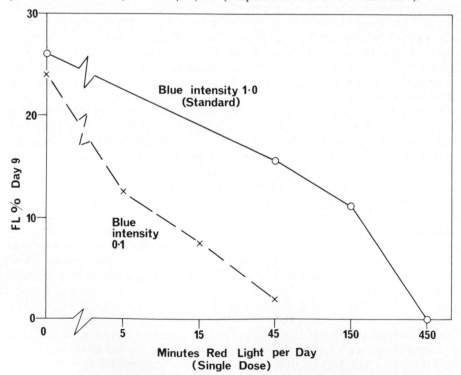

FIGURE 7-4. Relationship between the intensity of continuous blue light and the daily exposure to red light required to inhibit flowering. Cultures grown as in Table 7-1, standard blue and red light approximately as in Table 7-1.

If both are blue, flowering is permitted, but if either the main period is red and the light break blue, or the main period is blue and the light break red, flowering fails.

In addition to a red-blue synergism there is also an antagonism. This is evident in experiments to determine how much red light need be added to a continuous blue schedule in order to prevent flowering entirely. When two blue light schedules with a 10-fold difference in intensity are used, much more red is required to inhibit flowering under high intensity than under low intensity blue (Fig. 7-4).

A relationship between these effects of blue light and the action of phytochrome is indicated by the observations that with a blue main photoperiod far-red as a light break is no longer highly inhibitory and can thus partially reverse the effect of a red light break. Closing the main blue photoperiod with a brief red exposure abolishes this reversibility by making the far-red light break again fully inhibitory. However, this effect of red light terminating the blue light period is itself far-red-reversible.[16] It is important to note here that simply terminating a red main photoperiod with far-red, does not confer reversibility in the subsequent dark period – that is, does not reduce the inhibition caused by far-red as a light break (Hillman, unpublished).

The simplest explanation of all these results seems to be that phytochrome is the only photoreceptor involved, and that far-red, blue and red differ only in that they establish, in the order given, increasing proportions of P_{fr} (the far-red-absorbing form) at photoequilibrium. A detailed discussion of this hypothesis is undesirable here; the main purpose at present is to summarize observations rather than construct mechanisms. Nevertheless, consider the following tentative summary of the interactions between the quality of the main light period and reversibility in the dark period: if a high level of P_{fr} is present in the main photoperiod and in the early part of the dark period, then the later dark period process promoting flowering is extremely sensitive to P_{fr}, being easily inhibited by low levels.

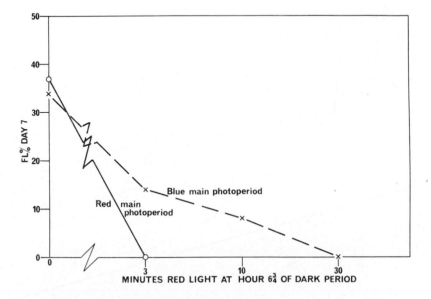

FIGURE 7-5. Relationship between color of main (10 hr) photoperiod and susceptibility to inhibition by red light in the middle of the dark period. Conditions as in Fig. 7-4.

Examining only a single aspect of this proposal, note that it suggests that the difference between light break reversibility with blue and red main photoperiods is that, with the latter, even the small amount of P_{fr} produced by far-red is highly inhibitory. In other words, though far-red presumably acts by removal of P_{fr} when it successfully reverses a red effect, it would act here by producing enough P_{fr} to saturate the system, since the system is very rapidly saturated. If this is so, it should be possible to demonstrate even with red light breaks that the dark period is far more sensitive to P_{fr} following a red than following a blue main photoperiod. This is easily done: a 3-minute exposure to the standard source is sufficient to abolish flowering completely in conjunction with a 10 hour red main photoperiod, while more than 10 minutes of red light are required to do so in conjunction with a blue main photoperiod, as shown in Figure 7–5.

No conclusive proof that the photoperiodic responses discussed here involve only phytochrome is possible at this time; in fact, Esashi and Oda[3] have decided

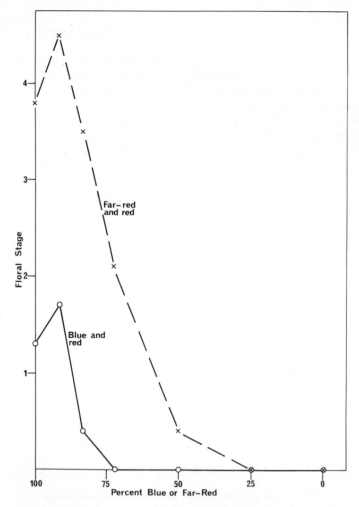

FIGURE 7-6. Flowering under constant energy (about 6 kiloergs cm^{-2} sec^{-1}) composed of different mixtures of red with blue or red with far-red. Plants grown in Hoagland's-type medium with 1 % sucrose and 5×10^{-5} M EDTA at about 26°C. Blue-red data from 9 days growth, far-red-red data from 11 days growth (adapted from Esashi and Oda[3]).

from complex studies of red, blue and far-red interactions on both *L. perpusilla* 6746 and *L. gibba* that phytochrome alone cannot account for their results and that another photoreceptor is active as well. Their conclusion rests heavily on the effects of continuous light of constant energy composed of various proportions of red and far-red, or blue and far-red. They find that 'notwithstanding the fact that the active P_{fr} level under the B light differs widely from that under the FR (reference given) the optimal (B/R) and (FR/R) values for the flowering . . . were relatively equivalent'. The relevant data from their paper are presented as Figure 7–6; while the conclusion with respect to the optimum ratios seems justified, a much greater effect is also clear: with red-blue mixtures, over 75 per cent blue is needed to permit any flowering at all, while with red-far-red mixtures, any level of far-red over 25 per cent permits flowering. This is what one would predict under the hypothesis that phytochrome alone is involved. Thus, these experiments are at best equivocal, and much more evidence is needed before the activity of a photoreceptor other than phytochrome can be regarded as established or even probable.

Studies of the role of light-quality, particularly far-red, on the flowering of *L. gibba* have been conducted by Kandeler.[19-22]

9 *Endogenous Rhythms*

Evidence for a significant role of endogenous circadian rhythms in the photoperiodic response of *L. perpusilla* 6746 on Hutner's medium is provided by the use of skeleton photoperiods – light-dark cycles in which the light period itself consists largely of darkness. If 10(14) indicates 10 hours of light alternating with 14 hours of darkness, the cycle 1(8) 1 (14) can be regarded as its skeleton. The first observations were that skeleton cycles such as $1(9\frac{3}{4})$ $\frac{1}{4}(13)$ permitted much less flowering than the corresponding full cycles – 11(13) – and this was interpreted simply as an inhibition due to the long dark interruption of the light period. The inhibition was reversible by brief light interruptions of the dark interruptions – that is, the schedule $\frac{1}{4}(2\frac{1}{2})$ $\frac{1}{4}(2\frac{1}{2})$ $\frac{1}{4}(2\frac{1}{2})$ $\frac{1}{4}(2\frac{1}{4})$ $\frac{1}{4}(13)$ permitted high flowering, indicating that the amount of light was not the factor involved, but rather its distribution.[13] However, the notion that a skeleton schedule such as $\frac{1}{4}(10\frac{1}{2})$ $\frac{1}{4}(13)$ was always simply inhibitory compared to its corresponding full schedule proved erroneous when it was observed that plants transferred from continuous light into the reverse of that schedule – that is, $\frac{1}{4}(13)$ $\frac{1}{4}(10\frac{1}{2})$ – flowered extremely rapidly.

It soon became clear that the effect of such skeleton schedules depended on which of the dark periods the plants experienced first after being transferred out of continuous light. Finally, experiments were conducted in which the effects of skeleton schedules were studied as a function of the length of a single dark period given between the end of continuous light and the start of the skeleton. In such experiments a circadian periodicity becomes obvious.[14] For example, the schedule $\frac{1}{4}(10\frac{1}{2})$ $\frac{1}{4}(13)$ repeated 7 days gives low flowering if preceded on the first day by 0 or 24 hours of darkness, but it gives high flowering if preceded on the first day by 12 or 36 hours of darkness. The apparent periodicity in such effects of the initial dark period length persists for at least 48 hours (Fig. 7–7). Note that in this experiment the skeleton schedule was presented as $\frac{1}{4}(13)$ $\frac{1}{4}(10\frac{1}{2})$ . . rather than as $\frac{1}{4}(10)$ $\frac{1}{4}(13)$ . . . , so that an initial 0 or 24 hours of darkness gave high rather than low flowering.

Consideration of the succession of treatments involved in such experiments – continuous light (stock conditions), followed by a single variable dark period, followed by seven repetitions of a skeleton schedule – leads to at least two simple conclusions. First, the rhythm apparently starts from the light-off signal pro-

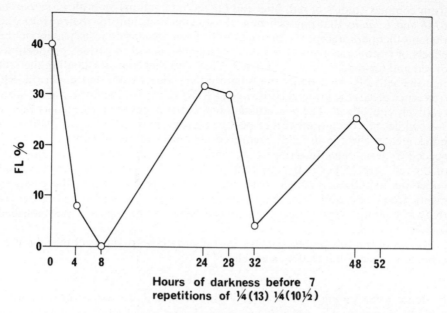

FIGURE 7-7. Flowering as affected by various durations of darkness before 7 repetitions of the schedule $\frac{1}{4}(13)\frac{1}{4}(10\frac{1}{2})$. Conditions as in Table 7-1 (red light) and Table 7-2 (adapted from Hillman[14]).

vided by the transition from continuous light to darkness; it is not likely to have been imposed by previous exposure to light-dark cycles, as the stock plants have been in continuous light for years. Secondly, the fact that the effects of a single variable dark period are evident after seven (or even nine) daily repetitions of the skeleton schedules suggests that such schedules themselves do not reset the rhythm, although they obviously interact with it. (In contrast, of course, the effect of seven repetitions of a full schedule such as 10(14) are not modified by a single preceding dark period of variable length.) Thus, the question arises, if the rhythm starts originally from a light-to-dark transition, why is it not constantly reset by the many such transitions experienced subsequently? The reason seems to be that the light periods used in skeleton schedules are insufficiently long.

To determine how long a light period is required to reset the rhythm, repetitions of a given skeleton schedule were tested either without an initial dark period, with a 12-hour initial dark period, or with a 12-hour initial dark period followed by light periods of varying lengths. The results (Table 7–2, part 1) indicate that from 4 to 6 hours of light are required to reset – that is, to abolish the effect of the 12-hour dark period and return the flowering to what it would be without any initial dark period. Stating this another way, after a 12-hour dark period 4 to 6 hours of light are required before turning the light off will give a new 'light-off' signal. A further experiment (Table 7–2, part 2) shows that the light need not be on through the entire time in question and that six 15-minute light periods separated by six 45-minute dark periods are roughly as effective as 4 hours of uninterrupted light. These results suggest that phytochrome is involved in the resetting, since the possibility of substituting repeated short exposures for one long one is characteristic of that system. However, the requisite far-red reversal studies have not yet been done. Resetting by short light periods given close enough together also, of course, explains the earlier observations that the

TABLE 7-2

Response to a skeleton schedule: resetting by various light treatments
after perturbation by a 12-hour dark period*

Hr of red light or (darkness) during the 24-hr between the continuous light stock conditions and the start of the skeleton schedule	Results after 7 repetitions of the skeleton 1(9) 1(13)
	Flowering percentage
1. a. 24	25
b. 12(12)	64
c. 10(12)2	62
d. 8(12)4	40
e. 6(12)6	22
f. 10(14) ⎱ Dark controls	62
g. 8(16) ⎰ for	58
h. 6(18) ⎰ c, d and e	55
2. a. 24	20
b. 12(12)	54
c. 10(12)2	58
d. 8(12)4	25
e. 6(12)6	26
f. $6(12)\frac{1}{4}(\frac{3}{4})\frac{1}{4}(\frac{3}{4})\frac{1}{4}(\frac{3}{4})\frac{1}{4}(\frac{3}{4})\frac{1}{4}(\frac{3}{4})\frac{1}{4}(\frac{3}{4})$	29

*Plants grown as in Table 7–1.

schedule $\frac{1}{4}(2\frac{1}{2})\,\frac{1}{4}(2\frac{1}{2})\,\frac{1}{4}(2\frac{1}{2})\,\frac{1}{4}(2\frac{1}{2})\,\frac{1}{4}(13)$ acts like 11(13) rather than like $1(9\frac{3}{4})\,\frac{1}{4}(13)$; the repeated flashes in the first schedule presumably reset in every cycle, unlike the true skeleton schedule itself but like the full schedule.

The analysis of relationships between endogenous circadian rhythms and other factors affecting the flowering of *L. perpusilla* 6746 is obviously just beginning, and many more questions arise than have been answered. One point implicit in the results already presented is that although a brief (e.g. $\frac{1}{4}$ hr) light exposure is insufficient to reset the rhythm it is sufficient to determine the end of a dark period which affects or interacts with that rhythm. Thus, the participation of more than one kind of light action (though not necessarily more than one kind of photoreceptor) in these effects seems evident. A detailed formal analysis of some of the results with skeleton photoperiods on *Lemna* has been presented by Pittendrigh[29] in connection with experiments on other organisms, including *Drosophila*, and may indicate a fruitful direction of future thought on these phenomena.

11 Photoperiodic Inhibition

In early experiments in which cultures were exposed to a single long night and then returned to long day conditions, the percentage of flowering fronds increased to a maximum five days after the long night and then fell off, but the actual number of flowering fronds per culture appeared constant from five days on. The conclusion was reached that the fall in percentage was due simply to dilution by the appearance of new vegetative fronds but that once induction had taken place a frond flowered normally no matter what the subsequent conditions.[5] This conclusion was not confirmed by Posner[30] who found, in similar experiments, a marked decline in total flowering fronds and concluded that adverse photoperiodic conditions actually caused regression in the development of flower primordia already induced. The reasons for these differences between two investigations conducted in the same laboratory are still not clear, but they might possibly be due to the use of slightly higher temperatures in all the later work (Section 13). At any rate, in a few recent experiments the kind of photoperiodic inhibition noted by Posner is quite evident.

For example, cultures were grown for several days under continuous light. Most were then given a long dark period: of these some received a post-treatment of continuous light of the kind in which they had grown; some of interrupted night conditions; some of extremely dim continuous red light. As controls, some received no long night at all either by staying always in continuous bright light or by receiving equivalent time under the dim red light. The results were that flowering was observed as a result of the long night only in those cultures receiving the dim red post-treatment. Although the controls showed that the dim red treatment itself was not equivalent to darkness, all the other post-treatments suppressed the flowering that would otherwise have taken place as a result of the long night (Hillman, unpublished). Hence, the photoperiodic inhibition of floral development in *L. perpusilla* 6746 is a real and potent phenomenon, and deserves further characterization.

13 Effects of Temperature

Landolt[23] originally observed *L. perpusilla* 6746 flowering in culture at various temperatures between 16 and 30°C. Under ordinary circumstances, temperatures in tubes and flasks are affected by illumination and can easily rise above those of the ambient air. Highly accurate temperature studies can be conducted only by immersing the vessels in thermostated water baths; such studies show fairly drastic effects of high temperatures. In Hutner's medium under short days flowering is vigorous at 27 and 29°C but fails completely at 31.5–32°C, although vegetative growth is still excellent at those temperatures. The dark period processes appear to be most sensitive to high temperature; with temperatures otherwise held at 28°C, a 4-hour period at 33°C in the middle of each dark period inhibited flowering by about 50 per cent, while the same treatment in the middle of each light period had essentially no effect.[6]

High temperatures also have interesting effects on the flowering that occurs in Hoagland-type media lacking EDTA and either contaminated or deliberately supplemented with low levels of cupric ion (Section 14). Under these conditions flowering takes place even under continuous red or white light but only if temperatures are kept at or below about 28°C. At 27°C, for example, flowering in the media described is almost as rapid with 16-hour white photoperiods as it is under 8-hour photoperiods, but at 29.5°C it occurs only under the 8-hour photoperiod, in which the temperature increase has little or no effect.[6]

No studies at all have been reported with low temperatures. Most work with these plants is done in the range 25–28°C; the extreme sensitivity of flowering to differences of even 2 or 3° even for a few hours means that slight temperature variations are likely sources of quantitative differences, and even perhaps of qualitative contradictions, between superficially similar experiments.

14 Effects of Mineral Nutrition

The possibility that the composition of the medium might be important for *Lemna* flowering was suggested by some field observations of Saeger[36] and first confirmed experimentally by Kandeler's work with *L. gibba*[18]. When *L. perpusilla* 6746 is grown in fresh Hutner's medium, flowering occurs only under short days, but when the medium has aged it occurs under long days also. This effect occurs much more rapidly in dilute medium (Table 7–3) suggesting that the aging is due to a change in medium composition rather than to the excretion of some florigenic substance by the plants.

TABLE 7-3

Flowering on full strength or dilute Hutner's medium
under 16-hour photoperiods*

Medium	Flowering percentage on indicated day, each value representing one culture		
	14	19	23
Hutner's	0	1, 2	11, 11
Hutner's + 1% sucrose	0	4, 7	9, 12
1/5 strength Hutner's	0	8, 10	16, 17
1/5 Hutner's + 1% sucrose	0	28, 32	44, 59

*Cultures in 125 ml Erlenmeyer flasks with 50 ml medium at 23–27°C and about 600 f.c. white fluorescent light (adapted from Table I. of Hillman[6]).

In an investigation to pursue this question further, other media were tested. The surprising result was that on a Hoagland-type medium L. perpusilla 6746 seemed daylength-indifferent. The short day response could be restored – that is, flowering could be inhibited under long but not under short days – either by raising the temperature to about 30°C (see Section 13) or by adding roughly 3×10^{-5} M EDTA to the medium. Not only EDTA but other chelating agents as well, including even tartaric acid, also had this effect, though at different, usually higher, concentrations.[6] Action similar to that of the chelating agents was exerted also by Hoagland-type medium aged by the growth of either L. gibba or L. perpusilla. Both chelating agents and aged Hoagland's medium were more effective at high pH (e.g. 4.6) than at low pH (e.g. 3.6). This relationship to pH was consistent with the idea that the chelating agents were indeed acting through their chelating properties; it also suggested that the aged Hoagland's medium contained naturally occurring chelating agents probably leached out during the growth (or senescence) of the cultures.[8,9]

An explanation for most of the foregoing phenomena arose from the finding that the response with chelating agents or aged Hoagland-type medium could be duplicated in fresh Hoagland-type medium if all materials, including the water, used to make the medium were highly purified. With full precautions of the kind used in studies of heavy metal deficiencies so that the medium was not heavily contaminated with extra metal ions, L. perpusilla 6746 showed a short day response even without added EDTA or other chelating agents. Adding $0.5–5 \times 10^{-6}$ M cupric ion to such purified media restored the original situation of daylength-indifference (Table 7–4). In short, the apparent conferring of a short day response by chelating agents is almost certainly the reversal of an effect of subtoxic concentrations of cupric ion. Excess cupric ion renders the short day plant L. perpusilla 6746 capable of flowering under long days.[12] This action of cupric ion has by now been repeated many times under red as well as under white light.[15] Numerous questions concerning mineral nutrition and flowering still remain, however.

First, of course, the mechanism of the cupric ion effect is unknown. The fact that apparently parallel but opposite effects have been obtained on a strain of L. gibba led to the suggestion that cupric ion affects photoperiodic sensitivity rather than flowering itself.[12] However, the interactions of medium composition with other factors on L. gibba are, if anything, even more complex[20–22] than those on L. perpusilla, and no satisfactory generalization can be reached at pre-

THE INDUCTION OF FLOWERING

TABLE 7-4

Effects of cupric ion and EDTA on flowering in highly purified
media under short or long days*

Cupric ion added, μM/L	EDTA μM/L	Photoperiod, hr	Flowering percentage Day 7
0.0	–	8	65
0.5	–	8	63
1.0	–	8	67
2.0	–	8	62
0.0	–	16	3
0.5	–	16	16
1.0	–	16	40
2.0	–	16	52
0.32	–	16	2
1.92	–	16	73
1.92	30	16	3

*Cultures in a Hoagland-type medium, without sucrose; vessels, light and tempera-
ture as in Table 7–3 (adapted from Figures 1 and 2 of Hillman[12]).

sent. Another puzzling point is that while the aging of Hoagland-type media,
with its effects on flowering in both *L. perpusilla* and *L. gibba*, is explicable by
the accumulation of naturally occurring chelating agents, this explanation will
not do for the aging of Hutner's medium. Fresh Hutner's contains a high level
of EDTA; it is thus no surprise that *L. perpusilla* 6746 is a strict short day
plant in this medium. However, aged Hutner's medium permits flowering under
long days and this can hardly be due to the accumulation of more chelating
agents. It may well be due to the loss of EDTA but neither this nor other possibilities have been tested. Much more work is needed on this question as well
as on the mechanism of copper action.

Several aspects of medium composition other than chelating agents seem to
interact with cupric ion. Dilution of the macronutrients increases the effect of
suboptimal (for flowering under long days) cupric ion; calcium and phosphate
have been implicated as the active ions in this interaction.[12] Mercuric ion, of
all the ions tested, is the only other material that seems to have an effect similar
to that of cupric ion; it probably acts by displacing copper from inactive sites.[12]

Attempts to observe the effects of EDTA on flowering have not been uniformly
successful, and reports have appeared in which EDTA either had no effect[28] or
an effect depending upon light intensity.[2] However, the initial cupric ion level
in these experiments was neither tested nor artificially increased, as if the investigators were unaware of the proposed role of copper in accounting for the
EDTA effect. Thus, relative purity of the initial conditions, plus temperatures
somewhat higher than those normally used, might easily create conditions in
which no major effects of chelating agents would be expected. Light intensity
probably plays a marginal role, since the copper effect is easily observed under
both high[12] and low[15] light conditions.

Of other mineral factors affecting flowering, iron has been studied in a few
experiments. Flowering is more sensitive to iron deficiency than is vegetative
growth: in Hutner's medium, reducing iron to one third or one tenth standard
level had little or no effect on frond multiplication but markedly reduced
flowering.[9]

15 Effects of Gas Composition

No work has been reported with *L. perpusilla* 6746. Kandeler has observed interactions of CO_2 and bicarbonate level with photoperiodism in *L. gibba*.[20-22]

16, 17 Translocation of the Floral Stimulus; Grafting Experiments

Although studies on this kind of question are presumably not impossible, they would probably require the use of a micromanipulator, or at least an unusually steady hand, and have not been done.

18 Effects of Growth Substances and Growth Retardants

Gibberellic acid (GA) autoclaved with the medium at concentrations of 0.1 mg/L and above markedly inhibits flowering and reduces frond size in *L. perpusilla* 6746 at the same time that it increases the rate of frond multiplication. Inhibition of flowering by 1 mg/L is complete under both short day and long day (high copper) conditions. Although parallel tests of the autoclaved medium on dwarf peas indicated that substantial gibberellin activity remained in it, it is of course possible that all or part of the effects on the *Lemna* were due to some decomposition product and not to the gibberellic acid itself.[7]

A number of growth-active substances, including napthaleneacetic acid, p-chlorophenoxyisobutyric acid and kinetin, as well as others, were used at many concentrations in early and unsuccessful attempts to reproduce the EDTA effect in *L. perpusilla* 6746.[6]

19 Effects of Metabolic Inhibitors

Investigations on the effects of exogenous amino acids and various antimetabolites on flowering in *Lemna gibba* have been reported,[27,37] as has also a promotion of flowering in *L. minor* by estrogens.[1]

Effects of X-irradiation

X-ray doses of 100–300 R/day under inductive conditions depressed flowering and fruiting of *L. perpusilla* 6746 probably as a consequence of depressed growth rather than in any specific manner.[30,33]

A clone of *L. perpusilla* designated aberrant 1073 was isolated by Posner from a culture of 6746 exposed to x-irradiation. Clone 1073 differs markedly from the parent strain in its flowering response not only with respect to light intensity, as shown in Table 7–5, but also toward cupric ion and probably other factors

TABLE 7-5

Effects of light intensity on flowering of
6746 and aberrant 1073 in short days*

Strain	Footcandles	Flowering percentage Day 9
6746	10	78
6746	100	82
1073	10	0
1073	100	37

*Cultures grown on 7/10 strength Hutner's medium with 1 per cent sucrose under 8 hr per day of white fluorescent light (adapted from Table V. of Posner[31]).

as well.[32] Other aberrant clones isolated in the same investigation[31] showed no abnormalities in flowering response, though a number were incapable of producing seeds or viable seeds under the standard conditions[34] in which 6746 does so abundantly.

APPENDIX A

Hutner's Medium

I: Composition

Compound	mg/L	mM
K_2HPO_4	400	2.3
KOH	200	3.6
EDTA	500	1.7
NH_4NO_3	200	2.5
$Ca(NO_3)_2.4H_2O$	354	1.5
$MgSO_4.7H_2O$	500	2.0
$FeSO_4.7H_2O$	24.9	0.09
$MnCl_2.4H_2O$	17.9	0.09
$ZnSO_4.7H_2O$	65.9	0.23
$CuSO_4.5H_2O$	3.95	0.016
$Na_2MoO_4.2H_2O$	25.2	0.10
H_3BO_3	14.2	0.23

pH adjusted to 6.2–6.5 with KOH, which of course affects total K level somewhat.

II: Stock Solutions

1. To make 5OX Stock, no Mg:

To about 200 ml H_2O, with magnetic stirring:

$Ca(NO_3)_2.4H_2O$, 17.7 g; EDTA, 25.0 g; K_2HPO_4, 20.0 g; NH_4NO_3, 10.0 g; KOH (85% pellets) 12–13 g (cool with cracked ice).

This makes solution A

To about 150 ml H_2O, with stirring:

$ZnSO_4.7H_2O$, 3.295 g; H_3BO_3, 0.710 g; $Na_2MoO_4.2H_2O$, 1.260 g; $CuSO_4$ .5H_2O, 0.197 g; at this point about 13 drops N HCl until cloudiness is gone; $Co(NO_3)_2.6H_2O$, 0.010 g; $MnCl_2.4H_2O$, 0.897 g.

This makes solution B

To about 50 ml H_2O:

$FeSO_4.7H_2O$, 1.245 g (solution C).

Now, with constant stirring, pour solutions A, B and C together and make up to 1000 ml. Keep refrigerated.

2. To make 5OX $MgSO_4$ stock:

$MgSO_4.7H_2O$, 25.0 g/1000 ml

3. For full strength medium, use 20 ml each of stock 1 and stock 2 per liter of medium, and adjust pH with 5 N KOH to 6.2–6.5. One-half x strength medium is usually best for growth.

4. Problems that may arise include the following:

Solution A may require more than the indicated amount of KOH to dissolve all the EDTA – this is likely if the KOH is not freshly opened, and has absorbed both H_2O and CO_2 from the air.

Stock 1 (A + B + C) often yields a fine precipitate as it ages, and should not be kept too long if the precise composition is critical for the experiment in question. If good growth is the only object, even stock solutions with heavy precipitates are satisfactory.

REFERENCES

[1] Czygan, F. C. (1962). Blütenbildung bei *Lemna minor* nach Zusatz von Oestrogenen. *Naturwiss* **49**, 285.

[2] Esashi, Y. and Oda, Y. (1964). Effects of light intensity and sucrose on the flowering of *Lemna perpusilla*. *Plant & Cell Physiol.* **5**, 513.

[3] Esashi, Y. and Oda, Y. (1966). Two light reactions in the photoperiodic control of flowering of *Lemna perpusilla* and *L. gibba*. *Plant & Cell Physiol.* **7**, 59.

[4] Hillman, W. S. (1958). Photoperiodic control of flowering in *Lemna perpusilla*. *Nature* **181**, 1275.

[5] Hillman, W. S. (1959). Experimental control of flowering in *Lemna* I. General methods. Photoperiodism in *L. perpusilla* 6746. *Amer. J. Bot.* **46**, 466.

[6] Hillman, W. S. (1959). Experimental control of flowering in *Lemna* II. Some effects of medium composition, chelating agents and high temperatures on flowering in *L. perpusilla* 6746. *Amer. J. Bot.* **46**, 489.

[7] Hillman, W. S. (1960). Effects of gibberellic acid on flowering, frond size and multiplication rate of *Lemna perpusilla*. Φyton **14**, 49.

[8] Hillman, W. S. (1961). Experimental control of flowering in *Lemna* III. A relationship between medium composition and the opposite photoperiodic responses of *L. perpusilla* 6746 and *L. gibba* G3. *Amer. J. Bot.* **48**, 413.

[9] Hillman, W. S. (1961). Photoperiodism, chelating agents and flowering of *Lemna perpusilla* and *L. gibba* in aseptic culture. In *Light and Life*, 673. Eds. McElroy and Glass. Johns Hopkins Press.

[10] Hillman, W. S. (1961). Test-tube studies on flowering: experiments with the Lemnaceae, or duckweeds. *Bull. Torr. Bot. Club* **88**, 327.

[11] Hillman, W. S. (1961). The Lemnaceae, or duckweeds. A review of the descriptive and experimental literature. *Bot. Rev.* **27**, 221.

[12] Hillman, W. S. (1962). Experimental control of flowering in *Lemna* IV. Inhibition of photoperiodic sensitivity by copper. *Amer. J. Bot.* **49**, 892.

[13] Hillman, W. S. (1963). Photoperiodism: an effect of darkness during the light period on critical night length. *Science* **140**, 1347.

[14] Hillman, W. S. (1964). Endogenous circadian rhythms and the response of *Lemna perpusilla* to skeleton photoperiods. *Amer. Nat.* **98**, 323.

[15] Hillman, W. S. (1965). Red light, blue light, and copper ion in the photoperiodic control of flowering in *Lemna perpusilla* 6746. *Plant & Cell Physiol.* **6**, 499.

[16] Hillman, W. S. (1966). Photoperiodism in *Lemna*: reversal of night-interruption depends on color of the main photoperiod. *Science* **154**, 1360.

[17] Hutner, S. H. (1953). Comparative physiology of heterotrophic growth in plants. In *Growth and differentiation in Plants* 417, Ed. Loomis. Iowa State College Press.

[18] Kandeler, R. (1955). Über die Blütenbildung bei *Lemna gibba* L. I. Kulturbedingungen und Tageslängenabhangigkeit. *Z. Bot.* **43**, 61.

[19] Kandeler, R. (1956). Über die Blütenbildung bei *Lemna gibba* L. II. Das Wirkungsspektrum von blühforderndem Schwachlicht. *Z. Bot.* **44**, 153.

[20] Kandeler, R. (1962). Die Aufhebung der photoperiodischen Steuerung bei *Lemna gibba*. *Ber. Deutsch. Bot. Ges.* **75**, 431.

[21] Kandeler, R. (1964). Wirkungen des Kohlendioxyds auf die Blütenbildung von *Lemna gibba*. *Naturwiss.* **23**, 561.

[22] Kandeler, R. (1964). Zweifache wirkung von Bikarbonat auf die Lichtsteuerung der Blütenbildung von *Lemna gibba*. *Ber. Deutsch. Bot. Ges.* **77**, 140.

[23] Landolt, E. (1957). Physiologische und ökologische Untersuchungen an Lemnaceen. *Ber. Schweiz. Bot. Ges.* **67**, 271.

[24] Maheshwari, S. C. and Chauhan, O. S. (1963). In vitro control of flowering in *Wolffia microscopica*. *Nature* **198**, 99.

[25] Maheshwari, S. C. and Seth, P. N. (1966). Photoperiodic control of flowering in *Wolffia papulifera*. *Plant & Cell Physiol.* **7**, 163.

[26] McClure, J. W. (1967). Flavonoid variation in clone 6746 of *Lemna perpusilla* from different laboratories. *Plant & Cell Physiol.* **8**, 523

[27] Nakashima, H. (1964). Effects of exogenous amino acids on the flower and frond production in duckweed, *Lemna gibba* G3. *Plant & Cell Physiol.* **5**, 217

[28] Oda, Y. (1962). Effect of light quality on flowering of *Lemna perpusilla* 6746. *Plant & Cell Physiol.* **3**, 415.

[29] Pittendrigh, C. S. (1964). The circadian oscillation in *Drosophila pseudoobscura* pupae: a model for the photoperiodic clock. *Z. Pflanzenphysiol.* **54**, 275.

[30] Posner, H. B. (1962). Permanent and temporary effects of X rays on the reproduction and aging of *Lemna perpusilla*. Ph.D. Thesis, Yale University.

[31] Posner, H. B. (1962). Characteristics of X-ray-induced aberrants of *Lemna perpusilla* 6746. *Plant & Cell Physiol.* **3**, 275.

[32] Posner, H. B. (1966). Some effects of copper and EDTA on flowering in *Lemna perpusilla*, aberrant strain 1073 (Abstract). *Proc. Annual Meetings, American Society of Plant Physiologists*, XXIX.

[33] Posner, H. B. and Hillman, W. S. (1960). Effects of X irradiation on *Lemna perpusilla*. *Amer. J. Bot.* **47**, 506.

[34] Posner, H. B. and Hillman, W. S. (1962). Aseptic production, collection and germination of seeds of *Lemna perpusilla* 6746. *Physiol. Plantar.* **15**, 700.

[35] Purves, W. K. (1961). Dark reactions in the flowering of *Lemna perpusilla* 6746. *Planta* **56**, 684.

[36] Saeger, A. C. (1929). The flowering of Lemnaceae. *Bull. Torr. Bot. Club* **56**, 351.

[37] Umemura, K. and Oota, Y. (1965). Effects of nucleic acid and protein-antimetabolites on frond and flower production in *Lemna gibba* G3. *Plant & Cell Physiol.* **6**, 73.

[38] Umemura, K. and Oota, Y. (1965). Flowering in *Lemna paucicostata* as compared with that in *Lemna perpusilla* 6746. *Plant & Cell Physiol.* **6**, 793.

8

Cannabis sativa L.

By J. Heslop-Harrison & Y. Heslop-Harrison

1 History of Use

Cannabis sativa L. (hemp) shares with Humulus japonicus L. (Japanese hop) the distinction of having been used in the first unequivocal demonstration of photoperiodic induction of flowering, by Tournois[39] (Fig. 1–1). The critical experiment was carried out in the period April to July, 1912, when Tournois compared the behaviour of groups of plants grown under full daylength with that of plants exposed to light only during the period 8 a.m. to 2 p.m. daily and enclosed in dark boxes during the remaining 18 hr of the daily cycle. The plants under short days showed precocious flowering, producing only 3 or 4 pairs of leaves and reaching a stature of 15 to 20 cm before inflorescence formation. In comparison, flowering in the natural-day controls was much delayed, and initiation did not begin until 7 or 8 leaf pairs had been formed accompanied by 50 cm or more of stem growth. Although the contribution of Tournois is rarely acknowledged in photoperiodic literature, his priority in the discovery of the short-day photoperiodic response is not in doubt.

In subsequent work with hemp, interest in the photoperiodic response was related principally to the effects daylength has on sex expression, phenomena also investigated by Tournois.[38,39] The contributions of Schaffner,[31-34] McPhee[27] and others have been reviewed elsewhere,[5] and some aspects of the influence of photoperiod on sexuality are considered in later sections. In the post-war period, the flowering behaviour of hemp has been studied by Petit,[30] Borthwick and Scully[1] and Cheuvart,[2] and there have been various contributions by Russian workers.[26,42] During the period 1949–1964 hemp has been used by the authors and collaborators in various studies of flower initiation and morphogenesis. These studies fall into three series: London (1950–1956), Belfast (1954–1959), and Birmingham (1960–1964). The principal co-workers have been Professor R. G. Thomas and Dr. M. P. Jagoe.

Many previously unpublished results are included in the following pages, and for brevity of reference these are referred to by period as (Lond.), (Belf.) and (Birm.). The experimental results marked (T) are due to Professor Thomas, and most appear in his thesis;[35] similarly those marked (J) are due to Dr. Jagoe (thesis[21]).

Hemp is cultivated for fibre, seed and drug production, and a great many races now exist, selected for different characteristics. These races differ widely in photoperiodic response: all are accelerated into flowering by short days, but many are relatively insensitive. In the period 1948–1956 races from several sources were tested, but the main work has been carried out using fibre hemp cultivars obtained originally from Liège (henceforth referred to as L) and two Portuguese localities, Sacavem (S) and Coimbra (C). The Coimbra race has been maintained in cultivation for 16 generations, but may now be suffering from inbreeding depression.

2 Growing Techniques and Growth Habit

Germination of more than 90per cent is readily obtained with fresh hemp seed, although viability declines quite rapidly, and with 4-year old seed germination may be reduced to 10 per cent. In most of the experimental work recorded here, seeds were germinated in flats either in vermiculite or in a standard potting compost. Seedlings were transplanted at a height of 2–3 cm to a mixture of equal parts of washed sand and sphagnum peat in 8–13 cm pots. In earlier work the potting mixture contained loam, sand and peat, but this was later replaced by a standard mixture of equal parts of washed sand and sphagnum peat, to which nutrients were added every second or third day. Under this regime very vigorous and healthy growth can be achieved, plants growing to heights of 4 metres in the 13 cm pots without any evidence of deleterious effects due to starvation or root constriction. There are no serious disease problems in the greenhouse culture of hemp, and pests are few and readily kept down by normal disinfestation practice. Seedling damping-off can be avoided by using a sterile medium and keeping watering to a minimum. A patchy drying or withering of the leaves of young plants is generally traceable to a fall in soil pH, which must be kept above 6.5 for healthy growth. In all, the fibre strains of hemp offer excellent experimental material, since apart from the ease of culture, the erect growth habit and absence of lateral branches means that a high plant density can be tolerated.

Several illumination sources have been used for day-length extension and supplementation, and for growth in wholly artificial environments. The experience with these may be summarised briefly as follows. For daylength extension when adequate photosynthetic energy is available in the daylight period, incandescent lamps are adequate. For daylight supplementation, high pressure mercury vapour lamps are economical, but the provision of long wave radiation from incandescent sources is necessary for normal photoperiodic response. For continuous illumination of plants growing without access to daylight banks of warm-white fluorescent tubes have been used successfully without supplementation from incandescent sources. Growth has been obtained with intensities down to 800 f.c., as measured with an EEL selenium cell meter, but 1000 to 1500 f.c. is required to give a reasonably normal plant form without stem weakness. Recently growth comparable to that in normal daylight has been obtained in chambers illuminated with Philips HPLR 400w mercury internal reflector lamps placed at 3 ft centres supplemented with light from equal numbers of 150w incandescent bulbs.

3 Inflorescence Structure and Criteria of Flowering Response

Wild *Cannabis* is dioecious; the chromosome number is $n = 10$, and the male sex is heterogametic. The cultivars vary substantially in the pattern of sex expression, and there has certainly been selection for monoecism. In consequence a great variety of sex forms now exists, and the genetical situation is complex (for full review, see Westergaard[41]). Selection for sex-type has been accompanied by selection for photoperiodic response, and in this attribute also considerable diversity now prevails in races of different provenance.[26,27]

The inflorescences of both sexes are basically compound racemes. Under conditions leading to full flowering, a determinate terminal inflorescence is formed. The male is the more copiously branched, and has the more reduced bracts (Fig. 8–1). The flowers of the two sexes are morphologically very distinct at maturity, and they are fundamentally unisexual in the sense that they do not reveal vestiges of the alternate sex,[5,7] nor are hermaphrodite flowers formed teratologically. The primordia do, however, pass through an undifferentiated state from which they are capable of developing either as staminate or carpellate[15,8] and in intersexual inflorescences, structures intermediate between stamens and carpels occur.[12] Molliard[28] used intersexual flowers to trace

FIGURE 8–1. Hemp (*Cannabis sativa* L.) in the early part of a flowering period. Male to the left, female to the right.

the affinities between the outer members of staminate and carpellate flowers.

In the pre-flowering state, the two sexes of hemp are indistinguishable morphologically, and notwithstanding the report of Walther and Lilienstern,[40] a long series of tests (Belf.) has failed to reveal any consistent differences in physiological characteristics, including respiratory rate, catalase and peroxidase activity, sap pH and pigment content, before the development of inflorescences. Subsequently to the passage into flowering very marked sexual dimorphism develops, and there is practically no physiological property in which the sexes do not diverge. The most striking differences are in growth rate during flowering, leaf size and pigment content[2] in the vicinity of the inflorescences, and longevity subsequent to anthesis. Compared with the females, genetically male plants show simultaneously a more rapid extension growth rate and a speedier reduction of leaves to the form of bracts, coupled with a diminution in relative chlorophyll content. Leaf-shape changes and their relationships with flowering are considered in later sections. The male plants have a much shorter life span after anthesis; under continuous inductive conditions they survive for periods three weeks to two months less than the females, according to variety.

In both sexes, the first evidence of a flowering response is seen in the formation of minute primordia at a node of the principal stem, within the stipules and adjacent to the axillary bud itself (Fig. 8–2A). As indicated above, these primordia are initially undifferentiated sexually, but later the males are betrayed by their rounded form, due to the differentiation of a radially symmetrical perianth, and the females by the enlargement of the single pointed bract which comes eventually to invest the flower (Fig. 8–2B and C).

FIGURE 8–2. Stages of inflorescence development in *Cannabis sativa*.

    A. Sterile node, with the stipules folded back to show the absence of flower primordia.

    B. Node with minute primordia in the axils of the stipules. These primordia, formed even in long days, are sexually undifferentiated, and may abort without further development.

    C. Developing female primordia.

    D. Developing male primordia.

    E. Male inflorescence, with the flower in the axil of a stipule at anthesis.

    F. Female inflorescences. The flower in the axil of the stipule at the centre left is forming a fruit.

    Primordium initiation is the first step to flowering, but as explained further in section 7 it occurs ultimately in non-inductive photoperiodic conditions (T), and does not necessarily lead to flowering. Flowering response can be measured in various ways. Criteria include (*a*) the nodal position of the first flower primordia; (*b*) the nodal position of the first opening flower; (*c*) the number of nodes on the principal axis with developing axillary inflorescences; (*d*) the fertility of axillary inflorescences, estimated from bud abortion, and pollen and seed sterility; and (*e*) the total numbers of flowers formed, per rode and per plant. These criteria relate to different components of the response, and they can be combined. In Figure 8–3, for example, the flowering response at successive nodes is recorded on a five point scale.

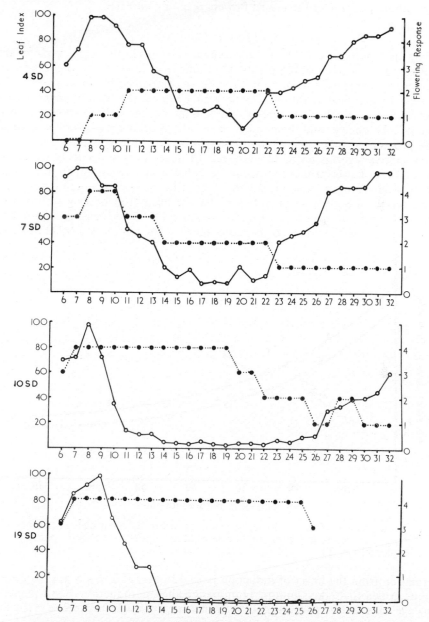

FIGURE 8.3. Flowering response in individual male plants given 4, 7, 10 and 19 short days after growth for four weeks in days of 21–22 hr light. Leaf shape index (open circles) calculated as in text (p. 210), and flowering response (closed circles) estimated on a 5-point scale, (0) node vegetative; (1) undifferentiated primordia present; (2) male primordia formed, but arrested in development; (3) male inflorescence formed but showing some sterility; (4) fertile male inflorescences present. The horizontal scale represents node number. (*C*, Belf.) (Heslop-Harrison and Heslop-Harrison[16]).

For the simple assessment of the effectiveness of an inductive treatment, the most efficient criteria are (*a*) time to flower, and (*b*) position of lowest developing primordium. Where growth rate is seriously influenced by temperature and nutritional treatments, comparison with controls is most effectively based upon nodal position of the lowest flowers reaching anthesis.

4 Effects of Plant Age

Hemp is characterised by a very regular heteroblastic leaf development. During the growth of young plants, the number of lobes of the digitate leaves increases progressively from node to node, accompanied by an increase in the number of marginal serrations. As flowering begins, the trend is reversed and lobe and tooth number, and area of the lamina, decline in both sexes. The product of lobe number and the number of serrations on one margin of the central lobe provides an index combining these two aspects of leaf shape.[4,22]

All cultivars so far tested have revealed a juvenile period during which the formation of flower primordia cannot be induced by any combination of treatments. The minimum period is slightly shorter for male plants than for females, and shorter for both sexes in cultivars, like the bushy Indian drug strains, with poor photoperiodic sensitivity. Figure 8–4 illustrates the decreasing requirement for short days before flowering as plants age (T). The minimum period to flower

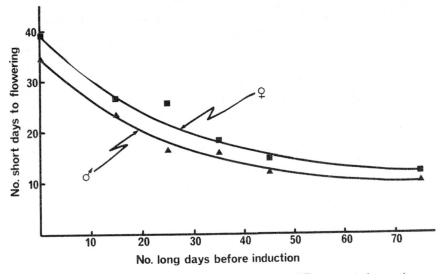

FIGURE 8–4. Time to flower in plants grown to different ages in continuous light before induction in 9-hr days. Mean values for the sexes plotted separately (*C*, T).

formation from the onset of induction is 10–12 days, and this is approached in plants grown to 45 days in long photoperiods before induction. Most plants of this age have started to form minute primordia, although these show no further development without exposure to short days.

Photoperiodic sensitivity is attained early in life. There is no evidence to indicate that the cotyledons respond, but the first unifoliate leaf is probably sensitive, and the next, usually trifoliate, certainly so (Belf.). This leaf expands from the 4th–6th day after germination.

Plants passing through a flowering period after restoration to long days after a short day episode show rejuvenation,[34] in the sense that they recapitulate the heteroblastic sequence apparent in the seedling, the nodal leaf sequence starting with the unlobed, unserrated inflorescence bracts and progressing to the digitate, serrated long-day leaf form. Rejuvenation is, however, incomplete to the extent that flower primordia continue to be formed (Fig. 8–3), although these undergo no development. Presumably in consequence, a further period of induction brings about flowering in the minimum 10–12 day period (Belf.).

Opposite and decussate phyllotaxis is another indication of juvenility. In a fibre strain (S) grown at a constant 22°C the transition to spiral phyllotaxy took place under 18 hour days at a mean node number of 11.4, and at a mean node number of 9.1 under 8-hour days (Belf.). A correlation exists between the position of the lowest flower primordia and the lowest alternate leaf, with the lowest alternate leaf on the average two nodes above the lowest primordium (T).

5 Vernalisation and Devernalisation

Hemp is naturally an annual plant of warm latitudes, and it reveals no vernalisation response as normally understood in plants of temperate climates. Low temperature treatment at any period from germination onwards delays growth and the passage into flowering, and may induce abnormalities in sex expression and floral morphogenesis (Section 13).

7 Photoperiod Response

Nature of the flowering reaction

All hemp varieties tested have revealed a short-day response, in the sense that the transition to flowering is accelerated with decreasing length of day. The nature of the effect requires unambiguous definition. As stated previously, the first sign of a transition to flowering is seen in the formation of undifferentiated primordia. In the Sacavem, Coimbra and Liège strains this occurs even under continuous illumination, and was observed by Borthwick and Scully[1] to occur also in cultivar Kentucky under non-inductive conditions. The time taken to form primordia is affected by photoperiod, increasing from 32 days to 91 days as daylength increased from 9 to 14.75 hours.[35]

In respect to primordium formation, therefore, all hemp varieties are probably to be looked upon as quantitative short-day plants. In contrast, for progress to anthesis – the production of open, fertile flowers – some varieties have an absolute requirement for short days. In these the primordia formed under long days fail to develop, or are shed. It seems that whether the response is 'absolute' or 'quantitative' depends upon the level of a reaction threshold. In a small-seeded Indian cultivar ('Cannabis indica') obtained through the kindness of the late Professor Maheshwari, the threshold was found to be low, and flowering occurred freely under continuous light; this race showed a quantitative short-day response. In contrast, the threshold in the Coimbra race was found to be high, so that it showed an absolute requirement for short days for fertile flowering. In other fibre cultivars, flowering occurs in continuous light, but only after a protracted period of growth. It is noteworthy that the responses of the sexes are different, since in the Liège race only the males showed any fertility under non-inductive conditions (Lond., T.).

Critical daylength

It is obvious from the foregoing that the concept of critical daylength only has meaning for those hemp varieties which fail to reach a stage of fertile flowering under continuous illumination. This is true for the females and all but an occasional male plant of the Portuguese fibre variety C in experiments over periods

of up to a year (Belf.). In daylengths of 20 hours, a significantly higher proportion of plants reached fertile flowering in such long term experiments, so if a
critical daylength had to be quoted, it would be in excess of 20 hours. In the
variety *C* there is essentially no further acceleration of flowering with daylengths
shorter than 9 hours, when flowering occurs in 33–35 days from germination.
This is also the minimum period for flowering in the small-seeded Indian cultivars: in these, flowering takes place in both sexes in 15–20 weeks under continuous light, although the variation between individuals is high, presumably
because such abnormally long daylengths are exposing otherwise concealed genetical diversity. It is probably safe to conclude that all varieties of hemp lie between the extremes defined by the Coimbra fibre strain and the Indian varieties.

As previously indicated, the sexual dimorphism extends to daylength sensitivity. In all recorded experiments, the male plants have been found to flower
earlier than the females under the same photoperiods. In Cheuvart's variety, for
example, the difference was 10 days under 16 hour photoperiods.

Effect of number of inductive cycles

In hemp, the relative effectiveness of a particular number of inductive cycles is
strongly dependent upon age: the younger the plant, the greater the number of
cycles required to produce fertile flowers. This is related to the fact that flower
primordia are produced as the plants age under all photoperiods. The effect of
short-day induction in accelerating primordium production is shown in Figure
8–5 for plants grown to an age of 15 days in continuous light before exposure
to 9-hour days (T). In this experiment, a significant response in respect to primordium formation was observed with 7 inductive cycles, but these primordia
did not develop into flowers in the course of the experiment, and indeed 15 short
days were required to induce a true flowering response.

In contrast, in a similar experiment with plants grown to an age of 26 days
in continuous light, 4 short days were sufficient to induce a full flowering re-
sponse(T, Fig. 8–6). Comparable results were obtained by Borthwick and Scully.[1]

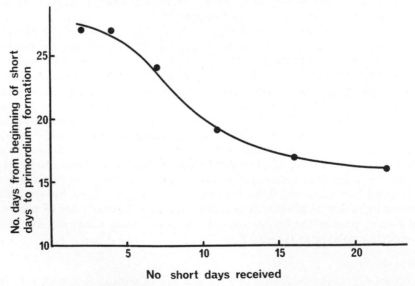

FIGURE 8–5. Effect of number of short days on time to form flower primordia. Plants grown to an age of 15 days in continuous illumination, then
given the indicated numbers of 9-hr days before restoration to continuous
light (*S*, T).

With the Kentucky variety, plants grown to an age of 3 weeks in 18-hour days required 8 short days of 8 hours light to produce an observable flowering response; those grown to 4 weeks, 6 short days; and those to 5 weeks, 4 short days.

A quantitative relationship can readily be demonstrated between the number of inductive cycles and the flowering response in male plants. Figure 8–3 shows the flowering response at successive nodes for individual male plants grown to an age of 28 days under non-inductive long-day conditions before exposure to 4, 7, 10 and 19 8-hour days ([16], Belf.). In this case, open flowers were obtained with a minimum of 7 inductive cycles, but some response to induction was seen in the plant receiving 4 short days.

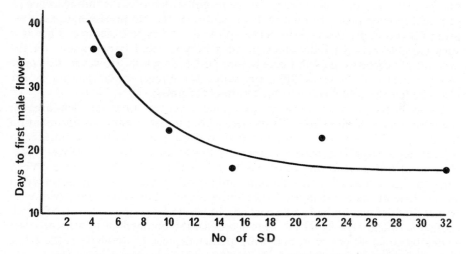

FIGURE 8–6. Effect of number of inductive cycles on time to anthesis in male plants. Plants grown to an age of 26 days in long days, then exposed to the numbers of 9-hr days indicated before transfer to continuous light. (*C*, T)

It is evident from Figure 8–3 that the leaf shape index provides a sensitive measure of the inductive experience of the hemp plant. The curve dips steeply with the passage into flowering, and even an experience of four inductive cycles that does not induce open flowers produces a downward inflection. Thomas has shown that one inductive cycle is sufficient to bring about a transient decrease in leaf serration number in plants grown to an age of 21 days in long days, although this treatment results in no detectable flowering response.

Effects of partial induction have been examined by varying numbers of inductive cycles, and by reducing the area of inducible leaf by defoliation to varying degrees (Belf.,Lond.).

For the varieties more sensitive to photoperiod, Figure 8–3 shows that as the number of inductive cycles is diminished a point is reached below which the flowering response is related quantitatively to the inductive experience. Following inductive treatments in this lower region the stem grows through a period of flowering – or at least incipient flowering – and then reverts to vegetative growth, with a concomitant rise in leaf lobe number and serration. Again, male and female plants show differential sensitivity to the same photoperiodic experience. Successive cycles of flowering can be caused by alternating minimal induction treatments with intervals of long-day rejuvenation. Provided that no inductive treatment is protracted enough to destroy the monopodial growth habit, the heteroblastic sequence is recapitulated after each flowering episode. The period required for recovery of the long day habit depends upon the length of the inductive treatment. With the C race, plants given 10 short days at an age of four weeks showed the first indication of recovery three weeks after the end of the inductive episode in a restoration of the trend to higher leaf lobe and serration numbers (Fig. 8–3). With an inductive period of 19 days, apical growth of male plants is usually brought to a halt; recovery, if it occurs at all, is erratic, and results from the outgrowth of vegetative buds in a lateral position; the time taken may be two months or more. In general, it may be said that a threshold exists for the number of inductive cycles below which rejuvenation is still possible on restoration to long days after the termination of main stem growth. In female plants, regeneration usually occurs in the neighbourhood of the inflorescence itself, and in male plants commonly lower on the stem. No precise figure can be given for this upper threshold in terms of number of cycles tolerated, since it is very variable between individuals in all genotypes, and is dependent on the amount of vegetative growth made before initial induction. However, it is once more evident that the sexes differ, the males losing regenerative powers sooner than the females under comparable treatment regimes.

Using the Sacavem race, Thomas examined the effect of reducing leaf area on the effectiveness of induction. Plants were grown under continuous illumination to an age of 35 days, and then defoliated to varying degrees before transfer to 8-hour days. Mean leaf areas and times to flower are shown in Table 8–1. Reduction of leaf area to one third barely affected the time of flowering. When only one leaf remained there was some indication of retardation, and reduction to one lobe at node 6 delayed flower initiation by about one week. Although 85 per cent defoliation had to be carried out before flowering time was affected, reduction of leaf area by 49 per cent decreased the numbers of flowers on male plants by some 40 per cent, and with greater degrees of defoliation the effect was relatively more pronounced.

TABLE 8–1

Effect of reduction of leaf area on time to flower (S). Plants grown to 35 days in continuous light, defoliated to the degrees shown, and then exposed to 8-hr days (T).[35]

Leaf area remaining:	10,400 mm² (intact)	6,450 mm²	3,250 mm²	1,350 mm²	700 mm²
Mean no. of days to formation of primordia					
Females:	11.8	15.3	–	13.0	21.5
Males:	12.5	11.0	13.0	18.5	18.5
Mean no. of male flowers open after 35 hr days	40.0	26.0	8.8	2.5	0.0

Threshold intensities

The light energy required to inhibit flowering has been investigated by Borthwick and Scully[1] using the Kentucky cultivar. Plants received 8 hours natural daylight, and then 16 hours light from an incandescent source at varying intensities, ranging from 0.001 to 60 f.c. All those receiving less than 0.02 f.c. flowered; at 0.05 f.c., five flowered out of six, and all higher intensities inhibited flowering. In a further experiment covering the range 0.002 to 0.25 f.c., 0.03 f.c. was found to be the threshold intensity.

Light break effects

There appear to have been no systematic studies with hemp on the relative effectiveness of light breaks of different intensities given at various times during the dark period, although in earlier experiments primarily concerned with sex expression several forms of night interruption were investigated (Belf.,Lond.). Using a 12-hour cycle, a retardation of flowering of up to 3 months was obtained with the fibre varieties on a 4-hour light, 8-hour dark regime, and even in varieties with a long critical daylength, fertile flowering could be delayed indefinitely on an 8-hour light, 4-hour dark programme.[19] What experience there is suggests that light breaks experienced midway through the dark period always reduce its effectiveness, but little is known of reciprocity relations, which are seemingly not simple. From the results of Borthwick and Scully[1] using continuous dark period illumination, light amounts as low as 2 f.c. hours should cause appreciable flowering delay. However, light amounts of 175 f.c. hours, given as a dark period interruption of 30 minutes duration with light at 350 f.c. from one 400 w mercury vapour source and four 100 w incandescent bulbs, delayed flowering by only a matter of one week in plants of the Liège stock grown from germination in an 8-hour light, 16-hour dark regime (T).

8 Spectral Dependence

Observations on hemp have hitherto been only of a casual nature. For the races *S*, *C* and *L* a source relatively rich in red is essential for daylength extension to inhibit or delay a flowering response. Light from filtered mercury sources, and from cool white and daylight fluorescent lamps, has been found relatively ineffective even at intensities exceeding 350 f.c.

11 Photoperiodic Inhibition

There is little evidence of photoperiodic inhibition phenomena in hemp. It follows from what has been said above that the intercalation of long days between short-day episodes is likely to have a perceptible effect only if the long-day experience is protracted enough to permit some degree of recovery. As Köhler[23] has shown, the experience of single long days during periods of short-day induction has no discernible inhibitory effect upon the flowering response.

12 Dual Photoperiodic Responses

Like all photoperiodically sensitive plants, hemp is adapted to respond to changing daylength in such a manner as to give greatest competitive advantage in a natural environment. The measure of success in an annual is fertility, expressed ultimately in seed output. The conditions maximising this parameter in hemp are undoubtedly offered by a photoperiodic regime beginning with short days and passing on to long days. This is clearly revealed by the factorial experiment referred to in Section 13, where under similar conditions of temperature plants exposed to 12-hour days following an inductive experience produced a seed yield of rather more than double that given by plants experiencing 8-hour days. Since the supplementary light received by the plants under 12-hour days was of low intensity, the effect was photoperiodic and not simply due to the greater availability of assimilates. It may thus be argued that *Cannabis sativa* is a short daylong day species in the common terminology, although this is no more than an awkward way of indicating that it is adapted to increasing daylength during the normal growing season.

13 Effects of Temperature

Nelson[29] found that higher temperatures accelerated anthesis in hemp plants grown under natural daylengths. In controlled conditions under continuous illu-

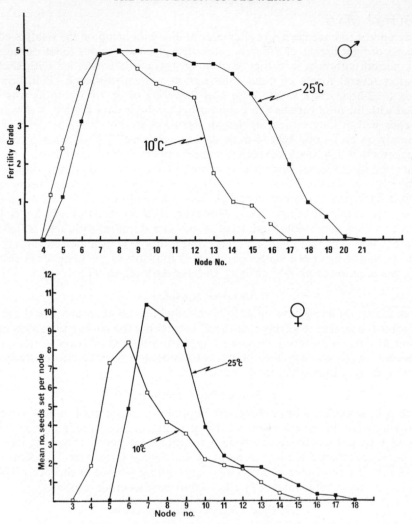

FIGURE 8–7. Effects of night temperature in the immediate post-inductive period on fertility in male and female plants. Treatments as in text. Male flowering per node scored on a 6-point scale ranging from vegetative to full development of axillary inflorescences, and female fertility estimated by mean number of seeds set per node. (C, Belf.)

mination, the time to formation of the first sterile primordium is significantly shorter in plants grown from an age of 10 days at 24°C than in those grown from the same age at 15.5°C (L, T). The effect is seen also in time to primordium formation and flowering in plants grown from an age of 3 days in 8-hour days, that is, in continuously inductive conditions. In an experiment with variety C, at a continuous temperature of 15.5°C, primordia were formed after an average of 24.5 days, and flowering occurred after 40.5 days; at 22°C, primordia appeared after 19 days, and flowering took place after 33 days, and at 26°C primordia appeared at 18 days, with flowering at 30 days.

The prevailing temperature during the inductive and early flowering period greatly affects node length,[36] but does not influence leaf shape as does nitrogen deficiency (Section 14). Temperature during primordium initiation and early flowering does, however, radically influence fertility in both sexes. Fig. 8–7 summarises part of the results of a factorial experiment in which plants (C) were exposed to varying combinations of light intensity, daylength and temperature after a 28-day period of growth in long days and an induction treatment of 10 short days at 22°C. The temperature regimes after induction were continuous 25°C, and 25°C day temperature and 10°C night, these treatments being confounded with two daylengths, 12 hours and 8 hours, and two light intensities, 1000 f.c. and 500 f.c. The curves of Figure 8–7 show how night temperature modified the fertilities of the two sexes under the most favourable conditions, 12-hour days at 1000 f.c., although the temperature effect was significant in other combinations also.

Apart from the diminution of fertility attributable to temperature, temperatures below 13–14°C also modify flower morphogenesis, especially in male plants. The effect is seen in increasing tendency to intersexuality and in enhanced meristic variation.[19] Tests to determine whether this effect is due to a local response in the apex itself or to some transmitted stimulus from the leaf have been carried out by exposing the apices of young plants to low air temperatures (5–10°C) in Dewar flasks throughout the dark period while the rest of each plant remained at 22°C (C, Belf.). Treatment was given during short-day induction and in the subsequent period of bud differentiation. Flowering was delayed in time almost to the same degree as in plants exposed completely to low night temperatures, but the incidence of floral abnormalities was reduced. This result seems ambiguous and the experiment requires repetition, but the indications are that part at least of the delaying effect of low temperatures on flowering is due to a direct response in the differentiating apex.

14 Effects of Mineral Nutrition

There have been many experiments on the effects of mineral nutrition on flowering behaviour in hemp, directed for the most part towards modifying sex ratio in populations or sex expression in individuals (see review[5]). Hitherto, however, there has been little published evidence concerning nutritional effects on flower induction. In work in London and Belfast several studies have been made on the response to different nitrogen levels, but no attention has been given to other elements.

Nitrogen deprivation retards growth and slows the trend towards increasing leaf complexity during early growth, an effect related to a lower rate of increase of growing point diameter from node node. However, notwithstanding this, the node at which the first flowers are formed is actually lowered under conditions of N deficiency. In one experiment with the C strain, plants were grown under two nutrient regimes, with normal N, and with nitrates replaced by chlorides, to an age of 16 days in long days before transfer to short days. With normal N, the mean node number of the first flower bud was 5.66 for the females and 5.08 for the males. Under N deprivation, the corresponding node numbers were 4.83 and 4.66. By the morphological index of nodal position of the first formed flowers, N deficiency thus promotes flowering, but in terms of the time to anthesis, the effect is one of retardation.

Thomas found no significant difference either in time of formation or location of flowers on cuttings rooted in media with normal and reduced N supply. Decapitated plants were grown to an age of 60 days in long days, and the paired lateral shoots at the uppermost node then removed and allowed to root for a further 70 days under long days, one of each pair in a medium with normal N, and the other in conditions of N deficiency. Following the beginning of short-day induction, the males in each series produced flower buds in a mean of 8.3 days, and the females in 13.8 with normal N, and in 14.4 with N deficiency.

N starvation severely reduced the numbers of fertile flowers formed in each sex, but in several experiments under well controlled conditions no consistent effects on sex expression or floral morphogenesis have been observed (Belf., Lond., Birm.). Borthwick and Scully[1] similarly found no influence of N nutrition on sexuality in the Kentucky strain. Some earlier reports of effects on sex ratio, such as that of Tibeau,[37] are of no significance because of the small numbers of individuals involved. The possibility that sexuality may be affected by other elements cannot yet be discounted; Herich,[3] for example, has indicated that boron, applied by seed soaking, may increase the proportion of male intersexes in a polyploid race tested by him.

15 Effects of Gas Composition

The only studies on the effects of gas composition on the flowering behaviour of hemp seem to have been concerned with the influence of carbon monoxide on sex expression.[15] In these experiments (C), plants were exposed to 1 per cent CO before, during and immediately after short-day induction. In all cases, the treatment induced some degree of intersexuality in genetically male plants if applied during the very early differentiation of the flower buds. In one experiment treatment was given before and during induction. Plants grown to an age of 15 days in long days were exposed nightly for five days to 1 per cent CO for periods of 16 hours with simultaneous illumination at 10–20 f.c., while controls received similar treatment without exposure to the gas. Thereafter the controls received 11, 8-hour days, while the treated plants were exposed to 6, 8-hour days in a normal atmosphere followed by 5 further 8-hour days with an atmosphere containing 1 per cent CO during the 16-hour night. After restoration to long days, flower bud differentiation began on the controls within five days, but their appearance was delayed for a further eight days in the CO-treated plants. The delay was related to a general retardation of development, but it was apparent also in the females in the level of the node bearing the first developing flowers, the mean number being $7.75 \pm .42$ in the controls and $9.17 \pm .26$ in the treated plants.

16 Translocation of the Flowering Stimulus

There have been no studies aimed at determining the rate of movement of the flowering stimulus from the leaf in hemp, although the plant would be well suited for this kind of investigation. Translocation of the stimulus between branches in different photoperiods has been examined by Thomas. Twin-branched plants (C) were produced by decapitating seedlings after growth to 19 days in long day conditions. After a further 23 days growth, donor branches were given 8-hour days in light-tight boxes, while receptor branches remained in long days. In half of the plants the receptor branches were defoliated, and new leaves appearing on these were removed as they grew. The results are summarised in Table 8–2. Flowering only occurred on defoliated receptors, and in both sexes was delayed in these by about a week compared with the controls.

17 Grafting Experiments

Several attempts have been made to demonstrate effects on sex expression by intergrafting male and female plants, but the results in all cases have been uncompromisingly negative.[5,36,25] This was found to be so even with micrografts, in which apical fragments of 4–5 mm were grafted onto mature stocks before, during and after induction to flower (Belf.).

The transmission of the flowering stimulus between graft partners, however, is very readily demonstrated (Belf., Lond.). In approach grafts between equal partners, the stimulus is transmitted effectively only if the receptor partner is defoliated. If the scion is small, the presence of young leaves does not inhibit the transmission. In one experiment (T) stem apices from non-flowering plants of both sexes were grafted onto female stocks, and the foliated parts of the stocks exposed to short days while the scions remained in continuous illumination. The

TABLE 8–2

Time to flower in donor and receptor branches of twin-branched plants (C). Treatments as in text. Data of Thomas.[35]

	Mean time in days from beginning of short-day exposure		
	Receptor defoliated		Receptor leafy
	Males	Females	Females
Donor Branch	7.3	13.0	11.5
Receptor Branch	13.0	20.0	no flowering

stocks flowered in 8 days and the male scions in 19; the females ranged between 19 and 29 days.

Apex grafting has been used to show that the effect of carbon monoxide on flower morphogenesis and sex expression is directly upon the apical tissues and not upon older parts of the plant.[15]

18 Effects of Growth Substances and Growth Retardants

Most experiments on the effects of growth substances on the flowering behaviour of hemp have been concerned with sex expression and flower morphogenesis, but a body of evidence relating to effects on flower initiation has arisen *pari passu*. The main data are summarised below for various growth substances.

Auxins

Foliar sprays of indole-3-acetic acid (IAA) and α-naphthalene acetic acid (NAA) given daily just before the dark period during an induction treatment of 10 short days suppress or greatly delay the flowering response in 20-day old plants (Belf.). The effectiveness of this treatment at other periods during the inductive cycle has not been examined.

NAA supplied through the leaf after a minimal induction period delayed flowering, reduced the total flowering response and induced intersexuality in genetically male plants.[4] In one experiment, plants (C) were grown to an age of 20 days in long days induced by 10 short days, and supplied with NAA at 0.5 per cent in hydrous lanolin through one leaf lobe for three days immediately after restoration to long days and through two leaf lobes five days later for a similar period. This treatment raised the nodal position of the first detectable flower bud from 6.0 to 7.9 and reduced the number of nodes with flowers reaching anthesis from 9.4 to 2.5.

A significant additional response to NAA treatment is a retardation of the heteroblastic trend that normally accompanies flowering. With both sexes, treated plants showed a more rapid recovery to higher leaf indices after a brief induction period than did the more copiously flowering controls. This response suggested that auxin treatment promoted a more rapid rejuvenation, and led to a demonstration that male apices induced to a degree which would normally cause death could be caused to resume vegetative growth by application of auxin exogenously.[16]

2, 3, 5-triiodobenzoic acid

On the assumption then current that 2, 3, 5-triiodobenzoic acid (TIBA) acted as an agent lowering endogenous auxin in plant tissues, its effects upon the flowering responses of hemp were examined in 1956.[14] Plants (C) were grown to an age of 20 days in long days, then given an inductive treatment of 10 short days. TIBA was applied in a hydrous lanolin medium at a concentration of 0.5 per cent through one leaf lobe for three days following the cessation of short-day treatment, and through two leaf lobes five days later for the same period. The morphogenetic abnormalities now known to be a common feature of plant response to TIBA were observed, and in several plants apical dominance was lost so that a bushy growth form resulted. There was some slight delay in the attainment of anthesis, but no shift in the node of lowest flowering in either sex. However, in both sexes the production of flowers was greater in the TIBA treated plants, very significantly so in the males (Table 8–3). The effect is probably to be attributed to the release of additional sites for flower production by the outgrowth of laterals following upon the loss of apical dominance. Male flowers in the treated plants showed remarkable morphogenetic modifications, the extreme being the total fusion of tepals and of anthers.

TABLE 8–3

Effect of 2, 3, 5-triiodobenzoic acid (TIBA) on the flowering response of male and female plants, assessed by the numbers of nodes bearing open flowers (C). Treatment as in text.

	Mean number of nodes with flowers	
	Males	Females
Controls	$14.0 \pm .28$	$12.1 \pm .24$
TIBA-treated	$23.5 \pm .43$	17.8 ± 3.21

Gibberellic acid

The effect of gibberellic acid (GA_3) on flowering in hemp has been analysed fairly fully,[17] and some apparently conflicting aspects of the responses reconciled. In summary, GA_3 supplied during short-day induction delays flowering and reduces flower production in genetically male plants, while treatment after induction increases flower production in both sexes. Male plants receiving GA_3 during induction showed a severe retardation of stem growth and lower flower production. Mean total number of flowers was, however, increased in plants receiving GA_3 at the end of the inductive treatment. The females showed no apex abortion, but the total yield of flowers was enhanced only in plants treated after the close of the short day episode.

Supplied to plants in non-inductive photoperiodic conditions, GA_3 produces a change in leaf shape simulating that induced by exposure to short days, although the formation of flower primordia is not promoted in these circumstances.[17]

Maleic hydrazide

The growth retardant maleic hydrazide (MH) inhibits stem extension growth in both sexes of hemp in all photoperiodic conditions (Belf.). In an experiment with twin-branched plants (C), one apex was dipped into a 0.5 per cent aqueous solution of MH on four occasions during short-day induction. Under subsequent long days the untreated apices passed through a flowering period and resumed vegetative growth. Few MH-treated apices survived, but those that did produced only aborted buds before resuming vegetative growth after a protracted delay.

Endogenous growth substances

In the period 1956–1958 (Belf.) several attempts were made to detect differences in the auxin metabolism of induced and non-induced plants of both sexes in the hope of finding evidence bearing upon the hypothesis that sex expression is governed, or at least affected, by natural auxins.[6,8,13] The then standard extraction, separation and assay methods were adopted, using straight growth tests for auxin activity. No consistent differences of any meaningful kind were observed, and although growth activity was obtained in ethanolic and methanolic extracts, no indole compounds were detected.

More consistent results have been obtained by Hulewicz[20] using a Hungarian cultivar. The auxins of the first three pairs of leaves were assayed for growth activity in the oat coleoptile and mesocotyl tests at various times during induction. According to Hulewicz, there is an initial rise on transfer to short days, then levels fall to the 5th day of induction. With continued SD treatment, there is a slow return to the long-day level. The auxins were not identified.

19 Effects of Metabolic Inhibitors

During 1958–1959, a study was made of the effects on flowering behaviour in hemp of a number of base analogues, including 8-azaguanine and 2-thiouracil. Only with 2-thiouracil (2–TU) were results of any significance observed,[9] presumably since other analogues penetrated less readily. In one experiment, plants (C) were grown 25 days in long days and then exposed to 10 short days. 2-TU was supplied by painting standard areas of the upper epidermis of the youngest fully expanded leaves with an aqueous solution containing 100 μg/ml immediately before the onset of each dark period. It was estimated that each plant received 15–30 μg per treatment, but the proportion penetrating could not be estimated. In male control plants, fertile flowers were uniformly produced at node 6; in the treated males, primordia were not produced until node 8, and these were sterile. In the control female plants the mean node number of the first fertile flowers was 7, while of the plants of this sex receiving 2-TU only one formed a distinguishable flower bud in the four weeks following induction, and this, at node 9, was sterile. Both by the morphological indicator provided by the position of lowest flower bud and in terms of true time, the 2-TU treatment delayed flowering, and the effect was related to a general retardation of development and the induction of morphogenetic abnormalties elsewhere in the plant.[11] In a response of this kind, the degree of specificity of the effect on flowering is in question, since this could be but one aspect of the general growth inhibition. However, treated plants reverted ultimately to vegetative growth with little or no flowering, suggesting that there had been practically no registration of the inductive stimulus when the analogue was present in the tissues.

Autoradiographic examination of the movement of 2-^{14}C-2-TU revealed that it was rapidly translocated to growing tissues above the level of application, and that it accumulated particularly in meristems. Since there is no reason to suppose that the analogue enters mature, photoperiodically perceptive leaves other than those through which it is introduced, it was argued that the response was not likely to be due to an effect on the synthesis or effectiveness of the products of the inductive dark period but rather that it was due to a loss of the capacity of apical meristematic tissues to react to leaf-generated stimuli.[9] A comprehensive study of the effects of 2-TU upon the apical meristem of hemp has been made by Jagoe.[21,18] Briefly, daily treatments given by dipping in 2-TU at 100 μg/ml under long-day conditions reduce mitotic frequency to very low values by the tenth day, when numerous blocked prophases are visible in the apex. Planes of division in the apex and in the sub-apical zone are modified from the third or fourth day, and after five days multinucleate cells are present throughout the apical meristem. Treatment for five days severely reduces the amount of cytoplasmic basiphilia (principally RNA) in the normally deeply staining cells of the flanks, and cells in this zone subsequently become necrotic. During recovery from a 10-day period of 2-TU treatment a normal apical meristem is usually restored, but only after a period of abnormal growth.[18] Cell division resumes in the sub-apical region first, and necrotic tissues are displaced. Symmetry is usually attained ultimately, but accessory growing points may be formed.

A substantial incorporation of 2-TU into RNA fractions has been demonstrated ([9], J), but whether the effects on development and morphogenesis are wholly due to interference with RNA metabolism cannot be said to be yet fully established.

21 Induction of Excised Apices

Preliminary experiments on the culture of excised apices for the study of induction *in vitro* have been carried out by Dr. J. Blake (Birm.). Explants ranging in size down to 500 μ have been grown successfully in synthetic media, and have been caused to develop without callus formation in the absence of exogenous auxin. Under these conditions, the terminal growing point continues to lay down primordia, but roots are not formed; uptake from the medium is through a basal nodule. Flowering has been obtained in culture in plantlets grown from pre-induced apices, but induction *in vitro* is still to be studied.

22 Chemical, Histochemical, and Ultrastructural
Changes at Induction

In the seed, the growing point of the stem is flattened, and constitutes merely two or three cell layers defined by their high pyroninophilia. The bulk of this pyroninophilia is RNAase digestible. During early germination, the apex progressively becomes domed, and by the fifth plastochron under long days it enters into a cycle of change characteristic of the vegetative period of growth. This cycle is related to the state of the plastochron, and the aspect of the apex intersection depends on the orientation of the section plane in relation to the leaf orthostichies during the period of opposite and decussate phyllotaxis. At the time of emergence of a pair of leaf primordia in one plane, the diameter of the apical dome reaches its minimum; maximum diameter, as observed in the same plane, is reached during the development of the next pair of leaf primordia in the plane at right angles. At all times during the vegetative cycle, a distinction can be made between a central region in the apex with weakly staining cytoplasm and small nucleoli, and a flank zone with smaller cells having cytoplasmic contents staining deeply with pyronin and larger nucleoli. Estimated by pyronin densitometry, RNA concentration in the flank regions may exceed that in the axial region by up to 50 per cent.

If short-day inductive treatment is given during the early vegetative growth period, the first response in the apex is a slight initial flattening and the extension of the region of basiphilic cells towards the centre. This change is correlated with the earlier definition of the primordia of lateral shoots in the axils of leaf primordia, and becomes apparent 4–6 days after the onset of induction, more rapidly in the male plant. Thereafter the growing point itself extends and narrows, and the outer cell layers become more uniformly basiphilic throughout the apical dome. The primordia of lateral axes, which by the 7th day of induction emerge high on the apical dome almost simultaneously with the appearance of the primordia of the subtending leaves, reveal high RNA concentrations, exceeding the maximum discernible in axial tissue by up to 66 per cent. This general pattern is apparent in both sexes, although in the female plant there is a less marked extension of the growing point during the early stages of inflorescence differentiation so that some of the features that characterise the transition to flowering are less prominent. The termination of flowering is marked in both sexes by the suspension of cell division and the loss of RNA throughout the apical dome.

Under protracted non-inductive conditions, the apex passes out of the cyclical pattern of behaviour characteristic of early growth, and assumes an aspect intermediate in some respects between that of the vegetative phase and that attained during flowering. The transition is correlated with the shift to spiral phyllotaxis, and follows upon the first appearance of abortive flower primordia associated with the stipules. The zonation of RNA in the apical dome becomes less evident, and the level at which axillary primordia can first be distinguished is advanced up its flanks. This condition prevails indefinitely under non-inductive daylengths in fibre strains showing absolute photoperiodic control of fertile flowering. In genotypes that do flower eventually in long days, the intermediate aspect slowly gives place, over several plastochrons, to that characteristic of normal flowering. The intermediate condition can thus be looked upon as indicative of a transition to flowering, a transition so slow in some genotypes that it is never completed in the course of the life span under non-inductive conditions. It is noteworthy however, that the progression to flowering is not irreversible, since it is to the intermediate pattern of apex that reversion occurs after a flowering episode following sub-optimal induction.

There is an abundant literature concerning chemical and biochemical changes accompanying the transition to flowering in hemp. Most papers have related to the development of sexual dimorphism, and have been concerned with later stages in the flowering process than are considered here. The most recent paper is that of Zemlyanukhin and Shenshina,[42] in which numerous differentiae are listed.

There have been no detailed fine structural studies of the hemp apex in transition to flowering.

23 Inflorescence Differentiation

The early changes in the transition of the hemp apex from vegetative growth to flowering have been outlined in the foregoing section. In this section, two further aspects will be given brief consideration, (a) the relationship of leaf-shape changes to flowering and inflorescence differentiation, and (b) the behaviour of the individual floral meristem, with particular reference to flower sexuality.

Leaf shape changes and flowering

The heteroblastic trend of early life is reversed with the transition to flowering. Leaves become progressively simpler in the neighbourhood of the inflorescence, and are ultimately reduced to tiny bracts at the tip of the male spike. This response is closely associated with the flowering reaction itself, and is certainly related to the change at the apex, mentioned above, in the relative rates of development of axillary bud primordia and the primordia of the subtending leaf. It has been shown that the principal shape features are determined very early in the life of the leaf primordium[16] and as a working hypothesis it might be suggested that one result of change in balance of growth between leaf or bract primordium and subtended bud primordium is to reduce the initial size of the former and so the potentiality for attaining complexity. A significant factor may be the area of the growing point available for occupancy by leaf primordia.

This is restricted as the balance of growth moves in favour of the axillaries; and it may also be noted that, due to the narrowing and attentuation of the male apex, the restriction is more pronounced in this sex, in which in consequence the transition to simplified leaf form is the more rapid.

The foregoing might suggest that the primary response is the enhanced growth rate of the lateral primordia, the leaf shape changes following; and here Thomas's observations on *Trifolium repens*[36] are very relevant. However, there is some reason to suppose that in lateral branches developing from formerly dormant buds in consequence of decapitation there may be a direct photoperiodic effect on the leaf primordium, independent of, or at least preceding, the flowering response itself.[16]

The floral meristem and flower sexuality

The individual floral meristems of each sex arise as simple, radially symmetrical domes of tissue; the male remains radially symmetrical throughout development, while the female becomes asymmetrical through the growth of the cupular investing prophyll.[28] In both genetical sexes it is well established that the primordium at the time of initiation is uncommitted sexually, and can develop into either a carpellate or a staminate flower. The particular interest of *Cannabis* lies in the fact that the pathway of development can be affected within limits by environmental variables and by chemical treatments.[4,5,29,32-34,42] From the point of view of inductive phenomena, the fact that photoperiod is one factor impinging upon the sex-determining process is noteworthy. *Cannabis* conforms with the bulk of well-investigated species whose development is accelerated by short days in that short-day treatment, at least during the juvenile phase, promotes female and depresses male sex expression.[5,6] It is tempting to associate this response directly with the induction process, and to suppose that 'florigen' is the link. An hypothesis containing the suggestion that the primordium-forming factor in hemp was primarily responsible for activating the respective male and female pathways of gene expression was put forward by Thomas.[36] The demonstration that an auxin, NAA, can simulate the short-day effect on male sexuality in hemp as it does in the monoecious cucurbits[24] and maize[10] may indicate another way in which photoperiod may affect the commitment of primordia, namely through its effect on the auxin metabolism of the plant.[12,13] There are numerous seemingly paradoxical features still to be reconciled, however, and understanding must await a fuller appreciation of the endogenous humoral agents concerned in flower initiation, in this as in other species.

REFERENCES

[1] Borthwick, H. A. and Scully, N. J. (1954). Photoperiodic responses in hemp. *Bot. Gaz.* **116**, 14.

[2] Cheuvart, C. (1954). Expériences fur le développement de *Cannabis sativa* L. (sexualité et pigments foliaires) à température constante et sous différents régimes de photopériodisme. *Bull. Acad. roy. Belg. Classe Sciences* **40**, 1152.

[3] Herich, R. (1956). K problemu pohlavnej determinacie a diferenciacie rastlin I. Posobenie boru na priebeh pohlavnej diferenciacie konopi (*Cannabis sativa* L.) *Act. Facult. Rer. Natur. Universit. Comenianae Bot.* **1**, 419.

[4] Heslop-Harrison, J. (1956). Auxin and sexuality in *Cannabis sativa*. *Physiol. Plant.* **9**, 588.

[5] Heslop-Harrison, J. (1957). The experimental modification of sex expression in flowering plants. *Biol. Revs.* **32**, 38.

[6] Heslop-Harrison, J (1957). The sexuality of flowers. *New Biol.* **23**, 9.

[7] Heslop-Harrison J. (1958). The unisexual flower. *Phytomorphology* **8**, 177.

[8] Heslop-Harrison, J. (1959). Growth substances and flower morphogenesis. *J. Linn. Soc. Lond., Bot.* **56**, 269.

[9] Heslop-Harrison, J. (1960). Suppressive effects of 2-thiouracil on differentiation and flowering in *Cannabis sativa. Science* **132**, 1943.

[10] Heslop-Harrison, J. (1961). The experimental control of sexuality and inflorescence structure in *Zea mays* L. *Proc. Linn. Soc. Lond.* 172 Session, 108.

[11] Heslop-Harrison, J. (1962). Effect of 2-thiouracil on cell differentiation and leaf morphogenesis in *Cannabis sativa. Ann. Bot.* **26**, 275.

[12] Heslop-Harrison, J. (1963). Sex expression in plants. In *Meristems and Differentiation*. Brookhaven Symp. Biol. No. 16, 109.

[13] Heslop-Harrison, J. (1964). The control of flower differentiation and sex expression. In *Régulateurs naturels de la croissance végétale*. Ed. J. P. Nitsch. Centre National de la Recherche Scientifique, Paris.

[14] Heslop-Harrison, J. and Heslop-Harrison, Y. (1957). Studies on flowering plant growth and organogenesis I. Morphogenetic effects of 2, 3, 5-triiodobenzoic acid on *Cannabis sativa. Proc. Roy. Soc. Edinburgh Sect. B.* **66**, 409.

[15] Heslop-Harrison, J. and Heslop-Harrison, Y. (1957). Studies on flowering plant growth and organogenesis II. The modification of sex expression in *Cannabis sativa* by carbon monoxide. *Proc. Roy. Soc. Edinburgh Sect. B.* **66**, 424.

[16] Heslop-Harrison, J. and Heslop-Harrison, Y. (1958). Studies on flowering plant growth and organogenesis III. Leaf shape changes associated with flowering and sex differentiation in *Cannabis sativa. Proc. Roy. Irish Acad. Sect. B.* **59**, 257.

[17] Heslop-Harrison, J. and Heslop-Harrison, Y. (1961). Studies on flowering plant growth and organogenesis. IV. Effects of gibberellic acid on flowering and the secondary sexual difference in stature in *Cannabis sativa. Proc. Roy. Irish Acad. Sect. B.* **61**, 219.

[18] Heslop-Harrison, J. and Jagoe, M. P. (1956). The effects of a pyrimidine analogue on apical organisation. In *Differentiation of Apical Meristems and Some Problems of Ecological Regulation of Development*, 105. Czechoslovak Acad. Sci.

[19] Heslop-Harrison, Y. and Woods, I. (1959). Temperature induced meristic and other variation in *Cannabis sativa. J. Linn. Soc. Lond. Bot.* **55**, 290.

[20] Hulewicz, D. (1964). The influence of growth regulators on development of Hungarian hemp. *Acta Agrobot.* **13**, 81.

[21] Jagoe, M. P. (1963). Effects of an Unnatural Pyrimidine on *Cannabis sativa* L-Thesis, University of Birmingham.

[22] Köhler, D. (1958). Die Entwicklung von *Cannabis sativa* unter den Einfluss Verscheidener Tageslängen. *Physiol. Plant.* **11**, 249.

[23] Köhler, D. (1963). Langtag und Bluhinduktion bei *Cannabis sativa. Naturwiss.* **50**, 158.

[24] Laibach, F. and Kribben, F. J. (1950). Der Einfluss von Wuchstoff auf die Bildung männlicher und weiblicher Blüten bei einer monözischen Pflanze (*Cucumis sativa* L.) *Ber. dtsch. bot. Ges.* **62**, 53.

[25] Limberk, J. (1959). The influence of photoperiodicity on the sexual index in hemp (*Cannabis sativa*). *Biol. Plant.* (*Praha*) **1**, 176.

[26] Lyushinskii, V. V. (1963). Comparative physiological evolution of various ecological types of hemp. *Tr. Prikladnoi Bot. Genet. Selek.* **35**, 204 (seen in abstract).

[27] McPhee, H. C. (1924). The influence of environment on sex in hemp *Cannabis sativa* L. *J. Agr. Res.* **28**, 1067.

[28] Molliard, M. (1898). De l'hermaphroditisme chez la Mercuriale et le Chanvre. *Rev. Gen. Bot.* **10**, 320.

[29] Nelson, C. H. (1944). Growth responses of hemp to differential soil and air temperatures. *Plant. Physiol.* **19**, 294.

[30] Petit, J. (1952). Sur la determination du sexe chez *Cannabis sativa* dans les conditions experimentales du phytotron de Liège. *Bull. Soc. Roy. Sciences Liège* **11**, 464.

[31] Schaffner, J. H. (1923). Influence of environment on sexual expression in hemp. *Bot. Gaz.* **71**, 197.

[32] Schaffner, J. H. (1923). Influence of relative length of daylight on reversal of sex in hemp. *Ecology* **4**, 323.

[33] Schaffner, J. H. (1926). The change of opposite to alternate phyllotaxy and repeated rejuvenations in hemp by means of changed photoperiodicity. *Ecology* **7**, 315.

[34] Schaffner, J. H. (1931). Fluctuation curve of sex reversal in staminate hemp plants induced by photoperiodicity. *Amer. J. Bot.* **18**, 242.

[35] Thomas, R. G. (1956). Sexuality and Flowering in Dioecious Angiosperms. Thesis, University of London.

[36] Thomas, R. G. (1962). The initiation and growth of axillary bud primordia in relation to flowering in *Trifolium repens*. *Ann. Bot.* **26**, 329.

[37] Tibeau, M. E. (1936). Time factor in utilisation of mineral nutrients by hemp. *Plant. Physiol.* **11**, 731.

[38] Tournois, J. (1911). Anomalies florales du houblon japonais et du chanvre déterminées par des semis hatifs. *C.R. Acad. Sci., Paris* **153**, 1017.

[39] Tournois, J. (1912). Influence de la lumière sur la floraison du houblon japonais et du chanvre. *C.R. Acad. Sci., Paris* **155**, 297.

[40] Walther, O. and Lilienstern, M. (1934). Contribution to the diagnosis of sex in hemp. *C.R. Acad. Sci. U.R.S.S.* (*Doklady*), n.s. **1**, 518.

[41] Westergaard, M. (1958). The mechanism of sex determination in dioecious flowering plants. *Adv. Genet.* **9**, 217.

[42] Zemlyanukhin, A. A. and Shenshina, S. V. (1961). Sex and its modification in hemp. *Fiziol Rastenii* (Translation) **8**, 158.

9

Kalanchoe blossfeldiana Poellniz.

By W. W. Schwabe

1 History of Use

Kalanchoe blossfeldiana is a native of Madascar, and the genus belongs to the *Crassulaceae*. This species of succulent has been of some commercial use for several decades, and numerous varieties are now under cultivation. The distribution of chromosome numbers in the genus was discussed by Baldwin.[1] Under normal glasshouse conditions, *Kalanchoe blossfeldiana* tends to flower in the late autumn and continues to do so for many weeks. (Fig. 9–1.)

FIGURE 9–1. *Kalanchoe blossfeldiana* left to right: Mature plant after prolonged short-day exposure (flowering); seedling grown in short-day throughout (flowering); mature plant grown in continuous light (vegetative).

The first recorded photoperiodic investigation with this species is by the Dutch investigator Roodenburg[66] who noted that short days accelerated flowering. His work, and the first papers by Harder and his school,[44] confirmed that *Kalanchoe* represents a typical short-day plant as originally defined by Garner and Allard. Because of the quantitative relation between induction and the number of flowers produced, this species has been useful in numerous investigations into photoperiodic behaviour and the underlying mechanisms. The varieties used chiefly are the ones originally worked with by Harder and his school (usually unnamed, but occasionally called var. 'Göttingen') and also 'Tom Thumb' and 'Feuerblüte'.

2 Growing Techniques and Growth Habit

Kalanchoe blossfeldiana is a relatively slow-growing species with an upright growth habit. The arrangement of leaves is opposite and decussate; occasionally tricussate specimens occur. Under optimum conditions of mineral nutrition and illumination, *Kalanchoe* tends to branch freely and becomes bushy. For the purpose of experimental investigation, these numerous laterals have often proved a disadvantage, and starting with the early experiments of Harder's school, it has been the usual practice to remove lateral branches to obtain single stemmed plants. For most of the experiments carried out by Harder, the plant material was raised from seed. The seeds of *Kalanchoe* are very small, but germinate readily and do not appear to have any obligate environmental requirements for doing so. In this way, large numbers of plants may be raised. However, because of the relatively slow growth rate and the small initial size, the production of plant material usable for photoperiodic experiments from seed requires a long time. For this reason, and also in order to ensure somewhat greater uniformity from working with a clone, most other experimenters have raised their plant material from cuttings. This technique is equally convenient, lateral shoots being used.

In a heated glasshouse rooting is usually complete after a week or ten days, and with the larger starting size suitable material is raised much more quickly. Wilson and Schwabe[92] determined the average period of growth for a single leaf pair, from initiation at the apex to maturity and full size. This amounted to approximately 90 days. The mean plastochrone is about 10 days per leaf pair.

The growth habits of short-day and long-day treated plants are very different. Leaves developed under long-day conditions are fairly thin (about 1.2 mm) and flexible for a succulent species.

Under short-day conditions the leaves are very much more thick, succulent and rigid. In the perception of the photoperiodic stimulus the leaf epidermis appears to play an important role;[83] also the lower leaf surface seems less sensitive to light break treatment than the upper.[8]

When leaves produced on plants in long-day are transferred to short-day conditions, even mature leaves are capable of becoming succulent, and their thickness may increase up to three times the original value.[27,79] This increase in leaf thickness is due entirely to cell expansion and increased water content. This is so in spite of the fact that the leaves of *Kalanchoe* can de-differentiate and produce a cork cambium capable of functioning to repair surface injuries.[83] Harder et al.[48] expressed succulence as mg water content per mm^2 leaf area and obtained values in short-day of 1.6 compared with 1.0 in long-day. If expressed as 'percentage dry matter' the water content in short-day may reach 2400 per cent against some 900 per cent in the long-day controls.[79] The growth habit of the entire plant is thus quite plastic and subject to control by photoperiod. The photomorphogenic effects appear to be transmissible along vascular strands. This was demonstrated by Harder and v. Witsch[45] (Fig. 9–2) who postulated the production of a specific morphogenetic hormone controlling leaf structure, viz., metaplasin.

The leaves of *Kalanchoe* are capable of rooting readily by themselves. Such isolated rooted leaves may survive for much longer periods and grow to considerably larger sizes than they would ever have attained when attached to the parent plant, growth being resumed as soon as roots are formed. Once again it has been found that such enlargement of leaves is entirely due to cell expansion. Such rooted leaves are capable of responding to length-of-day, i.e. increasing in succulence under short-day conditions. Leaves which would normally attain an area of 8–10 cm^2 may increase by 200 per cent and the thickness attained by typically rooted long and short-day leaves may be 1.7 mm and 4.4 mm respectively. This daylength response is not modified by application of indole-acetic acid or triiodobenzoic acid as lanolin paste.[79]

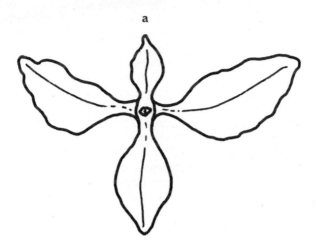

FIGURE 9–2. Effect on leaf shape of short-day induction given to single leaf in same orthostichy as leaf (a); note decreased leaf area in leaf above induced one (a) and reduction in half-leaves in adjoining orthostichies (after Harder[29]).

3 Inflorescence Structure and Criteria of Flowering Response

The structure of the inflorescence of *Kalanchoe* is a dichasial cyme which, however, terminates in cincinni.[29] But for this change in branching habit, in very large inflorescences the number of flowers produced could be expressed by the formula $2^{(n+1)} - 1$, n being the degree of branching. The transition to flowering in some varieties of *Kalanchoe* can be detected after some 8–9 days upon dissection of the terminal growing point, when a change of shape from a fairly flat apex to a raised dome-shape can be detected.[22,89] The particular advantage of using *Kalanchoe* for photoperiodic experiments has been the fact that the number of flowers produced bears a direct relationship to the degree of flower induction.[29]

No scale of developmental stages, such as that designed for *Xanthium*, has ever been suggested for *Kalanchoe*. The very minimum expression of photoperiodically inductive treatment in *Kalanchoe* is seen in some degree of precocious development of lateral shoots in the axils of very young leaf primordia. A detailed study of the mutual relations of main axis and lateral axes was carried out by Bünsow.[13] The next stage is represented by the disappearance or suppression of the terminal growing point itself, and the equal development of the uppermost two lateral shoots giving rise to dichotomous branching. The first flowering stage as such, is represented by a single terminal flower occupying the place of the original terminal meristem. Flower numbers then increase, usually in the following steps:

1, 3, 7, 15, 31 . . . in conformity with the degree of branching of the inflorescence.

With higher flower numbers the regularity in relation to the branching system is usually lost.

4 Effects of Plant Age

In *Kalanchoe* grown from seed and kept in continuous short days, flowering does not take place immediately, but there appears to be a minimum leaf number of approximately eight leaf pairs. However, in view of the small seed size, even with eight leaf pairs a flowering plant of *Kalanchoe* can still be very small (Fig. 9–1). The normal number of unexpanded leaf pairs in the terminal bud of *Kalanchoe* is about 3 and together with partly expanded leaves there are about eight pairs by the time the first leaf pair is fully expanded. There is no experimental evidence as to the age when the individual leaf becomes photoperiodically sensitive. However, the entire plant remains highly sensitive to daylength induction from this very early stage onwards.

Harder and v. Witsch[44,46] have noted that fewer short days are required with increasing plant age. They have also claimed that relatively old plants of *Kalanchoe* tend to become day-neutral, flowering even in non-inductive conditions. This claim has later been withdrawn,[47] the probable explanation being that old plants may have had some very slight short day exposure. In old stock plants, kept for many months in continuous light, occasionally individuals may be found which have initiated a single or even several terminal flowers.

5 Vernalization and Devernalization

Although Harder and v. Witsch[44] noted that about 3 weeks of chilling (at 3°C) given to germinating seed caused an acceleration of flowering, there is clearly no obligate vernalization requirement in this species, and the effect appears not to have been studied further.

7 Photoperiod Response

Kalanchoe blossfeldiana is a short-day plant, the minimum number of short days required for induction being two or more. With increasing numbers of short-day cycles, flower numbers increase exponentially and over a range from one to several hundred flowers, the logarithm of the flower numbers is linearly related to the number of inducing short-day cycles.[77] (Fig. 9–3.) When the number of

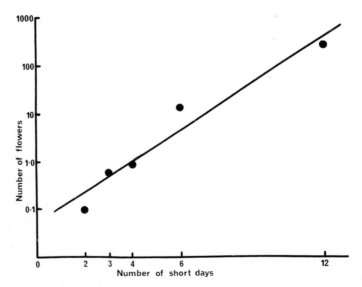

FIGURE 9–3. Effect of number of short days at induction on flower number (Schwabe[77]).

inductive cycles exceeds approximately 14 short days, the rate of increase in flower number drops, yielding a sigmoid type of curve.

Photoperiods effective for induction in 24-hour cycles range from about 11 hours of light to as little as 20 minutes, with hardly any reduction in flower numbers. With light periods in excess of 11 or 11½ hours in 24, flowering falls off rapidly, and 12 hours light represents the critical photoperiod.[39] Harder and Gümmer also investigated further reductions in the daily light period (10, 4, 3, 2, 1 minutes and 50, 40, 30, 20, 10, 5, 3 seconds) per day, and still obtained flowering. The shortest period they used yielded the remarkable result that as little as one second of bright light per day was enough to induce flowering, while uninterrupted darkness for some weeks failed to induce any flowering. This result was confirmed by Schwabe[80] using not daylight, but a bright incandescent light source. According to Oltmanns[64] the effect is temperature-dependent, and at 15°C flowering can also be induced in continuous darkness. Fredericq[23] also confirmed the Harder and Gümmer effect at slightly higher temperatures (> 18°C), using light of different wave lengths (see below).

A large number of experiments with cycles of total duration other than 24 hours, has been carried out by numerous investigators. A particularly interesting series by Harder and Gümmer[40] also has some bearing on the endogenous rhythms theory of Bünning.[6] The majority of these were summarised by Schmitz[73] in a useful diagram, an extended version of which is given in Figure 9–4. Although the experiments included in this figure were obtained

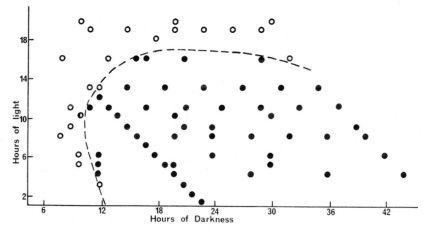

FIGURE 9–4. Combinations of light and dark periods tested in photo-periodic cycles of varying total lengths. Solid circles indicate flowering, open circles vegetative growth (re-drawn and amplified after Schmitz[73]).

under a variety of conditions, it is clear that in *Kalanchoe* flowering is invariably suppressed when the dark period in any one cycle is substantially below the critical (approximately 12 hours). However, another aspect revealed by the study of these collected data is perhaps equally important: there appears to be an upper limit to the light period which can be inductive, and, however long the dark period which may follow it, flowering is no longer possible when the light period exceeds 16–17 hours.

Kalanchoe is as sensitive to a light break in the dark period[32] as other short-day plants,[28] this response not being affected appreciably by temperature.[51] Light breaks have since been used extensively, particularly in the investigation of endogenous rhythms in this species. Relatively low light intensities (about

100 f.c.) saturate the response, for periods from some minutes to half an hour.[32] Very brief durations at high intensity (e.g. 1/40 of a second with a Vacu-Blitz lamp) were also effective.[50]

Over a narrow range of intensities the product of intensity × duration was related to the degree of flowering. Below about 2 f.c. flowering was not appreciably affected, and at still lower intensities induction occurred in continuous illumination.[32]

Another important result emerged from these experiments; the light breaks were given at different times during the dark period and the results obtained revealed striking differences in their effectiveness. The most effective time was slightly after the middle of the dark period, breaks close to the start or end of the dark being very much less effective. Twenty-one cycles with one-minute light breaks given after different durations of darkness from the start (1, 3, 5, 7, 9, 11 and 13 hours) within a fixed 15-hour dark period, gave the following flower numbers: 400, 386, 79, 9, 1.3, 312, 410.

In spite of the fact that *Kalanchoe blossfeldiana* is able to flower with as little as one second of light per day, this species nevertheless shows a high degree of sensitivity to light intensity during the much longer photoperiods which normally precede the inductive dark period. This can be seen from a comparison of flower numbers produced in winter or in summer under otherwise identical conditions, and may imply a direct effect of carbohydrate level. This would agree with the fall in flower numbers seen upon shortening the daily photoperiod from say eight hours to twenty minutes[39] and from the need for CO_2 in the light. However, this explanation is not supported by results of an investigation into the sensitivity to light intensity in relation to the critical daylength.[75] The experiments were designed to exclude effects of photosynthetic activity by changes in the duration of high and low intensity light periods, using either daylight or incandescent light sources. The use of suitable daylight comparisons was possible because the experiments were conducted during mid-summer at the Abisko Research Station of the Swedish Royal Academy, North of the Arctic Circle. The experiments established that a period of low intensity light immediately before the dark period was detrimental to flowering, and that this effect could be compensated by lengthening the total dark period. For instance, plants held in an 11-hour day of full light produced 26.3 flowers per plant; if the photoperiod included five hours of low intensity light flower numbers fell to 11.6; but if the dark period was increased to 14 hours by cutting the full light part of the photoperiod, flower numbers were restored to 24.2, although photosynthesis was reduced even further. Since the treatment which restored flower numbers differed from the reduced light treatment merely in having one hour less of full light, gross lack of carbohydrate must be excluded from any explanation, particularly also as far as carbohydrate level during the light period preceding the inductive dark is concerned; and this agrees well with Harder and Gümmer's results with very brief daily photoperiods. It also seems unlikely that merely reducing the intensity of illumination in daylight caused any changes in the equilibrium of the two forms of phytochrome and thus an explanation based on a change of P_r/P_{fr} balance may be ruled out. A possible explanation is that increased and inhibitory auxin levels produced under low light conditions are involved.[75]

8 Spectral Dependence

The effectiveness of light of different spectral composition needs to be tested in photoperiodically sensitive plants both during the main light period and also during the light breaks inserted in order to disturb the dark reactions. Fredericq[23] investigated the effect of light from different parts of the spectrum during the minimum main light period required by *Kalanchoe*. His evidence points clearly to the fact that phytochrome is involved, red light being much the most effective in promoting flowering, while subsequent irradiation with far red light diminishes flowering. The inhibition by far red light following short main light periods was further confirmed by Fredericq,[24] who also noted that the effect depended on light intensity; on the whole these observations agree well with data for other short-day plants.

The light-break effect in *Kalanchoe* is almost certainly mediated by phytochrome. The earliest tests on the effective spectrum were carried out by Wallrabe[91] and demonstrated that light from the red part of the spectrum was much more effective than other wavebands. Bünning and Engelmann's experiments[7] also confirmed the high efficiency of red light, suggesting the probable involvement of phytochrome in the photoperiodic responses of *Kalanchoe*. (See also Karvé *et al.*[54] on flower movements.)

9 Endogenous Rhythms

Kalanchoe blossfeldiana has been subjected to particularly extensive investigations into rhythmic changes in photoperiodic sensitivity, metabolic function, and flower movement.

Studies involving rhythmic changes which have been recorded for *Kalanchoe* are concerned among others, with the following characteristics:

(a) Sensitivity to photoperiod (numerous authors c.f. below).
(b) Floral movements.[11,12,30,54,100]
(c) Fresh weight of flowers.[2]
(d) Guttation rates.[53]
(e) Organic acid content.[2]
(f) Respiration rates.[73]
(g) Phosphatase activity.[19]
(h) Resistance to thermal death.[84]
(i) Stomatal opening in relation to photoperiod.[74]

In the present context we are particularly concerned with rhythmic changes in the sensitivity to flower inducing conditions. These have been investigated in two main types of experiment:

1. Involving combinations of light and dark periods differing more or less widely from the normal 24 hours to which endogenous circadian rhythms are tied.

2. Interrupting dark periods of up to 96 hours by a single light interruption given at different times.

In both types of experiment light given either as a full light period or as a light break should have favourable effects at times which coincide with the normal light period of a normal cycle, say 11 hours light, 13 hours dark, if Bünning's theory of a close relation between endogenous rhythms and photoperiodism is applicable. At other times light should inhibit flowering. The first type of experiment has not produced much support for this theory[73] (c.f. Figure 9–4).

The second kind of experimentation, with light breaks in very long dark periods, was first applied to *Kalanchoe* in a 72-hour cycle by Carr.[15] Single light breaks given during a 60-hour dark period promoted flower initiation when falling into the period in which the plant would normally have received light in a 24-hour cycle; given at times when the plant would normally have been in the dark, they inhibited flower initiation. This experiment was repeated by Schwabe[76] and by Melchers;[59] both confirmed the overall pattern of Carr's results. However,

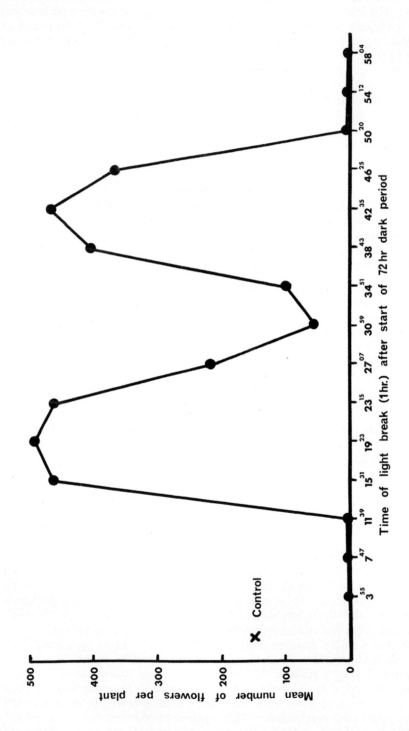

FIGURE 9–5. Effect on flower numbers of light breaks of one hour duration given at different times in a 72-hour dark period (after Melchers[59]).

they also indicated that light breaks given near the beginning or end of very long dark periods, i.e. during the time of the dark periods of the first and last 24-hour photoperiodic cycle, were more inhibitory than light breaks near the middle of the 60-hour dark period. Thus, the data lent considerable support to the suggestion by Claes and Lang[18] that the plant responds to two light periods, given with some dark interval of a few hours, as if there had been a period of continuous illumination. Melchers' data are shown in Figure 9–5. Similar data were obtained by Bünning and Engelmann.[7,20]

Extensive studies on the rhythmic opening and closing of the flowers in *Kalanchoe*, particularly by Bünsow,[11] have shown that if subjected to a variety of cycles of light and dark, the flower opening rhythm would adapt itself to a considerable number of these. However, when rhythms of light and dark periods (of equal duration) become shorter than 6 + 6 hours, the capacity to adapt begins to fail and the flower movements become disturbed or regain their previous periodicity. Under constant light or dark the movements are much reduced in magnitude and usually come to a halt after some time, entering a state of light or dark-rigor, but the onset of this may depend on light intensity and the carbohydrate status of the plant.[11] The adaptability of such rhythms represents one of the difficulties of making valid assessments on the regulatory action of the endogenous rhythmic system. In *Kalanchoe* for instance, the flower movement is clearly more adaptable than the rhythm which may be involved in flower induction, where even a homophasic 8 + 8 rhythm is quite ineffective and a 12 + 12 rhythm tends to represent the critical level.

More detailed attempts to interpret phase shifts in the floral movements of *Kalanchoe* have been made[9,10] but a detailed discussion of these would go beyond the scope of this chapter.

It is still impossible to assess the degree of control exerted by endogenous rhythmic changes over the photoperiodic responses of *Kalanchoe*. However, there is little doubt that circadian rhythms are somehow involved in the control of flowering, but the system may operate decisively only under conditions of very long dark periods.

10 Fractional Induction

Reference has already been made to the fact that the photoperiodic response in *Kalanchoe* is quantitative, the number of flowers produced by each plant approximately doubling for every extra short day between 2 and 14.

The short days must, however, be given consecutively to be fully effective. Summation fails to occur if inductive cycles are separated by non-inductive long-day cycles. Since the studies into the inhibition of flowering are inextricably involved with fractional induction, the evidence is discussed in the next section.

11 Photoperiodic Inhibition

Investigations of fractional induction in *Kalanchoe* have led to studies of the effects of non-inductive photoperiodic cycles. It has been known for some time that such cycles are inhibitory,[40] and the inhibitory effect was interpreted in relation to that of leaves in unfavourable daylengths when interposed between the induced leaves and the apical meristem.[52] This inhibitory effect itself was shown to be restricted to the same orthostichy as the treated leaf – much as had been shown for the morphogenetic effects of short-day (metaplasin).

Later experiments by Harder and Bünsow[33] showed that inhibitory effects of long days given prior to short-day induction could be also detected. Thus effects on translocation of the inducing stimulus could not be involved and the authors stated that the long day effect acted as 'Blühhemmstoff'.

If mature *Kalanchoe* plants are given 12 to 14 short days under optimum conditions each plant may produce several hundred flowers. Interruption by a single long day in the middle of induction by 12 short days reduces flower numbers by approximately 50 per cent. Insertion of single long days after every four short days (out of twelve) cuts flower numbers by 90 per cent and insertion of a long day after every three short days by 98 per cent. Alternation of long and short days, until a total of twelve short days has been given, prevents flowering altogether.[77] It is clear, therefore, that even when all treatments receive the same number of inductive photocycles the symmetrically intercalated long days have a very strong inhibitory effect. This can be assessed quantitatively by calculating how many of a fixed number of twelve short days are annulled by each intercalated long day, using a calibration curve of log. flower numbers v. days of induction (Table 9–1). This calculation shows that each intercalated long day can destroy the effect of approximately two short days. A similar calculation carried out with another parameter for assessing the degree of induction, the reciprocal of the number of the days from induction to the first appearance of the inflorescence, yields an almost identical result.

TABLE 9–1

Mean annulling effect of intercalated long days on the flowering of *Kalanchoe*. The number of inductive short days to which each of the induction treatments corresponds has been subtracted from the fixed total of 12 short days (column 2) and this indicates the number of short days which have been effectively annulled (Schwabe[77]).

Number of Intercalated long days in 12 short days	Number of short days annulled.	Number of short days annulled per long day
1	1.4	1.4
2	1.6	0.8
3	5.1	1.7
5	7.3	1.5
Mean		1.4

A short day with a light break in the middle of the dark period has exactly the same effect as a long day. In an experiment in which a total of 14 short days were given with light breaks of 30 seconds duration in the middle of the fifth and tenth nights, flower numbers were reduced to only 10 per cent of the controls.[77]

These responses raised a number of questions. If the inhibitory effect of long days were cumulative, maintaining a plant in long-day conditions could lead to the accumulation of so much inhibitor that subsequent induction by short days would be difficult. Moreover, the minimum induction period should then be proportional to the previous long-day period. This argument against flower inhibition was used by Borthwick.[3] Nevertheless, however long the previous long-day treatment, the variety of *Kalanchoe* used shows the first signs of flower induction with a minimum of two or three short days. Also, when plants were exposed to twelve short days in two groups of six separated by increasing numbers of long days (up to 16), it was found that the inhibitory effect hardly increased as more long days were given, at least up to twelve long days by which time the morphogenetic changes due to the first six short days had already begun to take place.[77] One may conclude from this that there is an upper limit to the amount of inhibition which can be accumulated and that this is approached after one long day. Once it is recognized that there is such a limit, the argument against counter induction can be dismissed.

Further experiments were undertaken to discover whether the inhibitory effect acts on the inductive stimulus produced during the short days preceding the interrupting long day, or whether the inhibitory effect prevents succeeding short days from becoming effective. The method used was to separate the inductive short days from the intercalated long day by a period which would allow either the short-day effect to become consolidated before exposure to the long day, or the inhibitory effect to disperse before exposure to the next short day.

Ideally, this neutral period should be neither promoting nor inhibitory, i.e. have neither short nor long-day effects. Since it is known (c.f. Figure 9–4) that a 16-hour light period followed by a 32-hour dark period does not induce flowering by itself, a 24-hour dark period was chosen as a neutral period to separate the long and short days. Added to a long day this yielded 16 hours light/32 hours dark; added to a short day it gave 8 hours light/40 hours dark. Since it was known that alternating short and long days prevent flowering,[71,77] this set of cycles was chosen for the test. With a constant total of 12 short days, the 24 hour dark period was inserted, either after the short day or after the long day. An alternation of short days and 24-hour dark periods, and an alternation of long and short days, served as controls. The results shown in Table 9–2 are very clear-cut indeed

TABLE 9–2

Effect of 24-hour dark periods (24D) preceding or following long days (LD), themselves alternating with short days (SD), on the flowering of *Kalanchoe;* 12 replicates (Schwabe[77]).

Order of cycle	Number of plants budded	Mean number of flowers per plant
SD: LD: 24D: SD:...	12	158.1
SD: 24D: LD: SD:...	5	2.5
SD: LD: SD:...	2	0.8
SD: 24D: SD:...	12	174.6

and suggest strongly, that insertion of the 24-hour dark period immediately after the long day, allowed dispersal of the inhibition to take place, thereby protecting the succeeding short day from its effect. By contrast the 24-hour dark period inserted after the short-day does nothing to consolidate the short-day induction. This result is easier to understand in terms of an inhibition produced in long day which reaches a maximum and which will prevent succeeding short days from having an effect, rather than a mechanism by which a light period of say, 8 hours is harmless to a previously manufactured promoting substance, but which tends to destroy the latter if the light period is extended to say, 16 hours.

If a single long day is inserted at various times among 12 short days, its effect is somewhat more inhibitory in the middle of the short-day period than near the beginning or the end. Although this is somewhat reminiscent of light break effects in a single dark period, the mechanism is unlikely to be similar.

In explanation of these phenomena Schwabe[77,80] put forward an hypothesis according to which photoperiodic induction leads to the production of an adaptively formed enzyme which in turn catalyses the flower hormone. The effect of long day, light breaks and other inhibitory conditions would operate through the production of an inhibitor which interferes with the formation of the enzyme. The level to which the inhibitor can accumulate is limited and the maximum may be attained after little more than 1 long day. Inhibition and promotion can then be quantitatively related, and as more of the enzyme is produced inhibition becomes less complete. It could be predicted, therefore, that such changes should lead to a change in the point of balance, i.e. in the critical daylength. Two experiments designed to test this hypothesis have borne out the prediction:[81] if partial induction periods were followed by days longer than the critical length these still promoted flowering, but they did not do so in controls without partial induction, or if presented in reverse order. In a similar experiment with a prolonged period of 12½-hour days following varying amounts of induction, flowering was again promoted compared with controls. Hence the suggested adaptive formation of the hypothetical flower hormone-producing enzyme was supported as well as the inhibitor hypothesis. Harder's study on the effect of daylength following short-day induction is very relevant here, and his results agree with those above.[31] Unfortunately, the promotive daylength of 12 hours which he used is still slightly inductive even on control plants, and thus could not be regarded as evidence for the shift in the critical daylength.

12 Dual Photoperiod Responses

The inhibitory response of long day and the promoting response of short day have been discussed in the previous section. For successful flower induction only one daylength treatment is required and not a sequence.

13 The Effects of Temperature

The photoperiodic responses of *Kalanchoe* are affected very much by temperature. The responses to temperature can be assessed quantitatively using the number of flowers produced per plant as a measure of the inductive effects. In the first such investigation, on the night temperature/daylength interaction, Harder *et al.*[48] noted a reduction of flowering as the temperature was reduced from 24°C to 8°C. At the lowest temperature flowering was entirely suppressed. The effects of relatively high and low temperatures (25°C v 10°C − 12.5°C) during the light and dark portions of inductive short days, of inhibitory long days, or of a 24-hour dark period after the long day are shown in Table 9–3. Reduction of the temperature in either light or dark slows down the promotive effects of flower induction. Flowering is also reduced at high temperatures, 30°C or above.[67,68] The inhibitory effects of long days were also reduced by low temperature. The effect of a light break, on the other hand, is independent of temperature.[51]

14 Effects of Mineral Nutrition

Not much is known concerning the effects of mineral nutrition in *Kalanchoe*. In general the nitrogen level of the medium in which *Kalanchoe* is grown may vary within fairly wide limits without apparently affecting photoperiodic responses. However, flowering is reduced when nitrogen-deficient plants are given a supply of ammonium sulphate just before short day treatment. But nitrogen feeding during induction seems favourable to flowering.[69]

It may be mentioned here that Harder and Lösing[41] showed that *Kalanchoe* is capable of withstanding water shortage to a considerable extent, but under these conditions prolonged exposure to short days does not induce flowering, even when the plants are subsequently supplied with adequate water.

TABLE 9–3

(a) Effect of temperature during light and dark periods of fourteen inductive cycles, 8 hours light 16 hours dark.

(b) Effect of temperature during the light and dark periods of 3 long days inter-calated singly between a total of twelve short days; i.e. after the 3rd, 6th and 9th short day. The short days were given at 25°C throughout.

(c) Effect of temperature during 24-hour dark period (24D) following or pre-ceding long days (LD) which are alternating with short-day inductive cycles (SD). High = 25°C, low = 10°C. A total of twelve such composite cycles was given (Schwabe[80]).

	Temperature during Light	Dark	Proportion of plants flowering	No. of flowers per plant
(a)	25°C	25°C	10/10	182.4
	25°C	10°C	10/10	10.9
	12–13°C	25°C	10/10	90.1
(b)	25°C	25°C	2/10	0.8
	25°C	10°C	10/10	13.4
	12–13°C	25°C	9/9	10.3

	Order of cycle	Temperature during 24D	Proportion of plants flowering	No. of flowers per plant
(c)	SD:LD:24D:SD:	High	10/10	223.0
	ditto	Low	10/10	95.9
	SD:24D:LD:SD:	High	0/10	0
	ditto	Low	2/10	0.3

15 Effects of Gas Composition

Studies carried out on the composition of the atmosphere surrounding the aerial parts of *Kalanchoe* during growth and photoperiodic induction have been mainly concerned with carbon dioxide level. Harder *et al.*[49] found that CO_2 was needed by *Kalanchoe* plants during the main light period preceding the inductive dark periods for normal induction subsequently to take place. Plants or induced leaves kept in a CO_2-free atmosphere during the main light period failed to promote initiation. In contrast, no CO_2 was needed to make long photoperiods inhibitory, a result later confirmed by Spear[87] and Fredericq[21]. Subsequently, Gregory, Spear and Thimann[25] showed that *Kalanchoe* develops a mechanism for dark-fixation of CO_2 when subjected to short day conditions, or to other photoperiodic cycles which are capable of inducing flowering.[86] The dark-fixation is usually as-sociated with an initial loss of CO_2 on return to light. Relatively high temperature has a similar effect and temperature-labile and photo-labile fixation products have been postulated.[88] Although this mechanism develops relatively slowly, it was initially suspected that this net fixation of CO_2 in the dark might be an integral part of the biochemical reaction chain involved in photoperiodic induction. However, subsequent work[65,95,96,97] with varieties 'Feuerblüte' and 'Tom Thumb', has shown that this somewhat optimistic suggestion does not hold true. It seems more likely that the phenomena of flowering and dark fixation of CO_2 may be parallel results of inductive treatment, rather than causally related to each other. Leaf succulence also appears to be independent of flowering and dark-fixation of CO_2, but may be related to the organic acid level.

16 Translocation of the Floral Stimulus

A considerable amount of work has been done on the pattern of effects of short days on leaf shape and leaf succulence thought to be mediated by metaplasin.[38] The results indicated that in Kalanchoe, with its opposite and decussate phyllotaxis, the stimulus passes acropetally along the orthostichy. There is, however, some lateral spread, and leaves in the next youngest pair, i.e. in the two adjoining orthostichies, are affected in the proximal halves (see Fig. 9–2). Although Harder considered that the translocated hypothetical substance specifically affected leaf shape rather than floral induction, it seems probable that the route taken by it is an indication of the translocation path of the flower stimulus.[45] When single leaves of Kalanchoe are induced in otherwise totally defoliated plants, the stimulus tends to by-pass the bud in the axil of the induced leaf itself.

Harder and Gall,[37] using chloroform, had some success in separating the morphogenic effects of short days from their flower-inducing action. 0.005 per cent chloroform in the atmosphere during short-day induction inhibited flower initiation, but not the development of leaf succulence. The mode of action of the chloroform is unknown, but it may have affected translocation of any stimulus from the leaf.

17 Grafting Experiments

Harder[29] failed in all attempts to get graft transmission of the flowering stimulus in Kalanchoe, but in 1954, Carr and Melchers[16] succeeded in transmitting the flowering stimulus from induced plants acting as donors to non-induced receptors. In these experiments the donors were placed as wedge grafts into the split, decapitated, stem of the receptor and merely tied with raffia. Flower induction subsequently occurred in lateral, completely defoliated, branches produced below the donor. Zeevaart[98] also included Kalanchoe in his extensive studies of translocation of the flowering stimulus in several genera and species. The flowering response of Kalanchoe receptors tended to increase when the Kalanchoe donors comprised some stem and more than one leaf. He also reported positive transmission of the flowering stimulus from Kalanchoe blossfeldiana to Sedum spectabile and S. ellacombianum and from both these long day plants to Kalanchoe. Attempts by Schwabe[79] to use isolated leaves which had been induced when separate from the plant as donors, grafted into the stem some distance below the growing points of non-induced receptors, failed to give any induction. Although the leaf grafts took with little difficulty, no transmission of the stimulus was found, regardless of whether the receptors were defoliated or not above the graft. However, in view of Carr's and Zeevaart's results, the failure in obtaining graft transmission from such leaves may well be due to some difference of technique only.

18 Effects of Growth Substances and Growth Retardants

Harder and Van Senden[43,85] showed that indole-acetic acid (IAA) applied during induction was detrimental or inhibitory to flowering in Kalanchoe blossfeldiana.

In these experiments leaves above those which were being induced were immersed in solutions of IAA ranging in concentration from 0·00005 per cent to 0.05 per cent. IAA was also inhibitory if supplied to the leaf below the induced one, causing increased leafiness of the inflorescence and reduced flower numbers. Triiodobenzoic acid, sometimes regarded as having anti-auxin activity, also caused flower inhibition, as well as malformation of stems and leaves.[42,99]

Harder and Bünsow[34,35,36] investigated the effects of gibberellic acid on flower induction in *Kalanchoe*, and again only inhibitory effects on flowering were noted. Concentrations used ranged from 0.1 to 50 p.p.m. and in all experiments these led to excessive elongation of internodes and leaves. When previously induced plants were treated, excessive elongation of peduncles took place.[cf.72]

20 Florigenic Extracts

No positive results of the application of extracts made from induced *Kalanchoe* plants to vegetative plants have been reported in the literature. Repeated attempts by the author to induce flowering, by means of aqueous extracts from induced leaves applied to non-induced leaves or apices, have not shown any positive promotion. However, in view of the great difficulty experienced in similar experiments with many other species by many investigators and over many years, this is hardly surprising, and cannot be regarded as evidence for the absence of any specific flower promoting substance produced as a result of induction.

22 Chemical, Histochemical, and Ultra-structural Changes at Induction

A variety of studies into the chemical changes occurring during flower induction have been carried out. Analyses of this kind can by themselves do no more than establish correlations between induction and metabolic changes, however. Only further experimentation can then produce evidence bearing on any causal connection, though the closeness of any such correlation may itself be suggestive.

The first products of photosynthetic carbon dioxide fixation in *Kalanchoe* exposed to long and short-day conditions were investigated by Norris and Calvin,[63] but the quantitative differences found did not suggest any fundamental differences in pathway or products which might be related to induction, e.g. increased C^{14} fixation in aspartic acid under long-day when expressed on a fresh weight basis. A great deal of work on the underlying mechanisms of the crassulacean acid metabolism and dark-fixation products has been carried out.[55,90] Kunitake, Saltman and Lang[56,70] confirmed the quantitative increase of CO_2 dark fixation on short-day treatment but found no significant differences in the pattern of labelling and no indication of any qualitative differences associated with induction.

The total organic acid content, which is subject to diurnal variation,[2] appears to reflect quantitatively the increase in dark CO_2 fixation after induction.[61] The net synthesis of malate and the metabolic pathways seem likely to be similar to those found[4,5] in *Kalanchoe crenata*. After prolonged exposure to differential daylength treatment the total acidity, and especially the malic acid content, of *Kalanchoe blossfeldiana* leaves is substantially higher in short-day than in long-day – if expressed on a dry weight basis: if expressed on a fresh weight basis the reverse holds true.[79]

· Considerable interest attaches to determinations by Caspar and Pirson[17] of the effects of blue and red light on organic acid metabolism in *K. rotundifolia*. Relative to plants grown in red light, those in blue light had a higher ratio of isocitric to malic acid, and this was paralleled by increased total N, protein, and RNA, while carbohydrate level was higher in red light.

Paper chromatographic analyses of the free amino-acid content of various parts of *Kalanchoe blossfeldiana*[58] and of the amino-acid composition of proteins,[60] have revealed changes in total quantity and also in the relative amounts of some acids. These changes may be merely a consequence of the morphological changes at the onset of induction.

Changes in the amounts of nucleic acids 5–7 days after the start of inductive treatment have been recorded in the leaves (especially younger ones) using dry matter as a basis for expressing the results.[26] An initial rapid rise of RNA is followed in the tip region of the plant by a steep fall to the original level and ultimately a slow decline. The DNA content changes follow exactly the opposite pattern. Older leaves show generally similar changes though of lesser magnitude.

Growth hormone contents and their diurnal variations showed no clear relation to the inductive processes.[2] Leaf anthocyanin content, however, is clearly related to daylength treatment.[62] In long day or light-break conditions only traces of anthocyanins are found, while considerable amounts are formed in short day, the major component in the leaves being chrysanthemin.

The acidity of the vacuole contents shows diurnal changes, but persistent differences between induced and non-induced plants can also be detected, e.g. the author found the pH of the expressed sap to be 5.15 in long-day and 4.35 in short-day.

Chromosome numbers in the leaves of *Kalanchoe* revealed a degree of polyploidy which varied in relation to the daylength condition to which the leaves were exposed.[93,94] Long-day leaves showed a high incidence of octoploidy, while the highly vacuolated cells in the short-day leaves were commonly 32-ploid.

Schwabe and Wilson[82] investigated the apparent viscosity of the cytoplasm of mesophyll cells in the leaves of *Kalanchoe* plants subjected to a variety of photoperiodic conditions. This was done by a centrifugation technique.[92] They found considerable differences in this physical character associated with daylength and light-break treatments. The effectiveness of red light breaks suggests that these changes are subject to phytochrome control. Immediate effects of light and darkness can also be demonstrated, but these are superimposed on diurnal variations. Viscosity increased progressively with increasing exposure to short days, particularly with prolonged SD treatment.

The resistance to thermal death also appears altered after photoperiodic induction. Lange and Schwemmle[57] found that leaves of vegetative plants in long-day were somewhat more susceptible to heat injury than short-day leaves, a difference equivalent to some 3°C (47°C–50°C) during a 30 minute exposure.

23 Inflorescence Differentiation

Floral differentiation at the apex of *Kalanchoe* was studied very early by Roodenburg.[66] The relatively flat dome of the apex gradually changes into a raised dome, becoming almost hemispherical. At the latest this can be detected within about 8–10 days of the start of inductive conditions, and after about 3 weeks the inflorescence becomes macroscopically visible. Subsequently, there is active development of lateral apices which, according to the degree of induction, may continue the inflorescence development, or alternatively may grow into vegetative lateral shoots. The anatomy of the shoot apex and the changes occurring during the initial stages of the transition to flowering have been described by Stein and Stein[89] with var. 'Brilliant Star', and by Fredericq,[22] and confirm the changes described earlier.

REFERENCES

[1] Baldwin, J. T., jr. (1938). *Kalanchoe*: The genus and its chromosomes. *Amer. J. Bot.* **25**, 572.

[2] Becker, T. (1953). Wuchsstoff-und Säureschwankungen bei *Kalanchoe blossfeldiana*, in verschiedenen Licht-Dunkelwechseln, *Planta* **43**, 1.

[3] Borthwick, H. A. (1947). Daylength and flowering. 1943–1947 Year Book, U.S. Dept. of Agric., *Science and Farming*, 273.

[4] Bradbeer, J. W. (1962–3). Physiological studies on acid metabolism in green plants, IX, The distribution of C^{14} in malate of darkened *Kalanchoe* leaf fragments after infiltration of labelled pyruvate, *Proc. Roy. Soc. Ser. B.* **157**, 279.

[5] Bradbeer, J. W. and Ranson, S. L. (1962/3). Physiological studies on acid metabolism in green plants, VIII. The utilisation of labelled pyruvate fumarate and glucose in *Kalanchoe* leaves in the dark. *Proc. Roy. Soc. Ser. B.* **157**, 258.

[6] Bünning, E. (1944). Endonome Tagesrhythmik und Photoperiodismus bei Kurztagspflanzen. *I. Biol. Zbl.* **64**, 161.

[7] Bünning, E. und Engelmann, W. (1960). Endogen-tagesperiodische Schwankungen der photoperiodischen Hellrot-Empfindlichkeit bei *Kalanchoe blossfeldiana* *Naturwiss.* **47**, 332.

[8] Bünning, E. und Moser, I. (1966). Unterschiedliche photoperiodische Empfindlichkeit der beiden Blattseiten von *Kalanchoe blossfeldiana*. *Planta* **69**, 296.

[9] Bünning, E. und Zimmer, R. (1962). Zur Deutung der Phasenverschiebungen und 'Transients' nach Exogener Störung Endogener Rhythmen. *Planta* **59**, 1.

[10] Bünning, E., Kurras, S. und Vielhaben, V. (1965). Phasenverschiebungen der Endogen Tagesrhythmik durch Reduktion der Atmung. *Planta* **64**, 291.

[11] Bünsow, R. (1953a). Endogene Tagesrhythmik und Photoperiodismus bei *Kalanchoe blossfeldiana*. *Planta* **42**, 220.

[12] Bünsow, R. (1953b). Über den Einfluss der Lichtmenge auf die endogene Tagesrhythmik bei *Kalanchoe blossfeldiana*. *Biol. Zbl.* **72**, 465.

[13] Bünsow, R. (1961). Zur Physiologie der Achsengestaltung bei *Kalanchoe blossfeldiana*, I. Mitteilung: Die Hauptachse, II. Mitteilung: Die Seitenachsen, *Planta* **57**, 71 and 88.

[14] Bünsow, R. und v. Bredow, K. (1958). Wirkung von Licht und Gibberellin auf die Samenkeimung der Kurztagpflanze *Kalanchoe blossfeldiana*. *Biol. Zbl.* **77**, 132.

[15] Carr, D. J. (1952). A critical experiment on Bünning's theory of photoperiodism. *Z.f. Naturf.* **7b**, 570.

[16] Carr, D. J. und Melchers, G. (1954). Auslösung von Blütenbildung bei der Kurztagpflanze *Kalanchoe blossfeldiana* in Langtagbedingungen durch Pfropfpartner. *Z.f. Naturf.* **9b**, 215.

[17] Casper, R. and Pirson, A. (1965). Grund–und Säurestoffwechsel in Blättern von *Kalanchoe rotundifolia*, HAW. bei Farblichtkultur. *Flora* **156**, 177.

[18] Claes, H. und Lang, A. (1947). Die Blütenbildung von *Hyoscyamus niger* in 48-stündigen Licht-Dunkelzyklen und in Zyklen mit aufgeteilten Lichtphasen. *Z.f. Naturf.* **2b**, 56.

[19] Ehrenberg, H. (1954). Einfluss verschiedenen Licht-Dunkel-wechsels auf die Rhythmik der Phosphataseaktivität in den Blättern von *Kalanchoe blossfeldiana*. *Planta* **43**, 528

[20] Engelmann, W. (1960). Endogene Rhythmik und Photoperiodische Blühinduktion bei *Kalanchoe*. *Planta* **55**, 496.

[21] Fredericq, H. (1958). On the significance of carbon dioxide of the air for flower bud initiation. *Biol. Jaarb. Dodonaea Gent.* **26**, 53.

[22] Fredericq, H. (1960). The change of the apex of *Kalanchoe blossfeldiana* towards inflorescence formation. *Biol. Jaarb. Dodonaea* **28**, 76.

[23] Fredericq, H. (1963). Flower formation in *Kalanchoe blossfeldiana* by very short photoperiods under light of different quality. *Nature* **198**, 101.

[24] Fredericq, H. (1965). Action of red and far-red light at the end of short-day, and in the middle of the night, on flower induction in *Kalanchoe blossfeldiana*. *Biol. Jaarb. Dodonaea* **33**, 66.

[25] Gregory, F. G., Spear, I. and Thimann, K. V. (1954). The interrelation between CO_2 metabolism and photoperiodism in *Kalanchoe*. *Plant Physiol.* **29**, 220.

[26] Gulich, L. (1960). Veränderungen in der Nukleinsäure Fraktion grüner Blätter im Zusammenhang mit Photoperiodischer Induktion. *Planta* **54**, 374.

[27] Gümmer, G. (1949). Einfluss der Tageslänge auf den Habitus, vor allem auf die Blattstruktur, einiger Langtags – und Kurztagspflanzen (Besonders von *Kalanchoe blossfeldiana*). *Planta* **36**, 439.

[28] Hamner, K. C. and Bonner, J. (1939). Photoperiodism in relation to hormones as factors in floral initiation and development. *Bot. Gaz.* **100,** 388.

[29] Harder, R. (1948). Vegetative and reproductive development of *Kalanchoe blossfeldiana*, as influenced by photoperiodism. *Symp. soc. exp. Biol. II. Growth*, 117.

[30] Harder, R. (1949). Über die endogene Tagesrhythmik der Fermentaktivität Guttation, und Blütenbewegung bei *Kalanchoe blossfeldiana*, und *Phaseolus multiflorus*. *Nachr. d. Akad. d. Wiss Göttingen Math, Phys.* **K1.,** 1.

[31] Harder, R. (1953). Über den Einfluss der Tageslänge Nach der Photoperiodischen Induktion auf die Infloreszenzen. *Planta* **42,** 19.

[32] Harder, R. und Bode, O. (1943). Über die Wirkung von Zwischenbelichtungen während der Dunkelperiode auf das Blühen, die Verlaubung und die Blattsukkulenz bei der Kurztagpflanze, *Kalanchoe blossfeldiana*. *Planta* **33,** 469.

[33] Harder, R. und Bünsow, R. (1954). Über die Wirkung der Tageslänge vor der Kurztaginduktion auf die Blütenbildung von *Kalanchoe blossfeldiana*. *Planta* **43,** 315.

[34] Harder, R. und Bünsow, R. (1956). Einfluss des Gibberellins auf die Blütenbildung bei *Kalanchoe blossfeldiana*. *Naturwiss,* **43,** 544.

[35] Harder, R. und Bünsow, R. (1957). Zusammenwirken von Gibberellin mit photoperiodisch bedingten blühfördernden und blühhemmenden Vorgängen bei *Kalanchoe blossfeldiana*. *Naturwiss.* **44,** 454.

[36] Harder, R. und Bünsow, R. (1958). Über die Wirkung von Gibberellin auf die Entwicklung und Blütenbildung der Kurztagpflanze, *Kalanchoe blossfeldiana*. *Planta* **51,** 201.

[37] Harder, R. und Gall, E. (1945). Über die Trennung der Blühhormon und Metaplasinwirkung bei *Kalanchoe blossfeldiana* durch Narkose. *Nachr. Ges Wiss Göttingen Math. Phys.* **K1,** 54.

[38] Harder, R., und Gümmer, G. (1944). Weiteres über örtlich beschränkte Wirkung und Leitung des formbeeinflussenden Metaplasins. *Jahrb. Wiss, Bot.* **91,** 359.

[39] Harder, R. und Gümmer, G. (1947). Über die Untere Kritische Tageslänge bei der Kurztagpflanze *Kalanchoe blossfeldiana*. *Planta* **35,** 88.

[40] Harder, R. und Gümmer, G. (1949). Über die Blütenbildung von *Kalanchoe blossfeldiana* in verschiedenen Licht-Dunkel-Rhythmen. *Planta* **37,** 12.

[41] Harder, R. und Lösing, J. (1946). Unterdrückung des Blühens bei einer Kurztagpflanze trotz Kurztags; Veränderung der Sukkulenz. *Naturwiss.* **33,** 190.

[42] Harder, R. und Oppermann, A. (1952). Einfluss von, 2, 3, 5 – Trijodbenzoesäure auf die Blütenbildung und die vegetative Gestaltung von *Kalanchoe blossfeldiana*. *Planta* **41,** 1.

[43] Harder, R. und van Senden, H. (1949). Antagonistische Wirkung von Wuchstoff und 'Blühhormon'. *Naturwiss.* **36,** 348.

[44] Harder, R. und v. Witsch, H. (1940a). Wirkung von Photoperiodismus und Yarovisation auf die Blütenbildung von *Kalanchoe blossfeldiana*. *Gartenbauwiss.* **15,** 226.

[45] Harder, R. und v. Witsch, V. H. (1940b). Über die Einwirkung von Kurztagsblättern auf im Langtag befindliche Blätter und Stengelteile der gleichenP flanze. *Planta* **31,** 523.

[46] Harder, R. und v. Witsch, H. (1940c). Über die Bedeutung des Alters für die photoperiodische Reaktion von *Kalanchoe blossfeldiana*. *Planta* **31,** 192.

[47] Harder, R., und v. Witsch, H. (1942). Weitere Untersuchungen über die Veränderung der photoperiodischen Reaktion von *Kalanchoe blossfeldiana* mit zunehmendem Alter der Pflanzen. *Planta* **32,** 547.

[48] Harder, R., Bode, O. und v. Witsch, H. (1942). Über Wechselbeziehungen zwischen Blütenbildung, Brakteenverlaubung und Sukkluenz der Laubblätter bei *Kalanchoe blossfeldiana*. *Flora* **36,** 85.

[49] Harder, R., Bode, O. und v. Witsch, H. (1944). Photoperiodische Untersuchungen in Kohlensäurefreier Atmosphäre bei der Kurztagpflanze *Kalanchoe blossfeldiana*. *Jahrb. Wiss Bot.* **91,** 381.

[50] Harder, R., Gümmer, G. und Gall, E. (1945). Über die Untere Zeitgrenze der blütenhemmenden Lichteinwirkungen bei *Kalanchoe blossfeldiana*. *Nachr., Ges. Wiss. Göttingen. Math. Phys.* **K1,** 48.

[51] Harder, R. Wallrabe und Quantz, L. (1944). Über die Rolle der Temperatur bei der Zerstörung des Blühimpulses durch Zwischenbeleuchtung bei der Kurztagpflanze *Kalanchoe blossfeldiana*. *Planta* **34,** 41.

[52] Harder, R., Westphal, M. und Behrens, G. (1949). Hemmung der Infloreszenzbildung durch Langtag bei der Kurztagpflanze *Kalanchoe blossfeldiana*. *Planta* **36,** 424.

[53] Heimann, M. (1950). Einfluss periodischer Beleuchtung auf die Guttationsrhythmik. *Planta* **38,** 157.

[54] Karvé, A., Engelmann, W. und Schoser, G. (1961). Initiation of rhythmical petal movements in *Kalanchoe blossfeldiana* by transfer from continuous darkness to continuous light or vice-versa. *Planta* 56, 700.

[55] Kunitake, G. M. and Saltman, P. (1958). Dark fixation of CO_2 by succulent leaves: Conservation of the dark fixed CO_2 under diurnal conditions. *Plant Physiol.* 33, 400.

[56] Kunitake, G. M., Saltman, P. and Lang, A. (1957). The products of CO_2 dark fixation in leaves of long and short-day treated *Kalanchoe blossfeldiana*. *Plant Physiol.* 32, 201.

[57] Lange, O. L. and Schwemmle, B. (1960). Untersuchungen zur Hitzeresistenz vegetativer und blühender Pflanzen von *Kalanchoe blossfeldiana*. *Planta* 55, 208.

[58] Madan, L. C. (1956). Die Verteilung der freien Aminosäuren in der Pflanze und ihre Beeinflussung durch photoperiodische Induktion. *Planta* 47, 53.

[59] Melchers, G. (1956). Die Beteiligung der endonomen Tagesrhythmik am Zustandekommen der photoperiodischen Reaktion der Kurztagpflanze *Kalanchoe blossfeldiana*. *Z.f. Naturf.* 11b, 544.

[60] Metzner, H. (1955). Veränderungen der Blattproteine bei photoperiodischer Induktion. *Planta* 45, 493.

[61] Neyland, M. and Thimann, K. V. (1956). Organic acid content of *Kalanchoe* leaves on different photoperiods. *Plant Physiol.* (*Meet.Suppl.*) 31, XXXV–XXXVI.

[62] Neyland, M., Ng., Y. L. and Thimann, K. V. (1963). Formation of anthocyanin in leaves of *Kalanchoe blossfeldiana* – a photoperiodic response. *Plant Physiol.* 38, 447.

[63] Norris, L. and Calvin, M. (1955). Photoperiodism and photosynthetic CO_2 assimilation. In *Biochemistry of Nitrogen. Annales Academiae Scientiarum Fennicae, Ser. A. II, Chemica* (*Helsinki*) 60, 32.

[64] Oltmans, O. (1960). Über den Einfluss der Temperatur auf die endogene Tagesrhythmik und die Blühinduktion bei der Kurztagpflanze *Kalanchoe blossfeldiana Planta* 54, 233.

[65] Priestley, C. A. (1959). The relation of dark fixation of CO_2 to daylength and flower induction in *Kalanchoe blossfeldiana* var. 'Tom Thumb', Ph.D. Thesis, Univ. London.

[66] Roodenburg, J. W. M. (1939). Vervroeging von de bloei bij *Kalanchoe blossfeldiana*. *Weekbl. v. d. Kon. Ned. Mij. v. Tuinb. en Plantenk* 13, 1.

[67] Rünger, W. (1958). On the effect of temperature and light intensity on the photoperiodic reaction and flower development of *Kalanchoe blossfeldiana*, var. 'Tom Thumb', IV. *Gartenbauwiss.* 23, 419. (c.f. *Hort. Abstr.* 29, 3907).

[68] Rünger, W. (1959). Über den Einfluss der Temperatur während verschiedener Zeitabschnitte der Kurztagperiode auf die Blütenbildung von *Kalanchoe blossfeldiana*. *Planta* 53, 602.

[69] Rünger, W. (1961). Über den Einfluss der Stickstoffernährung und der Temperatur während Langtag-und Kurztagperioden auf die Blütenbildung von *Kalanchoe blossfeldiana*. *Planta* 56, 517.

[70] Saltman, P., Kunitake, G. M. and Lang, A. (1957). Further studies on the effects of CO_2 dark fixation on the photoperiodic response of some short-day plants. *Plant Physiol.* 32, LV.

[71] Schmalz, H. (1959). Der Einfluss alternierender Kurz – und Dauertag – perioden verschiedener Länge auf die generative Entwicklung der Sojabohne und *Kalanchoe blossfeldiana*. *Naturwiss.* 46, 212.

[72] Schmalz, H. (1960). Der Einfluss von Gibberellin auf die Blütenbildung von *Kalanchoe blossfeldiana*. *Naturwiss.* 47, 20.

[73] Schmitz, J. (1951). Über Beziehungen zwischen Blütenbildung in Verschiedenen Licht-Dunkelkombinationen und Atmungsrhythmik bei Wechselnden photoperiodischen Bedingungen. *Planta* 39, 271.

[74] Schwabe, W. W. (1952). Effects of photoperiodic treatment on stomatal movements. *Nature* 169, 1053.

[75] Schwabe, W. W. (1954). The effects of light intensity on the flowering of *Kalanchoe blossfeldiana* in relation to the critical daylength. *Physiol. Plantar* 7, 745.

[76] Schwabe, W. W. (1955). Photoperiodic cycles of lengths differing from 24 hours in relation to endogenous rhythms. *Physiol. Plantar.* 8, 263.

[77] Schwabe, W. W. (1956). Evidence for a flowering inhibitor produced in long days in *Kalanchoe blossfeldiana*. *Ann. Bot. N.S.* 20, 1.

[78] Schwabe, W. W. (1957). Recent work on the inhibitory effect of long days on the flowering of some short-day plants. *Publ. No. 34, Ser. B. de l'U.S.I.B. Parma*.

[79] Schwabe, W. W. (1958). Effects of photoperiod and hormone treatment on isolated rooted leaves of *Kalanchoe blossfeldiana*. *Physiol. Plantar*. **11**, 225.

[80] Schwabe, W. W. (1959). Studies of long-day inhibition in short-day plants. *J. Exp. Bot.* **10**, 317.

[81] Schwabe, W. W. (1961). Tests of a new photoperiodic hypothesis. In *Recent Advances in Botany*, 1290. University of Toronto Press.

[82] Schwabe, W. W. and Wilson, N. R. (1965). Effects of photoperiod on the apparent viscosity of leaf cytoplasm in *Kalanchoe blossfeldiana*, 2. Some long- and short-term effects of daylength and spectral composition of light. *Ann. Bot., N.S.* **29**, 383.

[83] Schwabe, W. W. (1968). Studies on the role of the leaf epidermis in photoperiodic perception in *Kalanchoe blossfeldiana*. *J. Exp. Bot.* **19**, 108.

[84] Schwemmle, B. (1959). Endogen-tagesperiodische Schwankungen der Hitzeresistenz bei *Kalanchoe blossfeldiana*. *Planta* **53**, 134.

[85] Senden, H., van (1951). Untersuchungen über den Einfluss von Heteroauxin und anderen Faktoren auf die Blütenbildung bei der Kurztagpflanze, *Kalanchoe blossfeldiana*. *Biol. Zentralbl.* **70**, 537.

[86] Spear, I. (1958). The effect of modifying the dark period atmosphere on the flowering of short-day plants. *Plant Physiol.* (*Meet. Suppl.*) **33**, XIX.

[87] Spear, I. (1958). The CO_2 metabolism of *Kalanchoe* plants grown on long (96 hr.) cycles (B). *Plant Physiol.* (*Meet. Suppl.*) **33**, XIX.

[88] Spear, I. and Thimann, K. V. (1954). The interrelation between CO_2 metabolism and photoperiodism in *Kalanchoe*. II. Effect of prolonged darkness and high temperatures. *Plant Physiol.* **29**, 414.

[89] Stein, D. B. and Stein, O. L. (1960). The growth of the stem tip of *Kalanchoe blossfeldiana*, c.v. 'Brilliant Star'. *Amer. J. Bot.* **47**, 132.

[90] Thomas, M. and Ranson, S. L. (1954). Physiological studies on acid-metabolism in green plants. III. Further evidence of CO_2 fixation during dark-acidification of plants showing crassulacean acid metabolism. *New Phyt.* **53**, 1.

[91] Wallrable, E. (1944). Über die Wirkung von Licht verschiedener Wellenlänge auf die Blütenbildung und die Sukkulenz der Blätter bei der Kurztagpflanze *Kalanchoe blossfeldiana*. *Bot. Arch.* **45**, 281.

[92] Wilson, J. R. and Schwabe, W. W. (1964). Effects of photoperiod on the apparent viscosity of leaf cytoplasm in *Kalanchoe blossfeldiana*, – I. A. method for quantitative estimation and its sources of error. *Ann. Bot. N.S.* **28**, 647.

[93] Witsch, H., v. und Flügel, A. (1951). Über photoperiodisch induzierte Endomitose bei *Kalanchoe blossfeldiana*. *Naturwiss.* **38**, 138.

[94] Witsch, H., v. und Flügel, A. (1952). Über Polyploidieerhöhung im Kurztag von *Kalanchoe blossfeldiana*. *Z. Bot.* **40**, 281.

[95] Zabka, G. and Edelman, J. (1961). Pre-illumination as a factor in the dark-fixation of CO_2 by *Kalanchoe blossfeldiana*, var. 'Feuerblüte'. *Plant Physiol.* (*Meet. Suppl.*) **36**, lii.

[96] Zabka, G. and McMahon, E. (1965). Relationships among CO_2 dark-fixation, succulence, flowering and organic acid formation in *Kalanchoe blossfeldiana* var. 'Tom Thumb'. *Canad. J. Bot.* **43**, 447.

[97] Zabka, G., Gregory, F. G. and Edelman, J. (1959). Dark fixation of carbon dioxide in *Kalanchoe blossfeldiana* in relation to photoperiodism. *Nature* **183**, 1375.

[98] Zeevaart, J. A. D. (1958). Flower formation as studied by grafting. *Meded. Landbouwhogesch* **58**, 1.

[99] Zeist, W. van and Koevoets, T. C. M. (1951). *Kalanchoe blossfeldiana* treated with 2, 3, 5-triiodobenzoic acid (TIBA). *Proc. kon. Ned. Akad. Wetensch. Amst.* **54**, 126.

[100] Zimmer, R. (1962). Phasenverschiebung und andere Störlichtwirkungen auf die endogen tagesperiodischen Blütenblattbewegungen von *Kalanchoe blossfeldiana*. *Planta* **58**, 283.

10

Fragaria

By C. G. Guttridge

1 History of Use

The cultivated strawberry (*Fragaria X. ananassa* Duch.) is one of the world's finest fruits and much of the literature on flowering reports attempts by horticulturists to understand and control its flowering and fruiting habit. Darrow and Waldo's studies in the U.S.A. in the 1930s established the flowering response to short photoperiod and to low temperature[18] and the principles of varietal adaptation,[16] and Eguchi[21-25] did similar work in Japan.

The strawberry is interesting to students of the physiology of flowering chiefly because of (1) its perennial habit, requiring a physiological mechanism for balancing flowering and vegetative growth; (2) its strong vegetative response to photoperiod and other parameters of the environment[38]; (3) its habit of forming stolons and daughter offsets which are useful for the study of hormone translocation; and finally, (4) the possibility that flowering is regulated by inhibitors arising in non-inductive photoperiods.

The flowering and vegetative responses of different species and cultivars to environment vary greatly in degree. Because of the high polyploidy, one supposes that some responses may be poorly developed and difficult to demonstrate rather than totally lacking in a given cultivar and that differences, except for mutations, are of degree rather than of kind. Anderson[1] has compiled a comprehensive bibliography of world literature on strawberry.

2 Growing Techniques and Growth Habit

A high standard of plant management is necessary. Flowering is readily induced in some cultivars by mineral starvation before deficiency symptoms appear, or by drought or transplanting checks, so the provision of water and of mineral nutrients in adequate and steady supply is important. Sand culture is useful for long-term experiments and the Long Ashton nutrient formula[46] is satisfactory, but regular nutrient feeding in horticultural composts is also satisfactory. With horticultural composts there is a danger of excessive levels of nitrogen initially inducing tip-burn of the foliage, if the environment is conducive to vigorous growth, but later feeding may be needed. In some cultivars the presence of fruit trusses or dependent daughter runners can check growth and induce flowering in otherwise non-inductive environments. Plants are readily propagated from stolon offsets, known horticulturally as runners.

The growth habit of the tops[33] and of roots[58,59] have been described and White[91] has studied root and crown anatomy. The strawberry is an herbaceous perennial with a rosette habit. In cool temperate climates some 2 or 3 small leaves on each crown survive the winter. Stem internodes are usually about 2 mm in length and the leaves are inserted spirally 5 in 2 revolutions. Some 20–30 leaves may be formed annually on each crown, depending on climate. The plastochron is of the order of 8 days at 20°C. Flower trusses are initiated terminally, although the flower truss is laterally displaced later by the growth of the uppermost axillary bud to an apparently axillary position. A further truss may be initiated on the new axis after the initiation of at least 2 but commonly 3 or 4 leaves. Excepting under grossly unfavourable growing conditions, flower trusses on the main crown emerge and flower in sequence with the leaves. Axillary buds inserted lower on the crown stem may also initiate inflorescences but these usually emerge and flower only if growing conditions are good enough to cause the axillary bud to grow and form a branch crown. After several years a strawberry plant may have up to 40 crowns or more in some cultivars, all functioning with a measure of independence.

Stolons, bearing daughter runner plants, arise in axillary positions, being in effect branch crowns in which the first two internodes are elongated. Outdoors in cool temperate climates stolon initiation commences anew each spring, and the first runners of the season emerge some 5 or 6 plastochrons later. Stolon production is terminated by SD in autumn, but may be temporarily checked before this by drought or during a heavy fruiting period. Stolon production may be sparse in climates where winter chilling is inadequate.

There is no specialized winter resting bud. Each developing leaf is enclosed within the stipules of the next older leaf, there being from 4–8 leaves within the bud enclosed by the stipules of the youngest emerged leaf. This number is minimal (4–5) in late spring and maximal (6–8) in winter. Diploid species being smaller have fewer leaves in the bud. The increase in autumn results from a relative retardation of leaf emergence. When flower trusses are formed, the first two leaves of the uppermost axillary bud are frequently initiated in rapid sequence so that the numbers of leaves within the bud is not greatly altered and, later, after emergence, the plastochron recovers from the interruption caused by the emergence of the flower truss. Arney[2] has described leaf ontogeny.

3 Inflorescence Structure and Criteria of Flowering Response

The inflorescence (flower truss) is a cyme, with a very variable structure. Darrow[15] has illustrated 124 different variants in one cultivar. Figure 10–1, taken from Darrow's paper illustrates a basally branching type. More commonly, in some cultivars, the first branch arises several centimetres along the primary peduncle. The relative lengths of peduncle, branches and pedicels vary in response to photoperiod, temperatures and winter chilling.[65,77] In the field, the length of the peduncle is determined by the time of initiation of the inflorescence.[18] The peduncles of early-formed flower trusses (initiated in September in temperate regions of the northern hemisphere) develop in short autumn daylengths and are short, whereas, the peduncles of later formed trusses develop less in autumn than in spring and are longer because of the promotive effect of winter chilling on elongation.[50,77] Compensatory growth, as well as environment, seems to affect the size of branches and pedicels and the latter especially tend to be short when the peduncles are long. Bauer and Koch[7] have linked these and other characters with geographical adaptation of cultivars.

After initiation, further development of the truss is sensitive to photoperiod; exposure to long photoperiods (LD), induces earlier emergence and taller trusses with more flowers than does continued exposure to short days (SD).[25,29,64,74,84] Gosselink[29] suggests the early morphological changes described as initiation may proceed more quickly in LD than in SD and there is some indirect evidence from Jonkers'[50] data that initiation (not induction) is promoted by warm, long days. Eguchi[26] is reported as stating that the strawberry requires SD for induction and LD for inflorescence growth and emergence, but neither of these requirements is absolute in cultivated varieties, which often show greater tolerance to unfavourable photoperiod than wild species.

Flower induction is the process which results in the growing apex changing from vegetative to floral growth. An inflorescence can be recognized in dissection, by a high apical dome after about one plastochron, but recognition is much easier after about two plastochrons, when sepal primordia are present. A quantitative measure of inductive capacity of an environment is obtained from number of SD cycles needed to induce flowering or, from numbers of leaves formed before the inflorescence using the last emerged leaf, which may be tagged at the beginning of the experiment, as a base. If necessary the number of leaf primordia in the bud may be determined by dissecting a sample of crowns before treatment. Number

FIGURE 10–1. *Fragaria* X. *ananassa* Duch. This strawberry plant has a single crown. The single inflorescence is of the low-branching type, with no apparent primary axis or peduncle. The two secondary axes (A) are sub-tended by bracts (B and C) and are strongly developed and terminate in secondary flowers. Typically, as here, the lower one is larger. Tertiary (D) and quarternary (E) flower buds are present. The primary flower has set fruit.

Commonly the peduncle elongates and the secondary axes are then inserted higher, well clear of the bud.

As the inflorescence occupies a terminal poisition, extension growth of the crowns continues from the bud (F) subtended by the uppermost leaf (G). The bud may contain a second and possibly a third order inflorescence. Frequently the first two leaves of the extension bud emerge simultaneously and are comparable in size, but not in this illustration where one leaf (H) has emerged (after Darrow[15]).

of flowers on the inflorescence is not a measure of induction. The induction of flower trusses is almost always accompanied by changes in vegetative growth and it is sometimes possible to assay an environmental effect by measuring petiole length or some other accessible vegetative character.

Occasionally, but under a wide variety of conditions, flower trusses are induced on young attached runner plants only or before they are induced on the mother plant.[13,27,54] This happens naturally in some everbearing cultivars. The reasons for it are not understood.

For brevity the terms flower and truss are used to denote the whole inflorescence.

4 Effects of Plant Age

Jonkers[49] found that octoploid seedlings with fewer than 5–7 trifoliate leaves were not induced by SD, and Sironval[73] was able to recognise, by leaf dentation, a juvenile phase in the diploid *F. vesca semperflorens*, in which plants could not be induced. Leaf dentation may partly be a function of leaf size.

Flower initiation is also delayed in some cultivars in small runner plants where juvenility is unlikely.[3,48,72] The delay is possibly due to an insufficient leaf area. Jonkers[50] found that 3–4 leaves were necessary for flowering on young runner plants, and Ueno[85] found the most advanced stage of flowering in runner plants which had 4 or 5 leaves.

5 Vernalization and Devernalization

Jonkers[50] subjected germinated seeds of *F. vesca semperflorens* cv. Baron Solemacher and cv. Rügen and of the octoploid cv. Deutsch Evern to 2, 4, 6, 8 or 10 weeks of chilling at 3–5°C, but found this had no effect on subsequent flowering in either LD or SD. On the other hand Kruzhilin and Shvedskaya[52,53] interpret some observations on flowering behaviour in seedlings and runner plants as a vernalization effect, but they supply very little experimental data and confirmation is needed before a case can be made for a classical vernalization response.

By contrast, chilling of established plants inhibits the subsequent induction of flowers. This response is akin to the effects of low temperature in breaking dormancy or winter rest in woody plants and is associated with a promotion of vegetative growth.

V.d. Muijzenberg[65] noted that SD treatment in spring following winter chilling failed to induce flowering in cv. Deutsch Evern before mid-May and before June in some other varieties. Guttridge[35] obtained a quantitative assessment of the chilling effect by comparing the growth of chilled and unchilled (dormant) plants when transferred to the same inductive environment in growth rooms. In two experiments the photoperiod was 11 and 12 hours and the temperature 16°C in the growth room. Dormancy is not absolute in octoploid cultivars and the dormant groups in both experiments grew healthily except that vegetative development was severely restrained and no stolons were formed (Fig. 10–2).

Comparable groups were chilled either in the natural winter temperatures outdoors or in a cold store at 2–5°C. The chilled plants grew much more vigorously in the growth room than the unchilled plants had done, producing stolons, and larger petioles and laminae. Initiation of new flower trusses was delayed by 7 plastochrons in the cv. Royal Sovereign and by 3 in Auchincruive Climax compared with that in unchilled plants. Pre-existing trusses are especially responsive to chilling, which results in increased subsequent growth of the peduncle[77] and of the truss generally, particularly in the species *F. virginiana* and *F. elatior*.

Piringer and Scott[66] reported decreased flower formation following chilling in cv. Missionary, but not in some other cultivars and Takai[77] found large varietal

FIGURE 10–2. Effect of winter chilling on growth of strawberry plants (cv. Climax). The plant on the left was dormant when introduced into the growth room six weeks before photographing. The plant on the right was exposed to winter chilling outdoors for 10 weeks before being brought into the growth room, and differs from the left-hand plant mainly in respect of its prior chilling. Pre-existing flower trusses in both plants were removed upon their emergence. Note the stumps of severed stolons on the chilled plant.

ences in the amount of chilling required to induce vegetative responses, but wer formation is not mentioned in the English summary. Varietal variation may have its origins in the differing behaviour of *F. virginiana*, which has a strong chilling requirement, and *F. chiloensis*, at least some strains of which have a much weaker chilling response.[30] A distinction should be made between a chilling response and the amount of exposure to low temperature required to saturate it.

Inadequate chilling leads to a prolonged fruiting season because flower initiation continues throughout the winter (if mild enough for growth) and spring until terminated by long daylengths and/or warm temperatures in summer. For instance, some cultivars which are single-cropping in northerly regions of U.S.A. fruit over a long season in Florida[17] and in some circumstances in California[10,88] where winters are mild. This response, resulting from insufficient chilling, should be distinguished from late summer and autumn fruiting induced by a failure of photoperiodic regulation in summer, either because of relatively cool summer temperatures[48] or because of the genetically-induced everbearing habit of some octoploid cultivars which initiate flowers in the long daylengths of regions such as the northern states of U.S.A. and northern Europe. In these cultivars, the everbearing habit seems to result from flower induction being independent of photoperiod in the sense that long daylengths fail to inhibit it.

At least some of the octoploid everbearing cultivars exhibit a clearly defined post-chilling phase in spring in which flower induction fails, later causing a break in fruit production in summer.[89] This break in fruit production has also been seen in several French perpetual-fruiting cultivars growing outdoors at Invergowrie and suggests that the chilling and photoperiodic flowering responses may be genetically distinguishable in the octoploids, but neither the genetics of the responses nor the physiological interaction of the processes appear to have been studied.

7 Photoperiod Response

The single-cropping octoploid cultivars of temperate climates are facultative SD plants.[8,18,22,44,48,50,65] Both species and cultivars vary in photoperiodic sensitivity. *F. vesca* is relatively insensitive[11] and *F. virginiana* apparently the opposite, at least judging by the extreme sensitivity of its vegetative responses to photoperiod.[18] In the cultivars, which have been more widely studied than the species, flowers can usually be induced in long photoperiods when other environmental factors are unfavourable to growth. Chiefly these are low growing temperature, drought and mineral starvation. However, the summer-fruiting strawberries are SD plants in the sense that in some environmental conditions they are induced to flower only in photoperiods shorter than a critical duration. Further flower induction ceases when plants are transferred from inductive to non-inductive conditions, and an intervening chilling response is not necessary for reversion to vegetative growth. However, because chilling responses can be demonstrated,[35] it appears that prolonged exposure to SD must induce persistent changes that are reversed, at best only slowly, by photoperiod. These changes may result from accumulation of growth inhibitors rather than from persistent changes in metabolism such as have been postulated for annual species in which flower induction is irreversible.

The everbearing or perpetual-fruiting octoploid cultivars flower more freely in LD than in SD.[20,74] From seed *F. vesca semperflorens* did not flower in photoperiods shorter than $10\frac{1}{2}$ hours at 20°C or shorter than $11\frac{1}{2}$ hours outdoors according to Sironval[73], while in 8-hour photoperiods the seedlings died. The LD requirement is not absolute for the cultivars of this form Baron Solemacher and Rügen, which produced flower buds after 118 and 107 short days compared with 64 and 63 long days respectively for the two cultivars.[50] Although quantitatively

LD favours flowering in the everbearing types and in Sironval's variety is necessary for the attainment of puberty, neither of these responses is evidence for a specific photoperiodic regulation of flowering. No conditions are known to me in which the adult of any *Fragaria* species or variety will flower only in LD. The everbearing types may differ from the SD types in respect of flowering only in the lack or impairment of the photoperiodic or environmental control mechanism and the quantitative improvement in flowering in everbearing varieties in LD, compared with SD, may arise non-specifically from better growth.

Brown and Wareing[11] have shown that the everbearing habit in *F. vesca* is controlled by a single recessive gene. Thus the dominant gene in the non-everbearing wild type confers an environmental regulation of flowering (more by temperature than by photoperiod) whereas the recessive mutant allele results in a lack of environment control. If the mutation of a dominant gene to a recessive allele resulted in the loss of an enzyme-controlled reaction rather than the introduction of a new one, this would fit with the idea that flowering is controlled in non-everbearing forms by an inhibitory system, the loss of which gives an everbearing condition.

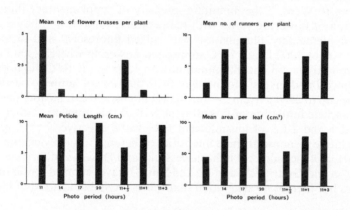

FIGURE 10–3. Effect of photoperiod on growth and flowering of strawberry plants (means of six cultivars). The photoperiod consisted of 11 hours daylight for the control plants. This was either extended to 14, 17 or 20 hours or the dark period was interrupted near the middle for $\frac{1}{3}$, 1 or 3 hours by irradiation from incandescent lamps (from data of Borthwick and Parker[8]).

With the photoperiodic regulation of flowering possibly genetically impaired to various degrees and with other environmental factors influencing the flowering response, the division between everbearing and summer-fruiting types is not surprisingly ill-defined, except in the diploid *F. vesca*, and that fruiting habits outdoors show great variety depending on climate. Generally speaking the fruiting seasons outdoors become longer towards lower latitudes, because of less winter chilling and longer growing periods with photoperiods shorter than about 14 hours. Darrow has discussed photoperiodic aspects of varietal adaptation.[17]

At temperatures above 16°–17°C and in the absence of a growth check, many cultivars will flower only in SD. In these conditions the threshold photoperiod has been reported to be between 12 and 16 hours,[29,48] 12 and 14 hours,[65] 11 and 14 hours,[8] 11 and 15 hours.[5] The threshold for vegetative responses – petiole length, leaf size and runner formation – is similar (Fig. 10–3).[8,29] This correlation between flower inhibition and vegetative growth suggests a link in the regulatory system. The promotion of lamina size, petiole length, runner formation and the greater development of the inflorescence in long photoperiods has been widely reported in the references quoted above. If threshold requirements are allowed for, the correlation between vegetative growth and flower inhibition is remarkably impressive for a wide range of influences besides the photoperiodic one, although there are possible exceptions.[72,90]

Substantial light breaks near the middle of the dark period replace long photoperiods. Borthwick and Parker[8] found that 1 hour of illumination near the middle of the dark period with 20–40 f.c. of incandescent light was as inhibitory as 3 hours immediately following 11 hours illumination with daylight. The light break was similarly effective on the vegetative responses.[8,87] Light breaks of 20 or 30 minutes were either much less effective[8] or ineffective.[87]

The lowest number of SD cycles reported to induce flowering at temperatures greater than 17°C is 6 for cv. Blakemore.[72] Others record 7 for Missionary,[44] 7–14 for Deutsch Evern,[65] 8 for Talisman,[83] 8–10 for Robinson,[48] 10 for Marshall,[90] 14 for Deutsch Evern,[50] 15 for Sparkle,[64] 20 for Sparkle[29] and 4–5 weeks for *F. vesca*.[11] Induction is affected by pre-treatments[48] and this rather than cultivar may account for most of the variation.

According to Went,[90] the minimum intensity of supplementary illumination for inhibition of flowering varies with temperature. Following 8 hours daylight at 23°C, supplementary illumination with mixed fluorescent and incandescent lighting of 800 or 1200 f.c. at 14°C suppressed flowering whereas 400 f.c. under the same conditions did not; illumination with 1200 f.c. at 10°C did not entirely suppress flowering. Jonkers[50] found light from fluorescent lamps to be ineffective at intensities up to 2500 μW/cm^2, – the highest intensity tried; incandescent lamps effected complete inhibition of flowering at 1/10 of this intensity. Other workers have found 1 and 2 f.c. of incandescent light to be effective,[48,71,86] and some noted vegetative response at these intensities or below.[86] Borthwick and Parker[8] used 20–40 f.c. of incandescent light successfully and Downs and Piringer 30 f.c.[20]

Thompson and Guttridge[83] and Ito and Saito[48] have reported flower induction in darkness but there is no suggestion that this is a reliable method of induction.

8 Spectral Dependence

The spectral sensitivity of the photoperiodic response has not been studied comprehensively. Horticulturists use incandescent lamps, which are more effective than fluorescent lamps for extending the daylength. As already noted, Jonkers[50] found incandescent lamps inhibited flowering at an intensity of 240 μW/cm^2 whereas fluorescent lamps failed to do so at 2,500 μW/cm^2, while other workers have found incandescent lamps to be effective even at intensities of 2 f.c. (approximately 10 μW/cm^2).[48,71,86] The low emission of fluorescent lamps in the far-red spectral region is usually held to account for their relative inefficiency.

For vegetative responses, a light regime of 10 hours of fluorescent and incandescent lighting at about 1,000 f.c. plus 8 hours of incandescent lighting at about 35 f.c. was more effective than 18 hours lighting with both sources together (Guttridge, unpublished).

Flower induction in autumn outdoors was delayed for 3 weeks by irradiating from dusk to midnight with red fluorescent lamps at an intensity of about 25 f.c.;[3] surprisingly, the light was just as effective when supplied during daylight hours. Incandescent lighting at an intensity of 230 f.c. delayed flowering for a further 9 days but was ineffective during daylight.[3]

Collins and Barker[14] exposed plants in a growth chamber at 20–23°C to continuous light from fluorescent and incandescent lamps at an intensity of 800–1000 f.c. with about equal wattage for the two lamp types. None of the mother plants and only 10 per cent of daughter plants attached to them flowered. When the incandescent lamp wattage was decreased to 20 per cent of the fluorescent lamp wattage none of the plants flowered. They suggest that induction was caused by the high proportion of incandescent light and therefore of the far-red component, which may have driven a sufficient proportion of the phytochrome pigment to the biologically inactive P_r form to result in failure of inhibition of flowering. In further trials[13] various types of fluorescent and incandescent lamps were used to give differing ratios of red and far-red radiation in continuous lighting, and the results were confirmed. Again flowering was confined to daughter plants; about 10 per cent of them flowered when the R/FR ratio was 1.30 or less. All plants remained vegetative when it was 2.86. Collins is cautious about differentiating between low energy photoreversible effects and high energy photosynthetic effects and the different light regimes in his experiments may have affected flowering in ways other than through differences in R/FR ratio.

9 Endogenous Rhythms

These have not been studied, although Hartmann experimented with 20 and 28-hour cycles.[44]

10 Fractional Induction

Intercalating a single LD in the middle of a series of SD cycles increased the number of SD cycles needed to induce flowering in cv. Talisman from an average of 16.5 to 18.0 (Guttridge, unpublished).

With cv. Deutsch Evern 2 trusses per plant were formed after two weeks SD induction and 3.7 after 3 weeks. When the three week period was twice interrupted – after the first and second weeks – by one week in long natural daylengths, flowering was decreased to 0.3 trusses per plant. With interruptions of 3 days duration 0.9 trusses per plant were formed.[65]

11 Photoperiodic Inhibition

There is no definitive evidence to show whether flowering is controlled by inhibiting or promoting hormones or both, but much circumstantial evidence suggests the former. Hartmann[44] used discrete mother-daughter units joined by the stolon and his results have been interpreted as demonstrating the transmission of a florigenic substance. By growing mother plants in SD of 10 hours in a growth cabinet and passing the stolon through the wall into LD of 15 hours in a second cabinet, he established a donor-receptor system, in which the daughter plant in LD flowered, apparently induced by a flowering stimulus transmitted from the induced mother plant in SD. Presumably because the daughter plants were at first too small to survive independently, Hartmann used extra mother plants as controls for comparison with the daughter receptor plants in LD. This lack of controls of comparable size is important because, judging by the size of the truss in the published photograph, induction may have occurred before the daughter plants were large enough to perceive the long photoperiod, and thus to generate an inhibitor. In fact, Hartmann commented that the flowering stimulus may have been translocated with the carbohydrate supply very early in the life of the daughter plants while they were still largely dependent on the mother plant plant for food materials. Another disturbing feature is the absence in Hartmann's photographs of any appreciable vegetative response to the long photoperiods in both the daughter receptor plants and the controls alongside them, perhaps because fluorescent lamps alone were used. His results do not establish the activity of a positive florigenic stimulus, and induction in the absence of an inhibitor could equally well be the explanation.

Several experiments suggest that long photoperiods, or light breaks of several hours' duration during the dark period, promote vegetative growth and delay or inhibit flower induction. The transmission of a stimulus to vegetative growth has been demonstrated in experiments with donor-receptor units composed of two adjacent runner plants from a runner chain.[34,36,37] In these units the mother and daughter differed in age by not more than 2 plastochrons.

Tracer experiments[36] showed that ^{32}P applied to the leaves moves naturally from mother to daughter plant but that movement in the opposite direction was induced by defoliating the mother plant or by exposing the daughter plant to longer daily durations of full lighting than the mother plant. These results suggest that ^{32}P may move from plant to plant together with the products of photosynthesis and the results of photoperiodic experiments indicate that the photoperiodic stimuli originating in LD are transported similarly.[36]

In one critical experiment daughter plants of cv. Redgauntlet were grown in a growth cabinet in SD at 18°C and attached mother plants in an adjoining cabinet at 13°C, a temperature difference calculated to enhance the transmission of photosynthates from mother to daughter plants along the stolon.[37] When the parent plants were exposed to LD (extension of the photoperiod by incandescent lighting of low intensity) daughter plants attached to them responded by greatly increased vegetative growth of petioles, leaves and stolons and by failing to initiate flower trusses. Control daughter plants, comparable in every way, except that they were attached to mother plants in SD, flowered. R. G. Hill (unpublished) confirmed these results with cv. Cambridge Favourite.

In another experiment daughter plants responded by increased vegetative development and delayed flower initiation to a light break of 3 hours duration with incandescent light of 25–45 f.c. intensity which was applied to attached mother plants.[36] In this experiment the mother plants, whether or not receiving the light break, were exposed to daylight 3 hours earlier each morning than the daughter plants. When no differential daylight treatment was applied the vegetative response of daughter plants to the photoperiodic stimulus arising in mother plants receiving a light break was much less and flowering was not significantly delayed, a difference attributable to less transmission of the stimulus.

In contrast, attempts to demonstrate the transmission of a SD stimulus, using differential temperature or differential daylight treatments calculated to promote transmission from donor to receptor, failed to show any evidence for promotion of flowering or for depression of vegetative growth in daughter plants in LD deriving from their attachment to mother plants in SD.[36,37]

In an experiment with cv. Royal Sovereign the growth of mother plants in SD was influenced by partial defoliation of daughter plants in LD.[34] Flower induction in the mother plant was progressively advanced by increasing the severity of defoliation of the daughter plants. Initiation took 9 plastochrons in mother plants that were attached to intact daughter plants compared with 3 in mother plants attached to defoliated daughter plants (less than 0–1 leaves present). The plastochron numbers suggest a delay caused by a flower inhibitor transported along the stolon from the daughter plants with leaves, rather than an advancement of flowering in the mother plants, caused by attachment to defoliated daughter plants. Transmission from daughter to mother was possible in this experiment because daughter plants were exposed to sunlight for up to 2 hours daily before the mother plants were uncovered. None of the daughter plants in LD flowered in response to the SD treatment of the mother plant except when completely defoliated and presumably unable to perceive photoperiod. In other experiments[43] (and unpublished) daughter plants in LD flowered only when defoliated.

Subsequently, Jonkers[50] has found with cv. Deutsch Evern that daughter plants in LD failed to flower in response to inductive treatment of the mother plants which flowered. In the reverse arrangement, 4 out of 6 daughter plants in SD were inhibited from flowering by attachment to mother plants in LD. Other results with cv. Glasa were less clear but provided no evidence for transmission of a flower-promoting substance.

Some further evidence for the dominance of the long-day stimulus comes from v.d. Muijzenberg's experiments[65] with single plants of cv. Deutsch Evern, which show that, with only a few exceptions, plants failed to flower if more than one leaf remained in LD while the remainder were in SD. With cv. Missionary, Hartmann[44] found that one leaf in SD induced flowering in 1 plant out of 5; 50 per cent of the leaf area in SD induced flowering in 2 out of 5 and 100 per cent of the leaf area in SD in 4 out of 5 plants, but this result, which gives no clear indication of dominance by either daylength is unreliable because the light source was entirely fluorescent lamps.

Whether a specific florigenic hormone has a role is not answered by this type of experiment. Defoliation experiments suggest that a specific flower promoting factor may be unnecessary. With cv. Talisman, induction in LD was promoted by the removal of foliage, suggesting that defoliation removed the source of a flower inhibitor.[83] All leaves in LD were inhibitory, but mature leaves were more so than young ones. Because plants do not long survive when totally defoliated, this condition could not be maintained for the duration of the experiment, and unfolding leaves were again present after about one week; green leaf bases were present throughout. These results therefore do not entirely exclude the possibility that flower induction may depend on the presence of a flower promoting factor originating in green tissue. However, defoliated plants initiated inflorescences equally freely in long or short photoperiods.

Other results point to the need for a small minimal leaf area for flower induction,[50,61,65] as well as for survival but provide insufficient evidence to conclude that a flower-promoting hormone is necessary for initiation.[61]

In some cultivars flower initiation sometimes fails in the field outdoors in Scotland and many crowns may be barren of flower trusses.[40,41,61,62] The condition can be corrected by defoliation of the plants after fruit harvest, but although the plants are defoliated in early August, initiation is often not promoted until late September. The time course of these events is not easily explained by assuming that defoliation removes the source of inhibitor even when a minimal recovery in leaf area is allowed for, because the older leaves would not be expected to inhibit flowering in naturally short autumn daylengths. Possibly flowering inhibitors accumulate during late summer in these varieties and the removal of foliage in August checks this accumulation. On different evidence Leshem and Koller[54] have suggested that a flower inhibitor may be stored in strawberry plants. The occurrence of barren crowns has not been satisfactorily explained either and it remains surprising that cultivars which are known to initiate flowers readily in response to a transplanting check, and in midsummer to competition with swelling fruits,[60] sometimes fail to initiate throughout the whole autumn growth period of about 6 plastochrons, a time which would be expected to offer abundant opportunity for induction and initiation.

Substantially on the basis of results discussed above Jonkers,[50] and later Mason,[62] have suggested that a flower promoter is formed when an inhibitor disappears or falls to a low level. This is a possible hypothesis because it accommodates the evidence that control is mediated by the level of vegetative growth and perhaps by the supply of a promoter of vegetative growth which is formed in greater amounts in LD than in SD. Consideration of the evidence for specific florigenic compounds in other genera encourages the acceptance of this hypothesis for strawberry, and so does the fact that applications of abscisin II[27] induce flowering in strawberry.

13 Effects of Temperature

Flower induction is strongly influenced by temperature. Darrow and Waldo in 1934[18] stated that 'At temperatures above 60°F (15.5°C) short daily light periods (10 hours or less) are necessary to initiate fruit buds' and 'at low temperatures fruit buds may form under longer daily light periods'. This has been widely confirmed.[44,48,65,90,93] However, at temperatures below about 15°–17°C photoperiodic effects remain although prolonged inhibition of flowering is not achieved. Went[90] and Saha[72] have shown that low night temperatures are operative but the effect of low day temperatures has not been explored. For *F. vesca* Brown and Wareing report that temperatures between 10° and 15°C are essential for induction and that long photoperiods delay but do not entirely suppress induction within this temperature range.[11]

The temperature-photoperiod complex largely determines the geographical variations in fruiting habit and the regional adaptation of cultivars.[16] For example, in California flower formation continues throughout the summer near the Pacific coast whereas inland, temperatures are higher and flower formation is inhibited in high summer.[16,45] Arney[3] considers that falling temperatures in autumn may be at least as important as declining photoperiod for induction in Scotland.

Went[90] compared the number of SD cycles of 8 hours light required for induction at different temperatures in cv. Marshall. Induction was most rapid at 17°C, requiring 10 cycles. At both higher and lower temperatures more cycles were needed viz. 12 at 14° and 20°C and 16 at 23°C. At 10°C, one batch of plants flowered after 12 cycles, but in another batch 16 cycles were insufficient to induce flowering.

Ito and Saito had similar results with cv. Robinson.[48] Flowering followed 9 daily light cycles of 4 hours duration at 17° or 24°C, and 8 or 10 cycles (in two experiments) of 8 hours at 17°C, 10 cycles at 24°C or 10 or 12 at 9°C. In 12-hour photoperiods 10 cycles at 9° and at 17°C sufficed but 14 or 16 cycles were needed at 24°C. With 16, 20 or 24-hour cycles flowers formed at 9°C but not at 17° or 24°C. Thus with temperatures above 17°C induction required SD. At 30°C no flowers were formed in 4, 8, 12 or 16-hour daylengths after 20 cycles.

Vegetative growth, measured as petiole length, leaf size or runner formation increases with increasing temperatures and photoperiod so that a negative correlation between flower induction and vegetative growth operates at temperatures above about 17°C. If temperature exerts its formative effects because of differing temperature quotients for different physiological processes then the situation above 17°C could be accounted for by postulating either a flower promoting process with a Q_{10} less than that of growth generally or a flower inhibiting process (but promotive of vegetative growth) with a Q_{10} higher than that of growth generally.

At temperatures below about 17°C induction is more easily achieved in the sense that short photoperiods are no longer needed. The photoperiod, however, continues to affect vegetative growth and it seems possible that flower induction is only quantitatively affected by photoperiod because threshold levels for photoperiod inhibition are not reached. The number of cycles needed to induce flowering increased slightly as the temperature decreased from about 17° to about 9° or 10°C in Went's[90] and Ito and Saito's[48] experiments. At still lower temperatures the required number of cycles increases substantially. Federov and Makaryceva[28] found 30–50 cycles at 2–7°C induced flowering. Jonkers[50] found that at 3–5°C 9 out of 9 plants of cv. Deutsch Evern initiated after 28 cycles but only 2 out of 9 after 14 cycles. With Glasa, prolonging the duration of exposure to a temperature of 3–5°C decreased flowering, so that the number of plants out of 40, later flowering in LD at 21°C, was decreased from 34 after 4 weeks exposure to 29 and 17 after 8 or 12 weeks exposure. Neither photoperiod, light intensity or light source – incandescent or fluorescent – were critical. The explanation, Jonkers suggested,[50] may be that the inductive process is overtaken by the inhibitory chilling process unless induction is completed within about 4 weeks. As fewer plants flowered after prolonged cool treatment, removal to LD at warm temperatures after 4 weeks must have promoted initiation of the truss, which is possible in a facultative SD plant especially as initiation itself may be promoted by conditions favouring vegetative growth.[29] The number of days to emergence of the trusses in LD at 21°C was decreased by prolonging the cool treatment, from 45 days after 4 weeks at 3–5°C to 24 days after 12 weeks and the enhanced rate of growth of the young truss which this implies is evidence for the activity of the chilling process. In some plants initiation was completed and trusses emerged after 30 weeks at 3–5°C.

Ito and Saito[48] subjected plants to diurnal cycles of 9°C and 24°C. The daily duration of low temperature ranged from zero to 24 hours by 4-hour steps. In 8-hour photoperiods, plants flowered after 10 cycles irrespective of the period at low temperature in each cycle, but in continuous illumination plants flowered after 10 cycles of continuous cold, after 12 cycles of 20 hours cold and 4 hours warm, after 16 cycles of 16 hours cold and 8 hours warm but did not flower after 30 cycles with less than 16 hours per day in the cold room. Accumulated hours at 9°C did not appear to be the criterion for flowering. They concluded that the daily period at 9°C must be of 16 hours duration or more to be effective. This suggests that each daily cycle must be individually promotive.

14 Effects of Mineral Nutrition

In spite of the many references both to horticultural experiments with fertilizers and to sand culture experiments with controlled nutrition in which fruit yields were the criterion of response, there is little information on the effects of mineral nutrition on flower induction per se. Direct effects on induction are inseparable from the effects of growth and plant size on the numbers of potential flowering sites. Where decreased flowering or fruiting occurs on plants of increased size, a decreased flowering response is implied, but where both flowering and plant size are increased, inferences on flowering response are seldom justified.

Long and Murneek's data[57] show that applications of nitrogenous fertilizers to a clay soil increased plant size and the number of fruit trusses approximately in proportion, an effect which was probably caused by an increase in number of crowns. However, in a rich loam soil the total leaf area was larger still but the number of trusses decreased to about two-thirds, indicating a reduction in number of trusses per crown. Whitehouse[92] earlier reported that increasing N from a deficiency level increased the number of flowering trusses by half, but that doubling the dose brought truss numbers down to the level of the deficient plants.

The same difficulty arises with other elements but it seems possible that flower induction per se may have been depressed by excessive feeding of P and Ca and by deficient feeding of P and Mg in the experiments of Davis et al.[19] Fruit yield and dry weight increments followed substantially similar curves with increasing levels of K, P and Mg in experiments by Gruppe and Nurbachsch.[31,32] An interesting interaction appears in results of Lineberry et al.[56] which show excessive N depressing yields that are already strongly limited by a deficiency of P.

Using the more direct method of assessing initiation by leaf counts, Arney[3] showed that three applications of nitrogenous fertilizer at monthly intervals in late summer delayed the natural autumn initiation by 10 or more days.

In a pot experiment (Guttridge, unpublished) mineral starvation induced flowering in the cv. Templar. After 5 months in summer, all 24 plants growing in a $\frac{1}{3}$ soil–$\frac{2}{3}$ sand mixture flowered in spite of long daylengths but only 3 out of 31 flowered in the same volume of undiluted soil. Later, nutrient solutions containing N, P or K separately or in factorial combinations were fed to the non-flowering plants and the response to natural induction in late summer observed. The result in Figure 10–4 shows that initiation was delayed by all nutrients and

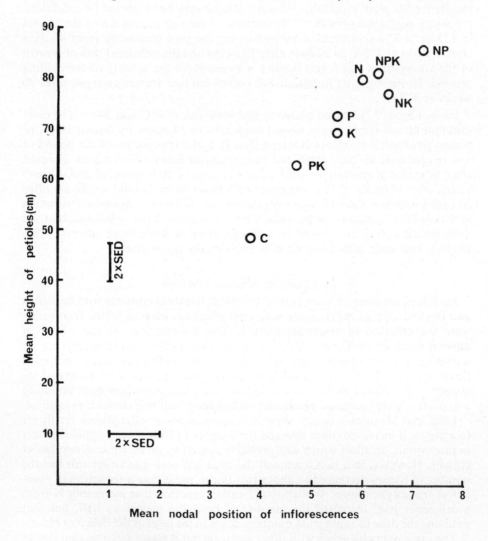

FIGURE 10–4. Effect of addition of N, P and K separately or in factorial combination on length of petioles and nodal position of the inflorescences (cv. Templar). (S.E.D. Standard error of the difference between control and any single treatment.)

that the delay was associated with increased petiole length, suggesting a general negative correlation between flower induction and vegetative growth rather than a specific effect of any one nutrient.

The limitation of fruit yields by flower inhibition in highly fertile soils or following heavy nitrogen feeding is not unknown in commercial plantations.

17 Grafting Experiments

Theoretically, grafting of the everbearing mutant with non-everbearing F. vesca in which flowering is controlled by environment should resolve the question of whether the mutational loss of control results from the loss of an inhibitory hormone or from a change to continuous production of a promotive hormone. Numerous attempts have been made at Invergowrie to devise a working system, but although runners can be grafted and virus transmission obtained, the transmission of effective amounts of hormone stimuli have not been clearly demonstrated.

18 Effect of Growth Substances and Growth Retardants

Auxins

Auxins do not affect flower induction in strawberry, although applications of I.B.A. increase petiole length (P. A. Thompson, unpublished). Extractable auxin levels in buds and leaves are affected by changes in photoperiod and temperature which induce flowering,[64,72] but such correlations do not imply a causal relationship.

Gibberellins

Applications of gibberellic acid inhibit flower formation.[43,69,82] Substantial doses, amounting to one or two sprays of a 100 ppm. solution, completely inhibit flower formation and lower doses decrease it. Plant size and environment affect the dosage required. If initiation is accomplished previously the development of the truss and its emergence are enhanced[69,78] as they are by long photoperiods or after chilling. Other effects of long daylengths and of chilling are also simulated; notably petiole length[42,43] and leaf size[4] are increased and stolons are formed. It is unlikely that gibberellic acid is the long-day hormone postulated by Guttridge[36,37] as it also causes elongation of the vegetative stem[43,69,82] – thus destroying the rosette habit – and also of the base of the receptacle of fruit, giving it a neck.[81] With large dosages, such as are needed to inhibit flowering, individual nodes become clearly separated and a dose of 1 mg per plant has given individual internodes of nearly 40 cm (Guttridge, unpublished). After 3 or 4 leaves have emerged following application of sufficient gibberellic acid to cause the stem to become elongated, petioles and laminae of leaves arising on the elongated portions of the stem tend to be small, probably because of unfavourable competition from the elongating stem for other growth factors.[4,42,43]

Gibberellins A_1, A_3, A_4, A_5, A_7, A_9 and possibly A_8 inhibit flower formation in the ever-bearing form F. vesca semperflorens, cv. Baron Solemacher in which environmental control of flowering is lacking.[43] The mode of action of gibberellins in inhibiting flowering is unknown. It may be by a secondary effect arising from unfavourable competition from the greatly stimulated vegetative growth. Other forms of competition, as from elongating runners or from swelling fruits (noted briefly by Mason [60]) tend to promote, rather than inhibit flowering, and in donor-receptor units, flowers can be induced in mother plants by attachment to strongly growing and presumably demanding daughter plants. However, applications of gibberellins may create a highly competitive situation for a specific substrate such as does not arise from the competition from fruits and runners.

It is also possible that applied gibberellins may interfere specifically in the endogenous regulatory system. It seems that in substituting for long photoperiods they may be acting more specifically than simply as promoters of elongation, because they induce the formation of typical stolons, which are distinguishable from branch crowns with elongated internodes.[43] Yet again exogenous gibberellins may block flowering directly but independently of the endogenous regulatory system. The flowering response has not been studied with sufficient precision for a proper discussion of these possibilities. Flowering has been slightly advanced in *F. vesca* by applications of GA but in this experiment the vegetative development of control plants was rather poor.[43]

Extracts of strawberry stolon tips and other parts have gibberellin-like activity.[55,68,80]

Growth retardants

2-Isopropyl-4-dimethylamino-5-methylphenyl-1-piperidine-carboxylate methyl chloride (Amo 1618) and 2-4-dichlorobenzyl-tributylphosphonium chloride (Phosfon D) are practically inactive but (2-chloroethyl) trimethylammonium chloride (CCC) and N-dimethylamino succinamic acid (B9) both depress vegetative growth, shorten petioles and shorten or inhibit altogether the elongation of runners, thus having the opposite effect to those of the gibberellins and of long daylengths.[39]

If CCC and B9 act by inhibiting the biosynthesis of gibberellins,[51] application of these chemicals would be expected to induce flowering in LD if native gibberellins inhibit flowering. In fact, neither of them are more than marginally promotive of flowering. In my own experience CCC has not induced flowering except slightly in marginal situations. El-Antably et al.[27] report 5 out of 10 plants of cv. Cambridge Favourite flowered after a 2000 ppm. soil drench with CCC. Similarly, aqueous sprays containing up to 8 per cent B9 slightly promoted flowering in daughter runner plants in the field (Mason, unpublished). The failure of these chemicals to induce flowering other than marginally is the only substantial break in the widely observed correlation between flower inhibition and promotion of vegetative growth in the non-everbearing strawberry.

Abscisin

El-Antably, Wareing and Hillman[27] recently report that daily sprays of 5, 10 or 20 ppm. of d, 1, abscisin in aqueous solution, in different experiments induced flowering in 23 out of 30 plants in total, while only 2 control plants flowered (cv. Cambridge Favourite). In another experiment with more vigorously-growing plants, 16 out of 30 flowered after 15 daily sprays of 10 ppm. Abscisin II has recently been extracted from dormant strawberry leaves at Invergowrie (Gabr and Guttridge[94]).

Vitamin E

According to Sironval,[73] when a young runner plant of *F. vesca semperflorens* is prematurely severed from the mother plant, the growth of existing inflorescences is stunted and the numbers of individual flowers drastically decreased. Some inflorescences revert to vegetative growth from a bud which arises in place of a secondary floral branch. Application of vitamin E to such isolated plants improved growth, slightly increased the number of individual flowers reaching anthesis and decreased the reversion to vegetative growth.[73] However, vitamin E did not promote the formation of new inflorescences either in isolates or in intact vegetative plants. In further work Sironval and Tannir-Lomba[75] extracted greater amounts of vitamin E from leaves of the same species growing in LD than from leaves in SD. They suggested a relationship with flowering, but as numbers of flowers per inflorescence and growth generally are both promoted by LD, this does not appear to be evidence that vitamin E regulates the induction of flower trusses specifically.

19 Effect of Metabolic Inhibitors

Thompson[79] observed that applications of weak solutions of maleic hydrazide prevented the initiation of inflorescences and also caused varying degrees of phyllody, and occasionally, reversion of the young inflorescence to vegetative growth. Time of application was very critical, the effects resulting only when the chemical was applied within one plastochron of flower initiation. Thompson cites a paper by Butenko and Baskakov[12] in which uracil is reported to overcome an inhibition of growth of callus tissue caused by maleic hydrazide, the implication being that the effects observed in strawberry may be mediated through the RNA system.

20 Florigenic Extracts

Sironval[73] has shown that the unsaponifiable fraction of leaf extracts of *F. vesca semperflorens* applied to isolated young runner plants of the same variety increased the numbers of flowers on existing trusses and decreased the incidence of reversion to vegetative growth as did applications of vitamin E, but a specific effect on induction of inflorescences on vegetative apices is not established by this result.

23 Inflorescence Differentiation

Hill and Davis[47] have described the sequence of morphological development of the inflorescence. Thompson[78] briefly reported that the numbers of flowers attaining anthesis in an inflorescence was increased 2 to 3 fold by application of gibberellic acid. Possibly the inhibitory effect of gibberellic acid on fruit set accounts indirectly for some of this response.

REFERENCES

[1] Anderson, W. (1966). Bibliography of world literature on the strawberry, 1920–1962. Thesis, Library Assn. Great Britain.

[2] Arney, S. E. (1953). Studies of growth and development of the genus *Fragaria*; 2. The initiation, growth and emergence of leaf primordia in *Fragaria*. *Ann. Bot.* **17**, 477.

[3] Arney, S. E. (1956). Studies of growth and development of the genus *Fragaria*. 9. An investigation of floral initiation under natural conditions. *Phyton* **7**, 89.

[4] Arney, S. E. and Ovenden, E. A. G. (1965). The mechanism of the stimulation of growth of strawberry plants by gibberellic acid. *Phyton* **22**, 93.

[5] Austin, M. E., Shutak, V. G. and Christopher, E. P. (1961). Responses of Sparkle strawberry to inductive cycles. *Proc. Amer. Soc. hort. Sci.* **77**, 372.

[6] Bailey, J. S. and Rossi, A. W. (1965). Effects of fall chilling, forcing temperature and daylength on the growth and flowering of Catskill strawberry plants. *Proc. Amer. Soc. hort. Sci.* **87**, 245.

[7] Bauer, R. and Koch, A. (1964). (Possibilities for the more precise characterization of the adaptation of varieties of the garden strawberry (*Fragaria ananassa* Duch.)) *Eucarpia Symposium*, Balsgärd, Sweden. (German)

[8] Borthwick, H. A. and Parker, M. W. (1952). Light in relation to flowering and vegetative development. 13th Int. Hort. Congress, 801, 1953.

[9] Bringhurst, R. S. (1958). Continuous summer bearing of non-everbearing strawberries in California. *Proc. Ore. St. hort. Soc.* **73**, 129.

[10] Bringhurst, R. S., Voth, V. and van Hook, D. (1960). Relationship of root starch content and chilling history to performance of California strawberries. *Proc. Amer. Soc. hort. Sci.* **75**, 373.

[11] Brown, T. and Wareing, P. F. (1965). The genetical control of the everbearing habit and three other characters in varieties of *Fragaria vesca. Euphytica* **14**, 97.

[12] Butenko, R. G. and Baskakov, Y. A. (1960). (On the mechanism of the effect of maleic hydrazide on plants.) (Russ. with Eng. summ.) *Fiz. Rast.* **7**, 385.

[13] Collins, W. B. (1966). Floral initiation in strawberry and some effects of red and far-red radiation as components of continuous white light. *Can. J. Bot.* **44**, 663.

[14] Collins, W. B. and Barker, W. G. (1964). A flowering response of strawberry to continuous light. *Can. J. Bot.* **42**, 1309.

[15] Darrow, G. M. (1929). Inflorescence types of strawberry varieties. *Amer. J. Bot.* **16**, 571.

[16] Darrow, G. M. (1936). Interrelation of temperature and photoperiodism in the production of fruit-buds and runners in the strawberry. *Proc. Amer. Soc. hort. Sci.*, **34**, 360.

[17] Darrow, G. M. (1955). Effect of temperature and daylength on varietal adaptation of strawberry. *Fruit Var. hort. Dig.* 10, 37 and 51.

[18] Darrow, G. M. and Waldo, G. F. (1934). Responses of strawberry varieties and species to duration of the daily light period. *Tech. Bull. U.S. Dept. Agric.* No. 453.

[19] Davis, M. B., Hill, H. and Johnson, T. B. (1934). Nutritional studies with *Fragaria*. 2. A study of the effects of deficient and excess potassium, phosphorus, magnesium, calcium and sulphur. *Sci. agr.* **14**, 411.

[20] Downs, R. J. and Piringer, A. A. (1955). Differences in photoperiodic responses of everbearing and June-bearing strawberries. *Proc. Amer. Soc. hort. Sci.* **66**, 234.

[21] Eguchi, T. (1932). (The flower bud differentiation in strawberry and the type of development.) *J. hort. Ass. Japan* **3**, 21. (Japanese)

[22] Eguchi, T. (1934). (Effects of the relative length of day and night before and after bud differentiation on formation and development of flower bud in the Victoria strawberry.) *J. hort. Ass. Japan* **5**, 42. (Japanese)

[23] Eguchi, T. (1934). (Effects of low temperature and soil moisture upon the time of flower bud differentiation in the strawberry.) *J. hort. Ass. Japan* **5**, 233. (Japanese)

[24] Eguchi, T. (1936). (On the effects of temperature and light upon the flower bud differentiation in strawberries.) *J. hort. Ass. Japan* **7**, 19. (Japanese)

[25] Eguchi, T. (1937). (Effects of the relative length of day and night before and after bud differentiation on formation and development of flower bud, fifth report.) *J. hort. Ass. Japan* **8**, 203. (Japanese)

[26] Eguchi, T. (1937). (Studies on the photoperiodic responses of plants before and after the differentiation of flower buds.) *Proc. Imp. Acad. Tokyo* **13**, 332. (Japanese with Eng. summ.)

[27] El-Antably, H. M. M., Wareing, P. F. and Hillman, J. (1967). Some physiological responses to d.l. abscisin (Dormin.). *Planta* **73**, 74.

[28] Fedorov, A. K. and Makaryceva, V. V. (1964). (The biology of the development of strawberry.) *Sadovodstvo* **7**, 24. (Russian)

[29] Gosselink, J. G. (1959). The effect of photoperiod and light quality on the vegetative and reproductive growth of the strawberry. Ph.D. Thesis, Rutgers University.

[30] Gruber, F. (1960). (Fundamental ideas about the choice of cross parents for the establishment of long term breeding work.) *Bull. Inst. agron. Stns. Res., Gembloux Hors ser.* **2**, 962 (French)

[31] Gruppe, W. and Nurbachsch, K. (1961). Studies on the mineral nutrition of strawberries. 1. Nitrogen, phosphorous and chloride increments. *Gartenbauwiss.* **26**, 415. (German)

[32] Gruppe, W. and Nurbachsch, K. (1962). Studies on the mineral nutrition of strawberries; 2. Potassium, calcium and magnesium increments. *Gartenbauwiss.* **27**, 64 (German with Eng. summ.)

[33] Guttridge, C. G. (1955). Observations on the shoot growth of cultivated strawberry plant. *J. hort. Sci.* **30**, 1.

[34] Guttridge, C. G. (1956). Photoperiodic promotion of vegetative growth in the cultivated strawberry plant. *Nature* **178**, 50.

[35] Guttridge, C. G. (1958). The effects of winter chilling on the subsequent growth and development of the cultivated strawberry plant. *J. hort. Sci.* **33**, 119.

[36] Guttridge, C. G. (1959). Evidence for a flower inhibitor and vegetative growth promoter in the strawberry. *Ann. Bot.* **23**, 351.

[37] Guttridge, C. G. (1959). Further evidence for a growth-promoting and flower-inhibiting hormone in strawberry. *Ann. Bot.* **23**, 612.

[38] Guttridge, C. G. (1960). The physiology of flower formation and vegetative growth in the strawberry. In (A colloquium on the problems of strawberry breeding and selection.) *Bull. Inst. agron. Stns. Rech., Gembloux* 1960. *hors. ser.* **2,** 941.

[39] Guttridge, C. G. (1964). The effects of (2-chloroethyl) trimethylammonium chloride on the growth and runnering of strawberry plants. *Hort. Res.* **3,** 79.

[40] Guttridge, C. G., Anderson, M. M., Thompson, P. A. and Wood, C. A. (1961). Post-harvest defoliation of strawberry plantations. *J. hort. Sci.* **36,** 93.

[41] Guttridge, C. G. and Mason, D. T. (1966). Effects of post-harvest defoliation of strawberry plants on truss initiation, crown branching and yield. *Hort. Res.* **6,** 22.

[42] Guttridge, C. G. and Thompson, P. A. (1963). The effect of daylength and gibberellic acid on cell length and number in strawberry petioles. *Physiol. Plant* **16,** 604.

[43] Guttridge, C. G. and Thompson, P. A. (1964). The effects of gibberellins on growth and flowering of *Fragaria* and *Duchesnea. J. exp. Bot.* **15,** 631.

[44] Hartmann, H. T. (1947). Some effects of temperature and photoperiod on flower formation and runner production in the strawberry. *Pl. Physiol., Lancaster* **22,** 407.

[45] Hartmann, H. T. (1947). The influence of temperature on the photoperiod response of several strawberry varieties grown under controlled environmental conditions. *Proc. Amer. Soc. hort. Sci.* **50,** 243.

[46] Hewitt, E. J. (1952). Sand and water culture methods used in the study of plant nutrition. *Tech. Comm.* No. 22. Commonwealth Bur. hort. plant Crops. E. Malling, Kent, U.K.

[47] Hill, H. and Davis, M. B. (1929). Studies in strawberry bud differentiation. *Can. Dept. Agr. Bull.* **110.**

[48] Ito, H. and Saito, T. (1962). Studies on the flower formation in the strawberry plants. I. Effects of temperature and photoperiod on the flower formation. *Tohoku J. agric. Res.* **13,** 191.

[49] Jonkers, H. (1958). Accelerated flowering of strawberry seedlings. *Euphytica* **7,** 41.

[50] Jonkers, H. (1965). On the flower formation, the dormancy and the early forcing of strawberries. Thesis published as: Meded. landbsch. Wageningen 65.

[51] Kende, H., Ninnemann, H. and Lang, A. (1963). Inhibition of gibberellic acid biosynthesis in *Fusarium moniliforme* by Amo 1618 and CCC. *Naturwiss.* **18,** 599.

[52] Kruzhilin, A. S. and Shvedskaya, Z. M. (1961). Characteristics of phasic development of strawberries. *Agrobiologiya* **4,** 525. (Russian.)

[53] Kruzhilin, A. S. and Shvedskaya, Z. M. (1964). Vernalization of vegetative buds in strawberry plants. *Fiz. Rast.* **11,** 1022. (Russian) *Soviet Plant Physiology* **11,** 870. (translation)

[54] Leshem, Y. and Koller, D. (1964). The control of flowering in the strawberry *Fragaria ananassa* Duch. I. Interaction of positional and environmental effects. *Ann. Bot.* **28,** 569.

[55] Leshem, Y. and Koller, D. (1966). The control of flowering in the strawberry *Fragaria ananassa* Duch. 2. The role of gibberellins. *Ann. Bot.* **30,** 587.

[56] Lineberry, R. A., Burkhart, L. and Collins, E. R. (1944). Fertilizer requirements of strawberries on new land in North Carolina. *Proc. Amer. Soc. hort. Sci.* **45,** 283.

[57] Long, J. H. and Murneek, A. E. (1937). Nitrogen and carbohydrate content of the strawberry plant. Seasonal changes and the effects of fertilizers. *Uni. Missouri ag. Exp. Sta. Res. Bull.* **252.**

[58] Mann, C. E. T. (1930). Studies in root and shoot growth of the strawberry. *Ann. Bot.* **44,** 55.

[59] Mann, C. E. T. and Ball, E. (1926). Studies in root and shoot development of strawberry I. *J. pom. hort. Sci.* **5,** 149.

[60] Mason, D. T. (1963). Seasonal growth pattern (of strawberry). 10*th Ann. Rept. Scot. hort. Res. Inst.,* 51.

[61] Mason, D. T. (1966). Inflorescence initiation in the strawberry. I. Initiation in the field and its modification by post-harvest defoliation. *Hort. Res.* **6,** 33.

[62] Mason, D. T. (1967). Inflorescence initiation in the strawberry. 2. Some effects of date and severity of post-harvest defoliation. *Hort. Res.* **7,** 97.

[63] Mason, D. T. (1967). Inflorescence initiation in the strawberry. 3. Some effects of cloching during induction. *Hort. Res.* **7,** 135.

[64] Moore, J. N. and Hough, L. F. (1962). Relationships between auxin levels, time of floral induction and vegetative growth of the strawberry. *Proc. Amer. Soc. hort. Sci.* **81,** 255.

⁶⁵ Muijzenberg, E. W. B. Van den (1942). (The influence of light and temperature on the periodic development of the strawberry and its significance in cultivation. *Meded. Lab. TuinbPlTeelt, Wageningen* No. 37. (Dutch.)

⁶⁶ Piringer, A. A. and Scott, D. H. (1964). Interrelation of photoperiod, chilling, and flower-cluster and runner production by strawberries. *Proc. Amer. Soc. hort. Sci.* **84**, 295.

⁶⁷ Porlingis, I. C. (1960). Growth and flowering of strawberry plants in relation to endogenous growth substances, applications of gibberellic acid and environmental factors. Ph.D. Thesis, Cornell Univ.

⁶⁸ Porlingis, I. C. and Boynton, D. (1961). Evidence for the occurrence of gibberellin-like substances in the strawberry. *Proc. Amer. Soc. hort. Sci.* **78**, 256.

⁶⁹ Porlingis, I. C. and Boynton, D. (1961). Growth responses of the strawberry plant, *Fragaria chiloensis* var. *ananassa* to gibberellic acid and to environmental conditions. *Proc. Amer. Soc. hort. Sci.* **78**, 261.

⁷⁰ Roodenburg, J. W. M. (1940). (The behaviour of plants in light of different colours. *Recl. Trav. bot. neerl.* **37**, 301. (Dutch)

⁷¹ Roodenburg, J. W. M. (1954). The physiological length of the photoperiod. *8th Inter. Bot. Congr. Paris Sect.* **11 & 12**, 318.

⁷² Saha, A. K. (1964). The relationship of photoperiod, night temperature, chilling, auxins and inhibitors to vegetative growth and flowering in the strawberry. Ph.D. Thesis, Missouri Univ.

⁷³ Sironval, C. (1957). (Photoperiod and the reproductive stage of red-fruited perpetual strawberries.) *C.r. Rech. Inst. Encour. Rech. scient. Ind. Agric.* **18**, (French.)

⁷⁴ Sironval, C. (1960). (Photoperiodism and development in cultivated strawberries.) In (A colloquium on the problems of strawberry breeding and selection.) *Bull. Inst. agron. Stns. Rech. Gembloux* 1960 *hors. Ser.* **2**, 950. (French.)

⁷⁵ Sironval, C. and El Tannir-Lomba, J. (1960). Vitamin E and flowering of *Fragaria vesca* L. var. *semperflorens* Duch. *Nature* **185**, 855.

⁷⁶ Smeets, L. (1956). Influence of the temperature on runner production in five strawberry varieties. *Euphytica* **5**, 13–17.

⁷⁷ Takai, T. (1966). The growth response of strawberry varieties to chilling. *Bull. Hort. Res. Stat. Morioka, Ser. C.* **4**, 73.

⁷⁸ Thompson, P. A. (1963). Development of the flower truss. *9th Ann. Rept. Scot. hort. Res. Inst. Dundee*, 41.

⁷⁹ Thompson, P. A. (1963). Reversal of photoperiodic induction of strawberries with maleic hydrazide. *Nature* **200**, 146.

⁸⁰ Thompson, P. A. (1964). Extraction of auxins and gibberellins from strawberry. *11th Ann. Rept. Scot. hort. Res. Inst. Dundee*, 50.

⁸¹ Thompson, P. A. (1964). The effects of applied growth substances on development of the strawberry fruit I. Induction of parthenocarpy. *J. exp. Bot.* **15**, 347.

⁸² Thompson, P. A. and Guttridge, C. G. (1959). Effect of gibberellic acid on the initiation of flowers and runners in the strawberry. *Nature* **184**, B.A.. 72

⁸³ Thompson, P. A. and Guttridge, C. G. (1960). The role of leaves as inhibitors of flower induction in strawberry. *Ann. Bot.* **24**, 482.

⁸⁴ Ueno, Y. (1962). (Flowering and vegetative growth of strawberry. I. Effect of photoperiod under constant temperature conditions.) *J. hort. Ass. Japan* cont. *as J. Jap. Soc. hort. Sci.* **31**, 81. (Japanese, Eng. summ.)

⁸⁵ Ueno, Y. (1965). (Flowering and vegetative growth of strawberry. 4. Effects of age and number of leaves on the floral differentiation.) *J. hort. Ass. Japan* cont. *as. J. Jap. Soc. hort. Sci.* **34**, 68. (Japanese, Eng. summ.)

⁸⁶ Ueno, Y. (1962). (Flowering and vegetative growth of strawberry. 3. Influence of intensity of supplemental light on the floral initiation.) *J. hort. Ass. Japan* cont. *as J. Japan Soc. hort. Sci.* **31**, 223. (Japanese)

⁸⁷ Ueno, Y., Ito, M. and Matsukawa, J. (1962). (Flowering and vegetative growth of strawberry. 2. Influence of the "light break" effect.) *J. hort. Ass. Japan* cont. *as J. Jap. Soc. hort. Sci.* **31**, 168. (Japanese)

⁸⁸ Voth, V. and Bringhurst, R. S. (1958). Fruiting and vegetative responses of Lassen strawberry in southern California as influenced by nursery source, time of planting and plant chilling history. *Proc. Amer. Soc. hort. Sci.* **72**, 186.

⁸⁹ Waldo, G. F. (1935). Investigations on runner and fruit production of everbearing strawberries. *Tech. Bull. U.S. Dept. Agric.* No. 470.

⁹⁰ Went, F. W. (1957). The Experimental Control of Plant Growth. *Chronica Botanica* **17**, Ch. 9. Waltham, Mass.

[91] White, P. R. (1927). Studies on the physiological anatomy of the strawberry. *J. agric. Res.* **35**, 481.
[92] Whitehouse, W. G. (1928). Nutritional studies with the strawberry. *Proc. Amer. Soc. hort. Sci.* **25**, 201.
[93] Yokomizo, T. and Sugiyama, C. (1960). (A study on the promotion of flower bud differentiation, flowering and fruiting of strawberry plants (Fukuba) by cool storage. *Bull. Kanagawa agric. Exp. Stat. hort. Branch.* **8**, 25. (Japanese Eng. summ.)
[94] Gabr, O. M. K. and Guttridge, C. G. (1968). Identification of (+) − abscisic acid in strawberry leaves. *Planta* **78**, 305.

11

Chrysanthemum morifolium (Ramat.) Hemsl.

By Henry M. Cathey

1 History of Use

The genus Chrysanthemum includes species which are found growing in nearly every part of the world. Some are found only in the extreme northeast of Asia; others are indigenous to various parts of western Europe.

Chrysanthemum morifolium (Ramat.) Hemsl. is a complex hybrid derived from several species that grow wild in China and Japan.[40,101] Two important ancestors were *C. indicum* and *C. sinense*. *C. indicum* is a misnomer, the wild species is not found in India. It is a native of China and southern Japan. It has single yellow ray inflorescences 2 cm in diameter, and flowers in December. *C. sinense* has white inflorescences with prominent orange discs, 3.5 cm in diameter, and flowers in November in its native habitat. Several other species also contributed to the development of the modern chrysanthemum. The first record of the cultivation of chrysanthemum was made in China about 550 B.C. Confucius, in the province now known as Shantung, described its yellow glory. Chrysanthemum was introduced to Japan from China in 724–749 A.D. Selection and crosses with

FIGURE 11-1. *Chrysanthemum morifolium* (Ramat.) Hemsl. cv. 'Old Purple'. Illustrated in the Curtis Botanical Magazine *t.* 327. 1796.

wild Japanese species continued over the centuries by many amateur gardeners. Captain Blancard of Marseilles returned from China in 1789 with three cultivars. Two of them died; the third became established in France and was called 'Old Purple'.

The new cultivar was named *C. morifolium* by the French botanist Ramatuelle for cultivar 'Old Purple', illustrated in Figure 11–1. By 1826, 68 distinct cultivars were grown in Britain from seedlings and sports. In 1843 The Royal Horticultural Society sent Robert Fortune to collect plants from China and Japan. Among the many brought back was an extensive collection of chrysanthemum cultivars. The Chinese cultivars collected prior to this time were tightly incurved flowers with a very limited color range. The seedlings introduced by Fortune in 1861 were reflexed and loosely incurving, with a wide range of colors. Most of the cultivars grown today are derived from this collection of seed. A miniature flowered chrysanthemum introduced in 1847 in England was called the Chinese Chusan Daisy, the progenitor of all pompon chrysanthemums. Other species such as *C. coreanum*, *C. articum*, and *C. nipponicum*, when crossed with *C. morifolium*, extended the types and flowering times of the chrysanthemum.

The horticultural classification of chrysanthemum cultivars is extremely arbitrary. They are usually divided into early, midseason, late, Korean, and Charm types with subdivisions as to color and flower form. The most comprehensive classification based on the physiological responses of the cultivars was proposed by Okada[58] (Table 11–1).

TABLE 11–1.

Classification of chrysanthemum cultivars (Okada[58]).

No. of group	Group	Response to photoperiod	
		Flower bud initiation	Flower bud development and flowering
I	Autumn flowering	Short day	Short day
II	Winter flowering	Short day	Short day
III	Summer flowering	Day neutral	Day neutral
IV	Late summer flowering	Day neutral	Day neutral
V	Early autumn flowering	Day neutral	Short day
VI	Okayamaheiwa type	Short day	Day neutral

Allard[1] found that by restricting potted chrysanthemum plants to a 10-hour day, starting in May, flowering time was advanced from mid-October to mid-July. The practical application of this information was made by Laurie,[45] Poesch,[61,62] and Post.[65,66] Year-round flowering of chrysanthemum was made possible by the selection of responsive cultivars and by appropriate temperature and daylength treatment of the plants.[67,69]

The chrysanthemum plant was classified as a short-day plant,[22] but has seldom been used in physiological experiments. It exhibits many of the responses to light and temperature that were first observed with *Xanthium* but is more demanding in that it requires exposure to many short days for induction to occur.

2 Growing Techniques and Growth Habit

Chrysanthemums grown from seed are heterogeneous and are better propagated by clonal cuttings from one parent plant. The position on the shoot from which the cutting is removed and the age of the stock plant have a profound effect on the responses of the cuttings, as discussed later. Cuttings 3 to 5 cm in length are rooted under intermittent mist at 17°C minimum night temperature with long photoperiods. Rooting requires 2 to 3 weeks. The rooted cuttings and stock plants are grown in a greenhouse whose temperature is kept at 15° to 17°C. The long photoperiod consists of the natural daylength with an interruption of the dark period from 10 p.m. to 2 a.m. with a minimum of 10 f.c. of illumination from incandescent-filament lamps. For short photoperiods, the plants are covered nightly from 4 p.m. to 8 a.m. with black sateen cloth or moved nightly into ventilated dark rooms. Chrysanthemums grow well in any type of growing medium, natural or synthetic, so long as it is well aerated and supplies the required nutrients in the proper balance.[35]

Chrysanthemums exhibit the typical growth characteristics of a caulescent perennial plant. The plants have mostly erect growth; they are much branched. The leaves are arranged spirally on the stem, practically entire to deeply lobed, depending on the cultivar, glabrous, pubescent, and strongly scented. At flowering, or before, stolons develop at the base of some cultivars. Stolons exhibit various degrees of transverse geotropism. The stolons terminate in rosettes of small, slightly lobed leaves. These rosettes are essential for the over-winter survival of a chrysanthemum cultivar when grown out-of-doors. These stolons must remain above ground and green for growth the following spring. Many of the cultivars used for year-round flowering of chrysanthemums never produce stolons under normal cultural procedures. They thus will not survive out-of-doors and must be carried over winter in greenhouses.

3 Inflorescence Structure and Criteria of Flowering Response

The flowers of the chrysanthemum are borne on a capitulum subtended by a peduncle covered with several series of involucre bracts. The outer ray florets are pistillate; the center disc florets bisexual. The literature on chrysanthemum is filled with many reports on modifications of the inflorescence by the environment and by applied growth regulators. Various kinds of flower buds observed on chrysanthemums have essentially the same basic structure but have initiated and developed to various degrees. Most chrysanthemum cultivars eventually form a potential inflorescence bud in non-inductive conditions; there does not appear to be a way to inhibit the flowering of chrysanthemums indefinitely. The kind of inflorescence that develops depends on photoperiod and temperature. The crown bud is an example of arrested development where the inflorescence differentiates partially, but development is arrested and the flower bud is surrounded by vegetative shoots. A terminal flower bud is one that differentiates to completion without any arrest in its development.

The criteria of flowering responses of chrysanthemums are often based on macroscopically visible responses – the number of leaves below the inflorescence, the number of days to the macroscopic appearance of the inflorescence bud, or the number of days to anthesis from the start of the experiment. Internode lengths are used as an indication of the effects on vegetative growth.

Borthwick and Cathey[4] used the stage method to determine the developmental condition of the chrysanthemum. They subjected plants to a fixed number of short days (8–12) and dissected them after a given interval (usually 14 days). The stage of development of each stem apex was described as follows:

0. Stem terminal flat; typical of vegetative condition.
1. Stem terminal slightly enlarged.
2. Stem terminal forming capitulum; first bracts of receptacle present.
3. Capitulum spherical with 12 or more bracts around its rim.
4. Capitulum becoming flattened; many bracts but no floret primordia present.
5. Two or three rows of floret primordia on rim of receptacle.
6. About six rows of floret primordia on capitulum.
7. Capitulum covered with floret primordia except at tip.
8. Entire capitulum covered with floret primordia.
9. A few floret primordia not yet having beginnings of perianth.
10. Perianth primordia present on all florets.

The individual scores were totalled and an average stage was used in the presentation of the data. Neither prolonged growing for visual observations nor the dissection method differentiates between effects on initiation and those on subsequent development. Since there are many stages in the transition from a vegetative to a generative shoot apex, a detailed separation of the processes is obviously impossible.

4 Effect of Plant Age

Chrysanthemums are grown primarily from clonal stock. The age of the stock plant, the length of shoot from which the tip cutting is removed, the part of the stock plant from which the cutting is removed, and the care with which the stock plants are grown greatly influence the flowering of the plant.[31] Tip cuttings are generally used from 3 to 5 consecutive shoots formed on a stock plant. Stock plants are then replaced with rooted cuttings and the cycle is repeated. Cuttings from chrysanthemum stock plants grown for more than 3 to 5 consecutive shoots form potential inflorescences.

Post found that when vegetative plants had their tips removed, the first 6 to 10 short photoperiods did not promote flower initiation of early flowering cultivars.[70] Late flowering cultivars required up to 20 inductive photoperiods following the pinch to initiate flowers. Chrysanthemums thus do not immediately start to initiate flowers when the growing point is removed and when the plants are placed on photo-inductive conditions. When the plants were given only a limited number of photo-inductive daylengths following the pinch and then returned to long photoperiods, they remain vegetative. Flower initiation occurs only on stems which are developing at the time of photo-induction treatments. Age of shoot bore no relationship to time of anthesis when short photoperiods were started 0, 2, 4, and 6 weeks following a pinch.[6] All plants, regardless of age, formed 8 to 10 additional nodes after the start of short photoperiods and anthesis occurred at the same time.

5 Vernalization and Devernalization

Schwabe[77] demonstrated in 1950 that certain cultivars of chrysanthemum had a vernalization requirement for early flowering. Using primarily the cultivar Sunbeam, he found that exposure of the plants for 3 to 4 weeks at a temperature of 5–7°C on natural short photoperiods reduced the number of nodes below the inflorescence bud from 114.7 for a non-vernalized plant to 28.6 for a vernalized plant. The further development and opening of the inflorescence bud after initiation depended primarily on the length of the day given. The cuttings grown from unvernalized long photoperiod stock plants flowered sooner and with a lower leaf number after vernalization than cuttings from stock plants grown on short photoperiods. The long photoperiod did not substitute for vernalization but produced a maximal effect of accelerating flowering when given for 4 to 6 weeks preceding an optimal duration of vernalization.

The shoot apex was the site of perception of vernalization.[80] Exposure of the other parts of plants to low temperature did not vernalize them; they continued to grow with the diageotropic growth habit typical of plants grown on short photoperiods. Unvernalized plants grown on long photoperiods remained vegetative with a normal geotropic growth habit.

Effective vernalizing temperatures need be given during only part of the day. Schwabe's experiments indicated that low temperature was more effective, when given during the dark phase than during the light phase. The experiments were confounded by the functioning of the leaves. Those plants chilled at night or throughout the 24 hours had dark green foliage with large amounts of a red pigment. Those chilled during the light period developed young leaves which were extremely chlorotic. Both symptoms quickly disappeared when the plants were returned to culture at 15–17°C. Exposure of plants to chilling for periods longer than 3 or 4 weeks did not alter the days to flowering or the leaf numbers to the inflorescence (Fig. 11–2).

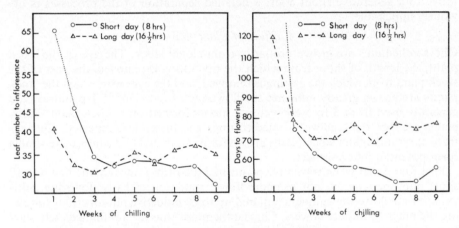

FIGURE 11–2. Effect of duration of vernalization treatment on leaf number and time to macroscopic appearance of inflorescence bud of Sunbeam chrysanthemum. One plant flowered in short photoperiods after 1 week of vernalization (Schwabe [77]).

Other cultivars tested by Schwabe[77,78] and by Mason and Vince[50,51,92,93,94,95] varied greatly in their requirements for vernalization, grading from those requiring no vernalization to those with an absolute requirement. Mason and Vince[51] proposed three different kinds of light and temperature sequences regulating stem elongation and flowering (Fig. 11–3). Sequence I dealt with terminal cuttings taken from vernalized plants. When these cuttings were grown at 10°C, they rosetted. The rosetted plants elongated, irrespective of daylength, at temperatures above 16°C. Transfer of elongated shoots to short photoperiods resulted in flowering at temperatures of 16°C or above. Transfer of elongated shoots to short photoperiods at temperatures below 16°C resulted in some cultivars flowering, some initiating but aborting the flowers, and some remaining vegetative and producing rosettes. The responses of the cultivars were also regulated by the light level during the photoperiod. Rosetting was observed in some cultivars even at normal winter light intensities. Sequence II dealt with non-chilled shoots developing at temperatures above 16°C. The plants of some cultivars produced rosetted growth when grown in short photoperiods (Fig. 11–3). When given a

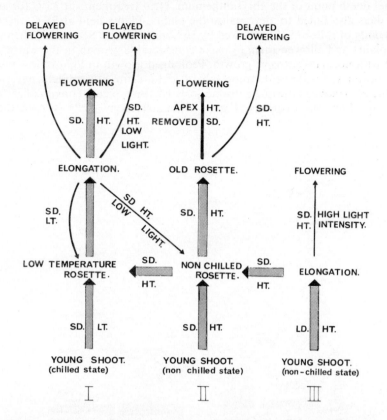

FIGURE 11–3. Scheme showing effects of different environmental sequences on growth and flowering in chrysanthemum. Key: SD = short photoperiods; LD = long photoperiods; LT = low temperature, 10°C or below; HT = high temperature, 16°C or above (Mason and Vince[51]).

vernalizing treatment, the plants rapidly elongated in high temperature. When grown on either short or long photoperiods, flower initiation eventually occurred. Cutting back the apex accelerated the flowering of the lateral shoots when compared with flowering time of the main axis. The delay in flowering without chilling varied widely with cultivar. Mason [50] observed that only 17 of 46 English cultivars were delayed for more than 10 weeks when compared with plants grown without chilling. Sequence III dealt with non-chilled shoots exposed immediately on emergence to long photoperiods. Plants of some cultivars grown from these cuttings flowered when given short photoperiods at high light intensities. Other cultivars, when transferred to short photoperiods for flowering, produced a terminal vegetative rosette. The three sequences illustrate the various possible interactions of light and temperature regulating stem elongation and flowering of chrysanthemums.

Devernalization

Schwabe's experiments with the cultivar 'Sunbeam'[81] indicated that the annual requirement of the basal shoots (stolons) of the chrysanthemum for vernalization was due to annual devernalization of these shoots as the main axis grew up and flowered. Short exposures of fully or partially vernalized plants to 40°C for up to 30 hours did not devernalize the plants. The 40°C heat treatment was near the thermal death point of the chrysanthemum. Heat treatments at 35°C for as long as 30 days also failed to devernalize the plants. Plants held at 35°C received 8 hours daily of full sunlight followed by 16 hours of dark. Schwabe[81] then vernalized plants and allowed them to make considerable growth in the warm greenhouse with normal geotropic growth. Prolonged growth in light of low intensity from incandescent-filament lamps (about 35 f.c.) caused complete devernalization and also induced the diageotropic growth habit typical of unvernalized plants grown in short photoperiods (Fig. 11-4). Later, Schwabe[82] showed that de-

FIGURE 11-4. Devernalization of Sunbeam chrysanthemum caused by low intensity ligh ttreatment. Left, controls. Right, devernalized plants. Note diageotropic growth of plant beginning above vernalized part of stem (Schwabe[81]).

vernalization was the result of an interaction between high temperature and low light intensity. Devernalization did not occur, even after 3 weeks of darkness, when the plants were held at a temperature of 18°C. One out of every three was devernalized. Plants held under similar low light conditions at 28°C for 4 weeks were completely devernalized. The mechanism for devernalization was not due to a temporary cessation of growth; maleic hydrazide suppressed growth without altering the vernalization status. Lowering of the carbohydrate level by removing the young leaves of shoots in full light did not cause devernalization. Feeding sugar to plants during the low light treatment failed to prevent devernalization, thus ruling out carbohydrate level as the controlling factor. Immediate revernalization by 3 to 4 weeks cold, without any additional carbohydrate either by normal photosynthesis or artificial feeding, was alone fully successful.

7 Photoperiod Response

Allard[1] found that 10 hours of sunlight from 5:30 a.m. to 3:30 p.m. and darkness from 3:30 p.m. to 5:30 a.m. promoted early flowering of chrysanthemums. Various short photoperiod regimes were compared by Laurie,[45] Poesch,[61,62,63] and Post.[65,66] They found the optimum photoperiod for early flowering was 10 or 11 hours of continuous light and 14 or 13 hours of dark. Four hours of darkening was more effective given in the afternoon than given in the morning; neither treatment promoted early flowering as much as darkening the end of the afternoon and the beginning of the morning.

Post[68] divided flower formation into three definable stages. These were:

1. Flower bud initiation and the adjustments which preceded this stage to the time when the first primordia became evident.

2. Flower bud development from the first morphological change to the stage in which the bud was macroscopically visible.

3. Flower bud elongation and growth from the time it was visible to the time the flower was fully open.

At latitude 42°N, Post[69] showed that flower bud initiation occurred from September 1 to March 25. The critical photoperiod was 14 to $14\frac{1}{2}$ hours. When plants were grown on a 14 to $14\frac{1}{2}$ hour photoperiod, the flower buds did not develop. A slight increase in photoperiod after flower bud initiation caused the flowers to develop into crown buds with extended peduncles and bract-like leaves on the stem. Furuta[30] found that cultivars which required 12 to 14 weeks from start of short photoperiods to anthesis required shorter photoperiods both for initiation and for rapid development of the flower than cultivars requiring 8 to 10-week time intervals before anthesis. Cathey[10] extended these observations to a wide range of chrysanthemum cultivars. His experiments showed that the 6, 8, and 10-week cultivars had critical photoperiods of more than 16, $15\frac{1}{4}$, and $14\frac{1}{2}$ hours, respectively, for flower bud initiation, but that the 12 and 15-week cultivars required photoperiods as short as 13 and 11 hours for formation of a flower at 15.7°C (Table 11–2). As shown by number of nodes and rate of development, a photoperiod of 12 hours or less was required for flower development of the 10-week cultivar. When the 10-week cultivar was grown on a 13-hour photoperiod, only the centre flower developed. The plants on a 12-hour photoperiod

TABLE 11–2.

Interrelation of temperature and critical photoperiod for flower initiation and development of 3 cultivars of chrysanthemum. Range of photoperiods 9 to 16 hours (Cathey[10]).

Cultivar	Period to flower	Minimum night temperature	Maximum light period for	
			Flower initiation	Flower development
	Weeks	°C	Hours	Hours
White Wonder	6	10.0	$13\frac{3}{4}$	$13\frac{3}{4}$
		15.7	16	$13\frac{3}{4}$
		26.5	16	12
Encore	10	10.0	$13\frac{3}{4}$	$13\frac{3}{4}$
		15.7	$14\frac{1}{2}$	13
		26.5	$15\frac{1}{4}$	12
Snow	15	10.0	12	12
		15.7	11	10
		26.5	10	9

had the same number of nodes to the flower as ones grown on a 9-hour photo-period. Doorenbos[27] and Seeley and Weise[84] reported that some of the garden chrysanthemums produced visible flower buds with photoperiods up to and including 24 hours. A few garden chrysanthemums were indifferent to photoperiod; their flowering was regulated by the temperature conditioning of the stock plants, as reported by Okada for Japanese chrysanthemum cultivars.[57,59]

The latitude at which the chrysanthemum was grown determined the date at which the normal flower bud initiation began in the fall. At 42°N, the critical date for flower initiation was August 15 to 25;[68] at 51–52°N the date was August 22.[90,91] Temperature and light conditions during these days altered the date by as much as 3 weeks on some cultivars.

Flower bud initiation was induced by a restricted number of short photo-periods. The number of flower buds formed increased as the number of short photoperiods increased. Most early flowering cultivars were completely budded with terminal sprays when they were exposed to 12 consecutive short photo-periods. Control of the type of flower spray was possible by the manipulation of the photoperiod.[43] Twelve short, 10 long, followed by short photoperiods, produced terminal sprays with crowned buds. Four or 6 short, 12 to 20 long, followed by short photoperiods produced crowned sprays with terminal clusters. Post and Lacey[73] reported that interrupting short photoperiods with long photo-periods also altered the type, shape, and number of florets in standard chrys-anthemums.

Poesch[62] showed that 5 to 10 f.c. of light from incandescent-filament lamps was sufficient to delay the flowering of many chrysanthemum cultivars; the low intensity light was used to supplement the normal daylight, the light regime was adjusted to give the plants a daylength of 15 to 17 hours. Emsweller, Stuart and Byrnes[29] and Stuart[87] demonstrated that light in the middle of the long night was more inhibitory to flowering than was light given on the end of the natural short photoperiod. Three to 4 hours of light from incandescent-filament lamps in the middle of the night was adopted as a procedure to prevent flower intiation. Post[71] reported that 25 f.c. hours were required to inhibit flowering of green-house chrysanthemums. He found that 100 f.c. for $\frac{1}{4}$ hour was as effective as 5 f.c. for 5 hours. These results indicated that reciprocity (intensity × time) held within these limits for the lighting of chrysanthemums.

Hume,[42] Emsweller, Stuart, and Byrnes,[29] and Post[68] reported using inter-mittent supplementary light to produce a long photoperiod response on plants. Later Waxman[98] found that 4 seconds of incandescent-filament light per minute for at least 4 hours in the middle of the night at a maximum intensity of 20 f.c. prevented the flowering of some chrysanthemum cultivars. Borthwick and Cathey[4,14,16,17] found that flowering in some experiments was prevented by lighting the plants intermittently only 5 per cent of the time during the dark period. A single 12-minute period of light (5 per cent of 4 hours) in the middle of the night slightly retarded flowering but did not keep the plants vegetative. When the 12 minutes were divided into several periods distributed at intervals through-out the 4-hour dark period, flowering was inhibited, provided that the dark in-tervals were no longer than about 30 minutes. Cycles in which the dark period was an hour were of marginal effectiveness and those with more than an hour of darkness were ineffective. Highly effective treatments included not only 30-minute cycles but others as brief as 2 seconds (Cathey and Borthwick, unpublished).

The intensity of light made little difference in the effectiveness of a cycle above some minimum level. For example, 10-minute cycles were effective provided an intensity of 5 f.c. was maintained 20 per cent of each cycle for 4 hours. Cycles longer than 1 hour were ineffective at this same intensity or at even 10 or more times that intensity.

8 Spectral Dependence

The requirements for photo-induction of the chrysanthemum have greatly limited its usefulness as a plant for studying the spectral dependence for regulating flowering.[89] Its requirements are: an adequate light intensity during a photo-period of several hours duration, a minimum of 8 short days for a measurable flowering response, and the presence of leaves on the plant during photo-induction.

Lane et al.[44] extracted chlorophyll and other pigments from green chrysanthemum leaves, freed the extract of chlorophyll and examined it photometrically for phytochrome but did not detect it in chrysanthemums, or in any other typical short day plant.

Phytochrome is present and plays an important role in regulating flowering of chrysanthemums, as is shown by the responses of the plants to red and far-red light. Floral initiation was inhibited by 1 minute of red light when given in the middle of a 16-hour night and was re-promoted by a few minutes of far-red given subsequently.[17] Repeated alternations of red and far-red radiant energies resulted, respectively, in repeated inhibited and repromotion of floral initiation with a gradually decreasing effectiveness of repromotion of far-red with repeated alternations. When far-red treatment was separated from the red treatment by a dark interval, repromotion of floral initiation was less as the duration of darkness increased and failed completely when the dark period was as long as about 90 minutes. Far-red alone or following a brief red treatment inhibited flowering when the duration of far-red treatment was about 90 minutes, presumably because of the inhibitory action of the low level of P_{fr} maintained by the prolonged far-red treatment.[15] Flowering of chrysanthemum was inhibited by a single conversion of P_r to P_{fr} by red light of at least 600 f.c. applied as briefly as 1 minute. The flower inhibition was a straightforward response to phytochrome as was shown by reversibility of the response by far-red. Treatment with red light was strongly inhibitory to flowering even after only 2 hours of darkness. Evidently phytochrome was not predominantly in the P_{fr} form at the end of 2 hours of darkness because treatment with red light at that time inhibited flowering. Two hours was as early and 11 hours as late in the 16-hour dark period as red light could act effectively.

Other light sources were also tested to determine if they could inhibit flowering with a 1-minute treatment. The failure of 1 minute of incandescent-filament light and sunshine to inhibit flowering of chrysanthemums was not due to inadequate radiant energy.[17] The energies used in the experiments were more than 100 times those required for inhibition of flowering when applied over a duration of several hours. The failure arose from the fact that the incandescent-filament lamps and the sun emitted similar amounts of red and far-red. When the conversion of phytochrome in the leaf reached a photostationary state under either incandescent-filament lamps or the sun, further increase in energy caused no change. The ratio of the two forms remained at the photostationary state amount of P_{fr} which was inadequate to last long enough in darkness to prevent flowering. However, incandescent-filament illumination was inhibitory to flowering when the plants were irradiated continuously for long periods. It was also inhibitory to flowering when used cyclically,[16] the pigment being partly converted to P_{fr} with each light pulse and with the P_{fr} allowed to act in darkness until its dark reversion began to reduce its effectiveness. The amount of P_{fr} phytochrome depends on the light source and on the differential screening of the leaves by chlorophyll and other pigments. Thus, fluorescent light was more effective in somewhat longer cycles than incandescent-filament light. For similar reasons light from ruby-red and BCJ photographic safety lamps, which had a higher ratio of far-red to red than unfiltered light from incandescent-filament lamps, was also effective on short cycles but the longest effective cycles of the ruby-red and BCJ lamps were shorter than the longest effective ones of incandescent-filament light.

The conversion of phytochrome in a leaf by radiation was altered by the filtering action of chlorophyll. The loss during transmission through a leaf was about 50 per cent at 730 mμ, and more than 87 per cent at 660 mμ. The radiation which reached the lowest parts of the leaf was predominantly far-red. This modified mixture of red and far-red radiation produced a low level of P_{fr}. When the leaf was placed in darkness, the P_{fr} in the cells of the lowest tissues of the leaf quickly reverted to the inactive form, thereby permitting those cells to have a promotive effect on flowering. Only when P_{fr} was maintained for an appreciable time by continuous irradiation, or frequently returned to that level by intermittent irradiation, was flowering completely inhibited.

The response to photoperiod discussed in the previous sections was based on the experimental procedure of growing the plants on an 8 or 9-hour photoperiod and a 16 or 15-hour dark period. A minimum of 3 to 5 hours of light per day are required for flowering.[55] Under very dim light, chrysanthemums require many short days to initiate flowers.[76,97] Plants grown on a very short photoperiod (e.g. 3 hours) did not flower as vigorously as those grown on 8-hour photoperiods. One to 8 minutes of far-red given at the start of these long dark periods inhibited flowering (Table 11–3). The inhibition of flowering with a brief period of far-red was reversible with red immediately following the far-red.

TABLE 11–3.

Inhibitory effects of far-red applied at start of dark period on floral initiation of (a) White Pink Chief and (b) Improved Indianapolis Yellow chrysanthemums (Cathey and Borthwick, unpublished data). Photoperiod consisted of 2000 f.c. cool white fluorescent and 80 f.c. incandescent-filament illumination.

Photoperiod (hours)	Far-red at start of dark period	Average stage of development	
		(a)	(b)
1.5	−	0	0
	+	0	0
3	−	2.7	3.9
	+	0	0
5	−	5.7	5.2
	+	1.9	3.
8	−	6.0	5.8
	+	6.0	5.7

Far-red – 8 minutes

Red also reversed the flower inhibiting action of far-red when given up to 6 to 8 hours after the far-red treatment. Multiple reversals were possible with far-red inhibitory, and red repromotive of flowering. Similar experiments with plants grown on cycles of 5 hours light–19 hours dark were less successful than those on 3 hours light–21 hours dark cycles. Far-red given at the start of the 16-hour dark period did not alter flower initiation.

Far-red was inhibitory to flowering at the end of an 8-hour photoperiod when the following 16-hour dark period was intermittently interrupted with cyclic fluorescent illumination (Cathey and Borthwick, unpublished). The plants were grown on 8-hour photoperiods of high intensity followed by low energy fluorescent illumination (60–80 f.c.) given intermittently 1 minute every 15 minutes throughout the 16-hour dark period (CFL in Table 11–4). The plants flowered but not as

TABLE 11–4.

Inhibitory effects of cyclic fluorescent light (CFL),[a] dark, 1 minute of red light (R),[b] and 1 minute of far-red light (FR) on the flowering of White Pink Chief chrysanthemum (Cathey and Borthwick, unpublished data).

8 hour day followed by:	Response
16 hr dark	Flowers
16 hr CFL[a]	Flowers
4 hr dark + 12 hr CFL	Vegetative growth
4 hr dark + R[b] + 12 hr CFL	Flowers
4 hr dark + R[b] + FR + 12 hr CFL	Vegetative growth
4 hr dark + R[b] + FR + R + 12 hr CFL	Flowers
4 hr dark + R[b] + 0.25 hr dark + FR + 11.75 hr CFL	Vegetative growth
4 hr dark + R[b] + 1 hr dark + FR + 11 hr CFL	Flowers

[a] CFL = Cyclic fluorescent light (1 min. every 15 min. – 60–80 f.c.).
[b] R = 2000 f.c. cool white fluorescent illumination filtered through 2 layers of red cellophane.

vigorously as ones grown with 16-hour dark periods. Plants grown with an interpolation of a 4-hour dark period following the 8-hour photoperiod and the 12-hour CFL were vegetative. One minute of intense red light (2000 f.c. cool white fluorescent illumination filtered through two layers of red cellophane) following the 4-hour dark period and prior to the 12 hour CFL repromoted flowering. The response was reversible – red light promoted while far-red light inhibited flowering when the interval of darkness between the red and far-red was 15 minutes or less. Reversibility was lost when 1 hour of darkness was interpolated between the intense red and far-red light treatments.

Phytochrome, primarily in the P_{fr} form for a certain number of hours, followed by reversion in the dark, was essential for flowering. If P_{fr} was present but not active during the first 3 to 5 hours of the 24-hour day and the plants were immediately placed in the dark for the remaining number of hours, P_{fr} was not functioning at a time when it was required for flowering. Phytochrome was also regulating the flowering of plants grown on 8-hour photoperiods – 16-hour CFL. Here, as previously, red repromoted while far-red inhibited flowering. Red was promoting the conversion of phytochrome to P_{fr} at a time that the plants required it for flowering. Other photo-reactions may also be involved in these displays but information is lacking at this time.

The phytochrome system in the chrysanthemum may be as follows:

1. 8-hour photoperiod – 16-hour dark period.
   (a) P_{fr} disappears in the first half of the night and must do so if flowering is to occur, since red light in the middle of the night converted phytochrome to the P_{fr} form, inhibiting flowering.
   (b) P_{fr} must act for nearly an hour to inhibit flowering.
   (c) Far-red repromotes flowering by converting P_{fr} to P_r any time within the hour following the red treatment.
   (d) Any light source which maintains even a low steady state of P_{fr} is inhibitory to flowering if continued for a sufficient duration of time.

(e) The higher the red to far-red ratio in the light source, the shorter the time required to convert phytochrome to P_{fr} and to inhibit flowering.

2. 3-hour photoperiods – 21-hour dark periods.

(a) Far-red at start of very long dark periods converts phytochrome to P_r at a time when it must be in the P_{fr} form, inhibiting flowering.

(b) A brief period of red repromotes flowering by converting phytochrome to the P_{fr} form.

(c) Red repromotes flowering by converting P_r to P_{fr} any time within the following 6 to 8 hours of darkness, but not later in the dark period.

3. 8-hour photoperiod – Cyclic fluorescent light (CFL) throughout the dark period.

(a) A dark interpolation between the photoperiod and CFL allows for the dark reversion of P_{fr} to P_r.

(b) Intense red light at the end of the dark interpolation and before CFL repromotes flowering by repromoting the conversion of P_r to P_{fr}.

(c) P_{fr} must act for nearly an hour to promote flowering.

(d) Far-red inhibits flowering by converting P_{fr} to P_r any time within the hour.

(e) Any light source which emits some far-red is inhibitory to flowering when given intermittently (CFL) throughout the night.

The chrysanthemum, in 8-hour photoperiods, behaves like other short day plants. In 3-hour photoperiods it behaves in a way comparable to *Xanthium* and soybean. Under cyclic fluorescent light chrysanthemum behaves in a way so far unique for short day plants, but is similar to certain long day plants. Under special conditions, the removal of P_{fr} prevents flowering while under other conditions its removal is necessary for flowering.

10 Fractional Induction

Post[66] found that 4 to 5 consecutive short photoperiods followed by long photoperiods caused plants to initiate crown buds with vegetative lateral growth. He failed to induce flower bud initiation with 6 short photoperiods when no more than 3 of them were in succession. Four consecutive short photoperiods were sufficient to cause flower bud initiation.[72]

13 Effects of Temperature

One cannot separate the effects of temperature from those of daylength in regulating the flowering of chrysanthemums. Temperature is the dominating factor in the summer-flowering cultivars while daylength dominates the responses of the autumn-flowering cultivars. The responses of the former were discussed in Sections 5 and 6. The autumn-flowering cultivars were classified by Post[71] as high temperature plants, since flower buds were initiated and developed above a critical temperature, about 15.7°C for many cultivars grown in the USA. Below this temperature only vegetative growth occurred. Above this temperature vegetative growth occurred when the plants were subjected to long photoperiods. The night temperature was more critical than the day temperatures.[32] Most rapid flowering occurred when the night and day temperature was maintained constantly at 15.7C. Night temperatures above or below this caused a delay in flowering. Cathey[6,8] divided chrysanthemums into 3 groups according to their response to temperature (Fig. 11–5); namely:

1. Thermozero – certain cultivars flowered at any temperature ranging from 10°C to 26.5°C, but earliest flowering occurred at a night temperature of 15.7°C. Flowering was delayed slightly at either end of the range.

2. Thermopositive – many of the early autumn-flowering cultivars required a minimum temperature of 15.7°C for vegetative growth and flower bud initiation. Flower bud initiation occurred in less time at 26.5°C than at 15.7°C, but flower development was delayed. Continuous low temperature (10–12°C) inhibited flower bud initiation. Low temperature (10°C) after flower bud initiation had occurred on plants grown at 15.7°C delayed flowering slightly in comparison with plants grown at 15.7°C continuously.

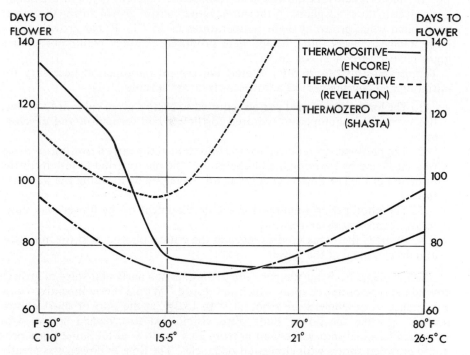

FIGURE 11–5. Number of days to flowering from the start of short photoperiods for thermopositive, thermonegative and thermozero cultivars planted in January from stock kept at 15.7°C, as affected by night temperature (Cathey[8]).

3. Thermonegative – most of the late autumn-flowering cultivars initiated flower buds at all temperatures from 10° to 26.5°C. High temperature, above 15.7°C, after the flowers were initiated inhibited flowering. These cultivars required a temperature of 15.7°C or below for flower bud development.

Night temperatures were more important than day temperatures. For a thermopositive cultivar grown at a day temperature of 21°C and night temperatures between 5 and 26.5°C, flowering time varied by over 36 days, but only over 11 days for the same range of day temperatures.[7] High day temperature did partially compensate for the inhibitory effects of low night temperature.

Okada[56] found summer-flowering cultivars to be unresponsive to daylength. The flowering date depended on the temperature requirements for flower initiation. The June-flowering cultivars initiated and developed flower buds at a minimum temperature of 7.7°C. The later flowering cultivars required the temperatures of August (11.6–15.7°C and above) for flower bud initiation.

Cathey[5] examined the effects of various temperature changes during the growth cycle of the chrysanthemum. The responses varied greatly among cultivars. A thermopositive cultivar, Encore, produced normal flowering plants when grown from cuttings produced at a minimum night temperature of 15.7°C. When the stock plants were grown at minimum night temperature of 21° or 26.5°C, the cuttings formed crown buds prematurely, flowering was delayed, and lateral shoots did not develop on plants when they were pinched. Plants grown from cuttings produced at 10° to 12°C exhibited delayed flowering with sprays containing a larger number of flowers than plants grown from cuttings produced at 15.7°C. The thermozero cultivars showed little response to different temperature conditions given to the stock plants. A thermonegative cultivar grown during the winter went blind when grown at night temperatures of 15.7°C. Rapid growth and a large number of very thin cuttings were produced on stock plants grown at a night temperature of 21° or 26.5°C.

Temperature (10° to 26.5°C) altered the critical photoperiod necessary for initiation and development of a flower as follows[10] (Table 11–2):

1. The longer the normal period required to bring a given cultivar to flower, the shorter the photoperiod required for flower bud formation and development.

2. The photoperiod required for the initiation of the early flowering cultivars was shortened by lowering the temperature. The photoperiod required for the initiation of the late flowering cultivar was increased by lowering the temperature.

3. The photoperiod required for the development of the flower was shortened by raising the temperature.

4. At 10°C there was no difference in the critical photoperiod for initiation and development of the flower.

Shifting plants from one temperature to another at a particular stage of growth altered the type of flower spray which developed.[9] With a thermonegative cultivar, reduction of temperature from 26.5° to 15.7°C at the start of short photoperiods or when the flower buds were visible, led to crowned sprays with elongated terminal sprays. Reduction from 26.5° to 10°C at the same times produced crowned sprays with elongated peduncles. The time to flower was greatly reduced on the plants grown at 26.5°C until the flower buds were visible and shifted to 10° for flower development.

14 Effects of Mineral Nutrition

The mineral nutrition regimen on which chrysanthemums are grown modifies their growth characteristics without appreciably altering flowering.

Waters[96] grew chrysanthemums with various ratios of nitrogen (N) and potassium (K). Increased K had very little effect on the plant responses other than the increased content in the leaf and flower tissue. When the N rates were increased, yield and post harvest keeping quality decreased and susceptibility to botrytis markedly increased. Optimum flower yields, in general, occurred when the young mature leaves contained 3.5 to 4.5 per cent N and 3.5 to 6.0 per cent K, and the flowers contained 1.5–2.5 per cent of both N and K. Chrysanthemums tolerated relatively large amounts of N and K without any interaction between the two elements.

Chailakhyan[25] found that it was possible to change the critical photoperiod of chrysanthemums by growing them with different nitrogen concentrations in the medium. He observed that nitrogen speeded flowering and that 5 days of darkness was more effective in bringing about accelerated rate of flowering than 5 short photoperiods. Nitrogen plus darkness increased the height of the plants, number of branches, and flowers.

15 Effects of Gas Composition

High levels of carbon dioxide (ca 1100 ppm) during the young plant stage increased the stem weight of many chrysanthemum cultivars and hastened slightly the time to flower.[85,86] High levels of carbon dioxide did not alter the temperature responses of thermozero, thermopositive, and thermonegative cultivars. They continued to exhibit the same temperature requirements as plants grown without additional carbon dioxide.

Low levels of ethylene (ca 1 ppm) in the atmosphere inhibited flowering of chrysanthemums grown on short photoperiods. Flower development was suppressed more than flower initiation.[74] Leaf and node elongation were inhibited. Normal elongation and prompt initiation of flowers occurred when the ethylene treatment was discontinued.

17 Grafting Experiments

Schwabe[80] was unable to detect the translocation of the vernalization stimulus as a result of movement through the mature tissues of the plants. He used both stock/scion and approach grafts with and without defoliation of receptors. Schwabe doubted[79] that the translocation of the daylength stimulus in the absence of any tissue union was demonstrated by Moshkov[54] and Gerhard.[34] The treatment of Moshkov and Gerhard consisted of repeated removal of the uppermost leaves of the chrysanthemum kept in long photoperiods and placing the cut petioles in contact with leaves cut from plants grown with short photoperiods. All new leaves and lateral shoots were removed. Schwabe suggested as an alternative explanation that all chrysanthemums eventually will produce potential inflorescence buds and will develop them under long photoperiods when the lateral shoots were removed continuously.[83]

The flowering stimulus was detected in intact chrysanthemum plants by Chailakhyan,[24] Lona,[49] and Weise and Seeley.[99] Chailakhyan blocked the movement of the flowering stimulus by girdling the stem.[23] The stimulus moved primarily into the stem sectors adjacent to the photo-induced leaves. Weise and Seeley grew two-branched plants, one branch receiving short photoperiods, the other receiving long photoperiods. Short photoperiods caused the flowering of the branch receiving short photoperiods and also the flowering stimulus moved through the graft and caused the flowering of the branch on long photoperiods. Earliness of visible flower buds and the number of flower buds on the receptor branch and scion were stimulated by defoliation of the receptor.

Harada[37] grafted a short day-requiring cultivar of chrysanthemum onto a cold-requiring cultivar. The cold-requiring cultivar was induced to flower by treatment with gibberellin. The short photoperiod requiring cultivar grafted on the gibberellin-treated plant flowered when grown with long photoperiods. Thus, gibberellin was capable of inducing indirectly the flowering of the short day-requiring cultivar.

18 Effects of Growth Substances and Growth Retardants

Regulation of the development of the chrysanthemum can be achieved through chemical substances. Auxins applied as dilute foliar sprays inhibited the flowering of chrysanthemums grown on short photoperiods. The auxins caused the cessation of stem elongation and blade expansion. The leaves exhibited epinasty and were permanently damaged. Application of an auxin paste to the developing flower bud inhibited the development of the inflorescence buds produced in short photoperiods.[78] Inhibition became progressively less effective with the advancing development of the bud. The latest stage which was arrested was that of ovule formation.

Gibberellin replaced the requirement for vernalization in promoting the flowering of certain Japanese chrysanthemums.[39,53] These cultivars, which were indifferent to photoperiod but required a period of low temperature to promote flower bud initiation, were induced to flower without low temperature under long photoperiods by a single application of 50 μg of gibberellic acid to the terminal bud.

Gibberellin did not induce the flowering of short-day requiring cultivars.[20] The greatest sensitivity for stem elongation occurred from the application of gibberellin to plants in the third week of short photoperiods.[20] Previous to this period, five times as much gibberellic acid was required to obtain similar elongation. Treatment with 5 consecutive daily sprays of gibberellic acid in the third week of short photoperiods had little effect on the fresh or the dry weight of the leaves; the length and dry weight of the stems were increased. The number of lateral inflorescences was decreased with rapid stem elongation of the plant. The period of greatest sensitivity of the peduncles occurred in the fourth week after the start of short photoperiods. Much later in the development of the flower, in the seventh week of short photoperiods, application of concentrated solutions of gibberellic acid accelerated the development of the florets.[88] The biological activity of gibberellins was characterized on chrysanthemum.[21] Gibberellin A_3 (gibberellic acid) was the most active, followed by $A_1 \geqslant A_4 > A_2$.

Growth retardants reduced stem elongation of chrysanthemums without malformations of leaf, stem, and flower.[11,12,13,46] Thus far, six groups of compounds have been termed growth retardants: nicotiniums, quaternary ammonium carbamates, hydrazines, phosphoniums, substituted cholines, and succinamic acids.

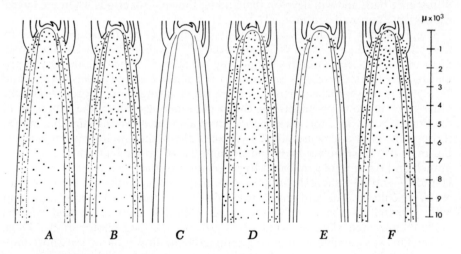

FIGURE 11–6. Number and position of mitotic figures in the median 60μ (6 median longisections, 10μ per section) of the apical portions of shoots of *Chrysanthemum morifolium* cv. 'Crystal Queen': A. control; B. plant treated with GA, collected 4 days after treatment; C. treated with Amo-1618, collected 18 days after treatment; D. treated with Amo-1618 plus GA, collected 4 days after treatment; E. treated with Amo-1618, observed 4 days after treatment; F. Amo-1618, after 14 days, followed by GA, observed 4 days after application of GA. Each dot represents a transverse mitotic figure. The pith tissue is bounded by the apical meristem at the top and the vascular tissue on the sides. The boundaries for the vascular tissue (and the lower limit of the apical meristem) are indicated by thin lines. Observations for cortical tissue were confined to the area bounded by the outer edge of the vascular tissue and the line connecting the leaf bases (Sachs *et al.*[75]).

Growth retardants not only reduced stem elongation but they increased the green color of leaves and increased the resistance of plants to adverse environmental conditions such as low temperature, saline soils and drought.[18] They did not interfere with the perception of photoperiod or temperature by plants. The action of one growth retardant on the chrysanthemum was given a histological basis by Sachs et al.[75] A quaternary ammonium carbamate, 4-hydroxy-5-isopropyl-2-methyl-phenyl-1-trimethylammonium chloride-1-piperidinecarboxylate (Amo-1618) prevented cell division in the sub-apical meristematic zone of the stem (Fig. 11–6). The apical meristem continued to function in the presence of Amo-1618. The lack of action of Amo-1618 on cell division in the apical region and the inhibition of cell division in sub-apical regions of the shoot produced the rosette habit of growth and normal leaf initiation and flowering. The action of all growth retardants on chrysanthemum appeared identical. The action of the growth retardants was mutually antagonistic with that of applied gibberellin.[12,75]

The lower alkyl esters of the C_8 to C_{12} fatty acids and the C_8 to C_{10} fatty alcohols selectively killed the terminal meristem without damaging the axillary meristems, foliage, or stem tissue of vegetative chrysanthemum plants.[19] The axillary meristems developed at nearly the same time as those of plants whose terminal meristems were removed manually. The action depended on the use of the proper surfactants to emulsify the fatty acid derivatives and the penetration of the emulsion into only the meristematic cells.

Alkylnaphthalenes and most aromatic compounds[22] caused abortion of partially initiated flower buds in chrysanthemum. The response depended on the stage and rate of flower initiation, the cultivar treated, and the surfactant used to emulsify the oil. Treatment when the terminal flower bud had completed flower initiation, but before the lateral flower buds had initiated all of the florets, caused abortion of the lateral flower buds only. The terminal flower bud was unaffected and developed at the same rate as terminal flower buds grown with the lateral ones removed by hand. Chrysanthemum cultivars other than Fred Shoesmith were less responsive to aromatic oil sprays.

Maleic hydrazide (MH) was used by Beach and Leopold[3] to break the apical dominance of the chrysanthemum plants. They found that 1000 ppm MH was the most effective concentration for producing plants comparable to plants pinched manually. Mastalerz and Campbell[52] observed that the growth of plants treated with MH was slower than that of plants pinched manually. A standard dosage was impossible to establish because of the variations in the responses of the plants. MH failed to break apical dominance at a concentration not toxic to plant growth.

19 Effects of Metabolic Inhibitors

Free amino acids, which were present in soils with relatively high pH, moisture, and temperature, caused frenching of chrysanthemums.[100] The plants had three common features; green netting or reticular chlorosis of leaves, narrow, strap-shaped leaves, and growth retardation and inhibition of flowering. Application of isoleucine and of D- and L-methionine caused the symptoms to develop.

5-Fluorouracil, an inhibitor of RNA synthesis and a complex fat (SKF 7997), an inhibitor of steroid synthesis, completely disrupted the growth of chrysanthemums (Cathey, unpublished). Since the chrysanthemum required 4 to 6 photo-inductive cycles for the initiation of flowers, the inhibitors were applied daily at the start of the long dark period. Stem elongation ceased immediately in response to the inhibitors, the plants were permanently damaged.

20 Florigenic Extracts

Harada[36] isolated a substance 'E' from vernalized plants of the cold-requiring cultivar Shuokan. The substance was purified by chromatographic technique, but was not crystallized, and caused the flowering of non-vernalized Shuokan plants. It was active on the standard mesocotyl, dwarf maize, and lettuce seed germination assays. Substance E had many of the actions of a gibberellin.

Paul and Biswas[60] prepared a floral initiating extract from chrysanthemum plants in flower. It was separated into 8 different fractions. Two fractions brought about an increased percentage of flower initiation in *Chrysanthemum* and *Xanthium*. Biswas, Paul and Henderson[3a] suggested that the active substance(s) might be a sterol(s) similar to sitosterol and stigmasterol or other related compounds.

22 Chemical and Histochemical Changes at Induction

Chrysanthemums had generally less growth substances under short than under long photoperiods. Harada and Nitsch[38,39] were unable to correlate a definite change in the growth-substance pattern with floral induction in chrysanthemum. Throughout the sampling procedure, many growth inhibitors were detected which undoubtedly altered the effectiveness and sensitivity of the bioassays.

Heuser and Hess[41] identified steam distillable terpenes in chrysanthemums, which acted synergistically with indoleacetic acid in the mung bean rooting bioassay. The structural characteristics of the various growth inhibitors in chrysanthemums have yet to be reported.

23 Inflorescence Differentiation

The floral anatomy of the chrysanthemum inflorescence has been extensively studied by Link,[47,48] Popham and Chan,[64] and Andrews and Watson.[2] Popham and Chan described the vegetative apex of a chrysanthemum as being almost flat or a broadly obtuse cone, 200 to 325 μ in diameter and 40 to 130 μ in height. The vegetative apex consisted of five zones: (1) a tunica 2–5 layers of cells thick; (2) a central area of highly vacuolated mother cells (block meristem); (3) cambial-like cells which were in a layer beneath the mother cell initials; (4) rib meristem which perpetuated the pith; and (5) peripheral zones where the procambial strands and cortex differentiated.

The pattern of floral initiation in chrysanthemum was established by Chan.[26] Number of short photoperiods and results:

1 – Plant vegetative.

3 – Disappearance of cambial zone and simultaneous elongation of cells in area (precursor of peduncle).

7–8 – Radial enlargement, round appearance of flower head.

12 – Marked flattening of dome of shoot apex occurred. Bract primordia at flanks of capitulum.

14 – Floret primordia, beginning at outside of capitulum, progressing acropetally toward top of dome.

20 – Differentiation of all florets on capitulum completed.

Doorenbos and Kofranek[28] reported that both an early flowering cultivar and a later flowering cultivar required about 24 short photoperiods to complete flower initiation but they required different numbers of weeks for flower development to anthesis.

REFERENCES

[1] Allard, H. A. (1928). Chrysanthemum flowering season varied according to daily exposure to light. *Yearbook USDA*, 1928, 194.

[2] Andrews, P. S. and Watson, D. P. (1952). Stages in anatomical development of the flower head of *Chrysanthemum morifolium* Bailey. *Proc. Amer. Soc. Hort. Sci.* **59,** 516.

[3] Beach, R. G. and Leopold, A. C. (1953). The use of maleic hydrazide to break apical dominance of *Chrysanthemum morifolium. Proc. Amer. Soc. Hort. Sci.* **61,** 543.

[3a] Biswas, P. K., Paul, K. B. and Henderson, J. H. M. (1966). Effect of *Chrysanthemum* plant extract on flower initiation in short-day plants. *Physiol. Plant.* **19,** 875.

[4] Borthwick, H. A. and Cathey, H. M. (1962). Role of phytochrome in control of flowering of chrysanthemum. *Bot. Gaz.* **123,** 155.

[5] Cathey, H. M. (1954). Chrysanthemum temperature study A. Thermal induction of stock plants of *Chrysanthemum morifolium. Proc. Amer. Soc. Hort. Sci.* **64,** 483.

[6] Cathey, H. M. (1954). Chrysanthemum temperature study B. Thermal modifications of photoperiods previous to and after flower bud initiation. *Proc. Amer. Soc. Hort. Sci.* **64,** 492.

[7] Cathey, H. M. (1954). Chrysanthemum temperature study C. The effect of night, day, and mean temperature upon the flowering of *Chrysanthemum morifolium. Proc. Amer. Soc. Hort. Sci.* **64,** 499.

[8] Cathey, H. M. (1954). Temperature classification of chrysanthemums. *Bull. N.Y. State Flower Growers* **104,** 1.

[9] Cathey, H. M. (1955). Chrysanthemum temperature study D. Effect of temperature shifts upon the spray formation and flowering time of *Chrysanthemum morifolium. Proc. Amer. Soc. Hort. Sci.* **66,** 386.

[10] Cathey, H. M. (1957). Chrysanthemum temperature study F. The effect of temperature upon the critical photoperiod necessary for the initiation and development of flowers of *Chrysanthemum morifolium. Proc. Amer. Soc. Hort. Sci.* **69,** 485.

[11] Cathey, H. M. (1964). Relation of phosfon structure to its growth retarding activity. *Phyton* **21,** 203.

[12] Cathey, H. M. (1964). Physiology of growth retarding chemicals. *Ann. Rev. of Plant Physiol.* **15,** 271.

[13] Cathey, H. M. (1965). Plant selectivity in response to variation in the structure of Amo-1618. *Phyton* **22,** 19.

[14] Cathey, H. M., Bailey, W. A. and Borthwick, H. A. (1961). Cyclic lighting – to reduce cost of timing chrysanthemum flowering. *Flor. Rev.* **129,** 21.

[15] Cathey, H. M. and Borthwick, H. A. (1957). Photoreversibility of floral initiation in chrysanthemum. *Bot. Gaz.* **119,** 71.

[16] Cathey, H. M. and Borthwick, H. A. (1961). Cyclic lighting for controlling flowering of chrysanthemums. *Proc. Amer. Soc. Hort. Sci.* **78,** 545.

[17] Cathey, H. M. and Borthwick, H. A. (1964). Significance of dark reversion of phytochrome in flowering of *Chrysanthemum morifolium. Bot. Gaz.* **125,** 232.

[18] Cathey, H. M. and Marth, P. C. (1960). Effectiveness of a quaternary ammonium carbamate and phosphonium in controlling growth of *Chrysanthemum morifolium* (Ramat.) *Proc. Amer. Soc. Hort. Sci.* **76,** 609.

[19] Cathey, H. M., Steffens, G. L., Stuart, N. W. and Zimmerman, R. H. (1966). Chemical pruning of plants. *Science* **153,** 1382.

[20] Cathey, H. M. and Stuart, N. W. (1958). Growth and flowering of *Chrysanthemum morifolium* Ramat. as affected by time of application of gibberellic acid. *Proc. Amer. Soc. Hort. Sci.* **71,** 547.

[21] Cathey, H. M., Stuart, N. W., Toole, V. K. and Asen, S. (1961). Enhancement of gibberellin-induced phenomena in gibberellins. *Advances in Chemistry Series* **28,** 135.

[22] Cathey, H. M., Yeomans, A. H. and Smith, F. F. (1966). Abortion of flower buds in chrysanthemum after application of a selected petroleum fraction of high aromatic content. *Hort. Science* **1,** 61.

[23] Chailakhyan, M. Kh. (1937). Hormone theory of plant development (Russ.) Moscow, Leningrad. Akad. Nauk. SSR.

[24] Chailakhyan, M. Kh. (1945). Photoperiodism of individual parts of the leaf; its halves. *C.R. Acad. Sci. U.R.S.S.* **47,** 228.

[25] Chailakhyan, M. Kh. (1945). On the relation between the reaction of flowering to the N food and photoperiodic reaction of the plant. *C.R. Acad. Sci. U.R.S.S.* **48,** 360.

[26] Chan, A. P. (1950). The development of crown and terminal flower buds of *Chrysanthemum morifolium*. *Proc. Amer. Soc. Hort. Sci.* **55**, 461.

[27] Doorenbos, J. (1959). Na-effecten van temperatuur en lichtintensiteit op Chrysanthemum. *Meded. Dir. Tuinb.* **22**, 19.

[28] Doorenbos, J. and Kofranek, A. M. (1953). Inflorescence initiation and development in an early and late chrysanthemum variety. *Proc. Amer. Soc. Hort. Sci.* **61**, 555.

[29] Emsweller, S. L., Stuart, N. W. and Byrnes, J. W. (1941). Using a short interval of light during night to delay blooming of chrysanthemums. *Proc. Amer. Soc. Hort. Sci.* **39**, 391.

[30] Furuta, T. (1954). Photoperiod and flowering of *Chrysanthemum morifolium*. *Proc. Amer. Soc. Hort. Sci.* **63**, 457.

[31] Furuta, T. and Kiplinger, D. C. (1955). Chronological age of cuttings, a factor influencing the spray formation of pompon chrysanthemums. *Proc. Amer. Soc. Hort. Sci.* **66**, 383.

[32] Furuta, T. and Nelson, K. S. (1953). The effect of high night temperature on development of chrysanthemum flower buds. *Proc. Amer. Soc. Hort. Sci.* **61**, 548.

[33] Garner, W. W. and Allard, H. A. (1920). Effect of the relative length of day and night and other factors of the environment on growth and reproduction in plants. *J. Agr. Res.* **18**, 553.

[34] Gerhard, E. (1940). Uber die Entwicklung der Pflanzen unter dem Einfluss der Tageslange and der temperatur im Jugendstadium. *Landw. Jb.* **87**, 162.

[35]Gosling, S. G. (1961). The Chrysanthemum Manual of the National Chrysanthemum Society, London.

[36] Harada, H. (1962). Etude des substances naturelles de croissance en relation avec la floraison. Theses a la faculte des Sciences de L'Universite de Paris.

[37] Harada, H. (1962). Etude des substances naturelles de croissance en relative avec la floraison. Isolement d'une substance de montaison. *Rev. Gen. Bot.* **69**, 201.

[38] Harada, H. and Nitsch, J. P. (1959). Extraction d'une substance provoquant la floraison chez *Rudbeckia speciosa* Wend. *Bull. Soc. Bot. Fr.*, **106**, 451.

[39] Harada, H. and Nitsch, J. P. (1959). Flower induction in Japanese chrysanthemums with gibberellic acid. *Science* **129**, 777.

[40] Hemsley, W. S. (1889). The history of the chrysanthemum. *Gardeners Chron.* **6**, 652.

[41] Heuser, C. W. and Hess, C. E. (1966). The role of oxygenated terpenes in the rooting of chrysanthemum cuttings. *Proc. XVII. Inter. Hort. Cong.* Paper 369.

[42] Hume, E. P. (1940). The response of plants to intermittent supplementary light. *Proc. Amer. Soc. Hort. Sci.* **37**, 1059.

[43] Kiplinger, D. C. and Alger, J. (1948). Interrupted shading of chrysanthemums. *Proc. Amer. Soc. Hort. Sci.* **52**, 478.

[44] Lane, H. C., Siegelman, H. W., Butler, W. L. and Firer, E. N. (1963). Detection of phytochrome in green plants. *Plant Physiol.* **38**, 414.

[45] Laurie, A. (1930). Photoperiodism – practical application to greenhouse culture. *Proc. Amer. Soc. Hort. Sci.* **27**, 319.

[46] Lindstrom, R. S. and Tolbert, N. E. (1960). (2-chloroethyl) trimethyl-ammonium chloride and related compounds as plant growth substances. IV. Effect on chrysanthemums and poinsettias. *Quart. Bull. Mich. Agr. Exp. Sta.* **42**, 917.

[47] Link, C. (1936). Preliminary studies on flower bud differentiation in relation to photoperiodic response. *Proc. Amer. Soc. Hort. Sci.* **34**, 621.

[48] Link, C. (1938). Further micro-chemical studies of flower bud differentiation in relation to the photoperiod. *Proc. Amer. Soc. Hort. Sci.* **35**, 810.

[49] Lona, F. (1950). Esperienze sull'anto-inibizione fotoperiodica e sulla fioritura delle brevidiurne a notte continua. *Humus (Milan)* **6**, 6.

[50] Mason, D. T. (1957). Chrysanthemum – 1. A. Classification of some mid-season and late-flowering varieties according to their vernalization requirement and to their rapidity of bud formation in long days. *Univ. Reading. Tech. Bull.* No. 1.

[51] Mason, D. T. and Vince, D. (1962). The pattern of growth in chrysanthemum as a response to changing seasonal environment. In *Advances in Hort. Sci. and their Applications* **11**, 374.

[52] Mastalerz, J. W. and Campbell, F. J. (1956). Maleic hydrazide – a substitute for pinching potted chrysanthemums. *Proc. Amer.Soc.Hort.Sci.***68**, 511.

[53] Matukhin, G. R. and Maksimova, E. V. (1960). Effect of gibberellic acid on growth and development in chrysanthemum. (Russ.) *Bot. Zh.* **45**, 1792.

[54] Moshkov, B. S. (1937). The photoperiodic response of leaves and the possibility of its utilization in grafts. (Russ.) *Tr. prikl. Bot., Genet. i. Selekts, Ser. A, Sotsialist. Rastenievodstvo* **19**, 107.

[55] Moshkov, B. S. (1940). On critical and optimal photoperiods. (Russ.) *Sovetsk. Bot.* 1940, 32.

[56] Okada, M. (1953). Effects of daylength and temperature on flowering of summer and August-flowering chrysanthemums. (Japanese.) *J. Hort. Ass. Japan* **21**, 251.

[57] Okada, M. (1955). Culture precoce des chrysanthemes (en Japonais). *Agr. et Hort.* **30**, 1597.

[58] Okada, M. (1957). Classification of chrysanthemum varieties in view of their environmental responses to flowering. (In Japanese with summary in English.) *Jour. Hort. Ass. Japan* **26**, 59.

[59] Okada, M. (1959). On the rosetting of suckers and measures for breaking rosetting in chrysanthemum (Japanese). *J. Hort. Ass. Japan* **28**, 209.

[60] Paul, K. B. and Biswas, P. K. (1966). Effect of chrysanthemum plant extract on flower initiation in short-day plants. *Proc. XVII. Intern. Hort. Cong.* Paper 297.

[61] Poesch, G. H. (1931). Studies of photoperiodism of the chrysanthemum. *Proc. Amer. Soc. Hort. Sci.* **28**, 389.

[62] Poesch, G. H. (1935). Supplementary illumination from mazda, mercury, and neon lamps on some greenhouse plants. *Proc. Amer. Soc. Hort. Sci.* **33**, 637.

[63] Poesch, G. H. and Laurie, A. (1935). The use of artificial light and reduction of the daylight period for flowering plants in the greenhouse. *Bull.* 559 *Ohio Agr. Exp. Sta.*, 1.

[64] Popham, R. A. and Chan, A. P. (1950). Zonation in the vegetative stem tip of *Chrysanthemum morifolium. Amer. J. Bot.* **37**, 476.

[65] Post, K. (1931). Reducing the daylength of chrysanthemums for the production of early blooms by the use of black sateen cloth. *Proc. Amer. Soc. Hort. Sci.* **28**, 382.

[66] Post, K. (1934). Production of early blooms of chrysanthemums by use of black cloth to reduce the length of day. *Cornell Univ. Agr. Exp. Sta., Bull.* 594, 1

[67] Post, K. (1939). The relationship of temperature to flower bud formation in chrysanthemum. *Proc. Amer. Soc. Hort. Sci.* **37**, 1003.

[68] Post, K. (1942). Effects of daylength and temperature on growth and flowering of some florist crops. *Cornell Univ. Agr. Exp. Sta. Bull.* 787, 1.

[69] Post, K. (1947). Chrysanthemum troubles of 1947. *Bull. N.Y. State Flower Growers* **27**, 4.

[70] Post, K. (1950). Accumulation of photoperiodic stimuli in chrysanthemums. *Proc. Amer. Soc. Hort. Sci.* **55**, 475.

[71] Post, K. (1953). Temperature and flowering of ornamentals. *Rep. 13th Inter. Hort. Cong.* 1952, 935.

[72] Post, K. and Kamemoto, H. (1950). A study on the number of short photoperiods required for flower bud initiation and the effect of interrupted treatment on flower spray formation in two commercial varieties of chrysanthemum. *Proc. Amer. Soc. Hort. Sci.* **55**, 477.

[73] Post, K. and Lacey, D. B. (1951). Interrupted short day improves standard chrysanthemum. *N.Y. State Flower Growers Bull.* **70**, 2.

[74] Rogers, M. N. and Tjia, B. O. S. (1966). Effect of ethylene in the atmosphere on photoperiodic responses of chrysanthemums. *Proc. XVII. Intern. Hort. Cong.* Paper 471.

[75] Sachs, R. M., Lang, A., Bretz, C. F. and Roach, J. (1960). Shoot histogenesis – subapical meristematic activity in a caulescent plant and the action of gibberellic acid and Amo-1618. *Amer. J. Bot.* **47**, 260.

[76] Schappelle, N. A. (1936). Effect of narrow ranges of wave lengths of radiant energy, and other factors, on the reproductive growth of long-day and short-day plants. *Cornell Memoir* **185**, 1–38.

[77] Schwabe, W. W. (1950). Factors controlling flowering in the chrysanthemum I. The effects of photoperiod and temporary chilling. *J. Exp. Bot.* **1**, 329.

[78] Schwabe, W. W. (1951). Factors controlling flowering in the chrysanthemum II. Day-length effects on the further development of inflorescence buds and their experimental reversal and modification. *J. Exp. Bot.* **2**, 223.

[79] Schwabe, W. W. (1952). Factors controlling flowering in the chrysanthemum III. Favourable effects of limited periods of long day on inflorescence initiation. *J. Exp. Bot.* **3**, 430.

[80] Schwabe, W. W. (1954). Factors controlling flowering in the chrysanthemum IV The site of vernalization and translocation of the stimulus. *J. Exp. Bot.* **5**, 389.

[81] Schwabe, W. W. (1955). Factors controlling flowering in the chrysanthemum V. De-vernalization in relation to high temperature and low light intensity treatments. *J. Exp. Bot.* **6**, 435.

[82] Schwabe, W. W. (1951). Factors controlling flowering in the chrysanthemum VI. De-vernalization by low-light intensity in relation to temperature and carbohydrate supply. *J. Exp. Bot.* **8**, 220.

[83] Schwabe, W. W. (1959). Some effects of environment and hormone treatment on reproductive morphogenesis in the chrysanthemum. *J. Linn. Soc. (Bot.)* **56**, 254.

[84] Seeley, J. G. and Weise, A. H. (1965). Photoperiodic response of garden and greenhouse chrysanthemums. *Proc. Amer. Soc. Hort. Sci.* **87**, 464.

[85] Shaw, R. J. and Rogers, M. N. (1964). Interactions. *Flor. Rev.* **135**, 73.

[86] Shaw, R. J. and Rogers, M. N. (1966). Relationship of day and night temperatures and carbon dioxide on vegetative growth and flowering of chrysanthemum. *Proc. XVII. Inter. Hort. Cong.* Paper No. 295.

[87] Stuart, N. W. (1943). Controlling time of blooming of chrysanthemums by the use of lights. *Proc. Amer. Soc. Hort. Sci.* **42**, 605.

[88] Stuart, N. W. and Cathey, H. M. (1962). Control of growth and flowering of *Chrysanthemum morifolium* and *Hydrangea macrophylla* by gibberellin. In *Advances in Hort. Sci. and their Applications* **11**, 391.

[89] Tincker, M. A. H. (1929). The effects of length of day, period of illumination upon the growth of plants. *J. R. Hort. Soc.* **54**, 354.

[90] Vince, D. (1954). Quelques aspects le chrysantheme. *Extrait du. Bull. Soc. fr. de Physiol. Veget.* **2**, 165.

[91] Vince, D. (1955). Some effects of temperature and daylength on flowering in the chrysanthemum. *J. Hort. Sci.* **30**, 34.

[92] Vince, D. (1956). Chilling will prevent rosetting. *The Grower (London)* **45**, 33.

[93] Vince, D. and Mason, D. T. (1954). Acceleration of flowering in non-vernalized chrysanthemums by the removal of apical sections of the stem. *Nature* **174**, 842.

[94] Vince, D. and Mason, D. T. (1957). The effect of removing apical sections of the stem on the flowering behaviour of non-vernalized chrysanthemums. *J. Hort. Sci.* **32**, 184.

[95] Vince, D. and Mason, D. T. (1959). Low temperature effects on internode extension in *Chrysanthemum morifolium*. *J. Hort. Sci.* **34**, 199.

[96] Waters, W. E. (1965). Influence of nutrition on flower production, keeping quality, disease susceptibility, and chemical composition of *Chrysanthemum morifolium*. *Proc. Amer. Soc. Hort. Sci.* **86**, 650.

[97] Watson, D. P. and Andrews, P. S. (1953). The effect of light intensity on the flowering of chrysanthemum variety Gold Coast. *Proc. Amer. Soc. Hort. Sci.* **61**, 551.

[98] Waxman, S. (1963). Flashlighting chrysanthemums. *Prog. Rpt.* 54, *Univ. of. Conn. Agr. Exp. Sta.*

[99] Weise, A. H. and Seeley, J. G. (1964). Translocation of the floral stimulus in chrysanthemum. *Proc. Amer. Soc. Hort. Sci.* **85**, 574.

[100] Woltz, S. S. and Jackson, C. R. (1961). Production of yellow strapleaf of chrysanthemum and similar disorders by amino acid treatment. *Plant Physiol.* **36**, 197.

[101] Woolman, J. (1961). Chrysanthemum History. *Nat. Chrysanthemum Yrbk*. London 1961, 136.

12

Arabidopsis thaliana (L.) Heynh.

By Klaus Napp-Zinn

1 History of Use

Arabidopsis thaliana is a cruciferous plant, originally named *Arabis thaliana* by Linnaeus in honour of Johannes Thal, 1542–1583, author of the first German flora. Local races occur all over Europe and in North Africa, Turkey, and Western Siberia. More recently, it has also been introduced into other countries, such as the U.S.A. As in other species of *Arabidopsis* floral nectaries are often rudimentary or missing,[12,34,35] and the species is autogamous and suitable for genetic studies.

Arabidopsis thaliana was introduced into work on the physiology of flower formation in 1937 by Laibach[18,19] who had counted its chromosomes (n = 5) as early as 1907.[17] Until 1952, studies on the induction of flowering in *Arabidopsis thaliana* were carried out exclusively in Laibach's laboratories. During this period, Laibach's main collaborators in the work on the physiology of flower formation were Härer,[10,11] Kribben[24] and Zenker.[25,71] Since then *Arabidopsis* has invaded laboratories all over the world, mostly from seed of many races supplied by Laibach. The local races mentioned in this chapter are Antwerpen (Antw), St. Blasien (Bla), Dijon (Di), Enkheim$_1$ (En$_1$), Estland (Est), Finnland (Fi), Graz (Gr), Kopenhagen (Ko), Krusenberg (Kru), Landsberg (La), Limburg$_{3,5}$ (Li$_3$, Li$_5$), Östhammar (Öst), Stockholm (St), Tenela (Te), Warschau (Wa), Wilna$_2$ (Wil$_2$), and Zürich (Zü).

2 Growing Techniques and Growth Habit

Arabidopsis thaliana is said to prefer acid soil, but has been found growing spontaneously also on calcareous soils.[63] In fact, *Arabidopsis* is not particular as far as the substratum is concerned. Seeds may germinate and produce plants even on vertical greenhouse walls.

Laibach[22] mentioned culture of the species in test tubes in 1951. Detailed accounts of aseptic culture on synthetic media have been published by Langridge,[27] Kvitko[16] and Ivanov *et al.*[15]

Arabidopsis thaliana is a semi-rosette plant; its main axis first forms a rosette of between 2 and 130 stalked leaves (besides the cotyledons), and then an elongated shoot which may bear between 0 and 45 usually unstalked leaves below the principal inflorescence. According to Laibach[22] the minimum number of true leaves can be as low as one (race Wa under poor nutrition).

3 Inflorescence Structure and Criteria of Flowering Response

As in Cruciferae in general, the inflorescences of *Arabidopsis thaliana* are open racemes. This is true for the terminal inflorescence as well as for the lateral conflorescences which usually originate from the axils of all stalk leaves and upper rosette leaves. A more detailed description of the inflorescences has been given by Müller,[34] while Barthelmess[2] has studied the correlation between flowering age and number of conflorescences. The formation of conflorescences in some leaf axils is suppressed in one race (Zü) under natural conditions, and in many late flowering races after application of gibberellins.[45,52,58,60] As in most crucifers, bracts are only rarely present in the racemes of *A. thaliana*, but they are a normal feature in those of *A. himalaica*.[68]

Laibach[22] originally took the visibility of flower primordia as the criterion of flowering response. Sometimes it is necessary to dissect a plant in order to find flower primordia. Recently, the time to opening of the first flower on the main axis, in doubtful cases the appearance of the stigma, has been widely used, as suggested by Napp-Zinn.[36,43]

Another useful index of flowering response is the total number of rosette and stalk leaves formed on the main axis below its first flower. However, this may be affected by relatively unspecific influences such as nutritional status of the plants.[38]

FIGURE 12–1. Plants of *Arabidopsis thaliana*, winter-annual race St, 5 weeks after vernalization at + 2°C for 70 days.

4 Effects of Plant Age

Those races of *Arabidopsis thaliana* which exhibit a cold requirement may be vernalized in the seed stage. All races investigated to date are long day plants, and Laibach[22] observed competence to respond to photoperiod immediately after germination.

5 Vernalization and Devernalization

Degrees of vernalization requirement

The numerous strains of *Arabidopsis thaliana* may be divided into four groups: (1) early summer-annual strains, flowering in less than 40 days at 20°C under continuous light of approximately 500 f.c.; (2) medium summer-annual strains flowering between 40 and 55 days; (3) late summer-annual ones (55–92 days); and (4) winter-annual ones (> 92 days under these conditions). These terms are applied here in a physiological sense; whether a given race is a winter-annual one also in an ecological sense depends upon its germination behaviour.

To the first group belong the strains Li_5, Wil_2, and La, which do not respond to vernalization when grown under a sufficient light intensity. With such strains some vernalization response can be found in plants grown in short days or low light intensity (40 f.c.).[50,51] The second group includes strains like the line H55-früh which have slight vernalization response under a light intensity of 500 f.c. The third group contains, among others, McKelvie's[29] artificially produced mutants f_1, f_2, f_3, and f_4 and Röbbelen's[65] strain V 13 with a medium cold requirement. Local strains like some Scandinavian ones (St, Te, and Öst), and McKelvie's mutant F, may be placed in the fourth group. By sufficient vernalization at the seed stage, their age at flowering may be reduced by 100 days, e.g. from 130 to 30 days. Thus, to some degree, the age at flowering of unvernalized *Arabidopsis* plants may indicate the extent of their vernalization requirement.

The genetical basis of the vernalization response

Laibach[20] crossed winter-annual and early summer-annual races. In the cross St × Wa the summer-annual character of Wa was dominant in the F_1; in the cross Di × Ko, however, the winter-annual character of Ko was dominant. In the F_2- generation of the first cross, Laibach obtained a segregation ratio of 2 summer-annual : 18 intermediate : 1 winter-annual.

Härer[10,11] crossed plants of 5 early, medium and late summer-annual local races. She concluded that one incompletely dominant major gene was chiefly responsible for the flowering behaviour and supposed (without sufficient experimental evidence) that the differences between several races were due to multiple alleles of a single locus. Besides this major gene some minor genes manifested themselves only under short-day conditions.

Napp-Zinn[39,42,50] studied the genetical basis of the vernalization requirement of the winter-annual race St in crosses with the early summer-annual strain Li_5. At least 4 different genes appear to be involved. For one of these genes, isolated in the line H55-früh (*kry kry*), the relatively small cold requirement is caused by the recessive allele, but with the other vernalization genes it is the dominant allele which elicits a marked cold requirement. Genes responsible for a greater cold requirement are more or less epistatic to others causing a smaller cold requirement.[49] The degree of epistasy may depend on light intensity and other conditions. The lines H51 ($+$ *kry* $+$ *kry Fri Fri*) and H53 (*kry kry Fri Fri*), for example, are both late summer-annual strains and flower about 55 days after sowing when grown under a high light intensity; under weak light, however, H51 may flower at an age of 80 days, and H53 after 110 days. Thus, low light intensity may convert epistasy of vernalization genes into additivity.

Because of this epistasy one cannot deduce the number of vernalization genes involved from the flowering age of a non-vernalized plant. McKelvie's mutant F, with probably one strong vernalization gene, flowers about the same time as the race St, the most effective vernalization gene of which does not even seem to be identical with that of F.[56]

Natural populations of *A. thaliana* are often mixtures of different genotypes. Thus, selection may be necessary before a given population can be used for physiological experiments.[55]

Other papers dealing with the genetics of flowering are those of Dierks,[6] whose heterosis genes seem to provoke a vernalization requirement; Seyffert,[67] on experiments under short-day winter conditions in which races with and without cold requirements did not differ remarkably; Rédei,[64] with late flowering, perhaps vernalizable mutants; and van der Veen,[70] whose crosses of two early summer-annual strains resulted in relatively late flowering F_1-plants with 2 genes responsible.

Laibach[23] investigated the genetics of flowering behaviour of hybrids between *Arabidopsis* species. He crossed the winter-annual race Fi of *A. suecica* with the early flowering races La and Di of *A. thaliana*. In all cases the behaviour of the mother was dominant in the F_1 (the reciprocal cross did not produce viable seed). Astonishingly, all the back crosses with *A. suecica* and with summer-annual races of *A. thaliana* (Di, En_1, and Li_5) gave exclusively winter-annual plants.

Effectiveness of different cold treatments

Napp-Zinn[46] treated imbibed seed of the winter-annual strain St for 0–70 days with temperatures between -3.5 and $+4°C$; afterwards, the plants were grown under continuous light at 20°C. Treatment at $+2°C$ for 70 days was the most effective; with cold treatments of up to 38 days duration, $+4°C$ was as effective as or even more effective than $+2°C$. Even treatment for only 14 days at -0.5, $+2$ or $+4°C$ provoked a marked acceleration of flowering. Vernalization at $-3.5°C$ was effective, after a duration of 58 days. Although the flowering behaviour of other *Arabidopsis* strains with and without vernalization requirements has been described by Laibach and Zenker[22,25,71] and others, the data is less complete than that for the strain St.

For effective cold treatment of imbibed grain, the addition of at least 60 mg of water per 100 mg of air dry grain is necessary.[41]

Relation between plant age and vernalization effect

A rather peculiar relation between plant age at the beginning of the cold treatment and its vernalizing effect was found with strain St. At the stage of imbibed seed a vernalization treatment has a relatively great effect; during and after germination the vernalizability diminishes rapidly for one to several weeks, and then increases again, reaching an optimum with plants between 45 and 90 days of age, after which it decreases again.[44]

The times of minimum and maximum vernalizability may vary with the experimental conditions, but neither light and darkness during vernalization nor the intensity or spectral composition of the light during the periods before and after the cold treatment determine the time of minimum vernalizability.[47,48] These factors may, however, influence the vernalizing effect of a given cold treatment and the possibility of devernalization. In one experiment, the effect of two light intensities, about 200 W/m² (L) and 550 W/m² (H) before and after vernalization was studied. The order of effectiveness for vernalization at 2°C for 40 days was $L \rightarrow H > H \rightarrow H > L \rightarrow L > H \rightarrow L$.[48]

A similar relation between age and vernalization effect has been found in other late flowering strains, like H53[47] and McKelvie's mutant F^{56}, regardless of whether vernalization had taken place in light or in darkness. In other strains, like H51, a period of slightly reduced vernalizability was only observed when plants were vernalized in darkness.[47]

Antivernalization, devernalization, stabilization of the vernalized condition, and revernalization

With regard to a heat treatment (e.g. 5 days at $+30°C$) immediately preceding or following vernalization, *Arabidopsis thaliana* behaves, in many respects, like other vernalizable plants. Most observations concern the winter-annual strain St.

Antivernalization (heat treatment followed by vernalization or not) delays flowering in St[36,46] and in the late summer-annual strain Gr[71], but not in early summer-annual strains (Napp-Zinn, unpublished). Under certain conditions, antivernalized St plants may flower at a lower node than controls, which may be due to starvation during the heat treatment in darkness.[36,38,46]

Complete devernalization is possible immediately after vernalization of up to 72 days with the winter-annual strain St.[36,46] In the late summer-annual strain Gr, only partial devernalization could be obtained by heat treatments at + 30° of up to 6 days.[71] In other, less cold-requiring strains devernalization, if any, is slight.[47]

Stabilization of the vernalization effect may be achieved by holding St plants at intermediate temperatures like + 20°C for 5 days between seed vernalization and heat treatment.[46] Among other factors producing varying degrees of stabilization in the race St are light, given during vernalization or heat treatment, and a period of normal cultivation before vernalization. A heat treatment in light was ineffective for devernalization when germinating seeds had been vernalized in light; a heat treatment in light or darkness was ineffective when the plants were 5 or more weeks old at the beginning of the cold treatment.[47]

After devernalization, *Arabidopsis* plants may be revernalized.[36,46,71] In the case of the winter-annual strain St, the duration of the first cold treatment manifested itself anew after uniform devernalization and revernalization.[36,46]

Vernalization and light

We have seen that light may influence the vernalization effect when given before, during, or after cold exposure. However, the light requirement is greatly reduced by a prolonged cold treatment; light intensity no longer influenced the vernalization response of St plants after 8 weeks of cold treatment.[41] Also, flowering of summer-annual strains, with little or no cold requirement under long-day conditions, may be greatly accelerated by vernalization if the plants are grown under short-day.[4,50,71] This may reflect a quantitative requirement for light rather than a photoperiodic one.

Interpretation of the vernalization behaviour

From the behaviour of the winter-annual strain St after seed vernalization and anti-, de-, and revernalization it has been concluded that there may be several thermolabile and thermostable intermediate stages in the vernalization process of this strain, as summarized in the following scheme.[36,46]

$$A \rightarrow A_1 \rightarrow A_2 \rightarrow A_3 \rightarrow A' \rightarrow B$$
$$\downarrow \qquad\quad \downarrow \quad\ \downarrow$$
$$X \qquad\qquad X' \quad Y$$

A = a thermostable precursor.

A_1 = a first thermolabile intermediate stage, demonstrated by the effect of antivernalization.

A_2 = a thermostable intermediate stage, demonstrated by the reappearance of the effect of a first cold treatment after de- and revernalization.

A_3 = a second thermolabile intermediate stage the existence of which is concluded from the fact that the partial processes between A_2 and B do not reach the final stage B at 20°C.

A' = a third thermolabile intermediate stage, demonstrated by devernalization, corresponding to the same symbol in the scheme of Purvis and Gregory[61] for the vernalization of Petkus winter rye, and to the thermolabile intermediate stage in that of Lang and Melchers[26] for the vernalization of biennial *Hyoscyamus niger*.

B = the thermostable final stage of vernalization.

X = a product to which A_1 is transformed at 30°C and which is different from A.

X′ = a product to which A_3 is transformed at 20°C.

Y = a product to which A′ is transformed at 30°C.

All the partial processes are thought to have normal temperature coefficients ($Q_{10} > 1$). At 20°C the process $A_1 \rightarrow B$ may circumvent A_2 and A_3.

With regard to the one gene-one enzyme hypothesis, this scheme obviously requires several vernalization genes, which are known to exist in this strain. The scheme can also explain other experimental results, such as a phase of reduced vernalizability which could correspond to the thermostable stage A_2, which has been found also in the probably unifactorial mutant *F*. The circumvention of A_2 and A_3 could have something to do with the replacement of cold by continuous light of high intensity.

6 Short Day Vernalization

Short-day vernalization is not possible in *Arabidopsis thaliana*. On the contrary, short-day conditions largely delay flowering.[22]

7 Photoperiod Response

Relatively little work has been done so far on the photoperiodic behaviour of *Arabidopsis thaliana*. The first observations are due to Laibach[18,19,21,22] who sowed 39 races at monthly intervals and cultivated the plants in a greenhouse under natural daylengths. As photoperiodic studies are most readily carried out with non-cold-requiring plants, Laibach's results with his earliest summer-annual races are most interesting. His quickest strain, Wa, showed flower buds only 11 days after germination in the case of July sowings, but 72 days after germination when sown in October or December. The corresponding times for the race Di were 12 days (July) and 112 days (October). All races proved to be long-day plants but there are great differences in the degree of long-day requirement. The genetical basis of these differences has not yet been investigated. Other experiments on the long-day requirement of *A. thaliana* have been done by Gregory and Hussey.[7]

Under continuous light of 135,000 erg sec^{-1} cm^{-2}, the race Wa shows flower primordia 8 days after germination, and must therefore, be competent to respond to photoperiod very early. Laibach[22] subjected germinating seeds of this strain to 4, 5, 6 . . . 11 days of continuous light, beginning with the day of sowing, and then to natural short-day in November/December. Germination occurred 2 or 3 days after sowing. Those groups which had received only 4 or 5 days of continuous light, did not show any flower buds within 50 days after sowing; with 6 days of continuous light flower primordia were visible on the 44th day, and with 7, 8, 9 or 10 days after 15, 13, 13, or 11 days, respectively, and the last group had flower buds already on the last day of continuous illumination. Thus, 4 days of continuous light immediately after germination are enough to provoke almost complete photoperiodic induction. The same is true with one third of the above light intensity, but with one twelfth of that intensity 9 days of continuous illumination after germination are required for induction. In a similar experiment with the Indian strain Saharanpur, exposure to 6 or more long days was necessary to obtain increased flowering.[1]

In another experiment, Laibach[22] exposed seedlings of the moderately early summer-annual race Li_3 to short days until 2 or 16 days after germination, and then to long days. In both groups flower primordia became visible 16 days after the beginning of the long-day exposure.

A. thaliana is a long day plant with a very low critical daylength; 4 hours for the early summer-annual race Wa and for the intermediate race Li_3, and 5 hours for the late summer-annual race Gr, at a constant temperature of 23°C.[22] Light intensity is much less important than cycle length, as may be seen in Table 12–1.

TABLE 12–1

The relative light quantities necessary for the formation of flower primordia in several summer-annual races of *Arabidopsis thaliana*. I = 135,000 erg sec^{-1} cm^{-2} (after Laibach[22]).

Daily Illumination

Race	24 hrs, I	8 hrs, I	4 hrs, I	24 hrs, I/3	8 hrs, I/3	24 hrs, I/12
Wa	1	1.15	1.05	0.46	0.44	0.29
Li₃	1	1.30	1.38	0.49	0.50	0.20
Gr	1	0.95	–	0.33	0.51	0.23
Est	1	0.83	–	0.52	0.38	0.35

8 Spectral Dependence

Meijer[30] studied flowering of 3 strains of *Arabidopsis thaliana* grown under 16 hours of light daily of 470 μW/cm^2 intensity and different colours, using plexiglass filters. Under these conditions, all strains initiated flower buds with a combination of blue (4000–5300 A°) and near infra-red light ($\lambda > 7000$A°). One strain also flowered in blue light alone. Another strain initiated flower buds in blue light if the intensity was raised to 650 μW/cm^2. Red (6000–7000 A°) or green light (5000–6000 A°) at 470 or 650 μW/cm^2 never induced flowering.

Napp-Zinn investigated the influence of light of different colours, using light from Philips coloured fluorescent lamps at an intensity of 550 W/m^2 on flowering of the summer-annual strain Li₅. Some plants were chilled in darkness for 81 days immediately after sowing. The results, summarized in Table 12–2, show that, up

TABLE 12–2

The effect of different light colours on days to flowering and on the number of rosette and stalk leaves in unvernalized and vernalized plants of the early summer-annual strain Li₅ of *Arabidopsis thaliana* (Napp-Zinn, unpublished data).

Treatment	Light Colour	Days to flowering	Rosette leaves	Stalk leaves
Unvernalized	White	35.7		2.1
	Blue	53.2	17.3	3.3
	Green	73.2	20.4	3.9
	Red	141.2	29.5	12.4
Vernalized	White	41.4	14.1	4.4
	Blue	50.3	10.0	2.5
	Green	61.0	16.5	3.3
	Red	96.1	17.5	4.8

to a point, the inhibitory influence of unfavourable light qualities could be overcome by previous vernalization.

Plants of the winter-annual strain St which had been vernalized for 81 days in the seed stage, behaved more like the unvernalized Li₅ plants than like the vernalized ones. In other experiments with strain St vernalized to varying degrees at various stages, the order of flowering was as in Table 12–2, with vernalization compensating to some extent for unfavourable light colours. Light quality before vernalization was less important than that after chilling. The phase of minimum vernalizability was only occasionally influenced by light colour.

9 Endogenous Rhythms

After the negative results of Hussey[14] with *Arabidopsis thaliana*, Clauss and Rau[5] tested anew Bünning's theory according to which photoperiodism has something to do with endogenous rhythms. Like Hussey they used the early summer-annual strain Li$_5$. After 24–42 days in short days of 8 hours, plants were exposed to five 72-hour cycles, each consisting of a main light period of 8 or 9 hours, a period of supplementary light for 3 hours at varying times after this main light period, and 61 or 60 hours of darkness. As expected from Bünning's theory, flowering was often favoured in those plants which received supplementary light about 12, 36 or 60 hours after the beginning of the main light period. However, the results were not very clear cut and differed between experiments.

13 Effects of Temperature

Apart from vernalization, the role of temperature in the flowering of *Arabidopsis* has not yet been investigated systematically. Laibach[22] studied the influence of cold during the daily dark period on flower formation of some summer-annual strains cultivated under threshold photoperiods. One group was kept at 23°C continuously, while the other received 1–3°C during the dark period and 23°C during the light period. The results are summarized in Table 12–3.

TABLE 12–3.

Influence of cold during dark period on the number of days from sowing to appearance of flower buds in several summer-annual strains of *Arabidopsis thaliana* (after Laibach[22]).

Length of light periods	Temperature	Races			
		Wa	Li$_3$	Est	Gr
4 hrs	Continuously 23°C		133	No flowering	No flowering
	Cold dark period		167	190	182
5 hrs	Continuously 23°C	82	106		98
	Cold dark period	102	154		123

Cold during the dark period favoured flowering in Est and Gr in 4-hour days; in all the other cases, cold delayed flowering.

14 Effects of Mineral Nutrition

In early summer-annual strains poor mineral nutrition (e.g. on sandy soil) slightly increases the number of days to flowering and reduces the number of leaves.[20] In certain cases (race Wa, cultivated on filter paper with tap water), only 1–3 leaves (besides the cotyledons) may be formed on the main axis.[22]

16 Translocation of the Floral Stimulus

Flowering normally occurs first at the tip of the main axis of *Arabidopsis thaliana*. Laibach and Kribben[24] wondered whether the axillary buds attain ripeness to flower at the same time as the terminal buds. If conditions become less favourable for flowering, e.g. by transition from long day to short day or from high to low light intensity after flower formation on the main shoot, the lateral buds produce vegetative rosettes. Laibach and Kribben concluded from this that the lateral buds obtain the floral stimulus later than the main bud. In this context these authors discuss the relations between the disappearance of apical dominance and the appearance of the floral stimulus in lateral buds.

18 Effects of Growth Substances and Growth Retardants

Auxins and antiauxins

The influence of some auxins and antiauxins during seed vernalization has been investigated. Unfortunately, *Arabidopsis* has the disadvantage that treatments which delay germination, such as extreme hydrogen ion concentrations or osmotically active substances, also diminish the vernalization response.[54] Therefore, plants so treated should be compared with controls germinated at the same time. On this basis, NAA, IAA, MH, and TIBA, when added to the imbibition medium of seed of cold-requiring strains of *Arabidopsis* before a vernalization of 40 days duration, did not cause a reproducible stimulation or inhibition of flowering.[54] By treating non-vernalized older rosettes with solutions of IAA or TIBA, Sarkar[66] succeeded in stimulating (with IAA) or delaying (with TIBA) flowering significantly in plants of the winter-annual strain St, and its hybrids with the early summer-annual strain Li_5.

TABLE 12–4

Influence of several gibberellins on flowering of some strains of *Arabidopsis thaliana* grown at 20°C in continuous light. $+++$ = acceleration of flowering by more than 20 days; $++$ = acceleration less than 20 days, but still significant at the 1 per cent level; $+$ = less significant acceleration; I = days between sowing and beginning of treatment (after Napp-Zinn[53]).

Strains	I	Gibberellins						
		A_1	A_3	A_4	A_5	A_7	A_8	A_9
Winter-annual:								
Öst	62	+	+ +	+ + +		+ + +		+ +
Te	62	+	+	+	+	+ + +	+	+
St	37	+ + +	+ + +	+ + +	+ + +	+ + +	+	+ + +
H 68 spät	37	+	+	+		+ + +		+
II 1	37	+	+ + +	+ + +	+	+ + +		+
III 18	37	+ +	+ + +	+ + +	+ + +	+ + +	+ +	+ + +
Late summer-annual:								
Kru	37	+	+ +	+ +	+	+	+	+
H 48 spät	37	+	+	+	+	+ +	+	+
H 51	37	+ +	+ +	+ +	+ +	+ +	+ +	+ +
H 53	37	+	+ +	+ +	+	+ + +	+ +	+ +
V 13	37	+	+	+	+ +	+	+ +	+ +
f_2	25		+	+	+	+ +	+	+
f_3	25	+	+	+	+	+	+	+
f_4	25	+	+	+	+	+	+	+ +
Med. summer-annual:								
Bla	23	+	+	+	+	+	+	+
Antw	23					+		
H 55 früh	23		+	+	+	+		
Early summer-annual:								
Li_5	23		+ +	+	+	+	+	+
V 4	23		+			+	+	
V 17	23		+			+		+

Gibberellins and antigibberellins

Several workers have succeeded in replacing both vernalization and photo-periodic induction by gibberellins. Langridge[28] grew plants of the early summer-annual strain Est in test tubes, and found that 4γ of gibberellic acid (GA_3) per plant led to a remarkable acceleration of flowering under short-day conditions, the age at flowering being reduced from 67.6 to 50.5 days and the number of rosette leaves from 12.3 to 8.3. Under continuous light, the gibberellin effect was much smaller (20.5 instead of 21.8 days, and 6.2 instead of 7.6 rosette leaves).

Laibach[23] and Sarkar[66] reported the induction of more rapid flowering by GA_3 in several cold-requiring races and hybrids, like St and its F_1-hybrid with the early summer-annual race Li_5,[66] the races Kru and Öst of A. thaliana, and in A. suecica.[23]

Napp-Zinn[53] treated plants of 23 strains over a period of 5 weeks with a total of 10γ per plant of 7 different gibberellins (A_1, A_3, A_4, A_5, A_7, A_8 and A_9). Most of these strains, especially those with a marked cold requirement, responded to most or all of the gibberellins by precocious flower formation (Table 12–4).

In other experiments seeds of 7 strains of Arabidopsis thaliana with different cold requirements were imbibed in solutions of CCC at concentrations from 3×10^{-7} to 1×10^{-2} prior to vernalization. The higher the CCC concentration, the more was flowering delayed in both summer and winter-annual strains; in some cases, the treated plants flowered even later than the unvernalized controls. As this is true also for strains without any cold requirement, it is not clear whether CCC affected the vernalization process or the photoperiodic induction.[59]

Napp-Zinn[57] discusses whether some gibberellin might be identical with vernalin, the hypothetical end product of vernalization. Although gibberellins may induce early flowering in cold-requiring strains of Arabidopsis, there are strong reasons against their identity with vernalin: (1) All cold-requiring strains of Arabidopsis thaliana may be vernalized in the seed stage, while imbibition of seeds with GA_3 is ineffective in hastening flowering, even when applied in combination with incomplete seed vernalization.[66] GA_3 may, however, induce germination of Arabidopsis seeds which need post-maturation. (2) Vernalization decreases, but gibberellins increase, the number of stalk leaves.[53,66] (3) In the strain Zü, vernalization decreases, but gibberellins increase, the number of empty leaf axils; they even provoke sterile axils in strains which normally do not show this phenomenon.[45,52,58,60]

Other substances

Michniewicz[31] obtained precocious flowering of a summer-annual strain under short-days (8 hour) after treatment with kinetin or vitamin E. Kinetin (10^{-7} M) also increased flowering slightly in the Indian strain Saharanpur under long day conditions.[1] Brown[3] has observed some acceleration of flowering from application of 5-iododeoxyuridine, as have Hirono and Rédei[13] with 8-azaadenine. These findings suggest that nucleic acid metabolism is involved in flower formation.

19 Effects of Metabolic Inhibitors

The findings of Gregory and Purvis[8,9] that vernalization in Petkus winter rye depends on the presence of oxygen and on a sufficient carbohydrate supply, suggested that vernalization might have something to do with respiration. Grain of the strains Li_5 (early summer-annual) and St (winter-annual) of A. thaliana were imbibed in solutions of several inhibitors of respiration (potassium cyanide,

2,4-dinitrophenol, o-phenanthrolin, and maleic hydrazide) prior to vernalization, but no significant, reproducible influence of these substances on flowering was found.[54]

With 2-thiouracil, which may replace uracil in RNA synthesis, neither seed treatment before cold exposure (races Li_5 and St) nor treatment of St rosettes during vernalization led to a noteworthy delay of flowering.[54]

20 Florigenic Extracts

Stimulated by a brief note of Purvis and Gregory[62] on the extraction of a florigenic product by chloroform from vernalized embryos of Petkus winter rye, Napp-Zinn[40] carried out similar experiments with Arabidopsis thaliana (winter-annual strain St) without success. Nor did paper chromatographic studies with ethanol or chloroform extracts of chilled and unchilled Arabidopsis seed (strains St and Li_5) give any hints for the understanding of the metabolic bases of flower formation of Arabidopsis.

22 Chemical Changes at Induction

There are reasons for assuming a connection between vernalization and respiration. Cold often lowers the respiratory quotient (RQ), and one could imagine that the RQ might be lowered in cold-requiring strains by vernalization to become comparable with the RQ of non-cold-requiring strains at normal temperatures (e.g. 20°C). Respiratory measurements with Arabidopsis seed revealed such a change; at every temperature studied between $+ 2$ and 30°C, the RQ was always higher in grains of St (winter-annual) than in those of Li_5 (early summer-annual), but in both strains the RQ diminished not only in the cold but also at the devernalizing temperature of $+ 30$°C.[37]

According to Lang and Melchers,[26] the partial processes leading from A to B in the vernalization scheme are presumably aerobic ones, while the destruction of thermolabile intermediate products may occur under anaerobic conditions.[8] Thus, a shifting of the equilibrium between aerobic and anaerobic processes in favour of the aerobic ones by addition of a product of anaerobiosis, like ethanol, should induce a vernalization-like effect in the absence of cold. Sarkar[66] therefore treated seeds of St, Li_5, and F_1 hybrid seeds of these two strains with ethanol (concentrations between 0.5 and 10 per cent), and obtained a significant, but small and scarcely reproducible acceleration of flowering (even in the summer-annual strain), which he did not regard as conclusive. The slight acceleration could be attributed to the evaporation of ethanol, which may also have served as an unspecific source of energy.

Thus, the metabolic links between the genes responsible for cold and long-day requirements on the one hand and the phenomena of flowering in Arabidopsis on the other remain unknown.

23 Inflorescence Differentiation

There is little information on the differentiation of the inflorescences of Arabidopsis thaliana. A clear distinction between tunica and corpus is possible beyond an age of 6 days.[32] The tunica is regularly composed of two layers. Like foliage leaves, the floral organs are initiated in the inner tunica layer, which indicates the foliar nature of the latter. In both groups of organs, the procambium strands develop acropetally.[69] Further observations on the development of shoot apices, e.g. with regard to the size of nucleoli in the tunica layers during vegetative and reproductive growth, have been published by Miksche and Brown.[33]

REFERENCES

1 Anand, R. and Maheshwari, S. C. (1966). Germination and flowering in *Arabidopsis thaliana* in sterile culture. *Physiol. Plantar.* **19**, 1011.

2 Barthelmess, I. (1964). Merkmalskorrelationen und Selektion bei *Arabidopsis thaliana* (L.) Heynh. *Z. Pflanzenzüchtung* **52**, 273.

3 Brown, J. A. M. (1962). Effect of thymidine analogues on reproductive morphogenesis in *Arabidopsis thaliana* (L.) Heynh. *Nature* **196**, 51.

4 Cetl, I. and Kučera, J. (1966). The effect of vernalization and photoperiod on the development of *Arabidopsis thaliana* (L.) Heynh. In *Differentiation of Apical Meristems and Some Problems of Ecological Regulation of Development of Plants*, 295. Proc. Symposium Praha-Nitra, 1964. Academia, Praha.

5 Clauss, H. and Rau, W. (1956). Über die Blütenbildung von *Hyoscyamus niger* und *Arabidopsis thaliana* in 72-Stunden-Zyklen. *Z. Botanik* **44**, 437.

6 Dierks, W. (1958). Untersuchungen zum Heterosisproblem. *Z. Pflanzenzüchtung* **40**, 67.

7 Gregory, F. G. and Hussey, G. G. (1953). Photoperiodic responses of *Arabidopsis thaliana*. *Proc. Linn. Soc. London* **164**, 137.

8 Gregory, F. G. and Purvis, O. N. (1938). Studies in vernalisation of cereals. II. The vernalisation of excised mature embryos, and of developing ears. *Ann. Bot.*, *N.S.*, **2**, 237.

9 Gregory, F. G. and Purvis, O. N. (1938). Studies in vernalisation of cereals. III. The use of anaerobic conditions in the analysis of the vernalising effect of low temperature during germination. *Ann. Bot.*, *N.S.* **2**, 753.

10 Härer, L. (1947). About the inheritance of the blossoming age of early and late blooming summer–annual strains of *Arabidopsis thaliana*. *Fiat Report* No. 1090. (German with English summary).

11 Härer, L. (1950). Die Vererbung des Blühalters früher und später sommereinjähriger Rassen von *Arabidopsis thaliana* (L.) Heynh. *Beitr. Biol. Pflanzen* **28**, 1.

12 Hildebrand, F. (1879). Vergleichende Untersuchungen über die Saftdrüsen der Cruciferen. *Jb. wiss. Bot.* **12**, 10.

13 Hirono, Y. and Rédei, G. P. (1966). Acceleration of flowering of the long-day plant *Arabidopsis* by 8-aza-adenine. *Arabidopsis Information Service* **3**, 10.

14 Hussey, G. (1954). Experiments with two long-day plants designed to test Bünning's theory of photoperiodism. *Physiol. Plantar.* **7**, 253.

15 Ivanov, V. J., Kasyanenko, A. G., Sanina, A. V. and Timoféeff–Ressovskaya, E. A. (1966). Studies of radiation genetics of *Arabidopsis thaliana* (L.) Heynh. I. Brief description of the experimental plant and some methods of its cultivation, crossing and estimation of variability. *Genetika* 1966, No. 8, 55–70.

16 Kvitko, K. V. (1960). Aseptic culture of *Arabidopsis thaliana* (L.) Heynh. and prospects of utilization of these methods in botanical investigations. *Vestn. Leningrad. Univ.* **15**, Ser. Biol. No. 3, 47. (Russian with English summary.)

17 Laibach, F. (1907). Zur Frage nach der Individualität der Chromosomen im Pflanzenreich. *Beih. Bot. Centralbl.*, *I. Abt.*, **22**, 191.

18 Laibach, F. (1940). Hormone im Pflanzenreich. I. Die Ursachen der Blütenbildung und das Blühhormon. *Natur u. Volk* **70**, 55.

19 Laibach, F. (1943). Zur Ätiologie der Blütenbildung. Naturwiss. **31**, 246.

20 Laibach, F. (1943). *Arabidopsis Thaliana* (L.) Heynh. als Objekt für genetische und entwicklungsphysiologische Untersuchungen. *Bot. Arch.* **44**. 439.

21 Laibach, F. (1949). Zur Blütenbildung bei Lang– und Kurztagpflanzen. *Ber dtsch. bot. Ges.* **62**, 27.

22 Laibach, F. (1951). Über sommer– und winterannuelle Rassen von *Arabidopsis thaliana* (L.) Heynh. Ein Beitrag zur Ätiologie der Blütenbildung. *Beitr. Biol. Pflanzen* **28**, 173.

23 Laibach, F. (1958). Über den Artbastard *Arabidopsis suecica* (Fr.) Norrl. X *A. thaliana* (L.) Heynh. und die Beziehungen zwischen den Gattungen *Arabidopsis* Heynh. und *Cardaminopsis* (C. A. Meyer) Hay. *Planta* **51**, 148.

24 Laibach, F. and Kribben, F. J. (1953). Apikaldominanz und Blühreife. *Beitr. Biol. Pflanzen* **30**, 127.

25 Laibach, F. and Zenker, A. (1954). Zur Kältebeeinflussung der Blütenbildung bei Langtagpflanzen. *Planta* **43**, 250.

26 Lang, A. and Melchers, G. (1947). Vernalisation und Devernalisation bei einer zweijährigen Pflanze. *Z. Naturforsch.* **2b**, 444.

27 Langridge, J. (1957). The aseptic culture of *Arabidopsis thaliana* (L.) Heynh. *Austral. J. biol. Sci.* **10**, 243.

[28] Langridge, J. (1957). Effect of day-length and gibberellic acid on the flowering of *Arabidopsis*. *Nature* **180**, 36.

[29] McKelvie, A. D. (1962). A list of mutant genes in *Arabidopsis thaliana* (L.) Heynh. *Radiation Bot.* **1**, 233.

[30] Meijer, G. (1959). The spectral dependence of flowering and elongation. *Acta bot. neerl.* **8**, 189.

[31] Michniewicz, M. (1966). Some remarks concerning the role of gibberellins in the process of vernalization. In *Differentiation of Apical Meristems and Some Problems of Ecological Regulation of Development of Plants*, 95. Proc. Symposium Praha – Nitra, 1964. Academia, Praha.

[32] Miksche, J. P. and Brown, J. A. M. (1963). Development of the vegetative and floral meristem of *Arabidopsis thaliana* under controlled conditions of growth. *Amer. J. Bot.* **50**, 616.

[33] Miksche, J. P. and Brown, J. A. M. (1965). Development of vegetative and floral meristems of *Arabidopsis thaliana*. *Amer. J. Bot.* **52**, 533.

[34] Müller, A. (1961). Zur Charakterisierung der Blüten und Infloreszenzen von *Arabidopsis thaliana* (L.) Heynh. *Kulturpflanze* **9**, 264.

[35] Müller, H. (1880). Einige thatsächliche und theoretische Bemerkungen zu F. Hildebrand's vergleichenden Untersuchungen über die Saftdrüsen der Cruciferen. *Jb. wiss. Bot.* **12**, 161.

[36] Napp-Zinn, K. (1953). Thermostabile und thermolabile Zwischenstadien im Vernalisationsprozess. *Ber. dtsch. bot. Ges.* **66**, 362.

[37] Napp-Zinn, K. (1954). Vergleichende Atmungsmessungen an Sommer- und Winterannuellen. Untersuchungen an Caryopsen und Embryonen von *Secale cereale* und an Samen von *Arabidopsis thaliana*. *Z. Naturforsch.* **9b**, 218.

[38] Napp-Zinn, K. (1954). Vernalisation und Blattbildung. *VIIIᵉ Congr. Internat. Bot., Rapp. et Comm., Sect.* 11/12, 288.

[39] Napp-Zinn, K. (1955). Genetische Grundlagen des Kältebedürfnisses bei *Arabidopsis thaliana* (L.) Heynh. *Naturwiss.* **42**, 650.

[40] Napp-Zinn, K. (1956). Zur Frage nach der Übertragbarkeit des durch die Vernalisation bewirkten Blühimpulses. *Ber. dtsch. bot. Ges.* **69**, 193.

[41] Napp-Zinn, K. (1957). Die Abhängigkeit des Vernalisationseffektes bei *Arabidopsis thaliana* vom Quellungsgrad der Samen und vom Lichtgenuss der Pflanzen nach der Kältebehandlung. *Flora* **144**, 403.

[42] Napp-Zinn, K. (1957). Untersuchungen zur Genetik des Kältebedürfnisses bei *Arabidopsis thaliana*. *Z. indukt. Abstamm. – u. Vererbungslehre* **88**, 253.

[43] Napp-Zinn, K. (1957). Physiologische Analyse des Vernalisationsvorganges. *Z. Botanik* **45**, 320.

[44] Napp-Zinn, K. (1957). Die Abhängigkeit des Vernalisationseffektes bei *Arabidopsis thaliana* von der Dauer der Vorquellung der Samen sowie vom Alter der Pflanzen bei Beginn der Vernalisation. *Z. Botanik* **45**, 379.

[45] Napp-Zinn, K. (1957). Untersuchungen über den Aufbau der Infloreszenz bei *Arabidopsis thaliana*. *Beitr. Biol. Pflanzen* **34**, 113.

[46] Napp-Zinn, K. (1957). Untersuchungen über das Vernalisationsverhalten einer winterannuellen Rasse von *Arabidopsis thaliana*. *Planta* **50**, 177.

[47] Napp-Zinn, K. (1960). Vernalisation, Licht und Alter bei *Arabidopsis thaliana* (L.) Heynh. I. Licht und Dunkelheit während Kälte- und Wärmebehandlung. *Planta* **54**, 409.

[48] Napp-Zinn, K. (1960). Vernalisation, Licht und Alter bei *Arabidopsis thaliana* (L.) Heynh. II. Die Rolle der vor und nach der Kältebehandlung herrschenden Lichtintensität. *Planta* **54**, 445.

[49] Napp-Zinn, K. (1961). Über die Bedeutung genetischer Untersuchungen an kältebedürftigen Pflanzen für die Aufklärung von Vernalisationserscheinungen. *Züchter* **31**, 128.

[50] Napp-Zinn, K. (1962). Über die genetischen Grundlagen des Vernalisationsbedürfnisses bei *Arabidopsis thaliana*. I. Die Zahl der beteiligten Faktoren. *Z. Vererbungslehre* **93**, 154.

[51] Napp-Zinn, K. (1962). Künstlich induziertes Vernalisationsbedürfnis bei sommerannuellen Pflanzen. *Naturwiss.* **49**, 473.

[52] Napp-Zinn, K. (1963). Zur Genetik der Wuchsformen. *Beitr. Biol. Pflanzen* **38**, 161.

[53] Napp-Zinn, K. (1963). Über den Einfluss von Genen und Gibberellinen auf die Blütenbildung von *Arabidopsis thaliana*. *Ber. dtsch. bot. Ges.* **76**, 77.

[54] Napp-Zinn, K. (1963). Über die Beziehungen zwischen Vernalisation, Keimung und Atmung. Untersuchungen an *Arabidopsis thaliana* (L.) Heynh. *Z. Botanik* **51**, 317.

[55] Napp-Zinn, K. (1964). Über genetische und entwicklungsphysiologische Grundlagen jahreszeitlicher Aspekte von Pflanzengesellschaften. In *Beiträge zur Phytologie*, 33. Festschrift für H. Walter, ed. K. Kreeb. Ulmer, Stuttgart.

[56] Napp-Zinn, K. (1965). Theory of vernalization – new experiments with *Arabidopsis*. In *Arabidopsis Research*, 56. Symposium Göttingen, 1965. Arabidopsis Information Service, Göttingen.

[57] Napp-Zinn, K. (1965). Physiologische Aspekte der Blütenbildung. *Scientia* **100**, 135.

[58] Napp-Zinn, K. (1966). Der Einfluss von Gibberellinen auf die Apikaldominanz bei *Arabidopsis thaliana*. *Arabidopsis Inf. Serv.* **3**, 12.

[59] Napp-Zinn, K. (1966). Antimetabolites in vernalisation. In *Differentiation of Apical Meristems and Some Problems of Ecological Regulation of Development of Plants*, 99. Proc. Symposium Praha – Nitra, 1964. Academia, Praha.

[60] Napp-Zinn, K. (1967). Zur Physiologie der Verzweigung krautiger Pflanzen. *Ber. dtsch. bot. Ges.* **80**, 218.

[61] Purvis, O. N. and Gregory, F. G. (1952). Studies in verr .sation. XII. The reversibility by high temperature of the vernalised condi⁺ .n in Petkus winter rye. *Ann. Bot., N.S.*, **16**, 1.

[62] Purvis, O. N. and Gregory, F. G. (1953). Acceleratinᵣ effect of an extract of vernalised embryos of winter rye on flower initiation iⁱ. unvernalised embryos. *Nature* **171**, 687.

[63] Ratcliffe, D. (1961). Adaptation to habitat in a group of annual plants. *J. Ecol.* **49**, 187.

[64] Rédei, G. P. (1962). Supervital mutants of *Arabidopsis*. *Genetics* **47**, 443.

[65] Röbbelen, G. (1957). Untersuchungen an strahleninduzierten Blattfarbmutanten von *Arabidopsis thaliana* (L.) Heynh. *Z. indukt. Abstamm.– u. Vererbungslehre* **88**, 189.

[66] Sarkar, S. (1958). Versuche zur Physiologie der Vernalisation. *Biol. Zentralbl.* **77**, 1.

[67] Seyffert, W. (1960). Untersuchungen über die Vererbung quantitativer Charaktere an *Arabidopsis thaliana* (L.) Heynh. *Z. Pflanzenzüchtung* **42**, 356.

[68] Troll, W. (1964). *Die Infloreszenzen. Typologie und Stellung im Aufbau des Vegetationskörpers*. VEB Gustav Fischer Verlag, Jena.

[69] Vaughan, J. G. (1955). The morphology and growth of the vegetative and reproductive apices of *Arabidopsis thaliana* (L.) Heynh., *Capsella bursa-pastoris* (L.) Medic. and *Anagallis arvensis* L. *J. Linn. Soc. London, Bot.* **55**, 279.

[70] van der Veen, J. H. (1965). Genes for late flowering in *Arabidopsis thaliana*. In *Arabidopsis Research*, 62. Symposium Göttingen, 1965. Arabidopsis Information Service, Göttingen.

[71] Zenker, A. M. (1955). Jarowisationsuntersuchungen an sommerannuellen *Arabidopsis*-Rassen. *Beitr. Biol. Pflanzen* **32**, 135.

There is a Journal, *Arabidopsis Information Service*, exclusively devoted to *Arabidopsis* research, under the editorship of G. Röbbelen, Institut für Pflanzenbau und Pflanzenzüchtung, Universität Göttingen, D–34 Göttingen, Germany.

13
Sinapis alba L.

By Georges Bernier

1 History of Use

The high photo-sensitivity of the crucifer *Sinapis alba* L. was recognized by Julius Sachs,[37] who selected *Sinapis* seedlings for showing phototropic curvatures in response to unilateral illumination. Today *Sinapis* is one of the plants most widely used for studies on photomorphogenesis (see Mohr[33]). Aspects of flower induction in this long-day species have been studied by several workers. However its high sensitivity to daylength was not recognized until recently. April 4, 1961, turned out to be a crucial moment in the history of use of *Sinapis* in the field of photoperiodism. On that day, the failure of the automatic clock of room 3 of the Liège phytotron produced an unexpected lengthening of the photoperiod from 8 to 24 hours, and vegetative mustard plants which had grown in that room for 8 weeks were induced to initiate a terminal inflorescence. Plants of the same age growing in the next room in non-disturbed 8-hour days did not flower. Since then *Sinapis* has been used at Liège as a suitable material for the study of flowering.

2 Growing Techniques and Growth Habit

All the studies at Liège have been carried out in the phytotron. Unless stated otherwise, the growth conditions were : day and night temperature : 20°C; relative humidity : 80 per cent; illumination by means of fluorescent white light (Phytor C.R.H.Lg. tubes) furnishing an intensity of 22,000 to 28,000 ergs/cm^2/sec at the level of the top of the plants. The spectral composition of light from the Phytor tubes was given by Bouillenne and Fouarge.[10]

Under these light and temperature conditions, *Sinapis* is a strict long-day plant. The photoperiodic behaviour of the plant is however quite different in higher light intensity. Plants raised in the same growth conditions as above except that light intensity was about 35,000 ergs/cm^2/sec during the whole daily light period were induced to flower in 8 and even in 7-hour short days.[11] *Sinapis* then behaves as a quantitative long-day plant.

That conditions other than daylength can influence the photoperiodic response of *Sinapis* probably explains why this plant was considered as an absolute long-day plant by some workers,[20] and as a quantitative long-day plant by others.[14,23,47]

The plants grown from seeds (supplied by Vilmorin-Andrieux, Paris) were selected for uniformity of size and singled out into 7-cm pots when 9 days old. The soil used was a sterilized mixture of 3 parts of leaf mould and 1 part of clay.

In the growth conditions of the phytotron, *Sinapis* is a monopodial caulescent plant both in long days and in short days (Fig. 13–1). As a result of a full flower induction, the plants become branched.

3 Inflorescence Structure and Criteria of Flowering Response

When using the one long day inductive treatment, the plants are returned to short days of 8 hours for 2 to 3 weeks before examination. The terminal buds are then dissected under the binocular microscope and classified as vegetative or as reproductive. At that time, reproductive buds have already produced 10 to 20 well developed flower buds. The terminal buds classified as vegetative after dissection were shown in a preliminary histological study to have a vegetative structure. The one long day inductive treatment has the great advantage that only the terminal bud of the shoot is induced, the axillary buds remaining in a vegetative condition. The inflorescence produced after induction by a single long day is quite short and the flowers, although complete, fail to open. However, induction in continuous long-day conditions results in the production of an elongated racemose inflorescence.

FIGURE 13–1. *Sinapis alba,* grown in test tube from an excised shoot tip (courtesy of R. Deltour).

4 Effects of Plant Age

Flowering is obtained when plants of ages from 3 to 90 days are exposed to long days.[3] This result indicates that there is no period of growth in which *Sinapis* is devoid of the ability to flower. However the minimum number of long-day cycles required for flower induction progressively decreases with aging of the plants in 8-hour days[2] (Table 13–1). An optimal sensitivity is reached by 3-month old plants which can be induced to flower by a single 16-hour day.

Ontogenetic changes in the apical meristem of the shoot parallel this progressive change in the ability of the plants to flower in response to a minimum number of long days.[1,3]

The young vegetative meristem of an 11-day old seedling raised in short days exhibits a typical cytohistological zonation (Fig. 13–2a). A centrally located zone is surrounded by an approximately ring-shaped zone (the peripheral zone). A third zone (the pith-rib meristem) lies below the central zone and includes ranks of flattened cells which function as a rib-meristem giving rise to the pith of the

TABLE 13–1

Effect of aging on the minimum number of long days (16 hr) required for flower induction. The plants were raised in 8-hour days before and after exposure to long days (after Bernier[2]).

Age (days) at the time of exposure to long days	Per cent of induced plants after . . . LD						
	1	2	3	4	5	6	7
15	0	10	15	30	50	75	90
30	50	100					
65	75	100					
90	100						

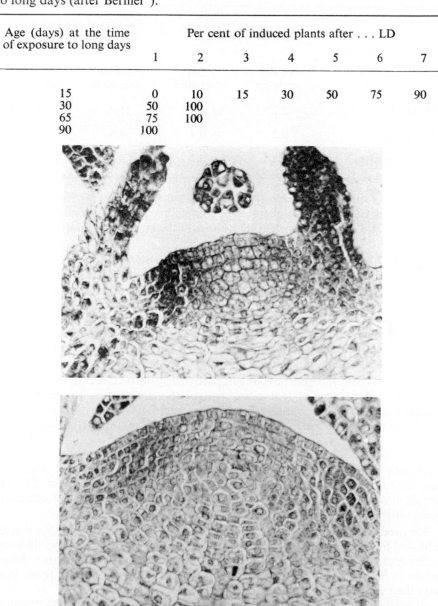

FIGURE 13–2. Vegetative meristems of plants raised in short days, stained with methyl green-pyronin (X 400). (a) top, plant 11 days old (b) bottom, plant 2 months old (Bernier[1]).

stem. DNA multiplication and mitotic index are much greater in the peripheral zone than in the central zone and the pith-rib meristem (Table 13–2). A distinct

TABLE 13–2

Effect of aging on the mitotic index and on DNA multiplication in the vegetative meristem. The meristems were collected at the end of the daily light period. Tritiated thymidine was applied during 4 hours.

Meristematic zone	Per cent of mitoses		Per cent of labelled nuclei after application of H^3 – thymidine	
	Young meristem	Old meristem	Young meristem	Old meristem
Peripheral	1.2	0.8	15.2	12.5
Central	0.2	0.4	3.8	5.0
Pith-rib meristem ..	0.5	0.3	4.5	6.5

zonation is easily recognizable when using histochemical stains for RNA and total protein. Cells of the peripheral zone contain markedly higher concentrations of RNA (Fig. 13–2a) and protein than those of the central zone and the pith-rib meristem.

In older plants, say 2-month old plants, the meristem enlarges in width and height. The number of cells is greater in all zones, particularly in the central zone and in the pith-rib meristem. The zonation, while still evident, is less marked than previously (Fig. 13–2b). This situation can be explained by a slight increase in the activity of the central zone and by a simultaneous slight decrease in the activity of the peripheral zone (Table 13–2). As a result of repeated cell divisions (essentially in the periclinal direction) the upper part of the central zone (just below the tunica) takes a more stratified configuration.

As most of these ontogenetic changes, particularly the stimulation of the central zone, are similar to some extent to the changes occurring during flower induction (see section 22), it looks as if some preparatory steps of the flowering process are already in progress in the meristem of plants grown in non-inductive conditions.

5 Vernalization and Devernalization

According to Sen and Chakravarti[40] and David,[16] the flowering of Sinapis in field conditions is promoted by a pre-sowing low temperature treatment. This observation was not confirmed however by Sen Gupta and Sen,[44] the discrepancy being attributed by Sen and Chakravarti[42] to varietal differences.

The promotive effect of seed vernalization in the strain we use at Liège was established by Bernier and Kinet.[8] In 16-hour days, the vernalized plants flowered earlier and produced fewer leaves before flowering than control plants. When grown in 8-hour days, the vernalized plants were shown to require fewer long days than controls to be induced to flower (Table 13–3).

As mustard is a crop of importance in India, a detailed study of some practical aspects of vernalization in this species was carried out by Indian workers.[40–43] They showed that sprouted seeds responded better than nonsprouted seeds to the same chilling treatment. Nonsprouted vernalized seeds are however far more interesting for practical purposes since they can be dried and stored at room temperature for at least 6 years without any resultant devernalization and without any loss of germinating capacity. Likewise no devernalization takes place when resoaked stored seeds or fresh vernalized nonsprouted seeds are subjected to 35°C for 48 hours.

In the varieties examined, vernalization is never absolutely required for flowering.

TABLE 13–3

Effect of seed vernalization on flower induction. The seeds were given 4 weeks at 2°C; afterwards the plants were given 2 weeks of 8-hour days at 20°C and then transferred to 16-hour days. The low per cent of induced plants is attributable to the low light intensity (18,000 ergs/cm^2/sec) given to the plants during their whole life.

Number of long days given to the plants	Per cent of induced plants	
	Control	Vernalized
4	0	44
6	12	83

7 Photoperiod Response

Under the particular growth conditions described in section 2, *Sinapis* is an absolute long-day plant with a critical day-length just below 10 hours.[3] When grown in continuous light or in long days (16-hour days) from sowing, the plants began to initiate flower buds during the second week of growth, macroscopic flower buds were visible before the end of the third week, and open flowers two weeks later. As the seedlings were without any foliage leaves at the time of flower induction and initiation, the cotyledons must have perceived the long days. Experiments by Zieriacks[52] showed that a single cotyledon or even less than a whole cotyledon is sufficient to perceive photoinduction in *Sinapis*.

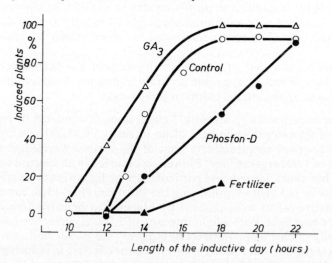

FIGURE 13–3. Flowering as a function of the length of the inductive day in control plants and plants treated with GA$_3$, phosfon-D and fertilizer. Description of the treatments in the text.

With plants grown in 10-hour days, flower buds were macroscopically visible only after three months, and the flowers usually failed to open. Plants kept in 8-hour days from sowing showed no sign of flowering during the first 6 months of growth.

With plants grown in 8-hour days under a light intensity of about 35,000 ergs/cm^2/sec, flower buds were visible after 3 months of growth and open flowers one month later.[11] This inductive effect of high light intensity suggests the participation of either photosynthesis or the high energy reaction of photomorphogenesis in the flowering process in mustard plants.

With 65-day old plants raised in short days and subjected to a single long day of increasing length, flower induction did not occur in photoperiods less than 13 hours. The longer the photoperiod the more complete was flower induction, with maximal response at 18 hours[5] (Fig. 13–3).

Holding plants in darkness for 1, 2 or 3 days before the inductive long day did not affect flower induction.[8] Likewise, keeping them in darkness for the second and the third days after the long day was without effect on induction. Darkness for the first day after the long day however greatly reduced the flowering response. Complete induction in *Sinapis* thus requires a period in light following the long day. A preliminary experiment showed that it was not possible to obviate the need for that second light period by a single hour of fluorescent white light.

The induction of flowering in *Sinapis* by means of night-breaks was recently investigated by Hanke.[27] The plants were cultivated in conditions very similar to those used at Liège. With 28-day old plants raised in 8-hour days of fluorescent white light, a long-day effect could be obtained by interrupting the long dark period with 2 hours of blue light. A nearly complete flower induction could be achieved when this treatment was repeated for six consecutive days. The night-breaks were most effective when given near the middle of the night.

8 Spectral Dependence

The spectral dependence of flowering in *Sinapis* – and in most Cruciferae – is uncommon, as first shown by the pioneer work of Funke[24] at the University of Ghent, Belgium. Using supplementary filtered radiation from incandescent lamps or from daylight, in addition to an 8-hour day in sunlight, he showed that mustard plants flowered with additional blue light as rapidly as they did with additional white light. The plants responded far more slowly to additional red light.

The peculiar behaviour of *Sinapis* in this respect has been investigated by several workers recently, using more accurate techniques. Light of different spectral regions was applied to the plants in three ways:

(*a*) In the experiments of Stolwijk[47] the treatment consisted of repeated 10-hour days of fluorescent white light at an intensity of 35,000 ergs/cm^2/sec, followed by 8 hours of supplementary light of the various wavelength regions, at an intensity of 1,000 ergs/cm^2/sec. Flowering occurred in all spectral regions after some time, but violet, far-red, and particularly blue light were more effective than green, yellow or red light in prolonging the short day (Fig. 13–4, curve A).

(*b*) Vegetative plants were exposed by Meijer[32] to repeated 16-hour days of red, green or blue light. With a light intensity of 2,500 ergs/cm^2/sec flowering was obtained only in blue light. With 6,100 ergs/cm^2/sec flower buds were initiated in all spectral regions, but blue light was the most effective in inducing flowering.

It is worth noting that Meijer's observation on the different photoperiodic behaviour of plants in low and high light intensities agrees with the results of Bouillenne *et al.*[11] (see section 2).

(*c*) The spectral dependence of flower induction in *Sinapis* is being investigated using a 2-hour break in the middle of the dark period.[27] The action spectrum (Fig. 13–4, curve B) shows a marked peak in blue light, a small response in red light and no response at all in green and far-red light. This action spectrum for the night break effect approximately matches the absorption spectrum for protochlorophyll,[31] a compound which is known to accumulate in the leaves during darkness.

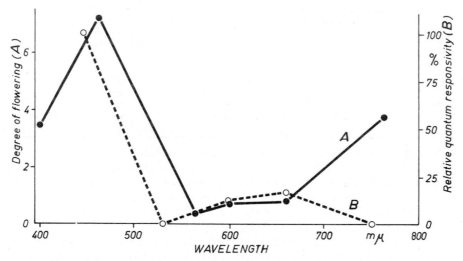

FIGURE 13–4. Action spectra for the induction of flowering using supplementary light (curve A, from the data of Stolwijk[47]) or night-breaks (curve B, from unpublished data of J. Hanke[27]) in addition to short days.

The participation of a single known photochemical reaction system in the flowering process of *Sinapis* is not easily deduced from the two action spectra of Fig. 13–4. The great effectiveness of blue light, in both cases, rules out the sole participation of the phytochrome system. The red action, in both curves, and the ineffectiveness of far-red light in curve B are hardly consistent with the sole mediation by a blue and far-red absorbing photoreceptor such as that postulated for the high-energy reaction of photomorphogenesis. Red action also excludes participation of the photoreactive system of phototropism. That flower induction would be exclusively mediated by the photosynthetic pigment system also seems unlikely. Gabrielsen[25] determined the rate/intensity curves for photosynthesis in different spectral regions in *Sinapis* and found that the maximum rate of photosynthesis was reached at different light intensities in the various wavelength regions. In opposition to what is found in flower induction, red-orange light was more effective than yellow-green and blue-violet light; the saturating light intensity (in Kerg/cm^2/sec) was 116 for red-orange, 174 for yellow-green, and 255 for blue-violet light.

In summary more than one photo-reaction appears to be involved in the long-day effect.

10 Fractional Induction

With plants raised in long days from sowing, additional long days after the 7th increased the proportion of plants flowering[3] (Table 13–4). However with alternation of single short and long days after the 7th long day about half of the plants were induced in all batches whatever the total number of long days.

TABLE 13-4

Effect of interposed short days on flower induction. Plants were grown for 7 days from sowing in long days and then submitted either to consecutive long days or to alternate short and long days. They were then returned to short days.

Number of long days given to the plants in addition to the first 7	Per cent of induced plants when receiving	
	Consecutive long days	Alternating short and long days
1	8	40
3	31	40
5	39	55
7	64	50

Reversion from the floral to the vegetative condition was observed in the terminal bud of about 10 per cent of plants receiving a sequence of alternate short days and long days. Some of these plants initiated a few flower buds and then reverted definitely to the vegetative condition. Other plants also flowered, then produced a few leaves, and finally resumed an irreversible floral functioning. The reversion was generally accompanied by serious disturbances of the phyllotaxis. The structure and functioning of the meristem were altered at the moment of reversion. The meristem had neither a typical vegetative organization nor a typical reproductive one. It exhibited an unusual configuration with a mixture of vegetative and reproductive characters. A detailed morphological and histological study of reversions in *Sinapis* was published by Bernier and Dath.[6]

These results show that fractional induction is possible in *Sinapis*.

As a minimum induction never induces morphogenetic reversions,[3] the disturbed functioning of some meristems is attributed to the repeated interruptions of the induction process.

11 Photoperiodic Inhibition

Interactions between induced and non-induced leaves were investigated by Chailahjan[14,15] using mustard plants on which all the leaves except two were removed. One leaf was kept continuously in short days while the other received repeated long days. It was found that the short-day leaf exerted an inhibitory effect on flower initiation only if it was situated between the long-day leaf and the terminal bud. This inhibitory effect was completely overcome by splitting off the short-day leaf by a longitudinal incision of the stem extending below the insertion of the long-day leaf.

It was concluded that the interactions between induced and non-induced leaves depended on their respective distances from the receiving bud rather than on their mutual disposition along the stem. These experiments were not sufficiently detailed, however, to propose an interpretation on the nature of the short-day inhibition in *Sinapis*.

13 Effects of Temperature

Using mustard plants raised in the phytotron and induced to flower by a single 14-hour day, Bernier *et al.*[5,8] showed that interruptions by low temperature (2 to 6°C) severely inhibited flower induction when applied during the first 29 hours after the start of the long day. The whole inductive process appears to be temperature-sensitive, different parts of it differing in their temperature-sensitivity. Flowering was inhibited most when the low temperature interruption occurred at the beginning or at the end of the long day and was less inhibited when the day was interrupted near the middle. Such an inhibition pattern is consonant with the assumption that hours of daylight at low temperature have an effect approaching that of hours of darkness. During the 10-hour short night, the inhibition was more pronounced when low temperatures were applied during the second half than during the first half.

14 Effects of Mineral Nutrition

Although mineral deficiencies do not alter the photoperiodic response of Sinapis, they do interfere with the rate of the flowering process in long days. Confirming previous observations by Chailahjan,[13] El Hinnawy[20] showed that the time of flower bud appearance was accelerated by low levels or by lack of nitrogen. High levels of nitrogen retarded and reduced considerably the flowering of mustard.

With our strain, we observed[8] a similar behaviour towards nitrogen. Weekly applications of NPK fertilizer greatly decreased the sensitivity of the plants to an inductive long day (Fig. 13–3), although vegetative growth was increased. Nitrogen was probably the active element of the fertilizer since applications of ammonium nitrate had the same effect.

It could be that nitrogen supply interferes with the perception of the photoperiodic stimulus by leaves or with the synthesis of the floral stimulus. The promotive influence of a lack of nitrogen remains a puzzling fact for it is known that flower initiation at the meristem sets in motion a great mitotic activity (see section 22) which in turn requires active protein synthesis. How this synthesis could occur in the absence of nitrogen remains unexplained.

El Hinnawy[20] also established that other mineral deficiencies affected the initiation and development of flower buds. The macroscopic appearance of flower buds was particularly retarded by magnesium deficiency.

15 Effects of Gas Composition

Fredericq[23] reported that removal of CO_2 from the atmosphere during the last 8 hours of repeated 16-hour days did not affect flower initiation in Sinapis. Likewise CO_2 was not required during the short dark periods of the long days. Attempts to keep the plants in a CO_2-free atmosphere throughout the light period caused death of the plants. Such results do not exclude possible participation of photosynthesis in flower induction. Such a participation is strongly suggested by the results of Deltour[19] (section 21).

16 Translocation of the Floral Stimulus

Attempts to study the translocation of the floral stimulus by means of defoliation experiments have always failed.[8] Flower initiation was suppressed when mustard plants, induced by a single 20-hour day, were defoliated at various times up to the 28th hour after the beginning of the long day. At the 28th hour however, pronounced changes were already visible within the meristem (section 22). The behaviour of Sinapis towards defoliation is difficult to explain for the present but is possibly connected with the need for a light period following the long day in order to achieve complete flower induction (section 7).

Plants defoliated at various times after the 28th hour flowered, a complete flower induction being reached when defoliation took place around the 56th hour after the start of the long day.

It is thus impossible to estimate the velocity of movement of the floral stimulus by means of such defoliation experiments. Yet the kinetic study of inhibition of flowering by 2-thiouracil (section 19) suggests that a sufficien amount of floral stimulus reaches the meristematic tissues around the 16th hour after the start of the long day. This result hardly seems consistent with a low rate of translocation for the floral stimulus in *Sinapis*.

18 Effects of Growth Substances and Growth Retardants

As expected in the case of a caulescent long-day plant, GA_3 has only a slight influence on flower initiation and stem elongation in *Sinapis*. Single applications of 20 µg of GA_3 per plant did not affect the vegetative condition of 65-day old plants kept in 8-hour days.[8] Repeated applications during several months, giving a total dose of 180 µg GA_3 per plant, led to the initiation of flower buds in about half of the plants after 200 short days (El Tannir-Lomba *et al.*[21]).

Single applications of 20 µg of GA_3 slightly increased the effectiveness of an inductive long day (Fig. 13–3) when applied just at the beginning of that day.[8] The critical daylength, which is normally 12 hours, was reduced by more than 2 hours.

The response of *Sinapis* to phosfon-D is also slight.[8] As shown in Figure 13–3, vegetative 65-day old plants grown continuously in a soil containing 5 per cent (dry weight basis) of phosfon-D could be induced by a single long day, the long day being somewhat less effective than in control plants. Stem growth, however, was greatly reduced by the retardant.

On the whole, GA_3 does not appear as an important regulator of flowering in mustard.

19 Effects of Metabolic Inhibitors

The influence of 2-thiouracil (2-TU) on the induction of flowering in plants exposed to a single long day was investigated by Kinet and Bernier.[29] Single applications of the inhibitor (7×10^{-3} M, 0.2 ml per plant) were made to the terminal bud of plants at various times during and after the inductive long day. Four hours after each application of 2-TU, orotic acid (saturated solution) was applied as an antidote. Preliminary experiments showed that the inhibitory effect of 2-TU was overcome by a simultaneous application of orotic acid but not by a simultaneous application of thymidine (1.4×10^{-2} M). As shown in Figure 13–5, 2-TU was most inhibitory to flower induction when applied from the 12th hour to the 20th hour after the beginning of the long day. It was not inhibitory after the 28th hour. When applied during the first 12 hours of the long day, 2-TU exerted an inhibitory effect which could be attributed to the synthesis of fraudulent nucleic acid molecules which persist in the tissues and perturb the reactions occurring from the 12th to the 20th hour.

If it is assumed that 2-TU acts within the meristem, like similar compounds,[9,22] it appears that synthesis of a nucleic acid, probably RNA, essential to induction occurs from the 12th to the 20th hour of the long day in the meristematic cells. This event will be discussed in section 22 in relation to other processes occurring in the meristem as a result of photoinduction.

21 Induction of Excised Apices

Excised shoot tips of mustard have been successfully grown *in vitro* by Deltour.[18] Shoot tips 1.5 mm-long were isolated aseptically from soaked seeds, and grown in test tubes on Ball's medium (modified[18]). The cultures were made in the phytotron under the conditions described in section 2. At the time of explantation, a shoot tip consisted of the shoot meristem, two leaf primordia and the upper

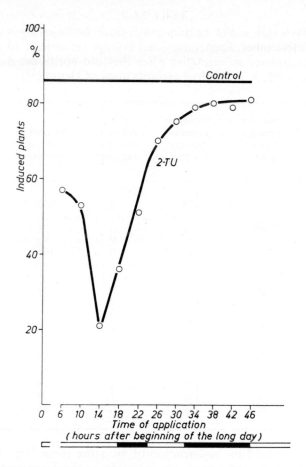

FIGURE 13–5. Inhibition of flowering in plants exposed to a single 18-hour day as a function of time of application of 2-thiouracil (7×10^{-3} M, 0.2 ml on terminal bud). (Kinet and Bernier[29]).

part of the hypocotyl. When composition of the medium permitted growth of the explant, an entire plant with numerous leaves and roots was finally regenerated.

The influence of daylength and of medium composition on flower initiation was investigated (Table 13–5). This study is still in progress but it has already been demonstrated[19] that:

the flowering response was promoted by long days;

4 per cent sucrose gave the highest per cent of induced explants in short days;

a low nitrogen supply promoted floral induction in short days but did not affect greatly the flowering response in long days;

low concentrations of GA_3 reduced the per cent of flowering explants in short days;

kinetin (from 0.1 to 10 mg/liter) induced morphogenetic abnormalities and caused rapid death of the explants in short days.

As expected from the results with high light intensities (outlined in sections 2 and 8), the presence of sucrose in the medium meant that some flowering plants were observed in all batches grown in short days, provided that the medium

TABLE 13-5

Effects of daylength and of medium composition on flowering of excised shoot tips grown in test tubes. Each value is an average on at least 10 explants. Explants were considered as vegetative when they did not flower during the first 5 months of growth. X = death of explants (data of Deltour[19]).

Daylength	Sucrose concen- tration g/liter	Nitrogen concen- tration mg/liter	GA$_3$ concen- tration mg/liter	Per cent of flowering explants	Days to macroscopic appearance of flower buds
16 hours ..	20	175	0	100	62
	40	0	0	X	X
	40	32	0	92	54
	40	175	0	100	53
8 hours ..	0	175	0	X	X
	20	175	0	35	116
	40	175	0	62	105
	60	175	0	45	102
	80	175	0	10	120
	40	0	0	X	X
	40	32	0	90	117
	40	175	1	13	88
	40	175	5	33	73
	40	175	10	43	101

composition permitted the regeneration of an entire plant. This fact, together with the great influence of sucrose concentration on the flowering response, suggests again the participation of photosynthesis in the flowering process in *Sinapis*.

22 Histochemical Changes at Induction

The histological and histochemical changes occurring in the apical meristem as a result of flower induction were studied using vegetative 65-day old plants induced by exposure to a single 20-hour day.[7,30] Instead of studying the meristem as a whole it was found more interesting to consider separately the changes occurring in each meristematic zone (the zones were described in section 4).

Mitotic activity

From the comparison of meristems of induced and control plants (Fig. 13-6), it appeared that there is a rise in the mitotic index within the peripheral zone in induced plants as early as 18 hours after the start of the long day. A first peak in mitotic activity was reached at the 26–30th hour. The mitotic index rose again after the 46th hour, reached a second maximum at the 62nd hour, and then declined.

Similar but more marked changes were recorded within the central zone, the major difference being that the two rises of the mitotic index began a few hours later in the central zone. The initiation of flower buds occurred at the same time as the second mitotic wave (section 23).

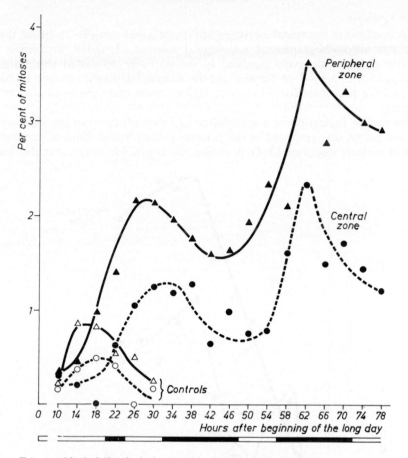

FIGURE 13–6. Mitotic index in the central and peripheral zones of the apical meristem at various times after the start of the 20-hour day.

Within the pith-rib meristem (Fig. 13–7) the mitotic index was usually very low in both control and induced plants. However, there was a sharp increase, in induced plants, between the 22nd and the 30th hour after the beginning of the long day.

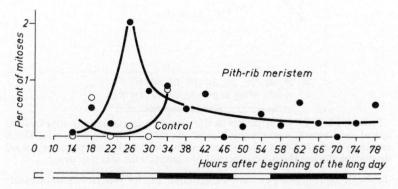

FIGURE 13–7. Mitotic index in the pith-rib meristem at various times after the start of the 20-hour day.

DNA synthesis

DNA synthesis in the apical meristem was investigated using H-[3] labelled thymidine and autoradiography of histological sections. Tritiated thymidine was directly and quantitatively supplied to the partially defoliated shoot tip according to the method of Bernier and Bronchart.[4] Different groups of plants received the precursor for 4 hours at various times after the beginning of the long day.

The earliest indication of a stimulation of DNA synthesis in the meristem of induced plants was recorded in the peripheral zone at the 22nd hour after the start of the long day (Fig. 13–8). A similar rise began 4 hours later in the central

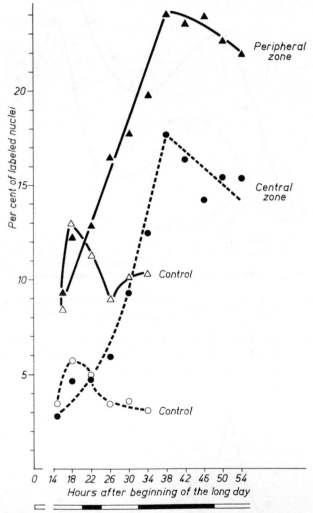

FIGURE 13–8. DNA synthesis in the central and peripheral zones of the apical meristem at various times after the start of the 20-hour day. DNA synthesis is expressed as the per cent of nuclei which incorporate tritiated thymidine during the 4-hour period of contact with this precursor.

zone. In both zones, the per cent of labelled nuclei reached a maximum value at the 38th hour and then slowly dropped. Relative to the values recorded in control plants the stimulation was obviously much more marked in the central zone than in the peripheral zone.

Within the pith-rib meristem (Fig. 13–9), the per cent of labelled nuclei was identical in control and in induced plants during the first 38 hours after the beginning of the long day. Afterwards, DNA multiplication in induced plants seemed to decrease slightly below the level found in control plants.

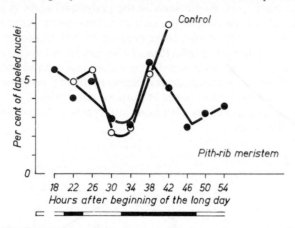

FIGURE 13–9. DNA synthesis in the pith-rib meristem at various times after the start of the 20-hour day. DNA synthesis is expressed as the per cent of nuclei which incorporate tritiated thymidine during the 4-hour period of contact with this precursor.

Cell growth

Rough estimates of cell cross-sectional area were carried out in induced and control meristems (Fig. 13–10). Owing to the large number of cells entering division

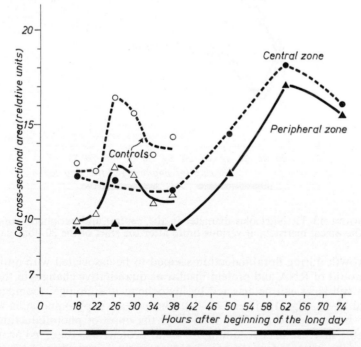

FIGURE 13–10. Cell cross-sectional area in the central and peripheral zones of the apical meristem at various times after the start of the 20-hour day.

from the 22nd to the 34th hour after the start of the long day in the peripheral and the central zones of induced meristems (Fig. 13–6), the mean cell cross-sectional area was smaller at that moment in induced meristems than in control ones. A great increase of cell cross-sectional area was observed after the 38th hour in induced meristems, particularly in the peripheral zone. A maximum cell size was reached about the time of the second mitotic peak. As the meristematic cells are more or less isodiametric, these changes in cell cross-sectional area can be considered as a rather good reflection of changes in cell volume.

The relative size of nucleoli is usually considered as a good indication of the rate of growth of tissues. A tremendous increase in nucleolus diameter was found in the peripheral and the central zones of induced meristems (Fig. 13–11). Nucleolus size began to increase at the 34th hour and reached a maximum value from the 46th to the 58th hour.

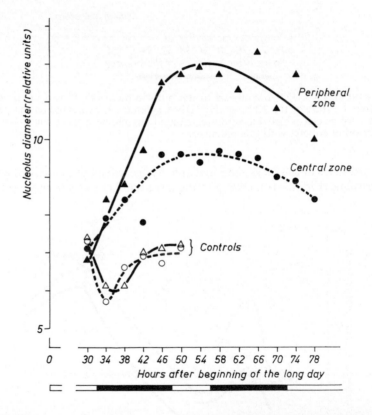

FIGURE 13–11. Nucleolus diameter in the central and peripheral zones of the apical meristem at various times after the start of the 20-hour day.

Cell growth during floral induction seemed to be associated with an increase in the amount of RNA and protein insofar as quantitative changes in their content on a cell basis can be detected by histochemical staining[26] (compare Figs. 13–2b and 13–12, Figs. 13–13 and 13–14). The increase in pyroninophilia was estimated to begin around the 32nd hour after the onset of photoinduction, while a detectable increase in the staining for total protein was observed around the 36th hour. An increased staining for RNA and protein was observed in both the nucleolus and the cytoplasm. A maximum staining was found around the 50th hour. As a matter of fact both RNA and total protein content increased more in the central cells than in the cells on the flanks so that the zonation partially faded away for a while (Figs. 13–12, 13–14). With the initiation of the first flower buds, heterogeneity in the meristem reappeared, owing to a drop in the RNA and protein content of the central cells (Fig. 13–15).

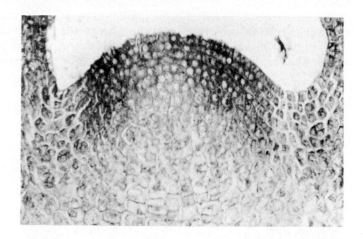

FIGURE 13–12. Meristem of a 2-month old plant subjected to a single long day. The meristem was collected 34 hours after the start of the long day, and stained with methyl green-pyronin. × 400 (Bernier[3]).

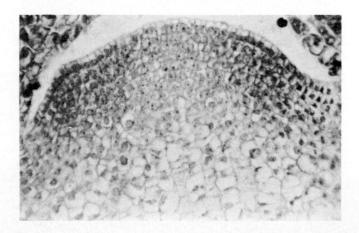

FIGURE 13–13. Vegetative meristem of a 2-month old plant raised in short days, stained with mercuric bromphenol blue for total protein. × 400.

Cell enlargement was also observed in the pith-rib meristem of induced meristems. In this case, the cells elongated in the direction of the plant axis and vacuolated (Fig. 13–15). Measurements (Fig.13–16) indicated that cell length was initially smaller in the pith-rib meristem of induced meristems than in the corresponding zone of control meristems, owing to the large number of cells entering a transverse division from the 22nd to the 30th hour in this zone of induced meristems (Fig. 13–7). Elongation began after the 34th hour. The pith-rib meristem rapidly lost its meristematic aspect and was transformed into a core of parenchymatous cells.

Interpretation of the results: the life history of meristematic cells during flower induction

The successive events which have been recognized in the meristem during the transition from the vegetative to the reproductive condition are shown diagrammatically in Fig. 13–17.

The first event we were able to detect is the inhibition by 2-TU of an essential process for flower induction occurring from the 12th to the 20th hour of the long day. The inhibited process is presumably a synthesis of new and specific RNA molecules. The reality of such molecules remains to be demonstrated, al-

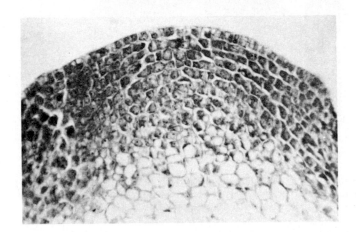

FIGURE 13–14. Meristem of a 2-month old plant subjected to a single long day. The meristem was collected 42 hours after the start of the long day, and stained with mercuric bromphenol blue for total protein. × 400.

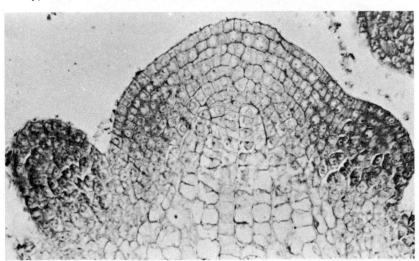

FIGURE 13–15. Reproductive meristem collected 78 hours after the start of the long day, and stained with methyl green-pyronin. The flanks of the meristem are producing flower buds. × 400.

though one may reasonably expect that one of the first effects of the floral stimulus when reaching the meristem is to initiate the synthesis of a specific floral RNA.[38,39]

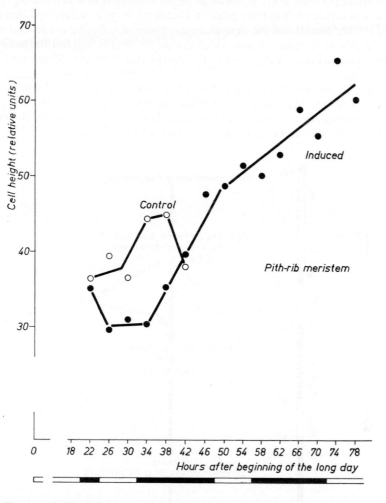

FIGURE 13–16. Cell height in the pith-rib meristem at various times after the start of the 20-hour day.

The next detectable event is the first rise of the mitotic activity occurring from the 26th to the 38th hour (Fig. 13–6). The comparison of the kinetic data concerning the mitotic index and those concerning DNA multiplication (Fig. 13–8) shows that a large number of meristematic cells enter mitosis before having synthesized DNA since the beginning of the long day. As it is generally considered that DNA replication is an essential prerequisite for cell division, the results point to the occurrence of a large population of cells, in the 65-day old vegetative meristem, that are in the G_2 phase of the mitotic cycle, between the end of DNA replication and prophase. One of the earliest results of flower induction within the meristem is thus the release of nuclei from the G_2 phase.

That cells can remain in G_2 for long periods and enter mitosis only in response to an appropriate stimulus is already known for other biological systems.[12,17,35,46] It may be suggested that short days considerably increase the length of G_2 in the meristematic cells. Anyway the block is never complete since a small number of cell divisions is always seen in the sections of apices from control plants kept in short days (Fig. 13–6).

An estimate of cells in G_2 at the onset of photoinduction was made by measuring the area under each mitotic peak of Figure 13–6. If it is assumed that all the cells of the peripheral and the central zones divide once during the second mitotic peak, then the proportion of cells which divide during the first mitotic peak (these are the cells in G_2) is 58 per cent in the peripheral zone and 52 per cent in the central zone.

The stimulation of the mitotic index at the 26th hour in the pith-rib meristem is a very interesting fact, since it shows that the release of cells from the G_2 phase is a very general effect of the floral stimulus. It is worth while to recall here that several growth regulators were also shown to act on cells in G_2.[12,36,51]

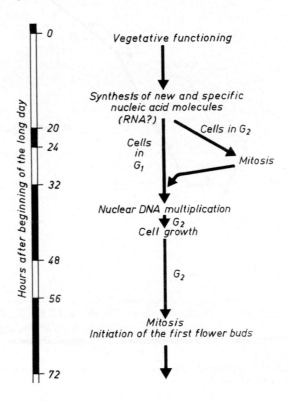

FIGURE 13–17. Tentative interpretation of the sequence of events in the meristem of *Sinapis* during the transition from the vegetative to the reproductive condition.

The third detectable event during flower induction at the meristem is the stimulation of nuclear DNA multiplication. Shortly after the peak of DNA synthesis, at the 38th hour, the regular production of leaves by the meristem stops (42nd–46th hour).

During the G_2 phase following the peak of DNA synthesis, an increase of cell size was observed as well as an increase of nucleolus diameter and of the amount of RNA and protein per cell. All these processes are probably closely related since it is well known that RNA and protein synthesis are essential for effective cell enlargement,[28,34] and that the nucleolus is the main site of nuclear protein synthesis. That all these changes occur in G_2 is not surprising since G_2 in plant cells has been shown to be a period of especially active RNA and protein synthesis.[45,48,49,50]

The last event is the second mitotic peak. The cells entering mitosis now are probably the cells which duplicated DNA during the peak of DNA synthesis. Since the histological study (section 23) reveals that flower bud initiation begins at the same time as the second mitotic wave, both nuclear DNA multiplication and the second mitotic rise appear as premises for the production of flowers. Both processes are thus related to flower initiation while the previous events – the synthesis of a specific nucleic acid and the first mitotic rise – appear to be related to flower induction at the meristem.

23 Inflorescence Differentiation

An inflorescence meristem is finally produced as a result of the various histological and histochemical changes occurring within the first two days after the inductive long day. The inflorescence meristem is composed of a superficial meristematic mantle 6–8 cells deep covering a core of elongated parenchymatous cells (Fig. 13–15).

The initiation of the first flower buds starts around the 58th hour after the beginning of the long day. The flower buds arise by periclinal divisions in the third or fourth cellular layers of the flanks of the meristematic mantle (Fig. 13–15, left flank). Simultaneously a distinct cyto-histological zonation reappears within the meristem. In plants induced by repeated long days new flower buds are produced for months at a high rate. A minimum of three flower buds is produced each day. In plants induced by a single long day, the meristem stops working and aborts after the production of a few dozen flower buds.

REFERENCES

[1] Bernier, G. (1962). Evolution of the apical meristem of *Sinapis alba* L. (long-day plant) in long days, in short days and during the transfer from short days to long days. *Caryologia* **15**, 303.

[2] Bernier, G. (1963). *Sinapis alba* L., a new long-day plant requiring a single photoinductive cycle. *Naturwiss.* **50**, 101.

[3] Bernier, G. (1964). Etude histophysiologique et histochimique de l'évolution du méristème apical de *Sinapis alba.*, cultivé en milieu conditionné et en diverses durées de jour favorables ou défavorables à la mise à fleurs. *Mém. Acad. Roy. Belgique, Cl. Sci.*, 4°(2) **16**, 1.

[4] Bernier, G. and Bronchart, R. (1963). Application de la technique d'histoautoradiographie à l'étude de l'incorporation de thymidine tritiée dans les méristèmes caulinaires. *Bull. Soc. Roy. Sci. Liège* **32**, 269.

[5] Bernier, G. and Bronchart, R. (1964). The steps of floral induction in *Sinapis alba* L. *Naturwiss.* **51**, 469.

[6] Bernier, G. and Dath, M. T. (1962). A propos de quelques cas d'apparition de fleurs le long d'entrenoeuds végétatifs ou de feuilles le long de l'inflorescence chez *Sinapis alba* L. *Rev. Cyt. Biol. Vég.* **25**, 241.

[7] Bernier, G., Kinet, J. M. and Bronchart, R. (1968). Cellular events at the meristem during floral induction in *Sinapis alba* L. *Physiol. Veg.* (in press).

[8] Bernier, G. and Kinet, J. M. In preparation.

[9] Bonner, J. and Zeevaart, J. A. D. (1962). Ribonucleic acid synthesis in the bud an essential component of floral induction in *Xanthium. Plant Physiol.* **37**, 43.

[10] Bouillenne, R. and Fouarge, M. (1955). La lumière artificielle en horticulture. Les tubes 'Phytor' adaptés à la croissance des végétaux. *Proc. XIVth Intern. Horticul. Congress, Netherlands*, 1114.

[11] Bouillenne, R., Parmentier, A. and El Tannir-Lomba, J. Unpublished results.

[12] Broadbent, D. and Radley, M. E. (1966). Some effects of 1-amino-2-nitrocyclopentane-1-carboxylic acid on flowering plants. *Ann. Bot.* **30**, 763.

[13] Chailahjan, M. Ch. (1944). Nitrogenous food as a factor increasing the rate of flowering and fruiting in plants. *C.R. (Dokl.) Acad. Sci. URSS* **43**, 75.

[14] Chailahjan, M. Ch. (1946a). Photoperiodic response of plants when their individual leaves go on different daylengths. *C.R. (Dokl.) Acad. Sci. URSS* **54**, 735.

[15] Chailahjan, M. Ch. (1946b). Influence of leaves exposed to different daylength upon development of shoots. *C.R. (Dokl.) Acad. Sci. URSS* **54**, 837.

[16] David, R. (1946). *Facteurs de développement et printanisation des végétaux cultivés.* Hermann et Cie, Paris.

[17] Davidson, D. (1966). The onset of mitosis and DNA synthesis in roots of germinating beans. *Amer. J. Bot.* **53**, 491.

[18] Deltour, R. (1966). La culture in vitro du méristème caulinaire de *Sinapis alba* L. Action de la photopériode, de l'A.I.A. et de l'acide gibbérellique. *Les phytohormones et l'organogenèse, Congrès et Colloques Univ. Liège* **38**, 359.

[19] Deltour, R. In preparation.

[20] El Hinnawy, E. I. (1956). Some aspects of mineral nutrition and flowering. *Med. Landbouwhogesch. Wageningen* **56**, 1.

[21] El Tannir-Lomba, J., Parmentier, A. and Bouillenne, R. (1962). Action comparative de la gibbérelline et de l'A.I.A sur des plantes de jours longs et de jours courts cultivées en diverses photopériodes et en conditions constantes dans le phytotron de Liège. *Proc. XVIth Intern. Horticult. Congress, Brussels*, 641.

[22] Evans, L. T. (1964). Inflorescence initiation in *Lolium temulentum* L. VI. Effects of some inhibitors of nucleic acid, protein and steroid biosynthesis. *Aust. J. Biol. Sci.* **17**, 24.

[23] Fredericq, H. (1958). On the significance of carbon dioxide of the air for flower bud initiation. *Biol. Jaarb. 'Dodonaea' (Ghent)*, **26**, 53.

[24] Funke, G. L. (1937). Proeven over photoperiodiciteit bij verschillend gekleurd licht. *Biol. Jaarb. 'Dodonaea' (Ghent)* **4**, 345.

[25] Gabrielsen, E. K. (1940). Einfluss der Lichtfaktoren auf die Kohlensäurenassimilation der *Laubblätter. Dansk. Botanisk Arkiv.* **10**, 1.

[26] Gifford, E. M. Jr. and Tepper, H. B. (1962). Histochemical and autoradiographic studies of floral induction in *Chenopodium album. Amer. J. Bot.* **49**, 706.

[27] Hanke, J. Unpublished results. *Botanisches Institut, Universität, Freiburg i. Br.*

[28] Key, J. L. (1964). Ribonucleic acid and protein synthesis as essential processes for cell elongation. *Plant Physiol.* **39**, 365.

[29] Kinet, J. M. and Bernier, G. In preparation.

[30] Kinet, J. M., Bernier, G. and Bronchart, R. (1967). Sudden release of the meristematic cells from G_2 as a primary effect of flower induction in *Sinapis. Naturwiss.* **54**, 351.

[31] Koski, V. M. and Smith, J. H. C. (1948). The isolation and spectral absorption properties of protochlorophyll from etiolated barley seedlings. *J. Amer. Chem. Soc.* **70**, 3558.

[32] Meijer, G. (1959). The spectral dependence of flowering and elongation. *Acta bot. neerl.* **8**, 189.

[33] Mohr, H. (1964). The control of plant growth and development by light. *Biol. Rev.* **39**, 87.

[34] Nooden, L. D. and Thimann, K. V. (1963). Evidence for a requirement for protein synthesis for auxin-induced cell enlargement. *Proc. Nat. Acad. Sci. (U.S.)* **50**, 194.

[35] Patau, K. and Das, N. K. (1961). The relation of DNA synthesis and mitosis in tobacco pith tissue cultured *in vitro. Chromosoma* **11**, 553.

[36] Patau, K., Das, N. K. and Skoog, F. (1957). Induction of DNA synthesis by kinetin and idoleacetic acid in excised tobacco pith tissue. *Physiol. Plant.* **10**, 949.

[37] Sachs, J. (1887). *Lectures on the physiology of plants.* Clarendon Press, Oxford.

[38] Salisbury, F. B. (1963). *The Flowering Process.* Pergamon Press, Oxford.

[39] Searle, N. E. (1965). Physiology of flowering. *Ann. Rev. Plant Physiol.* **16**, 97.

[40] Sen, B. and Chakravarti, S. C. (1938). Studies in vernalization of mustard. A preliminary report. *Indian J. agric. Sci.* **8**, 245.

[41] Sen, B. and Chakravarti, S. C. (1942). Vernalization of mustard. *Nature* **149**, 139.

[42] Sen, B. and Chakravarti, S. C. (1944). Cited in *Vernalization and Photoperiodism.* Eds. A. E. Murneek and R. O. White. Waltham, Mass., 1948.

[43] Sen, B. and Chakravarti, S. C. (1946). Effect of high temperature on vernalized mustard seed. *Nature* **157**, 266.

[44] Sen Gupta, J. C. and Sen, N. K. (1944). Cited in *Vernalization and Photoperiodism.* Eds. A. E. Murneek and R. O. White. Waltham, Mass., 1948.

[45] Sisken, J. E. (1959). The synthesis of nucleic acids and proteins in the nuclei of *Tradescantia* root tips. *Exptl. Cell Res.* **16**, 602.

[46] Stein, O. and Quastler, H. (1963). The use of tritiated thymidine in the study of tissue activation during germination in *Zea mays. Amer. J. Bot.* **50**, 1006.

[47] Stolwijk, J. A. J. (1952). Photoperiodic and formative effects of various wavelength regions in *Cosmos bipinnatus, Spinacia oleracea, Sinapis alba* and *Pisum sativum. Proc. Kon. nederl. Akad. Wet. C.* **55**, 489.

[48] Taylor, J. H. (1958). Incorporation of phosphorus-32 into nucleic acids and proteins during microgametogenesis of *Tulbaghia*. *Amer. J. Bot.* **45**, 123.

[49] Van't Hof, J. (1963). Deoxyribonucleic acid, ribonucleic acid and protein synthesis in the mitotic cycle of pea root meristem cells. *Cytologia* **28**, 30.

[50] Woodard, J., Rasch, E. and Swift, H. (1961). Nucleic acid and protein metabolism during the mitotic cycle in *Vicia faba*. *J. Bioph. Biochem. Cytol.* **9**, 445.

[51] Ying, H. K. (1965). Effects of phosfon on mitotic cycle, mitotic index, and DNA synthesis of *Pisum sativum* root meristem. *Plant Physiol.* **40**, suppl., xlix.

[52] Zieriacks, H. (1952). Über blüteninduktion durch Keim-und Primärblätter. *Biol. Zbl.* **71**, 210.

14
Lolium temulentum L.

By L. T. Evans

1 History of Use

Lolium temulentum, or darnel, has long been a plant of ill repute. A weed of cereal crops since pre-dynastic Egyptian times, it was the tares of the Bible,[38] and was referred to by Lyte in his herbal as 'a vitious grayne that combereth or anoyeth corne'.[1] Its success as a weed was due to the synchronization of its

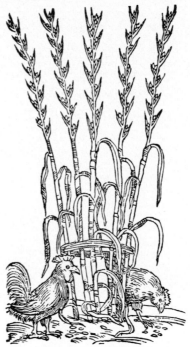

FIGURE 14–1. *Lolium temulentum* (from the *Commentarii* of Pierandrea Mattioli, 1560).

life cycle with, and the similarity of its seed to, those of several cereals. Its ill repute came from the toxicity of darnel seed to man and animals, due to an alkaloid, temulin, produced in the grains by the fungus *Endoconidium temulentum.*[43]

The morphological development of the inflorescence of *L. temulentum* was examined by Goebel in 1884,[29] and by Weber.[47] The species is self-fertile, and normally self-fertilising since the stigmas are not exserted at flowering and the anthers shed their pollen within the pales.[2] With self-fertilization goes uniformity of growth and flowering behaviour within populations, and since 1952 Cooper[5-10] has used the species extensively in his analysis of the physiological and genetic control of development in *Lolium,* for comparison with outbreeding species. He has shown it to be an annual long-day plant, usually without a requirement for vernalization. The finding in 1958 of a strain of *L. temulentum* which can be induced to flower by exposure to only one long day[14] has led to its extensive use in studies on the kinetics of photoperiodic induction. This is referred to as the Ceres strain, after the Canberra phytotron where much of the work with it has been done.

By the time plants are old enough to respond to one long day many potential sites for spikelet differentiation have accumulated at the shoot apex. This accumulation, which does not occur in dicotyledonous apices, offers several advantages, such as the built-in replication of inducible sites which is invaluable in histochemical, autoradiographic and electron microscope studies of induction. Also, the greater size and ease of excision of the shoot apex permits chemical studies of changes in both intact and excised apices during flower induction.

2 Growing Techniques, Growth Habit

Like many weeds, the species is easily grown. No problems with germination or seed dormancy have been encountered. Plants grow well in a range of soils, but are best grown individually in small pots of perlite or vermiculite, given a balanced nutrient solution daily. Growth is optimal at about 25°/20°C (day/night temperature), in which regime leaf primordia are initiated every 1.7 to 3 days, while leaves appear on the primary shoot every 6.4 to 9.6 days, depending on the light intensity.[17] The first formed leaves are relatively small, but leaf size increases up to the time of inflorescence initiation,[3] when they may be more than 45 cm long.

Exposure to one long day induces flowering in the Ceres strain only when the plants are at least 5–6 weeks old,[17] by which time many tillers have developed, some being almost as big as the primary shoot. It is often advisable to punch or mark the leaves on the primary shoot as they appear, and to remove all tillers prior to treatment of the plants. This does not affect the photoperiod response of the primary shoot.[8] The lower leaves on the primary shoot may also be removed since only 12 cm^2 of an upper leaf blade is required for maximal flowering response.[17] Exposure of the leaf sheaths alone to one long day does not cause induction.[18,19]

3 Inflorescence Structure and Criteria of Flowering Response

The inflorescence is a terminal spike bearing 8–30 sessile spikelets, depending no strain and on conditions during inflorescence development. In one strain, longer days led to more rapid development and a smaller number of spikelets.[8] In the Ceres strain, spikelet number was unaffected by the number of long day exposures.[14]

Several criteria of flowering response have been used. Where induction is marginal, the proportion of plants which flower, or which initiate inflorescences, is a convenient criterion of response.[17–20,26] As in other Gramineae, the best criterion for inflorescence initiation is the reaching or passing of the 'double ridges' stage of differentiation, in which the spikelet primordia between the leaf primordia become clearly convex, as in Figure 14–2. The length of the shoot apex at this stage depends on plant age and daylength conditions, and may range from 0.5 to 1.7 mm, being smaller the longer the photoperiod and the younger the plant.[15] Following the appearance of double ridges there is a marked decrease in the plastochron,[32] a sharp increase in apex length, and often more rapid internode elongation. But the 'double ridges' are the earliest unambiguous sign of inflorescence initiation. Subsequent differentiation leads to the successive appearance of primordial glumes, lemmas, florets and anthers, which may be used in a scoring system.[45]

The number of leaves below the inflorescence may also be used as a criterion of the earliness of flowering.[7–10,17,40] Values may vary between 4[10] and more than 37.[39] While the node of first flowering is a convenient criterion for some purposes, it can be misleading in that it is affected by conditions changing the rate of leaf initiation, even when these have no effect on the processes leading to flower induction. The number of days to earing or anthesis is a still less satisfactory criterion for flower induction since it may vary greatly with effects on postinductive inflorescence development. The interval from double ridges to earing usually ranges between 15 and 90 days, and adds not only confusion but also delay to flower induction studies. Periodic dissection to establish the time to initiation avoids both the confusion and the delay, but adds greatly to the number of plants that must be used in each treatment.[8]

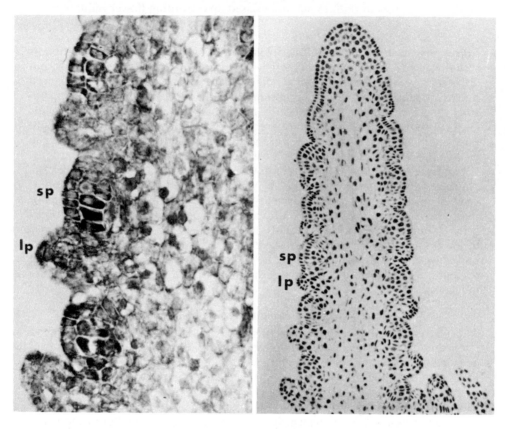

FIGURE 14–2. (a) Left. The flank of a shoot apex 3 days after long day induction (Day IV), stained with methyl green pyronin to show accumulation of RNA at potential spikelet sites (sp) between the leaf primordia (lp). (b) Right. Day V apex stained with Feulgen, showing more advanced spikelets and double ridges (Knox and Evans[32]).

Under standard conditions, the initiated inflorescences increase in length exponentially. The rate of their development increases with increase in temperature and photoperiod length, but is not affected by the extent of vernalization.[5,6,15] In short days at a given temperature, the rate of development increases in proportion to the logarithm of the number of long days given for induction.[14,15] The rate of inflorescence development, under standard conditions, thus provides a sensitive quantitative index of the intensity of induction. It can be presented as the relative growth rate of the inflorescence, as in Figure 14–3, or more simply as inflorescence length, on a logarithmic scale, a given number of days after treatment. Since there is no fixed relation between apex length and stage of differentiation,[15] both length and stage should be recorded. Spikelet primordia may be evident three days after exposure to a long day, as in Figure 14-2a, but dissection is best made 2–3 weeks after the long day. By that time plants given marginal inductive treatment have had time to initiate spikelet primordia, while those given an effective long day exposure may be differentiating floret primordia.

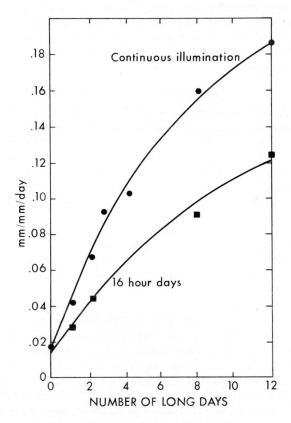

FIGURE 14–3. Effect of the number of long days at induction on the subsequent rate of inflorescence development in short days at 23°/17°C (Evans[15]).

4 Effects of Plant Age

When grown under continuous light in Arctic summer conditions, plants of *L. temulentum* flowered after forming 4 leaves.[10] Since there are 3 leaf primordia in the embryo, there can hardly be a juvenile phase in which the plants are unable to respond to long day conditions.

However, the sensitivity of the response to long days increases with increase in plant age. With the Ceres strain, for example, the number of long days required for induction was 6 at 14 days, 4 at 18 days, 2 at 28 days, and 1 at 34 days from sowing.[17] In young plants exposed to fewer long days than the threshold number for flower induction there was, nevertheless, an increase in apical growth and in the rate of leaf initiation due to long-day treatment.

The increase in sensitivity to induction with age is not due to increased leaf area, since only 3–5 cm^2 of an upper leaf need be exposed to one long day for full induction to occur. Either the distal 3 cm^2 of leaf 7 when it first appears,[26]

or the proximal 5 cm² of a mature sixth leaf,[17] is sufficient. This is equivalent
to the total leaf area of plants 14 days old.

Nor is the increase in sensitivity due to increasing leaf age, since the inductive
effect of a leaf is fairly constant once the blade has reached a certain minimum
area.[17,26] In *L. temulentum*, fully expanded leaves retain their full inductive capacity for a considerable period.

The higher photoperiodic sensitivity of older plants could be due to greater
responsiveness of the later formed leaves or of the older shoot apices. Further
analysis[17] suggested that the responsiveness of the shoot apex varied little with
age, whereas later formed leaves caused more effective induction per unit area
than the first formed ones.

5 Vernalization and Devernalization

The strains of *L. temulentum* most commonly used (Ba 3081 and Ceres) are summer annuals with no response to low temperature vernalization.[7,8,16,40] However, flowering in winter annual strains from Turkey and France is accelerated
by vernalization.[9] Four weeks at temperatures below 5°C saturated the vernalization response of most of these lines, but one line from Versailles (Ba 6902)
required 8 weeks.[9,40] The vernalization response was not affected by seedling
age, or by the photoperiod during cold treatment. However, exposure of seedlings to long days for 2 weeks before cold treatment eliminated the response to
vernalization, while vernalization slightly lowered the critical length of the photoperiod in which plants would subsequently flower.[40]

Presoaking seeds in gibberellic acid solutions increased their response to cold
treatments of intermediate duration, whereas auxin solutions seemed to reduce
the vernalization response.[39]

6 Short Day Vernalization

Strains which do not respond to low temperature vernalization (e.g. Ba 3081 and
Ceres) are merely delayed in their flowering by exposure to short days before
the inductive long days.[9,17,40] On the other hand, the winter annual strains
whose flowering in long days is accelerated by previous exposure to low temperatures also respond to short day vernalization.[9,40] For most of them, the leaf
number before flowering is not reduced as much by short days as by low temperatures, but slower leaf initiation at the low temperature could account for
this effect. Moreover, the data available are rather conflicting.[9,40]

7 Photoperiod Response

Photoperiod length

The effect of photoperiod length on the number of leaves or days before inflorescence initiation in 3 strains of *L. temulentum* is shown in Figure 14-4. The
Aberystwyth strain (Ba 3081) is a quantitative long-day plant which remains
vegetative for 120 days or so in 8-9-hour photoperiods, but will flower eventually
in short days.[6-8] The Ceres strain appears to be a qualitative long-day plant
with a critical photoperiod length of about 9 hours,[14,15] while the Turkish strain
(Ba 6139-7) may have a still longer critical photoperiod, even after 4 weeks of
vernalization.[39] Another Turkish strain (Ba 6137-21) apparently has a critical
photoperiod of more than 14 hours.[40]

The above results are for plants grown continuously under various daylengths.
For the Ceres strain, the critical photoperiod is much longer when only one inductive cycle is given, being then between 14 and 16 hours,[25-27] compared with
about 9 hours for repeated cycles.

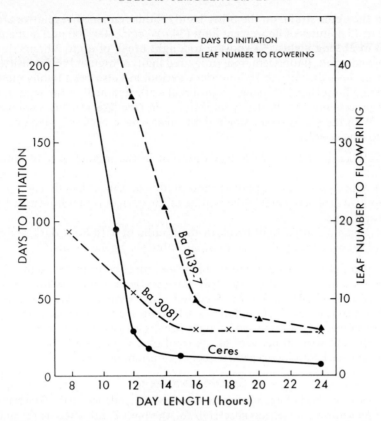

FIGURE 14–4. Relation between daylength and flowering response in three strains of *L. temulentum*: x = **Ba 3081** from Aberystwyth,[8] ● = Ceres from Canada,[14] ▲ = Ba 6139–7 from Turkey.[39]

Number of cycles

The number of long days to which plants must be exposed for flower induction to occur depends very much on plant age, as described above, and on the length of the photoperiod. Strains may differ in the number of long days they require, but this point has not been examined for *L. temulentum*. Strain Ba 3081 certainly responds to 4 long days,[8] and may respond to fewer.

Threshold light intensity

The light intensity for effective photoperiodic extension of a short day of daylight or high intensity light can be quite low. With the Aberystwyth strain incandescent light of 10 f.c. intensity was as effective as daylight.[8] With the Ceres strain, incandescent light of only 1 f.c. intensity (about 8 μW/cm^2 of 600–770 mμ light) was effective, and increasing the intensity beyond 100 μW/cm^2 of 600–770 mμ light had little effect on the flowering response.[27]

Effect of light interruptions

The flowering response of *L. temulentum* to brief light interruptions during long dark periods varies sharply between strains. With strain Ba 3081, exposure to 1 hour of red light (84 μW/cm^2) during each of 10 long nights caused induction, and exposure to 2 hours each night gave a greater flowering response. The red light breaks were most effective when given in the middle of each dark period.[45]

With the Ceres strain, on the other hand, plants remained vegetative after exposure to 15 minutes of fluorescent light (34 μW/cm^2, 600–700 mμ) in the middle of each of 21 long nights.[34] Exposure to a light break of up to 2 hours duration with incandescent, fluorescent, red, or far-red light, of high or low intensity, given at various times during one 16-hour dark period, has also been totally ineffective in inducing flowering.[20,27] Single light breaks affected neither the long-day promotive process nor the short-day inhibitory one (see later) to any significant extent.[27] With the Ceres strain single light breaks have been effective only under the following conditions:

(a) When of 4 hours or longer duration in the middle of a 16-hour dark period.[27]

(b) When given after a photoperiod of almost critical length, e.g. 5 minutes of red light (160 μW/cm^2) in the middle of the dark period following a 12-hour photoperiod.[27]

(c) When a 2-hour light break in the middle of a 16-hour dark period was combined with the application of auxin solutions to the plants.[20]

Repeated light breaks during one night are effective in inducing flowering in the Ceres strain, provided the interval between them is not too long. With red or far-red light, flower initiation occurred only when the darkness was interrupted at least once every 30 minutes of a 16-hour night, while with incandescent light some flowering was caused by light breaks every 4 hours. With light from all sources, and with 10 per cent of the total time illuminated, the flowering response increased with increasing frequency of illumination.[27]

8 Spectral Dependence

The classical method of examining the spectral dependence of the flowering process by determining an action spectrum for the light break effect is precluded in the Ceres strain by the ineffectiveness of light break treatments. Let us consider instead the relative effectiveness of light of varying spectral composition given over prolonged periods, usually as a low intensity extension to a day of high intensity daylight or artificial light. With the Ceres strain neither the intensity nor the spectral composition of the first 8 hours of a long day has much effect on the flowering response.[23,27] There is, however, a marked effect of the light intensity during early growth on the response to one long day.[41]

With single photoperiod extensions of 16 hours at very low intensities, red light was the least effective, possibly because of heavy screening by the uppermost chloroplasts in the leaves. At intensities above 100 μW/cm^2 the order of effectiveness was incandescent > red > far-red plus a little red > far-red alone. In other experiments the flowering response was greatest in light with about equal energy in the red (600–700 mμ) and far-red (700–770 mμ) bands, and fell progressively with increase in the proportion of either red or far-red light. With photoperiod extensions in low intensity monochromatic light, only 695 mμ light was effective.[27]

A similar response has been found with repeated photoperiod extensions of only 8 hours duration, in both Ceres and Ba 3081 strains, except that the latter remained vegetative with far-red extensions.[34,45]

Thus, an equal mixture of red and far-red light appears to be optimal for induction of *L. temulentum*. Attempts have been made to separate, both in space and in time, the action of red light from that of far-red light. When red light and far-red light exposures were given to separate leaves or parts of leaves, no synergistic effect was evident.[27] On the other hand, there was a marked synergism between red and far-red exposures when these were given sequentially to the same leaves, in short cycles. The synergism decreased as the cycle length increased from 2 minutes to 2 hours, and little was evident with longer cycles. Even when only 10 per cent of each short cycle was illuminated with red and far-red light, a marked synergism was evident, and occurred regardless of whether the far-red exposures were given before, during, or after the red exposures.[27]

At the moment, there is no convincing explanation of all these results. Several possible explanations have been excluded,[27] but at least two remain. One is that the far-red light participates in a high energy reaction, which is required in combination with phytochrome P_{fr} action throughout the photoperiod, though not continuously, to yield an effective long day. The relative ineffectiveness of high intensity fluorescent light, high in blue light for the high energy reaction and in red to maintain phytochrome P_{fr}, argues against this explanation.[27] The other possibility is that the long-day response is wholly mediated by phytochrome acting in a rather unusual way. Most of the results with *L. temulentum* could be explained on the assumption that the photoperiod response is mediated, not by P_{fr}, but by one of the short lived intermediates in phytochrome interconversion.[36]

9 Endogenous Rhythms

There is no evidence of persistent circadian rhythms in the photoperiodic response of *L. temulentum*. There is, however, evidence of a diurnal cycle in the response to red and far-red light which may indicate a rhythmic sensitivity to phytochrome P_{fr} action.

With strain Ba 3081, an interruption with 1 hour of red light in the middle of each 16-hour dark period caused induction to occur. However, if this interruption was preceded by 7 hours in red light, flowering was prevented, whereas 7 hours in far-red light before 1 hour in red stimulated induction. By giving 2–3½ hour exposures to red or far-red light at various times during the 7 hours before the 1 hour of red light at midnight, it was found that red light was most inhibitory, and far-red light most promotive, during the middle of the 7-hour period, i.e. about 12 hours from the beginning of the high intensity light period.[45] Brief (15 minutes) exposures to far-red light at that time were as promotive as prolonged irradiation. Their promotive effect could be annulled by subsequent red light for 15 minutes.[46] This is the best evidence there is of phytochrome action in the photoperiodic processes of *L. temulentum*.

A similar inhibitory effect of red light when given during the first four hours after each 8-hour period of daylight was also found with plants of the Ceres strain exposed to repeated long days.[34] With induction by exposure to a single long day, however, there was only a slight change in sensitivity to red and far-red light during the photoperiod extension, although red light was least effective, and far-red light most effective, when given during the first 4 hours after the high intensity light period.[27]

It remains an open question whether these changes are an expression of an endogenous circadian rhythm or of an accumulation of the product of the high energy reaction of photomorphogenesis during the main light period.[34] Also, the fact that the changes in response to red and far-red light were more marked with repeated long day treatments than with a single inductive cycle suggests that they may not play a primary role in photoperiodic induction of *L. temulentum*.

10 Fractional Induction

While exposure to one long day is sufficient for inflorescence initiation in the Ceres strain, exposure to additional long days increases the subsequent rate of inflorescence development. Interpolation of a number of short days between the long days, e.g. of 1, 2, 3 or 5 short days between two long days, did not reduce the flowering response significantly.[15] This finding is of interest in two connections. In the first place it implies that any inhibitory effect of an interpolated short day is evanescent and not cumulative. A similar conclusion can be drawn from the increase in sensitivity to induction with increase in age, or time in short days. Secondly, additional long days increase the rate of inflorescence differentiation even when they are given after induction has been consummated and differentiation has begun. This suggests that the long-day stimulus has a general effect on shoot apex activation quite apart from any specific effect it may have on floral induction.

11 Photoperiodic Inhibition

As noted above, short days given before, or interpolated between, inductive long days have no adverse effect on induction. There is thus no cumulative inhibitory effect of short days. However, exposure of some leaves to short day conditions while other leaves are exposed to an inductive long day causes a reduction in the flowering response.

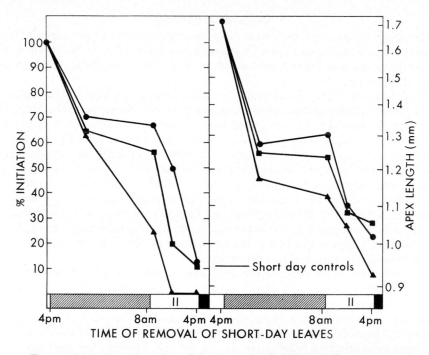

FIGURE 14–5. Translocation of the short day inhibitor. Effect of time of removal of lower leaf blades kept in short day conditions during exposure of the sixth leaf to one long day (*a*) on % plants initiating inflorescences, (*b*) on shoot apex length at dissection. Long day leaf area 26.6 cm², short day leaf area 21.1 cm² (●), 45.9 cm² (■), or 172.4 cm² (▲). The hatched area indicates the period when leaf 6 was under illumination while the lower leaves were in darkness (Evans[18]).

This inhibitory effect, generated in leaves in short days, appears to act outside the leaves, presumably at the shoot apex. Evidence for this conclusion comes from experiments in which the uppermost leaf was exposed to one long day, while the lower leaves were kept in short day conditions, and were cut off at various times during and after the long day.[18] The results of such an experiment are given in Figure 14–5, from which it may be seen that the later the short-day leaves were cut off, and the greater their total area, the greater was their inhibitory effect. A striking feature of these results was that an inhibitory effect of the short-day leaves was apparent even when they were cut off only 6 hours after the beginning of the dark period.

The conclusion that these effects were due to a transmissible short-day inhibitor has been questioned on the grounds that the short-day leaves may have acted as sinks for the floral stimulus from the long-day leaves, or may otherwise have reduced the amount of stimulus reaching the shoot apex, or may have diluted it with excess assimilates.[50,51] The pattern of movement of ^{14}C-labelled assimilates in such plants does not support these objections. Lower leaves in short days do not act as a sink for assimilates from a higher leaf in long-day conditions, nor do they reduce the flow of assimilates from the long-day leaf to the shoot apex. Moreover, they supply such a small proportion of the assimilates reaching the shoot apex that they could hardly cause much dilution of the inductive stimulus, even assuming such a phenomenon operated.[25]

The objection that the lower leaves in short days may have reduced the amount of floral stimulus reaching the shoot apex cannot be rigorously excluded because we have, at the moment, no direct way of assaying the movement of the floral stimulus. Although the experiments outlined above indicate that the presence of lower leaves in short days does not reduce the translocation of labelled assimilates from the upper leaf to the shoot apex, it is possible that translocation of the floral stimulus follows a different pattern. In fact, as will be discussed, the stimulus is translocated at a much lower velocity than are the assimilates, and can be exported from leaves too young to export assimilates.[26] Nevertheless, there is no reason to expect that lower, older leaves reduce translocation of the floral stimulus from the upper leaf to the apex, and known translocation patterns for many other compounds suggest this is unlikely. Thus, short-day leaves probably reduce the flowering response of L. temulentum by exporting to the shoot apex an inhibitor of flower induction.

The identity of this putative inhibitor is not known, but abscisin II is a possible candidate, since it occurs in increased amounts under short-day conditions.[11] With plants of L. temulentum exposed to one long day, abscisin II had no effect on induction when applied early on the long day, or two days after it, but was highly inhibitory when applied between 11 p.m. on the long day and 4 p.m. on the following day.[22] The fact that it was inhibitory when applied after the critical photoperiod had been passed and some stimulus had been translocated out of the leaves, suggests that abscisin was acting against induction at the shoot apex, as was deduced for the short day inhibitor.[18] The inhibitory effect of short-day leaves on induction in L. temulentum is eliminated when anaerobic conditions are combined with the long dark period.[19] It is of interest therefore that abscission is also inhibited by anaerobic conditions.[4]

12 Dual Photoperiod Responses

The evidence that flower induction in L. temulentum is antagonized by an inhibitor produced in leaves in short-day conditions, and translocated to the shoot apex, has been considered above. In the face of this, one may ask whether long-day induction in this species is due merely to the temporary absence of the short-day inhibition, or whether the long day also generates a stimulus to induction.

To resolve this question we need a condition other than daylength which prevents the short-day inhibitory process from occurring without affecting any long-day promotive processes. Holding the leaves under anaerobic conditions appears to have the required selective effect.[19]

Plants with an upper leaf exposed to one aerobic long day had their lower leaves in short-day conditions, either aerobic or in nitrogen. The presence of the lower leaves reduced the flowering response to the long day when they were in aerobic conditions, as shown previously, but not when they were held in nitrogen throughout the 16-hour dark period. Thus, anaerobic conditions eliminated the short-day inhibition. On the other hand, the promotive effect of a leaf exposed to a long day was the same whether it was kept in aerobic or anaerobic conditions throughout the 16-hour photoperiod extension. The flowering response to one long day was reduced, however, when the remainder of the plant was also held in nitrogen throughout the photoperiod extension.

When plants were kept in short-day conditions, but held in an atmosphere of nitrogen during one long night, 60–70 per cent of them subsequently initiated inflorescences, whereas all aerobic short-day controls remained vegetative. Thus, temporary prevention of short-day inhibition has caused induction to occur. However, the induction was minimal, and far less than that caused by exposure to one long day.[19] Long days must therefore have a direct, promotive effect on induction in addition to their indirect effect of preventing the short-day inhibition, and photoperiod a dual action in controlling the flowering of *L. temulentum.*

13 Effects of Temperature

For plants grown in long days, flowering was earlier the higher the temperature of growth, up to 30°/23°C.[16] This effect was probably due to the increased rate of inflorescence development at higher temperatures,[15] rather than to an acceleration of induction. Where differences in temperature were applied only during the exposure to one long day, the optimum temperature for induction was about 20°C, and induction was incomplete at 7.5°C or 30°C, and did not occur at 3°C. The optimum for the 8-hour period in high intensity light was 20°C, while that for the 16-hour low intensity photoperiod extension was 25°C. No initiation occurred when the low intensity light period was at 4°C.[18] This finding is further support for the existence of a long-day promotive process during the photoperiod extension, which is presumably retarded at 4°C.

Plants held in short days for two weeks with a day temperature of 25°C and a night temperature of 4°C did not show any subsequent inflorescence initiation in short days, which might have been expected if the short-day inhibitory process was eliminated at low night temperatures.[18]

15 Effects of Gas Composition

Evidence that anaerobic conditions suppress the short-day inhibition without affecting the long-day promotive process in *L. temulentum* has been given above. Exclusion of CO_2 during the low light extension of a long day had no effect on the flowering response.[19]

16 Translocation of the Floral Stimulus

Evidence for the production by long-day leaves of a stimulus to induction in *L. temulentum* has been given above. No direct evidence for the translocation of this stimulus is obtainable, but there is presumptive evidence from the effect on induction of the time at which the leaf blade exposed to one long day is cut off. Many experiments of this kind have been carried out,[18,22,25,26] and the results of one are shown in Figure 14–6. In all cases, the later the long-day leaf blade is cut off, the greater is the subsequent flowering response, presumably because more floral stimulus has been translocated out of the blade before cutting. There is a variation between experiments of about 8 hours in the time of apparent movement which is largely seasonal, later translocation being found in winter experiments.

Since all experiments have been done under the same temperature conditions, 25°/20°C, later translocation is probably associated with lower light intensities. Very low light intensity during the day after the long day greatly reduced the flowering response,[18] but this may have been through an effect on the capacity of the apex to respond to the stimulus rather than through an effect on the velocity of translocation. In fact, the velocity of translocation of the floral stimulus in *L. temulentum* was much the same at 60 f.c. as at 3000 f.c.[26]

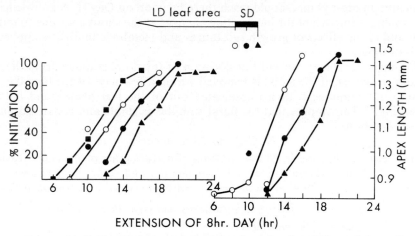

FIGURE 14–6. Translocation of the long-day stimulus. Effect of time of removal to darkness (■), or of cutting off the blade of leaf 7 at the base (▲), or 4 (●) or 8 (○) cm above the base on (a) % of plants initiating inflorescences and (b) apex length at dissection (Evans and Wardlaw[26]).

The velocity of translocation of the stimulus has been estimated in two quite different ways, and each has yielded a value of about 2 cm/hour. The first estimate was derived from the length of time after the critical photoperiod was reached that was required for the stimulus to traverse the amount of long-day leaf giving threshold induction.[25] Figure 14–6 illustrates the second, more direct, way of estimating the velocity. The basal 8 cm length of the leaf blade exposed to the long day was wrapped in foil at the beginning of the photoperiod extension. Thus it did not contribute to the generation of the floral stimulus but provided a zone through which the floral stimulus generated in the distal part of the leaf blade had to pass. By cutting the blade off at one of several positions in this zone, at different times during the photoperiod extension, the time taken for the amount of stimulus giving a particular flowering response to traverse a known distance could be found.[26]

Such experiments yielded velocities of 1–2.4 cm/hr for translocation of the floral stimulus, while determination of the velocity of simultaneous ^{14}C-labelled assimilate movement yielded values of 77–105 cm/hr. It seems unlikely, then, that the floral stimulus in this LDP is translocated in mass flow with assimilates. On the other hand, the velocity of translocation of the inductive stimulus in *Lolium* is comparable to that of gibberellin and auxin movement, and of protoplasmic streaming.

Independent translocation of floral stimulus and assimilates is also suggested by the different effect of leaf size on their export. As in many other plants, leaves about one quarter expanded exported hardly any assimilate, yet they apparently exported almost as much floral stimulus as larger leaves.[26] A point of difference between *L. temulentum* and *Xanthium* is that fully expanded *Lolium* leaves are as effective for induction as expanding ones.

Under favourable conditions, the stimulus begins to be exported from the leaf blade about 20 hours after the beginning of the long day, and enough to cause induction in most plants has left the blade by the beginning of the high intensity light period of the next day (II).[22,25,26] It then has to be translocated about 8–10 cm or so down the leaf sheath, and finally a few millimetres to the shoot apex. Assuming it moves at a velocity of about 2 cm/hr, the stimulus probably begins to reach the shoot apex at the end of the long day (I), while enough to cause induction in most plants should reach there by noon on Day II. A knowledge of this timing is important for interpreting changes at the shoot apex due to induction and in the effects of growth substances and metabolic inhibitors applied at various times.

Drought stress may prevent translocation of the floral stimulus from the leaf blades. However, if the stress is removed within a few days of the long-day exposure, the stimulus is then translocated out of the leaf blades, and induces flowering.[31] This implies that the floral stimulus is stable and conserved under these conditions.

17 Grafting Experiments

It has been widely considered that grafting of mature grass plants is not feasible. However, recent experiments with *L. temulentum* and some other grasses have shown that stem grafting can be carried out with a reasonable degree of success.[48]

18 Effects of Growth Substances and Growth Retardants

Gibberellins and growth retardants

Single applications of 3 μg or more of gibberellic acid (GA_3) cause inflorescence initiation in *L. temulentum* plants held continuously in short days, and greatly increase the effectiveness of induction in plants exposed to one long day. The method of application of GA_3 is not important, but the stimulatory effects depend strongly on the time of application. For plants exposed to one long day, GA_3 was most effective when applied at the end of the high intensity light period of the long day, with subsidiary peaks for applications at the same time on the day before and on the day after the long day. Applications at the beginning of the long day, and in the second half of the photoperiod extension have little effect.[20] Thus, GA_3 applications have their greatest effect at the same time that irradiation with far-red light is most favourable for induction, and their least effect when red light is most favourable.

Both for plants kept in short days, and for those given one long day, the order of effectiveness of the gibberellins was $GA_3 > GA_5 > GA_1 > GA_4$, GA_9, GA_8.[20] Other experiments have shown that GA_7 is also less effective than GA_3.[23]

For plants kept in short days, holding the leaf blade in nitrogen for one 16-hour dark period reduced the response to GA_3 injection.[20] This suggests that gibberellins may affect one of the photoperiodic processes in the leaves, in a step requiring aerobic conditions. Since the long-day promotive process is unaffected by anaerobic conditions, the gibberellin effect may be a suppression of the short-day inhibition. However, since GA_3 also stimulates flowering when given to plants during exposure to a long day, in the absence of short-day inhibition, it must play a further role in flower induction.

Experiments with growth retardants known to inhibit gibberellin biosynthesis[12] have not clarified the role of gibberellins in flower induction. In the early experiments Amo-1618 and CCC were injected near the shoot apex during the long-day exposure, and had no effect on induction or on the promotive effect of GA_3.[20] In more recent experiments[23] large doses of CCC solutions of high concentration (up to 10^{-1} M) have been applied to the root systems, at various times from 4 days before to 6 days after the long day. Although they have reduced growth markedly, they have had no effect on flower induction. These results suggest that endogenous gibberellins may play no role in the long-day induction of *L. temulentum*. However, other results do not altogether support this conclusion.

In treatments involving factorial combinations of CCC the day before the long day and GA_3 on the long day, the effects on vegetative growth were as expected: the more GA_3 applied, the greater the stem and leaf growth, the more CCC applied the less the growth, with a negative interaction between GA and CCC. For the flowering response, however, there was a pronounced positive interaction between them, CCC greatly increasing the response to GA_3, at all concentrations, in plants in short days and in those exposed to a long day. This positive interaction was evident even when the CCC applications were made after the long-day and the GA treatments.[23] A possible explanation of these results is that CCC has reduced competition between the growth of the rest of the plant and the development of the shoot apex stimulated by GA_3.

Another growth retardant, N, N-dimethylaminosuccinamic acid (B995) can be highly inhibitory to flower induction in *L. temulentum*. It is so only when applied at high concentrations (e.g. 6×10^{-2} M), particularly as leaf sprays but also when injected. Peak inhibition of induction by B995 occurs at two times, two days before the long day and towards the end of the long day. Later applications are only slightly inhibitory. Inhibition by B995 is accentuated by application of IAA, but relieved by GA_3 injection.[23] B995 may not inhibit gibberellin biosynthesis,[12] so interpretation is difficult. The later peak of inhibition suggests that gibberellins may play an important role following induction. However, the earlier inhibition, since it is reversible by GA_3 given during the long day, suggests that gibberellins may also play a role in induction. Further experiments are needed.

Auxins

Applications of IAA or NAA reduce the flowering response of plants given one long day,[20] or vernalized,[39] but cause some induction in plants held in short day conditions if combined with a light-break treatment which alone is ineffective.[20] The inhibitory effect of auxin on plants exposed to one long day is markedly time-dependent, occurring only with leaf applications made at the end of the high intensity light period or during the first half of the photoperiod extension.[20]

These results suggest that the long-day photoperiodic process in the leaves of *L. temulentum* is highly sensitive to auxin level. During a long-day extension the endogenous level may be near the optimum, and auxin applications make it too high, while in short days the endogenous level is low and applications raising it to near optimal levels allow a light break to effect induction.

Abscisin

Applied either as a spray to the leaves, or by injection near the shoot apex, abscisin II is inhibitory to induction by one long day only when applied during the photoperiod extension or during the following high intensity light period.[22] Such action suggests that abscisin could be the short-day inhibitor. When applied daily to the leaves of plants exposed to 15 long days, abscisin completely prevented flowering in *L. temulentum*.[13]

19 *Effects of Metabolic Inhibitors*

Many experiments with *L. temulentum* have utilised the technique of making single applications of specific metabolic inhibitors, to either the leaf or the shoot apex, at various times during induction by exposure to one long day. While the full interpretation of these experiments requires a knowledge of the rate of up-take and of the rate and pattern of transport of the applied compounds, of the rate of their metabolism, of changes in the pool size of related endogenous com-pounds, and of the specificity of their action, which is often not available, such experiments can provide clues to the nature of the component processes of induction.

Effects on photoperiodic processes in the leaf

The production of the floral stimulus in leaves during the photoperiod extension does not seem to involve either protein or nucleic acid synthesis in any specific way. Leaf applications of ethionine (5×10^{-3} M), chloramphenicol (2 mg/ml),[21] and p-fluoro-phenylalanine (2×10^{-2} M),[23] at various times during the long day, had little or no effect on induction, while 5-fluorouracil (5FU) applications to the leaves had only a slight inhibitory effect when made before the end of the long day.[21]

Leaf applications of cycloheximide and chlorpropham (CIPC) are inhibitory to induction when made during the long day, but this could be due to their being translocated to the apex and acting there.[23]

Steroid biosynthesis may be involved in the production of the floral stimulus. Tris-(2-diethyl aminoethyl) phosphate trihydrochloride (SK & F7997), which blocks the synthetic pathway between mevalonic acid and cholesterol, particu-larly at the conversion of lanosterol to zymosterol,[30] was highly inhibitory to induction when applied to the leaves (at 2–3 mg/ml) during the early part of the photoperiod extension, but had no effect when applied later, or on the day before the long day[21] (Fig. 14–7). Attempts to increase the response to one long day by spraying the leaves with mevalonic acid (1×10^{-2} M) at various times have yielded no effect.[23]

Two other compounds have had a marked inhibitory effect on induction when applied to the leaves at the end of the high intensity light period or during the early part of the photoperiod extension of the long day. One is 3 (3, 4 dichlor-ophenyl)-1, 1 dimethyl urea (DCMU), a specific inhibitor of electron transport in photosynthesis, and the other is 2, 4 dinitrophenol, an uncoupler of respira-tion.[23,26] The very pronounced inhibition by DCMU, at 3×10^{-5} M, was con-fined to applications made prior to translocation of the stimulus, which suggests that current photosynthesis is in some way involved in the generation or initial movement of the floral stimulus.

Effects on induction at the shoot apex

The results of serial injections near the shoot apex with Actinomycin D (8×10^{-5} M) and 5FU (5×10^{-3} M) suggest that ribonucleic acid (RNA) synthesis at the apex is an essential component of induction in *L. temulentum*.[21] It was concluded above (Section 16) that the floral stimulus begins to reach the shoot apex early on the morning of Day II, and this is the time at which injections of Actinomycin D were most inhibitory to induction (Fig. 14–7), whereas they were not inhibitory at either the beginning of Day I or the latter part of Day II. Injections of 5FU were also most inhibitory at the beginning of Day II, and this inhibition was relieved by injection of orotic acid (1×10^{-2} M) at the same time, but not by injection of thymidine (5×10^{-3} M). The failure of thymidine, and the ability of orotic acid, to antidote the inhibitory effects of 5FU suggest that RNA synthesis rather than DNA synthesis at that time is essential to induction. The fact that injections of 5-fluorodeoxyuridine (5FDU, 5×10^{-4} M) were only slightly inhibitory on Day II, and more inhibitory when injected on Days III and

IV, also suggests that DNA synthesis is not essential for induction, but is for floral differentiation. The fact that injections of 5FU are most inhibitory early in the morning of Day II could suggest that effective induction requires synthesis of transfer or ribosomal RNA, since these are supposedly most inhibited by 5FU treatment.[35]

Injections of 2-thiouracil and 6-azauracil were also very inhibitory to floral induction in *L. temulentum* if made before the end of Day II. The inhibition could be relieved by the injection of uracil or uridine, but not by injection of GA3.[44]

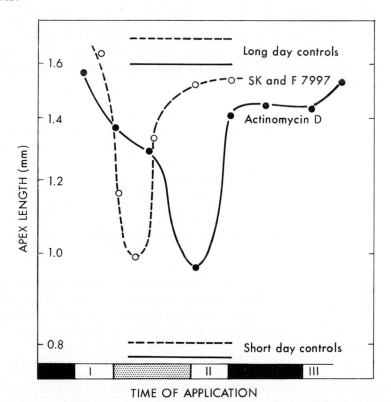

FIGURE 14–7. Effect of time of application of SK & F7997 to leaves (as spray, 3 mg/plant), or of Actinomycin D near the shoot apex (by injecting 10 μg/plant), on floral induction in plants exposed to one long day. The hatched area indicatest he low intensity light period of the long day (after Evans[21]).

Chloramphenicol (2 mg/ml) and p-fluorophenylalanine reduced the flowering response to some extent when injected at any time between Day I and Day III. Cycloheximide (1×10^{-4} M) or CIPC (30 ppm), on the other hand, were most inhibitory when injected near the end of Day I or early on Day II,[21,23,28] suggesting that protein synthesis at the shoot apex is also an essential component of induction. SK & F7997 was also inhibitory when injected near the shoot apex on Day II, and applications of DNP were similarly inhibitory.[23]

20 Florigenic Extracts

The procedure which has allowed some florigenic activity to be extracted from *Xanthium* plants[37] has been followed with plants of *L. temulentum* previously held in short days or exposed to 14 long days. The two extracts were then applied either to the leaves or near the shoot apex of *L. temulentum* plants kept in short days or given one long day. In no case was the slightest indication of florigenic activity in the extracts found, and both extracts reduced the flowering response to one long day.[52]

Extracts of vegetative and reproductive plants of *L. temulentum* have been analysed for their various lipid components, and have been assayed for florigenic activity on shoot tips of *Chenopodium rubrum* cultured *in vitro*.[49] Extracts from plants in long days increased the percentage of flowering explants, whereas extracts from plants in short days did not. Most fractions were found in both vegetative and reproductive plants, but two sterol fractions and one monoglyceride fraction were found only in plants in long days and only in the sixth leaf. A point of some interest, in view of the relative insensitivity of the early leaves to photoperiodic induction (section 4), was that the fifth and sixth leaves contained many fractions not found in the first leaf.

21 Induction of Excised Apices

Shoots cut off below the apex, reduced to one leaf, and kept in water, respond to one long day as well as intact plants do.[23] No attempts have been made to induce excised apices, but apices excised at various times before and after induction and incubated on appropriate media have been used to examine changes in their rate and pattern of RNA and protein synthesis as affected by long day induction, growth substances, and inhibitors. Patterns of incorporation of labelled precursors of RNA similar to those found in the apices of intact plants are obtained only when the excised apices are submerged in the medium, not when they are placed upright on top of it.[28]

22 Chemical, Histochemical, and Ultrastructural Changes at Induction

The floral stimulus probably reaches the shoot apex early on Day II. Since this is the time when injections of Actinomycin D and 5FU are most inhibitory to flowering, induction probably involves specific RNA synthesis at that time. Evidence for a transient increase during the morning of Day II in the incorporation of ^{32}P into nucleic acids in the shoot apices of plants exposed to a long day has been found. In experiments in which shoot apices were harvested 3–4 hours after ^{32}P-orthophosphate was applied to the leaves, exposure to a long day caused no increase in incorporation for ^{32}P applications before or at the beginning of the high intensity light period of Day II, a 30–40 per cent increase in incorporation of ^{32}P applied around 10.30 a.m. Day II, and little increase with afternoon applications or with those made during the succeeding night. By Day III, ^{32}P incorporation was consistently higher in the induced plants, by about 65 per cent. The increase in ^{32}P incorporation in Day II apices appeared to occur in all RNA fractions.[42]

A comparable transient increase in the incorporation of ^{35}S into protein has also been found in apices on Day II, but not on Day III. In at least one experiment (Fig. 14–8), the increase in ^{35}S incorporation preceded the increase in ^{32}P incorporation by 20 minutes.[24] Experiments with excised shoot apices have also provided evidence of an increase in RNA and protein synthesis associated with floral induction during the morning of Day II. With apices excised early on Day II, the rate of incorporation of ^3H-leucine or ^3H-uridine was the same whether or not the plants had been exposed to a long day. With apices excised later, however, incorporation was 20–50 per cent higher in those from plants exposed to a long day, this difference disappearing with still later excision.[28]

These results suggest that transient increases in both RNA and protein synthesis at the shoot apex are among the earliest effects of the arrival there of the floral stimulus. Moreover, the fact that both Actinomycin D and cycloheximide injections are most inhibitory to flowering when made early on Day II suggests that these increases are both essential components of induction.

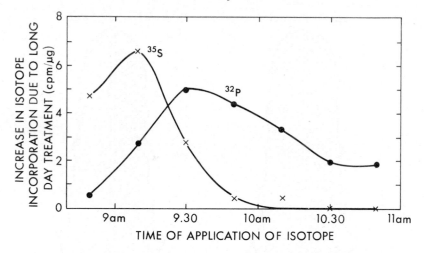

FIGURE 14–8. Effect of time of isotope application during Day II on the increase in incorporation of ^{32}P and ^{35}S by shoot apices due to long day treatment (from data of Evans and Rijven[24]).

Two other effects of induction on Day II apices were less clear, but suggestive for considerations of the nature of induction. Only a small proportion (7–17%) of the ^{32}P and ^{35}S reaching the shoot apices was incorporated into nucleic acids and proteins, yet the induced apices often imported more of the applied ^{32}P and ^{35}S than did vegetative apices, implying an early increase in their isotope uptake.[24,42] There was also a tendency for the leaf primordia subtending induced apices to incorporate more ^{32}P than did leaf primordia on vegetative apices.[42]

These observations suggest that the long-day stimulus may cause a general activation of the shoot apex, and a rapid increase in its sink strength. This latter effect could account for the marked increase in the amount of soluble nitrogenous compounds in Day IV apices.[41] The observations that the rate of leaf initiation at the shoot apex of young plants was increased by exposure to a number of long days insufficient for floral induction,[17] and that additional long days stimulated inflorescence development in mature plants regardless of when they are given,[15] also suggest a general activation of the shoot apex by the long-day stimulus.

However, floral induction also involves a localised activation of the cells between the leaf primordia, leading to precocious development of the axillary buds, as spikelet primordia. This can be seen histochemically in Day III apices by the accumulation of RNA in pockets of epidermal and hypodermal cells.[32] But it is evident even in Day II apices in the autoradiographic patterns of the incorporation of ^{32}P, ^{35}S and ^{3}H-orotic acid.[28,33] In vegetative apices the highest incorporation of all isotopes was at the summit of the shoot apex and in the leaf primordia accumulated down its flanks. The intervening pockets of cells in the axillary bud sites which ultimately give rise to the spikelets, were very low in activity, like the cells of the central core of the apex. By the middle of Day II, however, when the floral stimulus probably reached the shoot apex, there was a dramatic change in the pattern of incorporation. With ³H-orotic acid, for example, incorporation at the summit increased by 43 per cent and that in the leaf primordia by 38 per cent. In the cells of the axillary bud sites, however, incorporation increased by 184 per cent. A similar pattern was apparent with the other isotopes (Fig. 14–9).

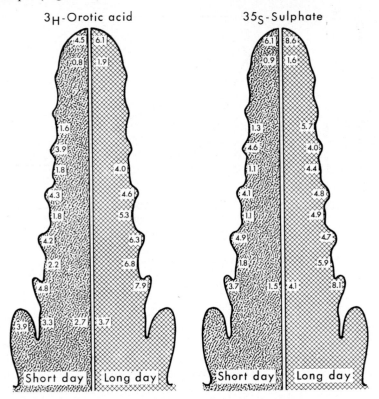

FIGURE 14–9. Pattern of incorporation of (*a*) ³H-orotic acid and (*b*) ³⁵S, as grains per 10.9 μ², in apices of *L. temulentum*. The left hand side of each apex gives average values for vegetative apices, the right hand side values for induced Day II apices (Knox and Evans[33]).

Thus, two elements are discernible in the early inductive events at the shoot apex, a general activation of apex metabolism, and a more striking but localized derepression of the cells at the axillary bud sites where the spikelets eventually differentiate. These two elements of floral induction in *L. temulentum* may be independent, since mere excision of the shoot apex from vegetative plants causes an immediate increase in incorporation by the cells at the axillary bud sites.[28]

23 Inflorescence Differentiation

Differentiation of the inflorescence following exposure to an inductive photoperiod begins more slowly in *L. temulentum* than in *Xanthium* or *Pharbitis*. One advantage of this is that it allows a clearer separation of the processes of induction and of differentiation.

No histochemical changes in DNA, RNA or histone patterns of the apices were evident on Day II.[32] By Day III a localized accumulation of RNA at the future spikelet sites was evident, and this was very marked in Day IV apices in which the hypodermal cells of the target areas expanded to produce the characteristic double ridges stage (Fig. 14–2*a*). Only after this stage did cell division in the target areas increase, causing rapid growth of the spikelet primordia, evident in Figure 14–2*b*.

These changes were reflected in changes in the chemical composition of shoot apices between Day I and Day IV.[41] In vegetative apices 58 per cent of the residual dry weight was protein, 27 per cent wall materials, and 14 per cent nucleic acids, half RNA and half DNA. Between Day I and Day IV, protein per apex increased by only 11 per cent, and DNA by 17 per cent, whereas RNA increased by 46 per cent. Although protein did not increase much in this interval, the soluble nitrogen content did so, from 23 to 124 mμg/apex. The relative growth rate (RGR) of the apices remained low during this interval, 0.07 g/g/day, compared with 0.05 g/g/day in vegetative apices.

After this latent period up to Day IV, the RGR of the apex rose rapidly to 0.45 g/g/day between Days IV and VI, and during this interval DNA content/apex increased by 95 per cent, RNA by 140 per cent, and protein by 160 per cent. During this period the rate of initiation of leaf primordia increased sharply, from one per 1.7 days in the vegetative apices to 5 or 6 per day. Spikelet primordia became morphologically evident on Day V (Fig. 14–2*b*); their cells were high in RNA, had large nuclei and nucleoli, and a marked heterogeneity within the nuclei in the density of DNA and histone staining.[32] Accompanying the marked increase in RNA staining at the spikelet sites between Day IV and Day V was an equally marked loss of RNA staining from the leaf primordia between them.

The shoot apices of *L. temulentum* accumulate a number (8–10) of potential spikelet sites before induction, and add rather more of them between Days IV and VII after induction. The cells of these latter sites do not exist when the floral stimulus reaches the shoot apex, yet normally it is these later formed upper spikelets which differentiate most rapidly, the terminal spikelet most rapidly of all. By contrast, when gibberellic acid was applied to plants in short days, it was the lowermost spikelets which were most advanced.[20] When ^{32}P was applied to the plants at induction, dissection 3 weeks later showed that whereas differentiation of the upper spikelets had proceeded more or less normally, that of the lower spikelets had not progressed beyond the earliest stages.[23] Presumably, decay of the ^{32}P incorporated at the lower spikelet sites at the time of induction, causing breakdown of the RNA synthesized there, has prevented further differentiation, whereas the upper spikelets, initiated several days later, were not affected.

Two kinds of induction may therefore occur; a direct induction of the lower spikelet sites by the photoperiodic stimulus from the leaves, and an indirect induction of the later formed sites, possibly by a quite different mechanism.

Conclusion

A recurrent theme in this chapter has been that flower induction in *L. temulentum* involves at least two components. There appear to be two separate photoperiodic processes in the leaves, one leading to the production of a floral stimulus in leaves exposed to a photoperiod of more than the critical length, the other to the production of an inhibitor of floral induction in leaves in short days. There is evidence that both stimulus and inhibitor are translocated from the leaves to the shoot apex where they interact quantitatively. Their identity is unknown, but the stimulus may be a steroid or a compound in the area of gibberellin metabolism. The effects of applied gibberellins could be due to the induced accumulation of some intermediate which stimulates a steroid pathway. The inhibitor may be abscisin.

When we look at inductive events at the shoot apex we also find evidence of dual action. There is a general stimulation of metabolism, involving increased uptake and increased RNA and protein synthesis, not only in the shoot apex but also in the leaf primordia. There is an increase in the rate of leaf initiation, which occurs in young plants even when flower induction does not. This general stimulation of apical activity by long days occurs whenever a long day is given, even after flower induction has occurred and inflorescence differentiation has begun. Besides this general stimulus there is also a more localised effect, evident in the activation of the cells which give rise to the spikelet primordia. Since prevention of the short-day inhibition by anaerobic conditions causes spikelet initiation without a general stimulation of the whole apex, the short-day inhibitor may specifically repress the cells of the axillary bud sites. Their activation following excision of the apex supports this suggestion. Thus, induction of flowering in *L. temulentum* by exposure to a long day probably involves de-repression of the cells of the axillary bud sites, during the temporary absence of the short-day inhibitor, combined with a general activation of apical metabolism by the long-day stimulus.

REFERENCES

[1] Arber, A. (1934). *The Gramineae. A study of cereal, bamboo and grass.* Univ. Press, Cambridge.
[2] Beddows, A. R. (1931). Seed setting and flowering in various grasses. *Welsh Plant Breed. Sta. Ser. H.*, 12.
[3] Borrill, M. (1959). Inflorescence initiation and leaf size in some Gramineae. *Ann. Bot. N.S.* 23, 217.
[4] Carns, H. R., Addicott, F. T. and Lynch, R. S. (1951). Some effects of water and oxygen on abscission *in vitro. Plant Physiol.* 26, 629.
[5] Cooper, J. P. (1951). Studies on growth and development in *Lolium* II. Pattern of bud development of the shoot apex and its ecological significance. *J. Ecol.* 39, 228.
[6] Cooper, J. P. (1952). Ibid. III. Influence of season and latitude on ear emergence. *J. Ecol.* 40, 352.
[7] Cooper, J. P. (1954). Ibid. IV. Genetic control of heading responses in local populations. *J. Ecol.* 42, 521.
[8] Cooper, J. P. (1956). Developmental analysis of populations in the cereals and herbage grasses. I. Methods and techniques. *J. Agric. Sci.* 47, 262.
[9] Cooper, J. P. (1960). Short day and low temperature induction in *Lolium. Ann. Bot. N.S.* 24, 232.
[10] Cooper, J. P. and Money-Kyrle, A. F. (1952). Inflorescence development in *Lolium* during the Arctic summer. *Nature* 169, 158.
[11] Cornforth, J. W., Millborrow, B. V., Ryback, G. and Wareing, P. F. (1965). Identity of sycamore dormin with abscisin II. *Nature* 205, 1269.
[12] Dennis, D. T., Upper, C. D. and West, C. A. (1965). An enzymic site of inhibition of gibberellin biosynthesis by Amo-1618 and other plant retardants. *Plant Physiol.* 40, 948.
[13] El-Antably, H. M. M., Wareing, P. F. and Hillman, J. (1967). Some physiological responses to D, L Abscisin (Dormin). *Planta* 73, 74.
[14] Evans, L. T. (1958). *Lolium temulentum L.*, a long day plant requiring only one inductive photocycle. *Nature* 182, 197.
[15] Evans, L. T. (1960). The influence of environmental conditions on inflorescence development in some long day grasses. *New Phytol.* 59, 163.
[16] Evans, L. T. (1960). The influence of temperature on flowering in species of *Lolium* and in *Poa pratensis. J. Agric. Sci.* 54, 410.
[17] Evans, L. T. (1960). Inflorescence initiation in *Lolium temulentum L.* I. Effect of plant age and leaf area on sensitivity to photoperiodic induction. *Aust. J. Biol. Sci.* 13, 123.
[18] Evans, L. T. (1960). Ibid. II. Evidence for inhibitory and promotive photoperiodic processes involving transmissible products. *Aust. J. Biol. Sci.* 13, 429.
[19] Evans, L. T. (1962). Ibid. III. The effect of anaerobic conditions during photoperiodic induction. *Aust. J. Biol. Sci.* 15, 281.
[20] Evans, L. T. (1964). Ibid. V. The role of auxins and gibberellins. *Aust. J. Biol. Sci.* 17, 10.
[21] Evans, L. T. (1964). Ibid. VI. Effects of some inhibitors of nucleic acid, protein, and steroid biosynthesis. *Aust. J. Biol. Sci.* 17, 24.
[22] Evans, L. T. (1966). Abscisin II: Inhibitory effect on flower induction in a long-day plant. *Science* 151, 107.
[23] Evans, L. T. Unpublished data.

[24] Evans, L. T. and Rijven, A. H. G. C. (1968). Inflorescence initiation in *Lolium temulentum L.* XI. Early increases in the incorporation of ^{32}P and ^{35}S by shoot apices during induction. *Aust. J. Biol. Sci.* **20,** 1033

[25] Evans, L. T. and Wardlaw, I. F. (1964). Ibid. IV. Translocation of the floral stimulus in relation to that of assimilates. *Aust. J. Biol. Sci.* **17,** 1.

[26] Evans, L. T. and Wardlaw, I. F. (1966). Independent translocation of ^{14}C-labelled assimilates and of the floral stimulus. *Planta* **68,** 310.

[27] Evans, L. T., Borthwick, H. A. and Hendricks, S. B. (1965). Inflorescence initiation in *Lolium temulentum L.* VII. The spectral dependence of induction. *Aust. J. Biol. Sci.* **18,** 745.

[28] Evans, L. T., Knox, R. B. and Rijven, A. H. G. C. (1968). The nature and localization of early events in the shoot apex of *Lolium temulentum* during floral induction. In *Cellular and Molecular Aspects of Floral Induction.* Ed. G. Bernier (in press).

[29] Goebel, K. (1884). Beiträge zur Entwicklungs-Geschichte einiger Inflorescenzen. *Jahrb. wiss. Bot.* **14,** 1.

[30] Holmes, W. L. and Di Tullio, N. W. (1962). Inhibitors of cholesterol biosynthesis which act at or beyond the mevalonic acid stage. *Amer. J. Clin. Nutrit.* **10,** 310.

[31] Husain, I. (1967). Ph.D. Thesis, University of Adelaide.

[32] Knox, R. B. and Evans, L. T. (1966). Inflorescence initiation in *Lolium temulentum L.* VIII. Histochemical changes at the shoot apex during induction. *Aust. J. Biol. Sci.* **19,** 233.

[33] Knox, R. B. and Evans, L. T. (1968). Ibid. XII. An autoradiographic study of evocation of the shoot apex. *Aust. J. Biol. Sci.* **21,** 1083.

[34] Lane, H. C., Cathey, H. M. and Evans, L. T. (1965). The dependence of flowering in several long-day plants on the spectral composition of light extending the photoperiod. *Amer. J. Bot.* **52,** 1006.

[35] Leaver, C. J. and Key, J. L. (1967). Polyribosome formation and RNA synthesis during aging of carrot-root tissue. *Proc. Nat. Acad. Sci.* **57,** 1338.

[36] Linschitz, H., Kasche, V., Butler, W. L. and Siegelman, H. W. (1966). The kinetics of phytochrome conversion. *J. Biol. Chem.* **241,** 3395.

[37] Mayfield, D. L., Lincoln, R. G., Hutchins, R. O. and Cunningham, A. (1963). Concentration of a floral-inducing entity from plant extracts. *J. Agric. Food Chem.* **11,** 35.

[38] Moldenke, H. N. and Moldenke, A. L. (1952). *Plants of the Bible* Chronica Bot., Waltham, Mass.

[39] Peterson, M. L. and Bendixen, L. E. (1963). Relationships of gibberellin and auxin to thermal induction of flowering in *Lolium temulentum L.* *Crop Sci.* **3,** 79.

[40] Peterson, M. L., Cooper, J. P. and Bendixen, L. E. (1961). Thermal and photoperiodic induction of flowering in darnel (*Lolium temulentum*) *Crop Sci.* **1,** 17.

[41] Rijven, A. H. G. C. and Evans, L. T. (1966). Inflorescence initiation in *Lolium temulentum L.* IX. Some chemical changes in the shoot apex at induction. *Aust. J. Biol. Sci.* **20,** 1.

[42] Rijven, A. H. G. C. and Evans, L. T. (1966). Ibid. X. Changes in ^{32}P incorporation into nucleic acids of the shoot apex at induction. *Aust. J. Biol. Sci.* **20,** 13.

[43] Steyn, D. G. (1933). Poisoning of human beings by weeds contained in cereals. *Onderstepoort J. Vet. Sci. An. Ind.* **1,** 219.

[44] Teltscherova, L., Seidlova, F. and Krekule, J. (1967). Effect of some pyrimidine analogues on flowering of long day and short day plants. *Biol. Plantar.* **9,** 234.

[45] Vince, D. (1965). The promoting effect of far-red light on flowering in the long day plant *Lolium temulentum.* *Physiol. Plantar.* **18,** 474.

[46] Vince, D. (1966). An interpretation of the promoting effect of far-red light on the flowering of long day plants. *Photochem. & Photobiol.* **5,** 449.

[47] Weber, H. (1939). Gramineen-studien I. Über das Verhalten des Gramineen-Vegetationskegels beim Übergang zur Inflorescenzbildung. *Planta* **28,** 275.

[48] Willing, R., Evans, L. T., Knox, R. B., Paton, L. and Wardlaw, I. F. (1968). Grafting of grasses (in preparation).

[49] Woodburn, T. L. (1965). A study into the lipid content of induced and non-induced leaves of *Xanthium pensylvanicum.* Wall., *Lolium temulentum L.*, and *Lycopersicon esculentum* Mill. var. Grosse Lisse. B.Sc.(Hons.) Thesis, Univ. New England, Armidale.

[50] Zeevaart, J. A. D. (1962). Physiology of flowering. *Science* **137,** 723.

[51] Zeevaart, J. A. D. (1963). Climatic control of reproductive development. In *Environmental Control of Plant Growth,* 189. Ed. L. T. Evans, Academic Press, N.Y.

[52] Zwar, J. A. and Evans, L. T. Unpublished data.

15

Silene armeria L.

By S. J. Wellensiek

1 History of Use

The caryophyllous *Silene armeria* L. was introduced as a long-day plant by
Liverman in 1952 and most, if not all, of the research with *S. armeria* has been
performed with strain 'N' of Liverman. His work is especially interesting with
regard to the interaction between temperature and different regimes of light and
darkness.

Since 1952 much work has been carried out in Japan, by Tashima on flowering
in total darkness, by Konishi on auxins, and by Takimoto on endogenous
rhythms and spectral dependence.

More recent work in Wageningen has resulted in the definition of induction
as the disappearance of an inhibition which occurs in vegetative plants. *S.
armeria* is characterized by the remarkable fact that induction is possible in at
least four ways:

1. Long day (LD), as already established by Liverman. In order to avoid
misinterpretation, it is necessary to indicate that the typical LD-action as such
takes place in a medium temperature region, around 20°C. This is symbolized
as '$LD_{20°}$'.
2. High temperatures in short day (SD), symbolized as '32° SD', as observed by Liverman.
3. Vernalizing low temperature in SD, symbolized as '5° SD'.
4. GA_7, which among the gibberellins acts very specifically in *S. armeria*,
according to Michniewicz and Lang.[11]

The inductive action of at least the first three of these factors follows from the
fact that after treatments of limited duration, which in themselves have no immediate visible effect, flower bud formation in $SD_{20°}$ starts and continues.
Konishi[3] characterized *S. armeria* as an irreversible bolting type in LD. In other
words, after optimal induction no desinduction takes place. However, after sub-
optimal induction, not resulting in flowering at $SD_{20°}$, complete desinduction
takes place in $SD_{20°}$, no matter what factor has induced.

2 Growing Techniques and Growth Habit

The growing of *Silene armeria* does not offer any difficulty. Seed dormancy is of
no importance. The seeds are sown in moist sand and germinate rapidly. The
seedlings are pricked out and potted in ordinary soil. Takimoto[16] grew *S. armeria*
in test tubes with a modified White's medium containing 5 per cent sucrose.
Water cultures are also relatively easy.

The growth habit in $SD_{20°}$ (8 hours light and 16 hours darkness, unless otherwise stated) is a vegetative rosette which is maintained indefinitely. When such
rosettes are transferred to LD (16 hours light and 8 hours darkness, unless otherwise stated) flower bud formation starts after 7–8 cycles, stem elongation 3 days
later, flower buds are macroscopically visible after 20–25 cycles, and open flowers
10 days later. These figures are of course subject to considerable modification
especially by temperature and light intensity.

When sown and grown in LD, the stem length of flowering plants is only

5–6 cm. When pregrown in SD and transferred to LD, the stem length may become 60 cm, after gibberellin treatment 100 cm according to Lang.[5] SD, when applied after LD-induction, reduces or destroys the apical dominance, resulting in up to 15 laterals growing out. This can be applied when growing *S. armeria* for decorative purposes. In this case rosettes at least 3 months old should be used when starting the LD-treatment.

3 Criteria of Flowering Response

The first visible flower bud arises from the terminal growing-tip. The number of days for visible flower bud formation can be accurately determined. The date of appearance of the first open flower is almost always 10 days later.

When a number of treatments end simultaneously, so that during the after-treatment all plants can be grown under the same conditions, the date of appearance of the first visible flower bud is a good criterion of flowering response. In most cases it is advisable to apply both $SD_{20°}$ and $LD_{20°}$ as after-treatments. In $SD_{20°}$, induction expresses itself by flower bud formation, while sub-optimal

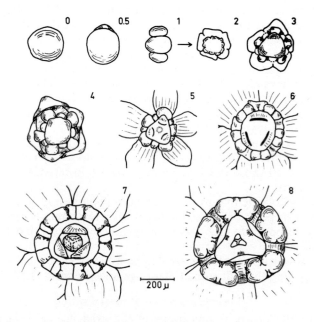

FIGURE 15–1. Scoring system for the development of the terminal meris-tems of *Silene armeria*, as seen from above.

0   = vegetative.
0.5 = first lateral inflorescence primordium.
1   = first and second lateral inflorescence primordia.
2   = calyx and earliest stamen differentiation in central terminal flower.
3   = 5 (+ 5) stamens.
4   = inner and outer circles of 5 stamens.
5   = 3 stigma primordia (calyx only partially indicated).
6   = inner circle of stamens with cross walls.
7   = outer circle of stamens with cross walls; placentae surrounded by 3 stigma primordia.
8   = inner stamens cover outer stamens; placentae still visible in centre.
9   = macroscopically visible flower bud.
10 = open flower.
(Wellensiek and Elings[27]).

induction does not give any flowering. The percentage of flowering indicates the degree of induction. In $LD_{20°}$ all plants will flower, but different treatments express themselves in differences in the number of days for visible flower bud formation. Plants of a certain treatment usually need two and a half times as many days for visible flower bud formation in $SD_{20°}$ as in $LD_{20°}$.

When treatments do not end simultaneously, the after-treatments should be carried out under strictly controlled conditions in order to allow comparison. This procedure is difficult and has turned out to be less satisfactory. A much better method is to score the stage of development of the terminal flower bud microscopically immediately after the treatments. Takimoto[13] used a scale from 0 to 6, Wellensiek and Elings[27] a scale from 0 to 10 (Fig. 15–1).

An unsolved difficulty is the separation of induction and realization. Flowering in $SD_{20°}$ means optimal induction, but realization may have already started before this after-treatment. Realization does not depend on any specific factor.

4 Effects of Plant Age

Higazy[2] exposed to LD plants previously grown for 6, 7, . . . 12 weeks in SD. The mean number of days to budding decreased from 71.2 to 45.3 respectively, with negligible differences between plants 10 and 12 weeks old. On the basis of these results it is safe to start experimental treatments with plants 3 months old. Next Higazy used plants 0, 3, 6, . . . 27 days old, one set grown in high and another in low light intensity (4773 and 942 μ W/cm^2 ϕ sphere respectively). Plants up to 15 days old when the LD-treatment started did not show any difference in flowering response, but as the age increased, the difference between the two sets increased in favour of the high light intensity plants. This difference amounted to 34 days with plants 27 days old.

In a recent experiment I have sown and grown plants in LD for 1, 2, . . . 9 weeks. After simultaneous transfer to SD, plants up to 4 weeks in LD did not flower, whereas all those in LD for 8 or 9 weeks flowered, with a transitional group in between.

These results indicate that in young plants a condition of low or no response to LD exists. This period of juvenility lasts only a few weeks. High light intensity increases the response to LD considerably which suggests that photosynthesis may be involved.

Juvenility towards vernalizing low temperature does not exist. No data are available regarding the influence of plant age on the effects of 32° SD and GA .

5 Vernalization and Devernalization

According to Wellensiek[20] indications of the existence of a vernalization response in *S. armeria* are:

(*a*) After exposure to 5° SD during 14 weeks 21 $LD_{20°}$ cycles were needed for visible flower bud, while unvernalized controls needed 28 cycles (c.f. Fig. 15–2).

(*b*) After the same vernalizing treatment flower buds were visible after 53 cycles of $SD_{20°}$ which indicates an optimal induction.

(*c*) Flowering may even occur during the vernalizing treatment in SD: plants 8, 12 or 16 weeks old were exposed to 5° SD, and 77, 100 and 92 per cent had visible flower buds after 357, 338, and 319 days respectively.

Exposure of plants to intermittent temperatures of 5° and 20° during SD, or to a short period of darkness at 5°, 20° or 32° before $SD_{20°}$, showed that the dark inhibition exists at 5°. The effect of 5° SD is, therefore, a true vernalization effect.

LD-action is not excluded at 5°, so that at 5° LD both vernalization and photo-periodic induction take place. The two processes can be separated almost completely by applying light of different qualities during vernalization. Fluorescent light has little photoperiodic effect compared with incandescent light. With these two light sources at 5°, no difference was found in SD, but a very large difference in LD in favour of incandescent light. This difference increased with the duration of the treatment.

The use of the two light sources at 5° in SD and in LD made it possible to estimate the vernalization effect and the photoperiodic effect for plants of different initial ages and for different periods. When plants 4, 8, 12 or 16 weeks old were treated, age, and duration of treatment above a minimum did not influence the vernalization effect, but did influence the LD-effect considerably: the older the plants and the longer the treatment, the better.

The absence of any age effect on vernalization is in harmony with results on seed vernalization. Germinating seeds in wet sand were exposed to 5° SD for different periods and after-treated in SD $_{20°}$. After 10 weeks at 5° SD some flowering occurred, while after 12 weeks 49 per cent flowering occurred after an average of 111 days. Longer treatments were not applied.

The demonstration of devernalization of plants by high temperatures[26] is complicated by the inductive action which takes place at those high temperatures. Several attempts were made to separate the inductive action from a possible devernalizing action. This was done by having vernalization followed by 32° SD and simultaneously determining the net vernalization effect and the net 32° SD effect. If the effect of these two was significantly larger than the combined vernalization + 32° SD effects, devernalization might have taken place. This was found sometimes, but the possible devernalization effect was only between 0.1 and 1.9 days. These values are so small that no definite conclusion about the existence of devernalization by high temperature is justified. If such a devernalization occurred, the devernalizing action of 32° SD would oppose its own inducing action!

6 Short Day Vernalization

SD at ordinary temperatures around 20°C never have a vernalizing action.

7 Photoperiod Response

Liverman and Lang[7] obtained a photoperiodic response curve in *S. armeria*, which is similar to that of *Hyoscyamus* in showing hardly any response in photoperiods of less than 11 hours and a rapidly increasing response between 11 and 16 hours, levelling off at longer photoperiods.

Liverman[8] found a critical daylength of between 10 and 11 hours for his strain 'C' and between 12 and 13 hours for his strain 'N', which is the one used almost exclusively in research on *S. armeria*. This points to genetic differences.

I have exposed groups of plants to 12 hours of high intensity illumination each day before exposure to 0 to 3 hours of low intensity incandescent light, for 3 to 6 weeks, followed by LD$_{20°}$. No response to 12 hours of light each day was found, but 12.5 hours was clearly inductive. The flowering response increased strikingly from 13 to 13.5 hours. In another experiment groups of plants received 0, 3, 6, 9 or 12 cycles of LD$_{20°}$, were then exposed to 7 photoperiods of 9.5 to 12.5 hours, and were finally exposed to LD$_{20°}$ if no flowering had occurred. Plants with a pretreatment of 9 or 12 LD$_{20°}$ were optimally induced when the different photoperiods started. The critical daylength of the others was not influenced by their pretreatment. It was above 12 hours.

The finding of somewhat different values for the critical daylength in different experiments is not surprising, since Liverman and Lang[8,9] established that the critical daylength is influenced by the temperature. The research on this relation is complicated by the fact that at rather low temperatures vernalization may occur, while very high temperatures may be themselves inductive. This implies that the actual effect of temperature on photoperiodism can be studied in only a limited region. Of Liverman's temperature series, 30°, 23°, 17° and 10°, the first must be excluded. At the other three, the critical daylength was longest at 10°.

I have studied the influence of temperature on the critical daylength by making use of the decreasing natural daylength in autumn and the increasing daylength in spring, at 6 temperatures from 9 to 24°C. Groups of vegetative plants were placed in each temperature at weekly intervals in spring and autumn for 3 weeks and then transferred to 24°C and 16 hours of artificial light daily. With increasing daylengths the critical day length was found near 13 hours 26 minutes (sunrise to sunset) without a detectable influence of the temperature. With decreasing daylength – which by visual observation of the plants was better – the critical daylength was near 12 hours 50 minutes at 9° and 12°C, it was perhaps somewhat lower at 15° and it was near 12 hours 22 minutes at 18°, 21° and 24°. This means that increasing temperature decreases the critical daylength.

In conclusion, Liverman's critical daylength between 12 and 13 hours can still be accepted, but this value holds for one genetical strain and it is influenced by temperature.

The number of LD-cycles for optimal induction was found by Liverman[8] to be 7. This number is variable, being influenced by genotype, temperature, photoperiod and light intensity.

In my own experiments with Liverman's strain 'N', virtually no flower bud formation in $SD_{20°}$ took place after 1 to 5 cycles of $LD_{20°}$, 100 per cent flower bud formation usually took place in $SD_{20°}$ after 10 or more cycles of $LD_{20°}$, with 6 to 9 $LD_{20°}$ cycles as a region of transition, in which the percentage of flowering increased rapidly. Selection during two generations for rapid or slow induction has resulted in a line in which there was 90 per cent flowering in $SD_{20°}$ after 6 cycles of $LD_{20°}$, and one which did not flower at all in $SD_{20°}$ after 12 cycles of $LD_{20°}$. Clearly, there are genetical differences in the number of LD-cycles required for optimal induction, rapid induction probably being recessive. The availability of genetically homogeneous, rapidly or slowly inducible lines will be useful for getting a deeper insight into the nature of floral induction.

The number of LD-cycles required for induction decreases rapidly with increasing temperature, and with increase in the daylength. Regarding the threshold intensity for photoperiodic action Liverman[8] has fixed it between 0.7 and 2.0 f.c. of continuous light.

I exposed plants at 21°C to photoperiods of 16 hours at intensities 100 ($= 30,000$ erg/cm^2/sec), 75, 50, 25 per cent. Vegetative plants, exposed to these conditions, needed 30.6, 33.5, 38.5 and 41.5 days respectively for visible flower buds. In a second experiment 6 rooms with temperatures 9° to 24°C were used, each with 4 light intensities, 55, 50, 30 and 4.5 $\times$ 10^3 erg/cm^2/sec. No flower bud formation occurred at 9° in 98 days, when the experiment was stopped. Otherwise, the numbers of days for visible flower bud decreased rapidly with rising temperature, except at the lowest light intensity, and increased with decreasing light intensity, except at 24°. Evidently the effect of the highest temperature was dominant.

The only reference to light break treatments is by Takimoto,[14] who found light from fluorescent and incandescent lamps equally effective.

This section is concluded by stating that critical daylength and number of cycles are influenced by genetic factors, temperature and light intensity, so that no fixed values can be given.

8 Spectral Dependence

Takimoto[14] compared continuous illumination from daylight fluorescent lamps with that from incandescent lamps and found the former almost completely ineffective, the latter fully effective. This is ascribed to the longer wavelengths (infra-red) in the latter. Indeed, Takimoto[16] obtained 100 per cent flower bud formation by exposing plants during 3 months to continuous infra-red only. Since plants in soil did not grow under infra-red irradiation, the plants were cultured aseptically on White's medium with 5 per cent sucrose. When light of other spectral regions was mixed with infra-red, flowering was reduced. Under SD flowering never occurred.

Following Takimoto's results, Wellensiek[20] has compared fluorescent lamps (Philips 55 and 29) with incandescent lamps. No flower buds were visible after 28 days of continuous illumination from the fluorescent lamps, and 7.3 and 9.1 more cycles of ordinary LD respectively were necessary. Plants had visible flower buds after 13.4 days of continuous illumination from incandescent lamps. At 5°C fluorescent light had hardly any effect.

In another study Takimoto[15] found that fluorescent light for 18 hours per day did not induce flowering during a period of 2 weeks. When 8 hours of incandescent light per day were included in the photoperiod, induction took place. This supplementary incandescent light was much more effective when given at the end of the fluorescent illumination than when given at the beginning. Takimoto concluded that two light processes are involved, one requiring relatively high light intensity, the other giving rise to a positive flower promoting effect and requiring light of relatively long wavelengths. Both processes are considered as different from the low intensity light process which destroys the dark inhibition, since in this process fluorescent and incandescent light are equally effective. Regarding this dark inhibition Takimoto concluded that it is stronger when preceded by fluorescent light than when preceded by incandescent light.

No literature on the action of phytochrome in *S. armeria* is known, but the available information makes it a promising plant for this purpose.

9 Endogenous Rhythms

Tashima and Imamura[17] reported that *S. armeria* is capable of initiating flower primordia in total darkness, i.e. independently of light. Further details about e.g. pretreatment, duration of treatment, or light during observations, are lacking. Takimoto[16] did not obtain any flower bud formation when growing *S. armeria* for 3 months on an artificial medium in total darkness. At the other extreme, in continuous light *S. armeria* initiates flower primordia most rapidly.

It seems as if neither light nor darkness is essential, but specific actions of these two factors evidently take place when they alternate. Since Lang[7] reported that after defoliation no flower formation was obtained in either SD or LD, the presence of leaves is essential for the perception of light.

The ratio of light and darkness in a 24-hour cycle has already been discussed. In a 48-hour cycle Liverman[8] found the critical daylength in strain 'N' to be 9 hours, which is much shorter than in a 24-hour cycle. In his 72-hour cycle most of the plants died, but flowering did occur with 48 hours light and 24 hours darkness.

Takimoto[13] studied the effects of 30 combinations of durations of light (4 to 24 hours) and 11 durations of darkness (4 to 36 hours). The plants received 10 cycles and were then transferred to SD of 8 hours light and 16 hours darkness. After 2 to 3 weeks the plants were scored. With a given light period, flower initiation decreased with increasing dark period. With a given dark period, flower initiation increased with increasing light period. With 12 hours light or less, no floral initiation took place with 14 hours or more darkness, but with 14 hours light or more, floral initiation took place with all dark periods applied, up to 36 hours, although the degree of flowering decreased as the dark periods increased. The conclusion is arrived at that flower initiation depends on the ratio of the durations of the light and the dark periods. This conclusion is in harmony with the concept of a dark inhibition which is destroyed by light or, as Takimoto suggests, the dark period may destroy the effect of a light period, unless the latter has been fixed after relatively much light.

In Takimoto's data there is no indication of a rhythmical change with increasing cycle length, but this was not the object of his investigations. There is perhaps one exception and this is a remarkable periodicity in the flowering response for cycles with equal periods in light and in darkness. The per cent flowering with cycle lengths of 8, 16, 24, 32 and 48 hours was 100, 66, 36, 71 and 100 respectively.

The meaning of this regularity remains open. It can be added that I have never found any flowering response from 12 hours light and 12 hours darkness, nor has Liverman[8] or Finn[1] in strain 'N' at ordinary temperatures. Takimoto combined 16 hours light with 6 durations of darkness, 8 to 32 hours, and found a decreasing flower-response which, however, did not go down to 0 per cent, but to 33 per cent. In addition, I applied 8 cycles of 16 hours light with 32 or 56 hours darkness, but found no flowering response with either. These investigations are limited, but yield no evidence in favour of a rhythmicity.

Finn[1] studied the effects of 12 hours light combined with 3 to 60 hours darkness and found the flowering response suppressed in cycle lengths of 24 to 36 hours, but reappearing with cycle lengths of 39 and 42 hours, with no flowering response to the longer cycle lengths. When 14 hours light were combined with 4 to 46 hours darkness, clear responses were found with cycle lengths of 18 and 24 hours only. When 15 hours light were combined with 3 to 45 hours darkness, flowering was suppressed with a cycle length of 30 hours, reappeared slightly with a cycle length of 36 hours, reappeared clearly with cycle lengths of 39 and 42 hours, and was suppressed with longer cycle lengths. Although in two experimental series some rhythmical response was apparent, as a whole experiments with *S. armeria* do not contribute to a solution of the problem of diurnal rhythmicity.

10 Fractional Induction

Wellensiek[18] interrupted a continuous light treatment after 0, 1, 2 . . . or 0, 2, 4 . . . days with 2 days of complete darkness. No effect of the darkness was observed. In a further experiment,[25] alternating $LD_{20°}$ and $SD_{20°}$ cycles were applied for 6 to 8 weeks but the SD cycles did not exert any inhibitory influence. However, the picture changes when several LD cycles are followed by several $SD_{20°}$ cycles.

When 2 to 8 LD cycles were followed by 1 week of $SD_{20°}$, the flowering behaviour in a LD after-treatment demonstrated that induction proceeded during the SD, to a greater extent the more LD cycles had been given as first treatment. However, when the LD cycles were followed by 2 weeks of $SD_{20°}$, a desinduction started in the second week of $SD_{20°}$, and this desinduction was greater than the increase of the induction during the first week of $SD_{20°}$, but did not destroy induction completely. Three to 4 weeks of $SD_{20°}$ destroyed all preceding induction completely, or completely rebuilt the inhibition of flowering.

To test the possibility that the inhibitory effect of leaves in $SD_{20°}$ is restricted to the youngest, just expanding, leaves, some partial defoliation experiments were done. Instead of diminishing the inhibitory effect it was, if anything, slightly increased.

Similar experiments were performed with 32° SD and 5° SD as inductive factors. The results were essentially the same. Certain discrepancies pointed to the possibility that the transition from $LD_{20°}$ to $SD_{20°}$ requires adaptation of the plant to the new light regime, while the transition from 5° to 20° needs a still greater adaptation to the new temperature. The desinduction after 5° SD, hence after vernalization, can be considered as a devernalizing action of $SD_{20°}$.

The fact that suboptimal induction by no matter what factor – $LD_{20°}$, 32° SD or 5° SD – is desinduced by $SD_{20°}$ of long enough duration, gives rise to the concept that all three factors influence one and the same process.

11 Photoperiodic Inhibition

Liverman[8] observed that high temperatures are inductive, also when applied only during the dark period. Cycles of 10 hours light and 14 hours darkness resulted in flower bud formation when the temperature during the dark period was 30°, but not when the temperature during the light period was 30° and during the dark period 23°C. Wellensiek[20,22] established this high temperature effect independently. Over 7 experiments with intermittent temperatures of 20° and 32°C in SD for 3 or 4 weeks, the numbers of subsequent LD for visible flower bud formation were:

8 hours light	16 hours darkness	
20°	20°	25.9
32°	32°	8.7
20°	32°	9.3
32°	20°	27.3

These results were interpreted by assuming an inhibition towards flower bud formation in vegetative plants, which exists at 20°C, but is destroyed at 32°C, when this temperature is given during both the light and dark periods or during the dark period only. This points to a dark-dependent inhibition. It is conceivable that the inductive action of $LD_{20°}$ is a destruction of this inhibition by light beyond the critical day length. There are no arguments against the reasoning that the vernalizing action of 5° SD is also a destruction of the inhibition. If this holds true, the inhibition evidently has a narrow temperature regime which lies between > 5° and < 32°C.

In recent experiments much higher temperatures, up to 42°C, in SD were applied and these were found highly inductive, even when applied only to the root system. This is interpreted as floral induction in the roots by a localized destruction of the inhibition.

Wellensiek and Elings[27] have concluded that the inhibition in *S. armeria* is not translocated from leaves in SD to the growing-point. Partially defoliated vegetative plants with elongated stems, obtained by administering low doses of gibberellic acid, were used. The upper and lower leaves were exposed to different daylength conditions. The treatments lasted 3 weeks, after which the stages of development of the terminal bud were scored. Plants with leaf pairs did not yield full conclusive results, but these were obtained when a comparison was made between (a) plants with one leaf in LD on the lower part of the stem and one leaf in SD on the upper part of the stem, but connected with a different vascular strand, and (b) plants with one leaf in LD on the lower part of the stem only. The average flowering-scores were 3.5 and 2.9 respectively, the difference not being significant. Hence no inhibitory action has been translocated from the leaf in SD to the growing-tip.

13 Effects of Temperature

Excluding inducing effects of rather low and high temperatures, the regime between 10° and 25°C remains. Liverman[8] studied the effects of 10°, 17° and 23° at
different day lengths. Above the critical day length exposures to 10° reduced the
flowering response, and between 17° and 23° there was little difference.

I have exposed vegetative plants to 6 temperatures of 9° to 24°C under 16 hours
artificial light. The treatments lasted 5 weeks and were followed by LD at 20°.
The average numbers of $LD_{20°}$-cycles for visible flower bud formation were
30.3, 25.1, 19.9, 12.7, 1.1 and 0.5 after 9, 12, 15, 18, 21 and 24° respectively, indicating an optimum near 24°. It should be kept in mind that both induction and
realization processes may contribute to this optimum.

Wellensiek[26] has studied the relations between the flower inducing conditions
5° SD and 32° SD, including $LD_{20°}$. To illustrate the methods used, the relation
between $LD_{20°}$ and 32° SD will be presented. Vegetative plants were exposed to
0, 2, ... 12 cycles of $LD_{20°}$, each followed by 0, 2, ... 12 days of 32° SD. While
4 cycles of $LD_{20°}$, or 8 days of 32° SD, caused no induction alone, their combination yielded 70 per cent flowering. Similar interactions were found between induction by $LD_{20°}$, by 32° SD and by 5° SD, and between these 3 conditions and

FIGURE 15–2. Vernalization and long day induction of *Silene armeria*.
The plants were treated with (left) 10 cycles of $LD_{20°}$, (centre) 6 weeks of
5°SD, and (right) 6 weeks of 5°SD and 10 cycles of $LD_{20°}$; all then received an after-treatment of 6 weeks of $SD_{20°}$ (after Wellensiek[26]).

GA_3 though less clearly. Desinduction in $SD_{20°}$ occurs with all the inducing conditions. These results are an argument in favour of the concept that all inducing
factors, at least $LD_{20°}$, 32° SD and 5° SD, influence the same process.

17 Grafting Experiments

The existence of a floral stimulus follows from grafting experiments as described
by Wellensiek.[23] The technique used was an ordinary split graft, which requires
elongated stems. Flowering plants used as donors (D) always have elongated
stems, but vegetative rosette plants, to be used as acceptors (A), must be brought
to stem elongation by a treatment with gibberellic acid. In order to avoid induction, the dosage of gibberellic acid was determined as not more than a total of
200 μg/plant. Induction by very high temperatures must also be avoided, and the
grafts were raised at $SD_{20°}$. Most of the experiments were done with $LD_{20°}$-
induced donors, but small scale experiments have revealed that essentially the

same results are obtained after induction by 32° SD, 5° SD or GA. In one experiment defoliation of D and/or A took place.

Grafts of D on A (D/A) gave a lower percentage of flowering A's, and required more days for the appearance of a visible flower bud on A, than A/D grafts, e.g. A in D/A gave 67 per cent flowering after 66 days, while A in A/D gave 100 per cent after 54 days.

The experiments were accompanied by an investigation of the flow of assimilates in grafted S. *armeria* plants by De Stigter.[12] who administered $^{14}CO_2$ to a leaf of either stock or scion in both the combinations D/A and A/D, and determined the presence of radioactive sugars in the other graft partner by autoradiography. He found that the upward movement of assimilates is much stronge- than the downward movement, which is in harmony with the above mentioned comparison between D/A and A/D, assuming that the floral stimulus is translocated with the mass flow of assimilates.

Other observations support this last assumption. Wellensiek[23] has found, that the flowers on D in D/A must be removed; otherwise apical dominance prevents the lateral buds on the A-stocks from growing out, and the floral stimulus from expressing itself. On the basis of these results the flowers on D in A/D were originally removed. However, the local apical dominance is destroyed by doing this, the laterals grow out and evidently attract the mass flow of assimilates, so that the necessary upward movement of the stimulus is hampered and the flowering of A is poor. The effect is less marked as in the case of D/A. De Stigter[12] has also studied the effect of removing the flowers on D in A/D and found a decided reduction of the upward translocation of assimilates.

Defoliation treatments also are in harmony with the translocation of the floral stimulus with the flow of assimilates. For example, A/D with defoliated A flowered after 45 days against 54 days when the leaves were kept on A. De Stigter confirmed this result in terms of the flow of assimilates.

In the treatments of Wellensiek and Elings[27] on the flower formation of partially defoliated plants some results point to a translocation of the floral stimulus: after 3 weeks of exposure to LD, plants with one leaf pair on the upper part of the stem reached score 6.1 of floral development, while plants with one leaf pair on the lower part of the stem reached the significantly lower score of 4.9. This low value must be ascribed to the longer distance which the floral stimulus has to travel to reach the terminal growing-tip.

The available evidence for S. *armeria* is in harmony with the generally accepted concept that the floral stimulus moves with the mass flow of assimilates.

The necessary minimal duration of a graft union in D/A can be studied by removing the D's at various times after the original graftings. Wellensiek[23] has done this after 2, 3, 4, 5 or 6 weeks and found no flowering A's after 2 weeks contact, but 70–100 per cent flowering in the other groups. This means that a union of 2 weeks is too short, but that a union of 3 weeks is sufficient. De Stigter[12] found no functional vessel union 5 days after grafting, a small downward translocation after 7 days and a distinct translocation in both directions after 9 days.

Further results refer to the necessary minimal duration of a graft union in A/D. The technique used was to start from a number of A/D grafts and to remove and regraft the original A_1's periodically on new A's, indicated as A_2. Graft unions of 2 or 3 days were too short to bring A_1 into flowering after regrafting, but this happened to a small percentage after graft contacts of 4 days, while the percentage of flowering A_1 increased rapidly with graft unions of 5 to 8 days. De Stigter has accompanied these experiments by an investigation on the translocation of $^{14}CO_2$

and found a pronounced translocation after 4 days of graft contact, earlier than in his above mentioned first investigation.

Hence the necessary minimal duration of graft contact is much longer in D/A than in A/D. The very small necessary duration of the graft contact in A/D implies that only a very small amount of the floral stimulus is necessary for ultimate flower bud formation.

Some defoliation treatments by Wellensiek[23] have given unexpected results. In both D/A and A/D the D's were defoliated and nevertheless flowering A's were obtained, 37.5 per cent after 78 days and 60 per cent after 63 days respectively, again showing better results in the case of upward translocation. These results indicate that leaves on D are not essential, once the stimulus is present.

The persistence of the floral stimulus has been demonstrated in a variety of experiments. First, in the experiment described above in which the D's were removed periodically from D/A, the D's were regrafted on new A's. As far as the graftings were successful, 100 per cent flowering was obtained in the new A's for all times of removal. Second, in the regrafting of A_1 from A_1/D on A_2 not only the regrafted A_1's flowered, but also the A_2's some 3 weeks later, so that the stimulus moved from the A_1's to their new stocks, where it functioned. Third, Wellensiek[23] has used flowering A's from both D/A and A/D as D's in new graftings and twice in 3 successive series obtained flowering A's in high percentages, up to 100 per cent. A similar series of 3 successive graftings was done, starting with D's which had been induced by 5° SD. The results were essentially the same.

The conclusion was drawn that the floral stimulus is an autocatalytically multiplying substance and this conclusion is corroborated by the above results on the small amount of necessary stimulus, on the fact that leaves on D are not essential, on the functioning of D from D/A when used in regraftings, and on the functioning of A from D/A and A/D as D in a new grafting. It explains why reversion to the vegetative state never occurs in generative plants.

The question: 'When does the production of the floral stimulus start?' is of paramount importance. In answering this question we start from the conclusions that a very small amount of the stimulus is sufficient for bringing about flower formation, and that in newly made grafts an inhibited vegetative partner and an induced stimulus-producing partner form one system where the stimulus is always able to express itself, however small its amount may be in the beginning. These conclusions exclude the possibility that stimulus production starts during induction as a direct effect of an inducing factor. The reason is that desinduction after sub-optimal induction could not exist, because tiny amounts of stimulus would express themselves by flower formation in the long run and this does not occur.

Hence stimulus production begins after optimal induction. This answer is also reached by considering a newly made graft combination of D and A. Evidently the inhibition in A does not influence the multiplication, the translocation and the functioning of the stimulus, so that an inhibition of the beginning of stimulus production in vegetative plants remains. Only when the inhibition has been removed by induction can the production of the stimulus start.

This concept is different from what was supposed earlier,[23] that in newly made grafts the first function of the stimulus was to remove the inhibition in the vegetative partner. For this process the term 'indirect induction' was adopted. The available information suggests, however, that in the acceptors the inhibition and the stimulus occur side by side, and that the stimulus functions and is not hampered by the inhibition. This renders the term 'indirect induction' superfluous.[24] The floral induction in roots by very high temperatures supports this view, because evidently the stimulus moves upwards from the roots and functions in the upper part of the plant which is inhibited.

One problem remains and this is when and how the stimulus, with its great persistence, disappears. It is evidently not present in the seed, but whether it disappears at meiosis or later is completely unknown.

18 Effects of Growth Substances

The growth substances which have been studied in relation to flower formation in *S. armeria* are auxins, gibberellins and dormin. Konishi[3] found much more auxin in bolting plants than in rosette plants, and less auxin-destruction in the former. Floral initiation and bolting were supposed to be correlated, but not to depend on the same factors.[4] In rosette plants and at the beginning of bolting little auxin was found due to IAA oxidation matching production. In bolting plants, high production and little destruction, due to inhibition of IAA oxidase, result in much auxin. High auxin was found before flowering due to high production and little consumption on account of a decreased growth rate. Konishi[4] states that bolting and flowering took place following spraying of plants with IAA solution (50 μg/ml) every day for about 2 months at 20°C. Liverman and Lang[10] obtained a similar result. They applied several concentrations of IAA under threshold photoperiod conditions during 1 or 2 weeks, followed by SD. The spraying was applied during 33 days. In one case 100 per cent flowering was obtained against 65 per cent in the controls, in another 50 per cent against 0 per cent in the controls.

Lang[5] reported a positive, but relatively weak and late flowering response to applied gibberellins, apparently as a secondary effect following stem elongation. With daily treatment of plants with gibberellins at different concentrations, Lang[6] obtained 100 per cent flowering with 50 or 100 μg per plant per day. Negative results were obtained by Wellensiek,[19] who treated vegetative plants in SD during different periods with gibberellin, although plants with stems of 6.5 to 14.1 cm were obtained. After transferring the plants to continuous light, they all flowered simultaneously. Higazy[2] also observed little if any effect from a treatment of limited duration.

Michniewicz and Lang[11] compared the responses of *S. armeria* to the 9 then known gibberellins. Flowering was obtained only with GA_7. The quantity administered was 150 μg/plant, and tenfold this amount of GA_3 did not give any flowering response. This indicates a great specificity among the gibberellins. It may also explain the earlier favourable effects which were obtained with commercial GA_3, which may be contaminated with GA_4 and GA_7 by as much as 10 per cent.

Dormin, applied in aqueous solution to the growing-tip, reduced apical dominance, retarded the flower bud formation on the main stem 8 to 9 days, did not influence the flowering of the laterals, and reduced the length of the main stem with approximately 50 per cent. Suppression of flower bud formation did not occur.

Conclusion

The processes which influence flower bud formation in *S. armeria* were dealt with by Wellensiek,[21] who stressed the existence of both an inhibition and a floral stimulus. In a very preliminary form[24] a new concept of the flower forming mechanism was presented. It is now possible to develop a more complete picture. For this purpose we shall first synthesize the conclusions drawn above. Three processes should be distinguished: inhibition, induction, and realization by the floral stimulus. We then find:

I.   *Inhibition*

   In vegetative plants in $SD_{20°}$ a non-translocated inhibition blocks the beginning of the production of a floral stimulus.

II. *Induction*

Induction is the removing of the inhibition, by $LD_{20°}$, $32°$ SD, $5°$ SD, or GA_7. That at least the first three inducing factors act on one process follows from:

(a) Desinduction to the completely inhibited state by $SD_{20°}$ of long enough duration after sub-optimal induction.

(b) The marked interaction between them.

III. *Realization by the floral stimulus*

Flower bud formation takes place through the action of a floral stimulus. Its production starts after optimal induction. Once present, it behaves as an autocatalytic substance. Its multiplication is not restricted to the leaves. After optimal induction flower bud formation is a neutral process, which takes place under all circumstances which permit growth.

In an attempt to understand the mechanism of flower bud formation, a starting-point is the resemblance of the floral stimulus to self-multiplying RNA viruses. If the floral stimulus is a specific RNA, a corresponding specific DNA must occur. Adapting our terminology to that of molecular biology, the inhibition in vegetative plants corresponds to a blocking or repression of the specific DNA, induction to derepression, and desinduction to rerepression.

The revised picture then becomes as follows:

I. *Repression*

In vegetative plants in $SD_{20°}$ a specific DNA is repressed.

II. *Derepression*

Derepression is possible by $LD_{20°}$, etc. Rerepression takes place in $SD_{20°}$ of long enough duration after sub-optimal derepression.

III. *Floral stimulus*

After optimal derepression the DNA is no longer blocked and forms a specific, self-multiplying RNA, which either is the floral hormone or is an important step in its synthesis.

This concept has been derived indirectly and by analogy. However, it fits the available experimental data, e.g. the non-translocation of the repression (histones?), and the floral induction in roots.

REFERENCES

[1] Finn, J. C. (1958). An investigation of long and short-day plants for an endodiurnal rhythmicity in the flowering response. Ph.D. Thesis, U. C. L. A.

[2] Higazy, M. K. M. T. (1962). Shortening the juvenile phase for flowering. *Meded. Landbouwhogesch. Wageningen* **62**, (8), 1.

[3] Konishi, M. (1954). Development of flowering stalks in *Silene armeria* in relation to auxin metabolism. *Proc. Japan Acad. Sci.* **30**, 24.

[4] Konishi, M. (1956). Studies in development of flowering stalks in long-day plants in relation to auxin metabolism. *Mem. Coll. Agric. Kyoto Univ.* **75**, 1.

[5] Lang, A. (1957). The gibberellins and their role in plant growth and development. *Un. int. Sci. biol. Serie B* No. 34, 55.

[6] Lang, A. (1957). The effect of gibberellin on flower formation. *Proc. Nat. Acad. Sci.* **43**, 709.

[7] Lang, A. (1965). Physiology of flower initiation. *Handb. Pflanzenphys.* XV/1, 1380.

[8] Liverman, J. L. (1952). The physiology and biochemistry of flowering. Ph.D. Thesis, Catltech. Pasadena, Cal.

[9] Liverman, J. L. and Lang, A. (1951). Influence of temperature on the photoperiodic response of *Silene armeria*. *Abstr. Ann. Meet. Western Soc. Naturalists*, Pomona Coll., Claremont, Cal.

[10] Liverman, J. L. and Lang, A. (1956). Induction of flowering in long day plants by applied indoleacetic acid. *Pl. Phys.* **31** (2), 147.

[11] Michniewicz, M. and Lang, A. (1962). Effects of nine different gibberellins on stem

elongation and flower formation in cold-requiring and photoperiodic plants grown under non-inductive conditions. *Planta* **58**, 549.

[12] Stigter, H. C. M. de (1966). Parallelism between the transport of C^{14}-photosynthates and the flowering response in grafted *Silene armeria L .Ztsch. Pflanzenphys.* **55**, 11.

[13] Takimoto, A. (1955). Flowering response to various combinations of light and dark periods in *Silene armeria. Bot. Mag. (Tokyo)* **68**, 308.

[14] Takimoto, A. (1957). Photoperiodic induction in *Silene armeria* as influenced by various light sources. *Bot. Mag. (Tokyo)* **70**, 312.

[15] Takimoto, A. (1957). Two processes involved in the light period of inductive photoperiodic cycles in *Silene armeria. Bot. Mag. (Tokyo)* **70**, 321.

[16] Takimoto, A. (1961). On the light controlling flower initiation of *Silene armeria. Plant & Cell Phys.* **2**, 71.

[17] Tashima, Y. and Imamura, S. (1953). Flower initiation in total darkenss in *Pharbitis Nil* Chois., a short day plant. *Proc. Jap. Acad.* **29**, 581.

[18] Wellensiek, S. J. (1960). Does darkness inhibit floral induction in long day plants? *Proc. Kon. Ned. Akad. Wet.* **C63**, 155.

[19] Wellensiek, S. J. (1960). Stem elongation and flower initiation. *Proc. Kon. Ned. Akad. Wet.* **C63**, 159.

[20] Wellensiek, S. J. (1964). The interchange of long day by low temperature in *Silene armeria.* In *Differentiation of apical meristems and some problems of ecological regulation of development of plants*, 299. Proc. Symp. Praha-Nitra (1966).

[21] Wellensiek, S. J. (1965). De bloemknopvorming bij *Silene armeria. Verslag afd. Natuurkunde, Kon. Ned. Akad. Wet.* **74** (9), 115–118.

[22] Wellensiek, S. J. (1966). Photoperiod and temperature in the long-day plants *Silene armeria* L. and *Trifolium pratense* L. *Ztsch. Pflanzenphys.* **54**, 377.

[23] Wellensiek, S. J. (1966). The flower forming stimulus in *Silene armeria* L. *Ztsch. Pflanzenphys.* **55**, 1.

[24] Wellensiek, S. J. (1966). The mechanism of flower formation in *Silene armeria* L. *Naturwiss.* **53** (16), 411.

[25] Wellensiek, S. J. (1966). Floral induction and desinduction in *Silene armeria* L. *Ztsch. Pflanzenphys.* **55**, 363.

[26] Wellensiek, S. J. (1966). The relations between the flower inducing factors in *Silene armeria* L. *Ztsch. Pflanzenphys.* **56**, 33.

[27] Wellensiek, S. J. and Elings, C. G. (1967). The non-translocation of the floral inhibition in *Silene armeria* L. *Proc. Kon. Ned. Akad. Wet.* **C70**, 187.

16

Brassica campestris L.

By Douglas J. C. Friend

1 History of Use

Brassica campestris L. is included in a complex of more-or-less freely inter-breeding species with a chromosome number of n equals 10, and is regarded as identical with *B. rapa* L. [1,11] This group includes the vegetable turnip and the spring and winter turnip rapes, grown principally for the oil contained in their seeds. This type of rape is distinct from two other forms of oil seed plants, often simply called spring and winter rape, with a chromosome number of n equals 19, belonging to the species complex *B. napus*.[1]

    B. campestris has been used by Wassink *et al.* in a re-investigation of Funke's experiments[6] on the spectral dependence of the photoperiodic reaction, and by Stolwijk, in experiments on the wavelength dependence of photomorphogenesis.[10,11,12]

    In 1965 a new strain of *B. campestris* was isolated. This proved to be a very sensitive quantitative long day plant that would flower in response to only one long day given as early as 4 days after sowing. This strain is particularly suitable for photoperiodic studies since up to 20 plants can be grown in a 2-inch diameter pot and only small scale facilities are needed to provide different photoperiodic treatments. The rapid flowering response allows completion of an experiment within ten days from sowing.

    This new strain, named Ceres because it was isolated at the Canberra Phyto-tron, was derived from the variety 'Arlo' of Polish spring turnip rape (*B. campestris* L. ssp. *oleifera* Metzg. f. *annua*[1]) while screening small annual species for possible use as sensitive long-day plants. When plants of the variety 'Arlo' were grown under continuous illumination at 25°C, about 2 per cent of the plants produced open flowers 15 days after sowing. No seed was obtained by selfing these plants, but good seed set was obtained in one cross. Further selection for a high degree of self-compatibility has been carried out from this initial cross, and after six generations of selfing, the strain is now very uniform in both flowering and vegetative characters. A brief description of the photoperiodic reactions of this strain has been published.[5]

2 Growing Technique and Growth Habit

A good seed supply is obtained by growing plants in soil in the greenhouse under a daylength of about 16 hours at a temperature of 25°C. Flowers open in about four weeks, and a high seed set is ensured by hand-pollinating daily with a brush. Seed ripens in about 8 to 12 weeks from sowing, and retains high viability for at least three years when stored at room temperature.

    No special conditions are required for germination, which takes place in white light, far-red or red radiation, or darkness, in 1 to 2 days at 25°C. Germination is most regular if a high humidity is maintained; shading from high light intensities prevents drying out. Seedlings are rather sensitive to damping off, which can be prevented by dusting the seed with 'Arasan' or some similar compound before sowing. Nutrient solutions are best omitted during the early stages of growth of the seedlings, as they seem to damage the cotyledons. Nutrients may be withheld entirely and the plants grown in plain sand or some other inert medium, in order to obtain small plants: the flowering response to one long day is not affected.

The emerged seedlings are placed under an 8-hour daylength at a high light intensity two days after sowing. Plants will grow well at lower light intensities and will also respond to only one long day, but the flowering response is somewhat slower. Photoperiodic treatments are usually given during the fifth dark period from sowing, when the plants are four days old. At this time the seedlings are 1–1.5 cm high, with two open cotyledons, each about 5 mm across. The first true leaf may be just visible.

FIGURE 16–1. *Brassica campestris*, Ceres strain, grown in soil in natural 15 hour days. Plant 40 cm high.

3 Inflorescence Structure and Criteria of the Flowering Response

The flowering response is usually determined ten days after sowing (six days after photoperiodic treatment) when the seedlings are 2–3 cm high, with the petioles of the first two leaves clearly visible. The developing inflorescence of a fully-induced plant can be seen under the dissecting microscope by parting the first and second leaves. Partially induced plants may show various stages of inflorescence initiation, from the first appearance of flower primordia to the extension of the pedicel. Vegetative plants have three to four young leaves present, with two or three leaf primordia developing on the apical growing point.

The flowering response can be measured by rating apices according to the stage of development, but in general it is simpler to record the percentage of plants that have reached or passed the earliest visible stages of flower bud development. This percentage, usually calculated from a sample dissection of about 50 plants, will be termed the percentage flowering. Another measure of the flowering response is provided by the number of leaves present on the main axis before the first flower bud, the final leaf number, which is inversely proportional to the earliness of floral initiation, and ranges from 3–4 in a fully induced plant, to 7–8 in a plant grown continuously under short daylengths. The number of flower buds produced depends greatly on nutrition, and is not a useful criterion of the flowering response, as the inflorescence is an indefinite raceme (Fig. 16–1).

4 Effects of Plant Age

Plants respond to one inductive long day as early as two days after sowing at 30°C (Fig. 16–2). At this time the cotyledons have only just started to unfold.

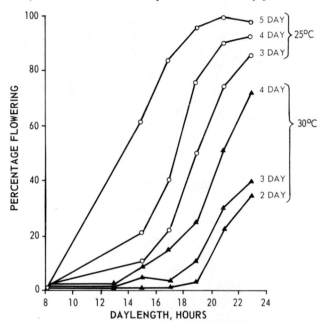

FIGURE 16–2. Effect of seedling age on flowering response to one long day provided by supplementary incandescent light (100 f.c.) given for different periods. Plants dissected at 10 days of age.

Germination is slower at 20°C, seedlings are only half-emerged on the second day and are not receptive to one long day. Three days after sowing, however, over 80 per cent of the plants initiate an inflorescence if 16 hours of supplementary light are given. The older the seedling before photo-induction, the greater was the flowering percentage obtained at a given daylength (Fig. 16–2).

5 and 6 Vernalization and Short Day Vernalization

There is no obligate cold requirement for this annual plant, and no investigations have been made of any possible hastening of flowering by low or high temperature given to the germinating seeds.

7 Photoperiod Response

As *B. campestris* is a quantitative long-day plant there is no critical daylength (or at least it is shorter than 8 hours) and flower initiation is more extensive and earlier the longer the daylength under which the plant is grown. In one experiment, plants were grown continuously with a basic 8-hour period of high intensity light supplemented with 50 f.c. incandescent light to give different daylengths. The number of days to 50 per cent initiation was 27, 21, 13 and 11, at daylengths of 8, 12, 16 and 24 hours respectively. Plants given only one long day showed a similar increasing flowering response with increasing daylength (Fig. 16–2).

When 4 day-old plants exposed to only one long day are returned to short day-lengths, the first visible flower primordia appear on a few plants on the 8th day. Nearly all plants have flower primordia by the 11th day (Fig. 16–3). Open flowers are formed about 26 days from sowing (Fig. 16–4). Plants grown continuously in

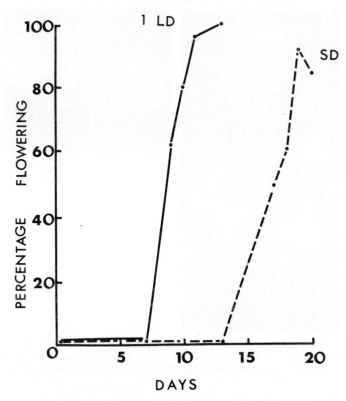

FIGURE 16–3. Rate of floral initiation after one long day, and under continuous short days (8 hours). Long day treatment consisted of 16 hours of supplementary incandescent light (100 f.c.) given four days after sowing.

8-hour daylengths show the first sign of floral initiation on about the 17th day, and reach 100 per cent initiation on about the 20th day. Once started, the rate of increase in the percentage flowering is just as rapid as in plants given one long day (Fig. 16–3). The flowering response becomes greater as the length and/or intensity of a single supplementary light period is increased.[5] Whereas 50 per cent flowering was obtained with only 5 hours supplementary light at an intensity of 1000 f.c., 15 hours were required at an intensity of 31 f.c. (Fig. 16–5).

As to be expected from the daylength and intensity interaction outlined above, light breaks have none of the dramatic effects so typical of the photoperiodic responses of short-day plants. Periods of one to four hours of red radiation (5 k erg . cm^{-2} . sec^{-1}) are without effect on flowering when given at any time during a 16-hour dark period, and even continuous irradiation at a peak wavelength of 660 nm (1 k erg . cm^{-2} . sec^{-1}) is without effect. When very high intensities of light were used (sunlight of about 8000 f.c.) interruptions of 30 to 60 minutes duration given once in the middle of the 16-hour dark period led to a small promotion of flowering (Fig. 16–6). The flowering response increased with further lengthening of the interruption up to at least 8 hours, by which time the interruption provided more than twice the energy of the main light period, in the visible region of the spectrum.

There is no absolute requirement for light prior to an inductive supplementary light period. When plants were grown in the usual 8-hour daylengths, and the length of the main light period immediately preceding the inductive supplementary

FIGURE 16–4. *Left*: Open flowers formed 26 days after sowing on plants given one long day when 4 days old. *Right*: Short day control of the same age with inflorescence initiated but hidden by the unexpanded leaves.

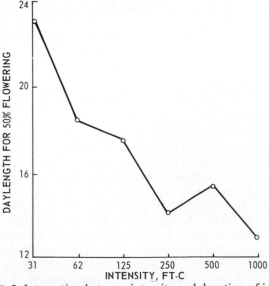

FIGURE 16–5. Interaction between intensity and duration of incandescent light used to supplement an 8-hour daylength, for one long day given four days after sowing.

light period was varied, flowering was still over 80 per cent even when the main light period was entirely omitted.

The effect of the main light period immediately succeeding the critical long day was strongly dependent on the intensity of the supplementary light. Flowering was little affected by reducing or even omitting the main light period when the supplementary light was given at an intensity of 500 f.c. (Fig. 16–7). After supple-

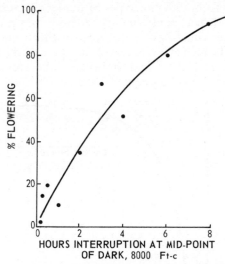

FIGURE 16–6. Promotion of flowering by interruptions with high intensity light (sunlight at about 8,000 f.c.) given at the mid-point of a 16 hour dark period, four days after germination. The main light period consisted of 8 hours of fluorescent and incandescent light of 3000 f.c. intensity.

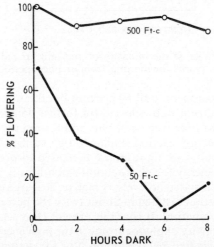

FIGURE 16–7. Effect of giving 0 to 8 hours of darkness, instead of light, at the beginning of the 8 hour main light period immediately following a period of 16 hours of supplementary light at two intensities.

mentary light at an intensity of 50 f.c. however, flowering was progressively reduced the shorter the length of the subsequent main light period. Supplementary light periods given at high intensities may have dual effects, one photoperiodic and the other providing energy substrates for the subsequent morphological expression of the photoperiodic response.

8 *Spectral Dependence*

As previously mentioned, short interruptions of a 16-hour dark period by red or far-red radiation were without effect on flowering. Promotion of flowering only took place when high energies of white light were used for long periods to supplement the main light period (Figs. 16–5 and 16–6). The spectral dependence of this high intensity reaction was first examined using rather broad bands of different wavelengths obtained from different types of fluorescent tubes in combination with Plexiglass filters. When supplementary radiation was given for 16 hours at an intensity of 20 k erg . cm^{-2} . sec^{-1}, the order of effectiveness was blue > far-red > green > red. The high effectiveness of the blue and the far-red agrees with the results of Wassink *et al.*,[11,12] and Stolwijk,[10] who grew plants in different spectral regions of supplementary light (1 k erg . cm^{-2} . sec^{-1}), giving repeated

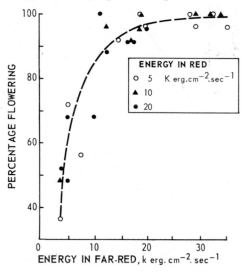

FIGURE 16–8. Effect of the intensity of red and far-red radiation given simultaneously to plants during one 16-hour photoperiod extension.

supplementary light treatment until 50 per cent floral initiation. The red and far-red regions of the spectrum were selected for further detailed study in the strain Ceres, because the high effectiveness of blue and far-red radiation suggested participation by a high energy reaction similar to that studied by Mohr.[8] After one long-day exposure, the flowering response increased in proportion to the logarithm of the incident energy for photoperiod extensions in both the red and the far-red, and was not saturated at levels as high as 30 k erg . cm^{-2} . sec^{-1}. A given energy of far-red radiation resulted in about twice the percentage flowering as at the same level of red radiation. It is not at present clear whether this type of response indicates the activity of phytochrome in the high energy reaction of photomorphogenesis (as suggested by Hartmann[7]) or the activity of a separate high energy pigment system, as initially proposed by Mohr[8] and recently implicated in the photoperiodic reactions of long-day plants by Schneider *et al.*[9] When red and far-red radiation was given simultaneously at different energy levels, flowering was dependent only on the level of energy in the far-red (Fig. 16–8). The addition of high levels of red energy did not lower the flowering response even when the level of far-red radiation was low. A similar promotion of flowering by far-red and lack of antagonism between red and far-red was also found for the long-day plant spring wheat.[3]

The spectral dependence of flowering has been investigated in more detail by irradiating plants with narrow spectral bands. The energy in these bands, although high (1 k erg . cm^{-2} . sec^{-1}) was not sufficient to promote flowering when used as the only source of radiation during the 16-hour supplementary light period. Plants were therefore given four hours of broad-band far-red radiation at high intensity (4–5 k erg . cm^{-2} . sec^{-1} excluding wavelengths longer than about 780 nm) immediately after the main light period, followed by 12 hours irradiation in the desired spectral region. Measured in this way, a peak of effectiveness was found at 710 to 725 nm (Fig. 16–9). This activity spectrum is rather similar to

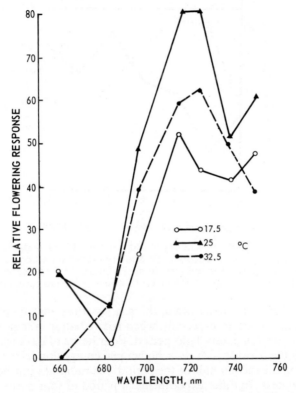

FIGURE 16–9. Relative effectiveness of different wavelengths in the red and far-red, at different temperatures. For details see text.

that of the high-energy reaction in morphogenesis, intensively investigated by Mohr.[8] A similar peak of effectiveness at about 710 nm also occurs for the promotion of flowering in wheat[4] and *Hyoscyamus*.[9]

Far-red radiation is also more effective than an equal energy of red when given in the absence of a preceding high intensity light period. Plants germinated and grown in darkness for three or four days can still be induced to 16 per cent flowering by 16 hours of high intensity far-red radiation, followed by the first main light period of 8 hours high intensity white light. As the cotyledons do not expand in darkness, the reduced level of flowering as compared with light-grown plants may partially result from the smaller area of photoperiodically sensitive tissue, as well as the low level of energy substrates within the etiolated seedling.

9 Endogenous Rhythms

The flower promoting effect of white light did not depend on the time at which it was given during a 16-hour dark period. When an 8-hour period of 200 f.c.

incandescent light was given at various times after the end of the main light period (at two-hour intervals) the flowering response varied only between 67 and 77 per cent. There is, however, a rhythmic change in sensitivity to red and far-red radiation given during the course of the dark period. In one experiment, plants were given four hours of either red radiation or darkness at various times during a 16-hour supplementary photoperiod consisting of far-red radiation (Fig. 16–10).

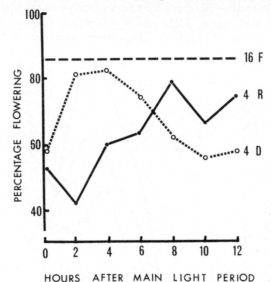

HOURS AFTER LIGHT PERIOD

FIGURE 16–10. Effect of 4 hours of red radiation (4 R) or darkness (4 D) given at different times during a 16 hour photoperiod extension, far-red radiation being given for the remaining 12 hours. 16 F indicates the level of flowering reached with plants given 16 hours of far-red radiation.

Flowering of plants given red radiation was less than that of plants given 16 hours of far-red radiation, especially when red radiation was given during the first half of the supplementary light period. Four hours of darkness given during the first half of the period produced a higher percentage flowering than red radiation, but during the second half of the period, red radiation promoted flowering more than darkness. In other experiments, a period of four hours far-red radiation produced the highest percentage flowering when given soon after the beginning of the supplementary light period, red radiation being given for the rest of the time.

It is not known at present whether these changes in sensitivity to red and far-red radiation are endogenous, or initiated by the timing or spectral composition of the preceding light period.

There is evidence that the promotion of flowering during the first few hours of the supplementary light period (Fig. 16–10) is phytochrome-dependent. If the main light period ends with 5 minutes of red radiation, a period of four hours darkness followed by 12 hours high intensity supplementary far-red does not promote flowering as much as when the main light period ends with five minutes of far-red radiation. Flower promotion is restored when the brief red irradiation is followed by 5 minutes of far-red radiation. Conversely, flower promotion is reduced if far-red is followed by red radiation.

The photoperiodic response during the last part of the 16-hour supplementary light period has not yet been examined in this way, but another type of experiment provides evidence that phytochrome may be involved. When a level of farred energy sufficient to induce about 20 per cent flowering was given continuously during a 16-hour supplementary light period, four hours of red radiation given simultaneously further promoted flowering only during the last four hours.

The photoperiodic reactions taking place during the supplementary light period may thus depend on both conventional phytochrome and high-energy reactions.

13 Effects of Temperature

A high temperature (30°C) brings the plants to a photoperiodically sensitive stage sooner than a lower temperature, as stated previously. Once plants had expanded cotyledons however, the optimal temperature for floral initiation in response to one long day was 25°C (Fig. 16–2). Both growth and flower initiation were slower at 15°C. Under an 18-hour daylength for instance, 50 per cent flowering was reached in 10 days at 25°C but required 13 days at 15°C.

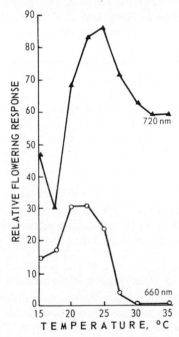

FIGURE 16–11. Relative effectiveness of 12 hours supplementary irradiation in the red and far-red regions of the spectrum for promotion of floral initiation. Plants were grown at 25°C, but subjected to different temperatures during the 12 hour irradiation period.

Specific effects of temperature on floral induction, rather than on the later morphological expression of the flowering stimulus, have been studied by growing plants at 25°C, and subjecting them once to different temperatures for 16 hours, while giving them a long day of different lengths. In general, temperature had relatively little effect. There was 64 per cent flowering at 25 and 20°C, and 48 per cent flowering at 15°C, taking mean values over all daylengths from 14 to 24 hours.

An increase in temperature over the range 15 to 35°C during 12 hours irradiation at different wavelengths did not cause any shift in the peak of the wavelength response, which remained at 710–725 nm. In Figure 16–9 the values are means from three series of experiments at temperatures 2.5°C apart, the points marked 17.5°C for instance being the means of series at 15, 17.5 and 20°C. The relative effectiveness of the red and far-red regions of the spectrum does however depend to some extent on temperature, the flower promoting effect of far-red radiation being especially marked at high temperatures (Fig. 16–11). Similar temperature effects in the response to red and far-red have been found in spring wheat.[4]

14 Effects of Mineral Nutrition

When seedlings are exposed to one long day, flower initiation is not affected by the presence or absence of Hoagland's solution applied to an inorganic substrate very low in mineral salts. In the case of plants maintained under 8-hour day-lengths however, watering with Hoagland's solution retards the initiation of flowers. After 21 days there was 80 percent flowering in plants given only water, and only 27 per cent flowering in plants given Hoagland's solution. This inhibition is probably caused by nitrates. The absence of a nutrient effect in plants given one long day can probably be attributed to their extremely rapid flowering, the initials of flower primordia being laid down while the cotyledon reserves are of more importance than the external medium.

16 Translocation of the Flowering Stimulus

B. campestris is not a suitable species for studies on the translocation of the flowering stimulus, because of its small size. Removal of one cotyledon has little effect on the flowering response to one long day, but removal of two, either just before, just after, or 24 hours after the long day completely prevents flowering. Because the cotyledons provide the main energy substrate of the young seedling, lack of flowering cannot be attributed solely to interruption of the translocation of the flowering stimulus.

18 Effect of Growth Substances

Flowering is promoted under both long and short day conditions after spraying the cotyledons of seedlings with 10 to 500 ppm gibberellic acid. It is not at present known whether floral initiation is hastened or the later stages of inflorescence development.

23 Inflorescence Differentiation

The anatomy and morphology of inflorescence differentiation has not been studied. The initiation of an inflorescence is first visible two days after long day treatment as a protuberance on the apical meristem. Further outgrowth of the developing flower buds is probably very similar to that in Sinapis.[2]

REFERENCES

[1] Berggren, G. (1962). Reviews on the taxonomy of some species of the genus Brassica, based on their seeds. Svensk Bot. Tidsk. **56**, 65.

[2] Bernier, G. (1962). Evolution of the apical meristem of Sinapis alba L. (long-day plant) in long days, in short days and during the transfer from short days to long days. Caryologia **15**, 303.

[3] Friend, D. J. C. (1964). The promotion of floral initiation of wheat by far-red radiation. Physiol. Plantar. **17**, 909.

[4] Friend, D. J. C. (1964). Promotion of flowering of wheat by far-red radiation. (Abstract.) Plant Physiol. **39**, Supplement, XLIX.

[5] Friend, D. J. C. and Helson, V. A. (1966). Brassica campestris L.: Floral induction by one long day. Science **153**, 1115.

[6] Funke, C. L. (1948). The photoperiodicity of flowering under short-day with supplemental light of different wave lengths. Lotsya **1**, 79.

[7] Hartmann, K. M. (1966). A general hypothesis to interpret 'high energy phenomena' of photomorphogenesis on the basis of phytochrome. Photochem. & Photobiol. **5**, 349.

[8] Mohr, H. (1962). Primary effects of light on growth. Ann. Rev. Plant Physiol. **13**, 465.

[9] Schneider, M. J., Borthwick, H. A. and Hendricks, S. B. (1966). Light-mediated control of nastic leaf movements, flowering, and stem length in *Hyoscyamus niger*. (Abstract.) *Plant Physiol.* **41**, Supplement xv.

[10] Stolwijk, J. A. J. (1954). Wavelength dependence of photomorphogenesis in plants. *Meded. Landb. Whogeschool Wageningen* **54**, (5), 181.

[11] Wassink, E. C., Sluysmans, C. M. J. and Stolwijk, J. A. J. (1950). On some photoperiodic and formative effects of coloured light in *Brassica-rapa*, f. *oleifera*, subf. *annua. Proc. Kon. Ned. Akad. Wetensch. Amsterdam* **53**, 1466.

[12] Wassink, E. C., Stolwijk, J. A. J. and Beemster, A. B. R. (1951). Dependence of formative and photoperiodic reactions in *Brassica rapa* var. *cosmos* and *lactuca* on wave length and time of irradiation. *Proc. Kon. Ned. Akad. Wetensch. Amsterdam* **C54**, 421.

17

Anagallis arvensis L.

By L. A. T. Ballard

1 History of Use

This plant – pimpernel, poor man's weatherglass, mouron rouge, Gauchheil – has provided material for experimental botanists for many years. In the 1800s, even prior to the recognition of Mendel's results, it had been used for studies of inheritance of flower colour.[21] The main facts in this field are now well documented[30,33,41] and the species has been appreciated as useful material for teaching purposes.[27,28]

The first recorded observations on flowering in relation to environmental factors were probably made by Marchand,[29] when he noted abnormal flowers and vegetative reversions in natural populations in autumn.

The first experimental work appears to be that of Chouard[15,16] who initially showed *Anagallis arvensis* L. to be a qualitative long-day plant. Later, Brulfert and Chouard[11] reported that exposure to a single long day was sufficient to induce flowering. Since then, a large proportion of the information available on this species has come from Chouard's laboratory. A little later, work on *Anagallis* in London in F. G. Gregory's laboratory,[24,25] and in Australia,[5,23] was commenced about the same time, the latter, at least, arising from Chouard's descriptions.

This species does not boast an impressive literature and most of the published findings have come from the three sources just mentioned.

2 Growth Habit and Growing Techniques

Three features combine to give this species some individuality; it is variable in form, apical dominance is virtually absent, and it readily produces both root and shoot adventitious meristems.

A member of the Primulaceae, floras describe it as a branched, procumbent, herbaceous annual; but mostly they fail to indicate the very great range of form and development which individuals may have in response to environment. Under severe water and nutritional stress, small plants are produced with perhaps a single stem a few cm long and carrying greatly reduced leaves, though they are still able to initiate flower buds. With water and minerals available optimally, particularly under non-inductive conditions, a plant becomes a luxuriant, sprawling, much-branched system, covering 1 m^2 or more. Not only total plant size, but also the sizes of leaves and flowers vary greatly in response to environment.

The weak, quadrangular stems bear decussately arranged, sessile, ovate leaves which, at maturity, under average glasshouse or growth room conditions, may be 15–22 mm long at the base of the plant. Leaves are usually smaller than this in the field and, even under favourable growth conditions, their size declines after approximately 10 nodes have formed.

At the end of each axis an apical meristem and 2 pairs of leaf primordia are enclosed in 2 partly expanded leaves. The elongation of each internode becomes apparent when 3 pairs of leaves above it have been differentiated. Because of the absence of apical dominance, axillary meristems which are detectable histologically at the lower primordial leaf pair (Fig. 17–1A) become macroscopic about 2 nodes lower. Under non-inductive conditions their rapid further development

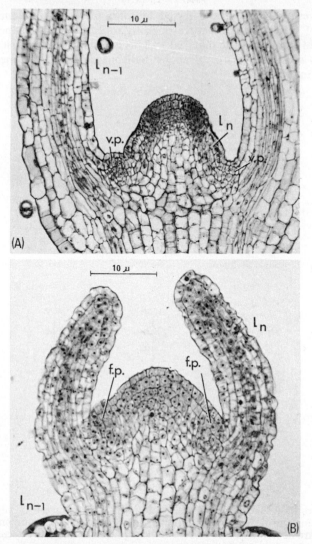

FIGURE 17–1. Median longitudinal sections through apices of similar ages (A) vegetative apex, through the plane of second youngest leaf primordia (L_{n-1}), (B) apex three days after the end of inductive treatment, through the plane of youngest leaf primordia (L_n), and thus at right angles to (A). Note the similarity of the vegetative bud primordia (v.p.) and the flower primordia (f.p.), the latter being apparent one node higher. In each case primordium development is unequal on the two sides.

(Grant Lipp[22])

produces axes like those from which they originated, and the plant assumes its semi-prostrate, branched condition.

The terminal meristems behave similarly under both non-inductive and inductive conditions, but, under the latter, axillary meristems become determined as flowers which are thus always solitary and laterally situated. Flower initiation continues only so long as inductive conditions prevail (Fig. 17–2).

Under continued inductive conditions, anthesis occurs 5–6 weeks after the first long day and seeds in the first capsules formed are mature 6–8 weeks later, though they are germinable after about 3 weeks. Seed is produced prolifically and no potential investigator need be deterred by fears of shortage of material, since seed yields of 150 g per plant, corresponding to 2.5×10^5 seeds per plant have been recorded for glasshouse material.[12] This is in marked contrast to the value of 902 ± 54 seeds per plant, given by Salisbury[37] to be the mean for field material in England.

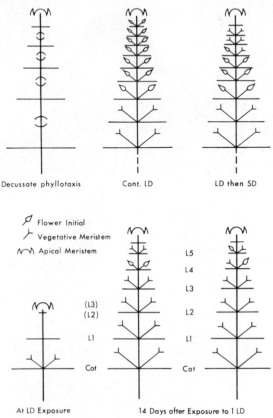

FIGURE 17–2. Schematic representation of the distribution of vegetative meristems and flower initials following various long day treatments. The leaves are depicted in one plane but the phyllotaxis is actually decussate as suggested in the top left diagram.
    Top row – any axis; Bottom row – the seedling system described in the text. Unexpanded leaves are shown in brackets.

Small, young plants make the most favourable material for studies of flowering. These may be obtained either from seed or cuttings, each method having its advantages.

The seeds are light sensitive[23] and, after a period of imbibition in the dark, germination may be uniformly initiated by exposure to red radiation. By selection when planting the germinated seed, and also on emergence, stands of plants whose development is uniform to at least half a plastochron are easy to obtain when grown in an inert substrate such as vermiculite or perlite flushed with solutions of the Hoagland type. Care should be exercised to keep solutions off young leaves as they burn readily.

The early development from seed, at 20°C and under short days is shown in Figure 17–3, which also provides a general impression of growth rate. In growth rooms, unless very high light intensities are combined with marked day/night temperature alternation, the small plants are somewhat fragile on their elongated hypocotyls. Advantages are that they can be ready for treatment 14–16 days after initiating germination and some experiments can be terminated 8–10 days later (Fig. 17–4). Large numbers can be treated in a minimum of space, either individually in small pots or tubes, or in bulk in dishes.

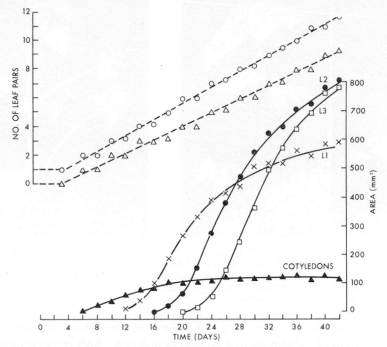

FIGURE 17–3. Leaf initiation and leaf growth of the young *Anagallis* plant. Time is measured from the irradiation which initiated germination. Areas are for the leaf pair at each node. ▲ cotyledons; × first leaves; ● second leaves; □ third leaves. △ number of leaf pairs (including cotyledons) visible macroscopically; ○ number of leaf pairs (including cotyledons) visible at a magnification of 30 diameters. (Ballard and Grant Lipp[5])

More robust plants can be produced by rooting cuttings. Brulfert[9] takes standard cuttings each with 2 pairs of expanded leaves. In a sandy medium they root quickly and are ready for use 10 days later and, if taken from an established clone, make very uniform material.

Taxonomists recognize two subspecies of *Anagallis arvensis* L. and it now seems reasonably clear that all the material used for flowering studies belongs to *Anagallis arvensis* L. subsp. *arvensis* (believed taxonomically the same as *A. arvensis* subsp. *phoenicea* Scop. of Chouard, Brulfert and co-workers).

Within this subspecies there are five recognized varieties, differing mainly in flower colour.[31] Experiments have been reported only on the red-flowered form (var. *phoenicea* Scop.) and the blue-flowered form (var. *coerulea* Ludi). However, even within the same flower colour-group, red in this case, Hussey[25] has isolated strains with differing characteristics, so it is not unexpected that there should be differences in the results secured by different workers, irrespective of the flower colours of their materials. Workers of the Paris group have used a clone with red flowers. They do not identify it further and, for convenience, it is referred to in this chapter as the Paris clone. Australian workers have mainly used a line with blue flowers, derived from a single plant collected at Glen Osmond, South Australia.[23] It is referred to here as the GO strain. This was previously[5,23] wrongly identified as *A. arvensis* subsp. *foemina* (Mill.) Schinz and Thell., but in its more critical characters[31] it corresponds with the commoner subspecies, *arvensis*.

FIGURE 17–4. Young seedling plants, left to right, (*a*) 15 days old, ready for long day exposure (*b*) 25 days old ready for dissection (*c*) 30 days old, showing first open flower at node 2, after continuous high intensity illumination since germination. The lower vegetative axillaries are at the first leaf and coty- ledonary nodes.

3 Inflorescence Structure and Criteria of Flowering Response

The proportion of individuals in a natural population which respond positively to any given treatment reflects both the variability of the population and the intensity or efficacy of the treatment. Thus, the most useful index of the flowering response in *Anagallis* material derived from seed is the proportion of plants in the test population that initiates flower buds, following a given treatment. For survey purposes, useful information can be obtained from groups of 10 plants but, for more accurate and comparative purposes, estimates should be based on 20–40 plants.

In clonal material, because of its genetic uniformity, this index is somewhat less informative, tending to reflect on uniformity of conditions, rather than on treatment differences.

On plants which have at least one pair of mature leaves, flower initiation can be detected histologically in the axils of the most apical leaf primordia some 3 days after an inductive treatment[9] and a little later than this in seedling material which is going through the process of accumulating leaf primordia at the apex[5] (Fig. 17–1B). However, it is usually more convenient to defer assessment until 8–16 days after treatment, when the terminal buds of the axes concerned can be examined under a dissecting microscope at 20–30 diameters magnification. The longer period is necessary only if the number of flowers is required. To ensure accuracy in such cases the first vegetative axillary bud after the flowers must be observed, and the vegetative buds develop more slowly.

The material can be dissected fresh but, if there are too many apices to deal with at once, they can be preserved and dissected at leisure. Fixatives such as formalin-acetic acid-alcohol, with the alcohol more dilute than for histological purposes, are satisfactory. In fact, dissection of preserved material is, in some ways, easier than fresh, because the small leaves are more readily pushed aside by dissecting needles and, having become limp, do not spring back. It is un-necessary to dissect under liquid because evaluation usually takes only one to three minutes and drying out is not a problem.

For some purposes, rate of flower bud development is valuable and this may be assessed by allotting arbitrary values to stages of development so chosen that the relation with time is linear, as Salisbury[38] has done with *Xanthium*. Either the slope of the lines, or the flower stage reached after some standard time after induction, indicates rate of development (Fig. 17–5). This procedure is valid for 2–3 weeks after induction, but it should not be extended to accepting number of days to anthesis, an index useful in other species, unless the inductive treatment is continuous or, at least, prolonged. This is because in *Anagallis* flower bud de-velopment is irregular in a certain proportion of cases under conditions of mini-mal induction (Section 23).

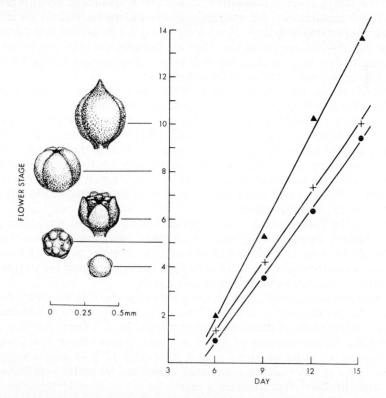

FIGURE 17–5. Development of the oldest flower initials induced by various long-day treatments. Time measured from start of each long-day treatment. Flower initial development assessed by allotting scores corres-ponding to selected stages, some of which are depicted. Stages greater than 10 defined by length. ● 2 long days; + 3 long days; ▲ continued long-day treatment. The slope of the continued long-day line differs from that of each of the other two (P < 0.01); the slopes of the latter do not differ significantly (P > 0.05).   (Ballard and Grant Lipp[5])

In some species, the number of flowers produced has been taken as a measure of the flowering response. In *Anagallis*, however, this quantity, which corresponds closely to the number of floral nodes, indicates rather the duration of an effective inductive treatment, since reversion to vegetation occurs extremely rapidly under non-inductive conditions. A single cycle of an effective condition (Section 7) usually produces flower initials at only a single node, continuous induction produces initials at all nodes subsequent to that of the first flower. Inductive periods consisting of an intermediate number of cycles produce a roughly proportional number of floral nodes. For example, in a glasshouse experiment with weakly inductive conditions for 2, 4, 6, 8 and 10 cycles, flower initials were produced at 0, 1, 3, 4 and 6 nodes respectively.[6]

4 Effects of Plant Age

In some respects *Anagallis* does not conform to the normal pattern of change in response to photoperiod with age. However, it is not particularly notable that induction by long days can occur in very young plants. Flowers can regularly be produced at the second leaf node (Fig. 17–4c) and, in a proportion of cases following low temperature vernalization, at the first node (Table 17–2). There are no particular requirements for ripeness to flower and the cotyledons are effective organs for perceiving long days. However, it could not be proven that cotyledons on their own could cause induction. They are less effective than true leaves since their contribution may be detected only after 5–8 exposures to conditions for which 3 cycles given to first leaves cause induction.

In the GO strain, very small amounts of leaf tissue, 20 mm² or less, suffice for induction. Because leaf primordia are able to contribute to the total photoperiodic stimulus while they are no more than 2–3 mm² in area, it is difficult to isolate the action of any given leaf rank, including cotyledons. Whether real efficiency only of leaves is responsible, or else variation in meristematic responsiveness in some manner linked with leaf size is also involved, leaves are found maximally effective in flower initiation when they are only one-twentieth fully expanded. Unlike leaves of other species the efficacy has declined considerably by the time they are half expanded.[5]

However, the Paris clone does not appear to behave in this way, since partly expanded leaves, although they may contribute to induction, are insufficient on their own.[9a] Thus either 2 pairs of adult leaves[9] or one pair in combination with even minute expanding leaves is the minimum leaf requirement for complete induction following exposure to a single long day.[9a]

The efficiency of leaves of corresponding size and stage of development declines with increase in ontogenetic rank, and leaves on laterals inserted at a higher level are less effective than on those inserted at a lower level.[5] These features would tend to make *Anagallis* harder to induce as it ages, and not easier as is usual, and are consistent with the length of time it is possible to hold plants vegetative. Hussey[25] kept plants which accumulated more than 60 nodes vegetative for 2 years, while Brulfert[9] kept some for 3 years.

Nothing is known about any possible effect of plant age on the general level of meristematic activity throughout the plant, but some interesting facts are available about the activity of an individual meristem in relation to its age (size).

Vaughan's[40] descriptions show that vegetative and floral meristems are not distinguishable histologically in their early stages, but only by their rates of development. Floral meristems develop more rapidly and can be detected earlier, i.e. nearer the apex (Fig. 17–1). However, they are not recognizable histologically at the time of induction nor when the stimulus from the leaves reaches the apex[6] and thus it seems probable that at the time of determination a meristem consists of a few cells only. Moreover, it appears to be labile for only a brief period. Data of the type presented in Table 17–1 show that during a single day some meristems at a lower node (4) become too old, i.e. are committed vegetatively; while some at a higher node (5) arise or reach some required minimal stage to become floral.

TABLE 17-1

Effect of time of photoperiodic stimulus on the distribution of induced flowers (Ballard and Grant Lipp[6]).

Occasion on which 1 long cycle given	Node 4			Node 5		
	% individuals with FF FV VV			% individuals with FF FV VV		
	FF	FV	VV	FF	FV	VV
Day 15	54	35	10	0	2	98
16	0	31	69	0	57	43
15 and 16 ..	88	12	0	2	94	4

FF = both lateral positions floral; FV = mixed;
VV = both lateral positions vegetative.
There were no flowers at nodes other than 4 and 5.

In the following way it is possible to derive information about the relative ages of the meristems which either become floral or remain vegetative at the two nodes in question. The two lateral meristems at any node are not equal in size and development (Fig. 17-1). The advanced and retarded ones are so disposed as to trace two separate helices, the combination of which (for their subtending leaves) produces the decussate phyllotaxis.[34,35,39] The direction of rotation of the helices is the same within any plant and random between plants.[6] Observation of the sizes of meristems at nodes above and below any particular node permits allocation of one of the meristems at that node to the advanced helix and the other meristem to the retarded helix.

In the case in question, where there are two flower initials at node 4, one is larger, with a higher flower stage (Section 3) and this one takes its place in that helix tracing the advanced (older) meristems. Where the meristems at nodes 4 and 5 are mixed (FV), following inductive treatment on the second day, at node 4 the vegetative meristem is the older, as is the floral meristem at node 5. This clinches the argument that developing meristems remain labile only briefly before being committed to further vegetative, or changed to floral, development.

5 Vernalization and Devernalization

Since *Anagallis* will flower under an appropriate photoperiod when grown at constant 30°C, it is clear that it has no absolute cold requirement.

The results of Table 17-2 from an early glasshouse experiment[3] show that low temperature treatment of imbibed seed hastened flowering in one of the two strains investigated, as measured both by position of the first floral node and time to anthesis. As is usual with long-day plants, the relative effect is greater the shorter the photoperiod and in the GO strain the vernalization permitted flowering in 8 hour photoperiods.

Nothing further is known about this low temperature vernalization (range of effective temperatures, time required etc.) nor is anything recorded about devernalization.

6 Short Day Vernalization

There are no recorded observations on this feature; but in view of the facts of Section 4 it seems unlikely either that positive effects exist, or that they could be demonstrated if they did.

TABLE 17–2

Acceleration of flowering by low temperature treatment of imbibed seed (Ballard[3]).

	Photo-period (hours)	GO strain		Red flowered form	
		Untreated	Cold treated	Untreated	Cold treated
Lowest floral node	8.0	Veg	16.2	Veg	Veg
	14.6–13.6	3.9	2.2	4.3	4.4
	20.0	2.8	1.7	2.9	2.8
Days to anthesis..	8.0	> 195	121.8	> 195	> 195
	14.6–13.6	47.9	33.2	44.5	44.8
	20.0	35.0	32.7	38.3	36.9

Seeds of the two strains were held imbibed at 25°C until they had just germinated and then at approximately 3°C for 35 days. These, and another group germinated at 25°C to be at the same stage of development, were sown in soil in a glasshouse. Photoperiods were (a) 8 hours obtained by drawing black curtains over the plants (b) the prevailing natural day length (c) 20 hours obtained by supplementing the natural day with incandescent light of 50 f.c. intensity. The node (true leaf) of first flower, and the number of days from sowing to anthesis were recorded.

7 Photoperiod Response

This section will lean heavily on the results of Brulfert[9] who has presented the most complete analysis.

Critical day length

There is general agreement between investigators for all strains that the critical light period below which induction is not possible is 12–12.5 hours – at least this is so for temperatures above 10°C (Section 13).

Number of cycles and light intensities required

The flowering response is markedly affected by light intensity. The most important inter-relations, for the Paris clone, are summarized in Table 17–3, which

TABLE 17–3

Minimum number of cycles necessary for complete flower initiation in the Paris clone in relation to length of photoperiod and intensity of radiation (data of Brulfert[9]).

Intensity of supplementary radiation (ergs/cm²/sec.)	Total duration of photoperiod (hours)			
	16	18	20	22
50,000	2	2	2	1
20,000	3	2	2	1
5,500	10	7	3	1
500	> 17	> 12	> 22	20

All groups received 9 hours of mixed fluorescent and incandescent light (50,000 ergs/cm²/sec) and then supplementary periods at the intensities indicated to give the various total photoperiods.

clearly points to a requirement for high light intensities. So far as it is known, the behaviour of the GO strain is similar at medium to high intensit es, but not at low intensities, since it required one cycle of a 24-hour period (i.e. 32 hours continuous light) at 2000 f.c., but only 2–3 cycles of 20-hour photoperiods, 12 hours of which were at 40–50 f.c. One such cycle was quite ineffective; but increasing the intensity to 150 f.c. permitted initiation in 9 per cent of the plants.

That the photoperiodic requirements are not saturated at low intensities is notable, particularly since the results of Section 8 suggest the response, at least in the Paris clone, to be mediated by phytochrome. Possibly the availability of lateral meristems at the required degree of development is the critical factor. This could depend on the general activity of the shoot apex which, in turn, could be affected by the level of assimilates. An interesting finding by Hussey suggesting that sucrose can replace the high light requirement supports such an idea. He observed initiation in 4 out of 10 cuttings held in 2 per cent sucrose for 32 hours at the low intensity of 25 f.c. from incandescent lights.[25]

It is also consistent that the light intensity at the compensation point is high in this species,[9] and that the general sensitivity of response of plants appears to be affected by the light intensity obtaining during previous development.[3] Table 17–4 shows two examples of greater sensitivity to induction in plants raised under higher light intensities. This behaviour could lead to seasonal effects.

TABLE 17–4

Flower initiation in relation to conditions during development of experimental plants (Ballard[3]).

Inductive treatment	Light intensity during development	Flower initiation (%) after treatments of the indicated number of long days						
		0	1	2	3	4	5	6
A	High (glasshouse)	0	0	100	92	–	–	–
	Low (growth room)	0	–	17	92	100	–	–
B	High (glasshouse)	0	–	0	0	15	77	–
	Low (growth room)	0	–	0	0	0	0	30

Plants were raised under short days either in a glasshouse under natural illumination (approximately 3000–5000 f.c.) or in a growth room with mixed fluorescent and incandescent light (approximately 750 f.c.). They were exposed to inductive conditions when each group was at the same stage of development.

The two inductive treatments differed, thus comparison between the two halves of the table is not valid.

Light break effects

There is some divergence of behaviour. Plants from three different sources agree in responding positively to interruptions of long nights at the mid point.

(a) Light break of 2 hours at 30–50 f.c. following an 8-hour day – Chouard[15] in his earliest account, and thus probably before the development of the Paris clone.

(b) Light break of 0.5 hour at 700 ergs cm²/sec from fluorescent lamps following a 9-hour day – Brulfert[9] with the Paris clone.

(c) Light breaks of 0.5 hour at 25 f.c., repeatedly given, following non-inductive days of 10, 11, or 12 hours–Hussey,[25] red-flowered form.

However, the GO strain does not follow this pattern. Light breaks of one hour at even the relatively high intensity of 1700 f.c., following 8-hour days, and repeated for 2, 5 or 8 cycles produced no flower initiation.[6]

8 Spectral Dependence

Evidence presented by Brulfert[9] for the Paris clone suggests that its flowering response is mediated by phytochrome. Ineffective short days of high light intensity could be prolonged to effective long days by yellow or red radiation of medium intensity (400–900 ergs/cm^2/sec), but not by blue, green or far-red radiation. More significantly, flowering could be induced by interruptions of 0.5 hour of white or red radiation (at intensities roughly equivalent to those just cited) given at the middle of the dark period, and reversed by following far-red radiation. Blue radiation for similar times and intensities was indifferent – it neither induced, nor reversed the effect of radiations which did.

The response of the GO strain is not known with certainty. The ineffectiveness of night breaks, as described above, precludes the investigation of spectral effects by this method. Short days (8 hours) supplemented by either red or far-red radiation (to a total of 20 hours) were quite ineffective in induction,[6] but this may have been due to the rather low intensities used (red, 600–700 mμ, at approximately 65 ergs/cm^2/sec; far-red, 700–900 mμ, at approximately 300 ergs/cm^2/sec).

9 Endogenous Rhythms

An experiment by Hussey[24] provides the only reported evidence on the possibility of circadian rhythms. Groups of plants were held on 72-hour cycles comprised of 12 hours at 1000–1200 f.c. in all cases, and either 60 hours darkness or periods of 12 hours at 10 f.c. intercalated at various points in the dark period. Nine such cycles were given. Flower initiation occurred only in the two cases where the intercalated light period, together with the high light period, made a continuous 24-hour light period.

This experiment was done at the height of the controversy concerning Bünning's endogenous rhythm theory of photoperiodism. The results themselves are unequivocal. The absence of any intermediate optimum, such as had been found by Carr[13] with *Kalanchoe* on 72-hour cycles, did not support Bünning, but was held rather to support the additive interpretation of light breaks adopted by Claes and Lang.[20] Today, with our more detailed knowledge of the light requirements of *Anagallis*, of its reluctance to respond to fractional induction, and of some of the properties of its meristems, it might well be considered that the results are less informative about rhythms, and suggest rather that the species is not good material for this type of study.

10 Fractional Induction

The possibility of fractional induction can be investigated, because it is easy to select conditions under which one cycle is ineffective, and more than one cycle effective, for induction. With the GO strain, interpolation of even one short day between two single long days reduced the flowering response to zero, under conditions where two consecutive long days gave 60–100 per cent initiation.[3] Although there are no further supporting records available this result is consistent with other properties of the species, such as the brief lability of meristems and the prompt and complete reversion to vegetation in the absence of inductive conditions.

13 Effects of Temperature

The information of previous sections probably suggests that *Anagallis* is a qualitative (obligate) long-day plant; but, under very low temperature regimes, both the GO strain and the Paris clone initiate flowers in short days. The latter remains vegetative in short days at 10°C[9] but flowers in 15 weeks at 2°C on 8-hour photoperiods.[9a] The GO strain initiates flowers on photoperiods as short as 7 hours and responds quantitatively to long days when subjected to temperatures around 5°C for 4–6 hours during the night. Under 8-hour photoperiods flowers were initiated at the mean node 9.0, and at node 8.2 when 4 long days of 20 hours were given when the plants had 5 macroscopic leaf nodes.[3] Perhaps these low temperature responses are related to the response to seed vernalization (Table 17–2) and it is unfortunate that data on this feature are lacking for the Paris clone, as they are for the response of the GO strain to intermediate temperatures.

The temperature response of the Paris clone is unusual since increase of temperature facilitates flower initiation. For photoperiods of 16 hours the number of cycles required falls from > 7 at 10°C to 2 at 35°, and for photoperiods of 24 hours from 15 to 20 at 2°C to 3 and 1 at 10°C and 35°C respectively. Consistent with this is the further finding for the Paris clone concerning the action of single continuous high light 24-hour inductive periods. When these were divided into 9-hour and 15-hour periods, each at a different temperature, the efficacy of the single day increased when the longer period was at the higher temperature e.g. for the 9-hour/15-hour periods, 10°/20° and 10°/16° were respectively more effective than 20°/10° and 16°/10°.

However, in the GO strain, for temperature alternations of 21°/16° and photoperiods of 20 hours, Ballard and Grant Lipp[4] found a small difference in favour of a programme that instituted the lower temperature at the start of the supplementary low light period of 12 hours, rather than at the start of the dark period of 4 hours, thus providing the low temperature for a longer period.

16 Translocation of the Floral Stimulus

No estimates of the velocity of movement of the stimulus in this species are available, but defoliation experiments establish the time required for enough of the stimulus to move out of the leaf and to be effective at an apical meristem. Translocation and any other concerned processes start during the day following the inductive treatment, are well advanced in 48 hours and completed 72 hours after the beginning of the long light period.[6,9] The results of Table 17–5 show that the presence of the cotyledons, even in short days, greatly increases the flowering response when the first leaf is removed soon after the inductive long day. In this case, the data do not permit discrimination between 2 possibilities: (1) that the assimilates provided by the cotyledons in short days assist the translocation of the floral stimulus from the leaf; (2) that such assimilates are necessary for proper function of the meristem. Results of other sections favour the second alternative.

Since defoliated plants can be prepared so that the only leaves exposed to inductive conditions are situated 3 or more nodes distant from the apical region where flowers subsequently appear, it is reasonable to assume that the floral stimulus travels, as is normal, in the conducting tissue. The extent to which this is possible is not quite so evident.

Brulfert interprets her 1965 defoliation experiments to indicate that the stimulus moves freely throughout the plant, unrestricted as to direction or axis. But in some cases where the flowers occurred on branches of an axis which carried the leaves believed to be the source of the floral stimulus, it is feasible that leaf

TABLE 17–5

Effect of time and conditions of defoliation on the flowering response (Ballard and Grant-Lipp[6]).

Treatment	Organs given 1 LD	Organs excised	Time of excision (hours)	% Flower initiation	
				Expt. 1	Expt. 2
No masking	cots + L1	Nil	—	88	84
	cots + L1	cots + L1	32	0	—
	cots + L1	cots + L1	48	5	0
Cots. masked to have SD	L1	Nil	—	88	90
	L1	L1	32	0	0
	L1	L1	40	—	11
	L1	L1	48	71	39

Plants bore cotyledons (cots.) and first leaves (L1) only, and were exposed to a single period of 32 hours of light at 2,000 f.c. In some groups the cotyledons were masked by aluminium covers to receive a short day of 8 hours light. Time of excision was counted from the start of the long light period.

primordia of sufficient size for perception (Sections 4 and 21) were already present at the time of induction in the axillary buds producing the branches, and that the stimulus need not have travelled out of one axis into another. However, in later experiments[9a] this possibility seems to have been excluded.

In the GO strain, the pattern of flower production suggests that, if movement of the stimulus from one axis to another occurs at all, it is not frequent and may only be recognized after substantial induction. Direct attempts to demonstrate such a transfer in two-branched plants, one branch held in inductive, and the other in non-inductive conditions have failed. In these experiments[6] only young leaves were left on receptor branches, and controls enclosed in transparent vessels demonstrated that enclosing the receptor branches in opaque vessels to produce short days did not produce conditions (other than photoperiodic) which inhibited flowering. Hussey[25] has also failed to demonstrate transport in two-branched plants, and further experiments in this general area seem desirable.

Another of Brulfert's results seems to propound a paradox. Her earlier disbudding experiments suggested that either apical or axillary meristems must be present during the exposure to long days for this to be effective in induction. In later experiments[9a] she has obtained as much as 70 per cent flowering after exposure to one long day during which neither terminal nor lateral meristems were present. Whether meristems were not present at all, or present during exposure to the long day and removed the following day, secondary or adventitious meristems became organized and, on the branches arising from them, flowering took place some 20 days later. This seems to imply a relatively long life for the flower-forming substance.

It does not seem to matter whether one envisages that it is the original stimulatory substance formed in the leaf during the photoperiodic exposure that is preserved, or that this stimulatory substance is transformed in a meristem to some other all-pervading, persistent product which has the property of directing floral development (Carr[14] has produced evidence of this latter type of activity in Xanthium). In either case a long-lived substance is invoked, and, if it exists, it is difficult to understand the pattern of flowering produced in intact plants exposed to similar inductive conditions. Here, flowering is restricted sharply to 1 or 2 nodes (Fig. 17–2, Table 17–1), whereas, with a persistent stimulus freely available, flowering over a very large number of nodes would be expected. When flowering over many nodes does occur, it is related to the duration of the inductive treatment (Section 4).

17 Grafting Experiments

Grafts may readily be made by the method suggested by Went[42] and a satisfactory proportion of them show union in 10–14 days, but no use of this appears to have been made in flowering studies. It is possible that previous ideas on reversion may have suggested that such experiments would be unprofitable. However, in view of the discussion of Sections 16 and 21, the possible value of grafting should be re-evaluated.

18 Effects of Growth Substances and Growth Retardants

Gibberellins

After Lang produced flowering in *Hyoscyamus niger* by the application of gibberellic acid, plants in general were sprayed, smeared and injected with gibberellins. *Anagallis* did not escape the onslaught, though only gibberellic acid, GA_3, has been used.

In an early report Chouard[19] stated that *Anagallis* could not be induced by GA_3. Grant Lipp[22] has confirmed this in a careful study which established that neither single doses of 0.3–8.0 μg GA_3 applied to the apical bud just before the end of an 8-hour day, nor doses of 1–2 μg repeated over several weeks, produced flowering. *Anagallis* thus takes its place as a member of the class of non-rosette, caulescent long day plants in which flowering is not induced by GA.

However, GA_3 accelerated the development of flowers on plants receiving long days and it also appeared to interact with long day treatment to raise the percentage of individuals flowering after sub-maximal induction, e.g. after 2 LD and application of 0, 0.3, 1, 3 and 6 μg GA_3 per plant the percentage flowering was 77, 100, 90, 90, and 97 respectively. Such a result could stem from a general effect of the GA_3 on meristem development.

Brulfert[7] has also noted that a single dose of GA_3, administered some days after a minimal induction, hastens by 3 weeks or more the appearance of abnormal flowers which are often produced under these conditions (Section 23).

Auxins

2,4,-dichlorophenoxyacetic acid (2,4-D) produces flower abnormalities distinguished by suppression of floral members, coalescence of them and even of individual flowers formed very close together by abnormal shortening of internodes. In some cases, the resultant structures simulate the flowers of other Primulaceous, or closely related, plants.[1,2] Although these abnormalities are the result of effects on growth rather than on induction they are of interest in indicating that, even after induction, there still remain possibilities of variation in developmental patterns.

21 Induction of Excised Apices

Stem fragments consisting of as little as the apical meristem proper and no more than one or two pairs of leaf primordia can be cultured by standard techniques on solidified media containing minerals and carbohydrate. Rooting occurs rapidly and small, normal plants are produced.[9,25,36]

However, it was left to Brulfert[9] to record the interesting feature that, when cultured in continuous light, very early flower initiation occurs – in fact, at the first node produced after placing an apex in culture. Whatever may be the reasons why, in other circumstances, induction is only associated with the presence of larger amounts of leaf tissue, it is clear that here very small amounts of leaf tissue are sufficient to generate an effective photoperiodic stimulus. This is in contrast to the 4 leaves required by this strain as a normal, rooted plant, when receiving a single long day (Section 4). One could speculate whether, when carbohydrate is supplied, the small leaf tissue system is effective because of greater efficiency in transport of the stimulatory substance, with less retained in the leaves. Alternatively, since in the absence of carbohydrate leaves on intact plants must supply both assimilates and floral stimulus, one could consider that the minimal leaf area required is much greater for assimilate than for stimulus supply. Perhaps the weight of evidence presented in earlier sections tends to favour the second alternative.

23 Inflorescence Differentiation

There is no inflorescence proper and the following refers to the individual flowers located singly in the axils of leaves on any branch.

Vaughan[40] has given a detailed description of flower differentiation which is largely supported by other observations,[9,22] though there may be slight differences in the interpretation of the facts.

The flower primordium develops in the axil of a leaf primordium in the flank region of the main meristem. In fact, Vaughan maintains that the floral meristematic zone is a detached portion of the main apical meristem. When first recognizable, it consists of a 2-layered tunica and a deeper layer in which periclinal divisions will occur, thus giving rise to the bulk of the primordium.

Floral primordia develop more rapidly than vegetative primordia, being detectable consistently one node nearer the apex. In fact, in the early stages this is the only visible difference between them. Vaughan remarks, 'The development of all buds is essentially the same up to the stage where they protrude above the plant surface . . .' . These features, together with the unequal development of both types of buds on the two sides, are brought out in Figure 17–1.

With the histological situation now in mind, reference is made again to what was deduced concerning the nature of the meristem just when it is committed florally. The number of cells involved must be few, and it is remarkable that rates of development can be altered so profoundly and yet cause no visible differences when the primordia appear the same size, at different times later. And it is further noteworthy that these two structures, when they are still morphologically identical, can be situated in tissues so disparate in properties such as degree of vascularization and cell wall thickening.

Shortly after the flower primordium reaches the stage shown in Figure 17–1B the differentiation of sepals, stamens, carpels and petals, in that order, commences and their further development is not considered here.

Atypical Development

Any account of flowering in this species would be incomplete without some reference to the atypical flowers which it often produces. These structures are partly vegetative or foliaceous in character. Many other species produce similar structures but, in *Anagallis*, the environmental control of their production is very clear. Moreover, the Paris group has devoted much effort to studying this phenomenon,[8,10,11,17,18] and we probably owe much of their valuable general analysis of flowering in *Anagallis* to their requirement for background information for this study.

Heslop-Harrison[26] has stressed the desirability of maintaining an open mind about the causes and implications of such plant teratisms, and the non-committal term 'proliferous flowers' (fleurs prolifères) seems preferable to 'vegetative reversions', 'vegetative flowers'[32] etc.

The salient features of these proliferous flowers are:

(a) They display a continuous range of forms, from being mostly foliaceous and possessing no reproductive organs (stamens or carpels), to being reproductively complete. In all cases, the characteristic feature is the organization, at some central undifferentiated region of the flower initial, of an adventitious vegetative meristem, from which arises a more or less normal leafy shoot.

(b) They occur at the same places as do normal flowers, and their abnormality only becomes detectable 12 or more days after induction, when flower differentiation is proceeding. Their subsequent development is irregular and slow.

(c) They appear either under conditions of minimal induction (one cycle) or, if induction has been prolonged, they appear just at the node marking the return to vegetation. This has suggested that they result from an insufficiency of the floral stimulus.

(d) They may be produced at will – a single exposure to 22 hours of light at 50,000 ergs/cm^2/sec at 25°C produces them on 20–60 per cent of individuals. However, it has not been possible to control the precise proportion, nor the character, of the proliferous flowers by systematically varying the intensity of inductive treatments.

A study of these structures provokes speculation on, and evidence towards the solution of, such questions on the nature of floral induction as . . . is it a unitary process, the flower as a whole being committed, or does each flower part, in turn, require its own appropriate stimulus? Is induction an all or none process?

Conclusion

Since flower initiation depends on at least two sets of processes, one occurring in the leaves and the other at meristems, neither set can be held more important than the other. While this is so, the information discussed in this chapter suggests that *Anagallis* presents material more favourable for investigating meristematic rather than leaf events – certainly the more interesting findings so far appear to be in this territory.

It is worth observing that while many far-reaching differences are apparent in the behaviour of the two strains most investigated, they do agree in the meristematic properties of note – very early competence, brief lability and marked dependence on non-specific substrates.

REFERENCES

[1] Aymard, M. (1959). Phenocopies florales produites chez *Anagallis arvensis* L. par l'action de l'acide 2, 4-dichlorophénoxyacétique. *Bull. Soc. bot. Fr.* **106**, 457.

[2] Aymard, M. (1960). Coalescences florales chez *Anagallis arvensis* L. traité à l'acide 2, 4-dichlorophénoxyacétique. *Bull. Soc. bot. Fr.* **107**, 1.

[3] Ballard, L. A. T. Unpublished data.

[4] Ballard, L. A. T. and Grant Lipp, A. E. (1963). The effect of programme systems on flower initiation. *C.S.I.R.O. Division of Plant Industry Annual Report* 1962-63, 104.

[5] Ballard, L. A. T. and Grant Lipp, A. E. (1964). Juvenile photoperiodic sensitivity in *Anagallis arvensis* L. subsp. *foemina* (Mill.) Schinz and Thell. *Aust. J. Biol. Sci.* **17**, 323.

[6] Ballard, L. A. T. and Grant Lipp, A. E. Unpublished data.

[7] Brulfert, J. (1961). Action de l'acide gibbérellique sur l'expression des fleurs prolifères, chez *Anagallis arvensis* L. *C.R. Acad. Sci., Paris* **253**, 517.

[8] Brulfert, J. (1963). Etude expérimentale de la formation de fleurs prolifères chez *Anagallis arvensis* L. *Bull. Soc. bot. Fr.* **110**, 138.

[9] Brulfert, J. (1965). Etude expérimentale du développement végétatif et floral chez *Anagallis arvensis* L., ssp. *phoenicea* Scop. Formation de fleurs prolifères chez cette même espèce. *Rev. Gén. de Bot.* **72**, 641.

[9a] Brulfert, J. Unpublished data.

[10] Brulfert, J. (1965). Physiologie de la mise à fleurs d'*Anagallis arvensis* L. ssp. *phoenicia* Scop., et du développement végétatif en retour des méristèmes floraux. *Bull. Soc. Fr. Phys. Veg.* **11**, 247.

[11] Brulfert, J. and Chouard, P. (1961). Nouvelles observations sur la production expérimentale de fleurs prolifères chez *Anagallis arvensis* L. *C.R. Acad. Sci., Paris* **253**, 179.

[12] Buchwald, T. Unpublished data.

[13] Carr, D. J. (1952). A critical experiment on Bünning's theory of photoperiodism. *Zeit. Naturf.* **7**, 570.

[14] Carr, D. J. (1966). The relationship between florigen and the flower hormones. *New York Acad. Sci. Ann.* **144**, 305.

[15] Chouard, P. (1947). Sur le photopériodisme chez les plantes vivaces II. *Bull. Soc. bot. Fr.* **93**, 399.

[16] Chouard, P. (1949). Expériences de longue durée sur la photopériodisme; leçons qui en découlent. *Mem. Soc. bot. Fr.* **1949**, 106.

[17] Chouard, P. (1950). Réversibilité de l'état reproductif à l'état végétatif sous l'effet du photopériodisme. *C.R. Acad. Sci., Paris* **231**, 1245.

[18] Chouard, P. (1957). Réversibilité de l'état reproductif à l'état végétatif par le photopériodisme, et production expérimentale de fleurs prolifères chez *Anagallis arvensis*. *C.R. Acad. Sci., Paris* **245**, 2351.

[19] Chouard, P. (1957). Diversité des mécanismes des dormances, de la vernalization et du photopériodisme, révélée notamment par l'action de l'acide gibbérellique. *Mem. Soc. bot. Fr.* **1957**, 51.

[20] Claes, H. and Lang, A. (1947). Die Blütenbildung von *Hyoscyamus niger* in 48-stundigen Licht-Dunkel-Zyklen und in Zyklen mit aufgeteilten Lichtphasen. *Zeit. Naturf.* **2**, 56.

[21] Focke, W. O. (1881). *Die Pflanzenmischlinge*. Berlin. Cited by [27,31].

[22] Grant Lipp, A. E. Unpublished data.

[23] Grant Lipp, A. E. and Ballard, L. A. T. (1963). Germination patterns shown by the light-sensitive seed of *Anagallis arvensis*. *Aust. J. Biol. Sci.* **16**, 572.

[24] Hussey, G. (1954). Experiments with two long-day plants designed to test Bünning's theory of photoperiodism. *Physiol. Plantar.* **7**, 253.

[25] Hussey, G. Unpublished data.

[26] Heslop-Harrison, J. (1952). A reconsideration of plant teratology. *Phyton. Ann. Rei Bot.* **4**, 19.

[27] Lehmann, E. (1938). *Anagallis* als erbbiologische Schulmaterial. *Der Biologe* **7**, 303.

[28] Lehmann, E. (1943). *Der Erbversuch*. Stuttgart.

[29] Marchand, L. (1864). Monstruosités végétales. *Adansonia* **IV**, 150. Cited by [9].

[30] Marsden-Jones, E. M. (1935). The genetics of *Anagallis arvensis* Linn. and *Anagallis foemina* Mill. *Proc. Linn. Soc. Lond.* Session 147, 105.

[31] Marsden-Jones, E. M. and Weiss, F. E. (1938). The essential differences between *Anagallis arvensis* Linn. and *Anagallis foemina* Mill. *Proc. Linn. Soc. Lond.* Session 150, 146.

[32] Murneek, A. E. (1940). Length of day and temperature effects on *Rudbeckia*. *Bot. Gaz.* **102**, 296.

[33] Nilsson, H. (1938). *Anagallis arvensis* L. s.l. und die Natur Ihrer Farbenvarianten. *Hereditas* **24**, 97.

[34] Plantefol, L. (1946). Fondements d'une théorie phyllotaxique nouvelle. La théorie des hélices foliares multiples. *Ann. Sc. Nat. Bot.* 11th Series, **7**, 158.

[35] Plantefol, L. (1946). Fondements d'une théorie phyllotaxique nouvelle. La théorie des hélices foliares multiples. *Ann. Sc. Nat. Bot.* 11th Series, **8**, 1.

[36] Rijven, A. H. G. C. Unpublished data.

[37] Salisbury, E. J. (1942). *The reproductive capacity of plants. Studies in quantative biology*. G. Bell and Sons Ltd., London.

[38] Salisbury, F. B. (1955). The dual role of auxin in flowering. *Plant Physiol.* **30**, 327.

[39] Schoute, J. C. (1936). On whorled phyllotaxis. III True and false whorls. *Rec. trav. bot. néerl.* **33**, 670.

[40] Vaughan, J. G. (1955). The morphology and growth of the vegetative and reproductive apices of *Arabidopsis thaliana* (L). Heynh., *Capsella bursa-pastoris* (L.) Medic., and *Anagallis arvensis* L. *J. Linn. Soc. (Bot.)* **55**, 279.

[41] Weiss, F. E. (1910). Report Brit. Assoc. Sheffield, 1910, 779.

[42] Went, F. W. (1938). Transplantation experiments with peas. *Am. J. Bot.* **25**, 44.

18

Pisum sativum L.

By Wolfgang Haupt

1 History of Use

Mendel, in his classical paper on plant hybrids, paid attention to the flowering behaviour of peas, comparing early and late flowering varieties.[34] Since this genetically fixed characteristic is one of the most important factors determining flower initiation in peas, an understanding of initiation requires knowledge of the inheritance of early versus late flowering. Important papers along this line have been published by Tedin,[51] Wellensiek,[52] Hänsel,[10,11] Barber,[1] and Rowlands.[46]

External factors also influence flowering of peas, particularly photoperiod, as first shown by Kopetz,[27] vernalization, first mentioned by McKee,[33] nutritional status and growth substances and retardants.

Many investigations have been inspired by the question whether flower inducing or flower inhibiting substances are involved, making use of the fact that peas can be grafted easily and with a good chance of success. However, in contrast to many of the plants treated in this book, there seems to be no all-or-none response in flower induction of peas because most factors in question have only quantitative rather than qualitative effects.

In the following pages a distinction will be made between flower initiation, the physiological changes in the growing tip resulting in development of a flower primordium, and induction, the effect of a certain factor which brings about flower initiation.

2 Growing Techniques and Growth Habit

There is no need for special growth techniques because pea seeds are very rich in food reserves, localized in the cotyledons. As a result, peas are able to grow for a relatively long time on pure sand or on an agar medium without any addition of sugar and salts.[12] Early varieties initiate flowers under these conditions, even in total darkness; thus development up to flower initiation (and occasionally to anthesis) may take place at the expense of reserves in the cotyledons. Care must be taken to prevent contamination of the cotyledons by bacteria or fungi in the early stages of growth, under certain greenhouse conditions.[18] Pea seeds are readily sterilized by soaking in solutions of mercuric chloride[12] or other disinfectants.

If peas are deprived of their cotyledons at an early stage of their development, from before soaking until they become photosynthetic, the food reserves of the cotyledons have to be replaced by sugars, salts, and vitamins in the medium. Plants must then be cultivated under strictly sterile conditions.[12,17,26] However, flower initiation may take place so early on artificial media that only traces of the above mentioned substances are needed.[14,15]

Grafting can be done by connecting both partners either with a small glass tube[13,18,55] or with transparent adhesive tape.[26] The ability to regenerate not only guarantees a high proportion of success in grafting, but also ensures ample formation of adventitious roots in cuttings which can then be grown as easily as intact plants in normal soil.[13,16,50] Only cuttings of very young plants, isolated during the soaking period, have to be cultured on an organic medium.[26] These

FIGURE 18–1. *Pisum sativum* L. with a flower bud, an open flower and three pods (after L. Reichenbach *et al.*, *Deutschlands Flora*, Vol. 22, Leipzig und Gera 1900–1903).

techniques are very important in investigations concerned with the influence of the cotyledons on flower initiation.

The growth habit of peas needs only a few comments. Normally it is monaxial, with one main stem on which the leaf axils bear dormant stem buds or flowers. Once a leaf axil gives rise to a flower primordium, all younger nodes normally do so as well until growth is terminated (for exceptions see[1,26]). No terminal flower is developed in peas, except apparently in plants in which shoot apex senescence is delayed by removal of flowers.[32a]

In certain varieties, there are deviations from this general picture, the most important ones being:

(*a*) Due to inhibition of growth of the upper internodes, nearly all flower-bearing nodes are concentrated near the tip.[34,52]

(*b*) Instead of a single flower, each axil bears a small inflorescence with 2 to 3 or even more flowers.[23,40,52]

(*c*) Flower initiation takes place so early that only the cotyledons bear vegetative buds in their axils; the first or second leaf bears reproductive buds which give rise to extensive racemose inflorescences instead of single flowers.[28]

(*d*) The buds on the lower nodes give rise to lateral stems instead of being dormant, the extent of lateral growth depending on external conditions. These stems in turn give rise to additional flowers.[10,23,41]

Important as these deviations may be in practical agriculture, they seem to be less so in the physiology of flower induction, and normal growing peas are to be preferred for experimental work.

Later, we mention the difference between tall and dwarf varieties which seems largely to be due to difference in the extension growth of the internodes rather than in the number of nodes, and has little bearing on differences in floral behaviour. However, in some kinds of experiments dwarf varieties are more suitable from the practical point of view.[54]

3 Inflorescence Structure and Criteria of Flowering Response

As has been mentioned, there are either single flowers in the leaf axils or small inflorescences. It is not yet clear whether the inflorescence structure is determined only by nutritional factors or also influenced by the strength of the flower induction.

Since flower initiation at one node is normally succeeded by flower initiation at all following nodes, most investigators confine themselves to observing the first visible flower, be it macroscopically or microscopically, and to stating at which physiological age this flower or flower primordium appears. This age can be measured simply by time, i.e. days from sowing to flowering, or it can be measured by the number of vegetative nodes which are formed prior to the first flower-bearing node.

Both parameters are, within a certain range of environmental conditions, roughly correlated with each other,[46] but even in a pure line, there is some independent variation between individuals concerning time of flowering and node number.[10,11] Thus, the two parameters are not equally well suited to all kinds of experiments. Retardation or acceleration of growth, e.g. by temperature, may result in a retardation or acceleration of the time the first flower appears which is not due to any specific influence on flower initiation. From this point of view it seems better to take the node of first flower as an expression of the physiological age. However, here also an objection can be made. If young stems of a late variety are cut off and either regrafted on their own stocks or allowed to root as cuttings, it is observed, eventually, that flower initiation takes place at about one to two nodes earlier without any promotion in time. This effect can be enlarged by repeatedly cutting and rooting the stems.[13,16] With these treatments the growth of the apical meristem is arrested or strongly retarded for about one week, during which time about two new nodes normally are formed. It is concluded that some chemical reactions which result in ageing and therefore in flower initiation, are not as strongly retarded as growth. In this special case, small differences in the node number are not conclusive for a specific effect on flower initiation. It must be stated with emphasis, however, that not all inhibition of growth results in such a shift of node number.[49a] At any rate, in doubtful cases, both parameters should be taken, or the growth of the apical bud followed in addition to evaluating the node of first flower.[15,18]

Instead of taking the absolute node number for the first flower, it is sometimes preferable to take the difference between this and the youngest node visible at the start of the experiment. By this method, allowance is made for different stages of growth at the start of the experiment.[26]

By measuring only the time or position of the first flower, two types of information are lost. Firstly, whether or not a flower primordium develops into a full-grown flower or is aborted prematurely may depend upon factors which also influence flower initiation.[6,48] Secondly, in contrast to the general rule, there may be a kind of reversible induction, i.e. flower initiation at one or a few nodes followed by further vegetative nodes. This can be found in grafts performed under certain conditions[26] (section 17) or if an inducing factor acts only for a short time.[1] The problem arises then which factor determines the second initiation of flowers some nodes later. Thus, it has proved useful to score all nodes above that with the first flower for the vegetative or reproductive condition.[26]

4 Effects of Plant Age; Genetics of Flowering

For most plants in which the physiology of flowering has been investigated, only one or a few varieties have been used, to ensure that the genetic constitution is as constant as possible. In peas, one of the most important factors determining flower initiation is age. This factor cannot be influenced experimentally like day length or light intensity. However, the critical age is determined by the genetic constitution, and variation of this factor can be obtained indirectly by using several varieties. Many different varieties are used in investigations on flower initiation in peas, some of which are listed in Table 18–1 with their flowering behaviour and growth habit. Each characteristic is mainly governed by one pair of genes, Le/le for the growth habit and Sn/sn for the flowering behaviour. These segregate independently and thus belong to different linkage groups.[1,46,52]

TABLE 18–1

Some pea varieties which have been used in experiments concerning flower initiation.

Variety	Flowering type	Growth habit	Reference
Massey	early	dwarf	1, 2, 35, 43
Kleine Rhein-länderin	early	dwarf	12–18, 26
Vince	early	dwarf	10
Meteor	early	dwarf	6
Alaska	early	tall	1, 2, 21, 29–31, 35
Unica	intermediate to late	dwarf to medium	1, 2, 10, 20, 35
Supreme	late	dwarf	48, 49
Greenfeast	late	dwarf	1, 2, 42, 47, 50
Dwarf Telephone	late	dwarf	4, 35, 38, 39
Zelka	late	tall to medium	1, 20
Alderman*	late	tall	13, 17, 18, 26
Tall Telephone*	late	tall	1, 2, 4, 35, 43

* probably synonymous with each other.

The inheritance of flowering behaviour requires some additional comments. Firstly, late flowering (Sn) is dominant over early flowering(sn), pointing to something being present in late varieties which is absent from early ones, be it a transmissible flower inhibitor or an inhibitor of florigen synthesis.[1] Secondly, the allelic genes Sn/sn alone cannot explain the broad range of flowering behaviour between varieties which covers nodes of first flowering from 2 to about 50.[28,51] It is, therefore, assumed that at least two different pairs of allelic genes are responsible for lateness,[51] or, that besides the Sn/sn system, there is a polygenic control system.[1,46] Furthermore, Wellensiek[53] found evidence to assume a multiple allelic gene system with alleles each for late, intermediate, and early flowering, each later gene being incompletely dominant over the earlier one(s). All these results suffer, at the moment, from being obtained in different groups of varieties, and therefore being not strictly comparable. Thirdly, though the main effect of the combined Sn and polygenic system seems to be the determination of the physiological age at which flower initiation occurs, this effect is not completely fixed but can be modified by external factors such as photoperiod, vernalization, or chemical treatments. The range of these effects is commonly from nodes 8 to 11 for early varieties, and from 17 to 24 for late ones. However, these ranges can be broadened further by special experimental conditions, even to the extent of an overlapping of the two kinds of varieties.

One of the main tasks in analyzing flower initiation in peas is to clarify the physiological differences between early and late varieties. With regard to the importance of age for flower initiation, it may be assumed that juvenility has adverse effects. This has been confirmed in an intermediate to late flowering variety which is very sensitive to daylength; here, an inductive period of 2 weeks in long days is much less effective in very young than in older plants. The juvenile phase discovered in this way seems to end after about 4 weeks.[54] In some grafting experiments, older plants of a late variety are more sensitive than younger ones.[26] In addition, young plants of late varieties have a retarding effect on flower initiation which is graft transmissible.[43] However, whether or not this is comparable with a transmissible juvenility factor as in *Hedera*[8] is not yet clear.

5 *Vernalization and Devernalization*

Late varieties show pronounced responses to vernalization. A flower promotion of several nodes can be observed after cold treatment (1° to 7°C) for one to four weeks in the varieties Greenfeast, Dwarf and Tall Telephone, Unica, Zelka, and some others,[1,2,20,22,38,39,41] and also a reduction in time to flower initiation has been found.[39] Sometimes, this effect is more marked in conditions unfavourable for flowering such as short days (Table 18–2).

TABLE 18–2

The effect of vernalization, photoperiod and temperature of growth on node of first flower in the late variety Tall Telephone (after Barber[1]).

	Short day (12 hours)			Long day (24 hours)		
Growth temperature	10°	17°	23°	10°	17°	23°C
Unvernalized	21. 4	25. 2	27. 7	19. 5	19. 2	19. 0
Vernalized	18. 9	19. 6	22. 9	16. 9	16. 8	16. 2

Between varieties also, the earlier is flowering the less the vernalization effect;[54] early varieties can even be delayed by vernalization by about one node.[1,2,21,30,31,35] Whether or not this means a genetical linkage between cold requirement and late flowering[1] will be discussed in section 7.

Though the effects of vernalization are rather small in peas, and though the time until flower initiation occurs is limited, devernalization has been observed. In Dwarf Telephone, Unica, and Zelka, exposing plants to 30°C for 10 days following vernalization cancels the flower promotion partially or completely.[20,39]

Vernalization and devernalization not only influence flower initiation but also growth. It is interesting to note that the dose dependence for both kinds of vernalization and devernalization effects may differ to a certain degree.[1,20,21,38,39,41]

There are interesting interactions between vernalization and the effects of growth substances, the latter being synergistic or antagonistic to the former (see section 18).

7 *Photoperiod Response*

Late flowering varieties have been reported to be quantitative long day plants.[1,2,26,42] The effect of long days compared with short days can amount to a difference of more than 10 nodes (Table 18–3), and, in terms of time to

TABLE 18–3

Flower initiation of late varieties as influenced by photoperiod length (after Barber[1]).

Variety	Node of first flower in daylength of		
	8[hr]	12[hr]	24[hr]
Greenfeast	29.4	25.7	16.5
Tall Telephone	29.0	24.0	16.0
Zelka	37.5	..	17.0*

* only one week of continuous light, beginning 10 days after germination.

flowering, to a difference of 60 days.[42] In contrast, early flowering varieties are normally day neutral[12,30] (for exceptions see[29]), and as in the case of vernalization, photoperiodic sensitivity is the more pronounced the later the variety flowers.[41,46] This has been explained in terms of pleiotropic effects of the Sn gene responsible for late flowering.[1]

However, another explanation arose from anatomical and physiological investigations which showed that in the early variety 'Kleine Rheinländerin', initiation of flowers at the 9th or 10th node takes place about the 5th day after soaking.[12] Thus, there is almost no time for flower initiation to be influenced by either vernalization or photoperiod, apart from the fact that pea seedlings five days old are still underground and therefore not able to receive a photoperiodic stimulus. Although they appear to be independent of photoperiod, it does not follow that early varieties are insensitive to photoperiod.[10] Flowering in 'Kleine Rheinländerin' is markedly retarded, both in terms of node number and time if, during the first hours of soaking, the cotyledons are excised and the plants then grown in sterile artificial nutrient medium.[12] Under these conditions flowering in the decotylized plants has a strong daylength dependence (Fig. 18–2). This favours the second explanation, viz. flower initiation in early varieties occurs too early to be able to respond to photoperiod.[17]

It is curious to find, in Figure 18–2, that complete darkness is not as inhibitory as short days of 4 hours but corresponds to a 10 to 12-hour photoperiod. Similar effects have been reported by other authors.[5,7,29] However, some of these results have been questioned,[12] as they have been obtained with intact seedlings of early strains which do not respond to photoperiod. There are no comparable reports about late varieties grown under extreme short days or darkness, because it has not yet proved possible to grow them to the stage of flower initiation under light periods shorter than 8 hours.[26] To be effective, long days are not required during the whole period of development. With late varieties one or two weeks of long days can markedly promote flower initiation in plants otherwise grown in short days[1,54] (cf. Table 18–3), provided they are applied at the right time (see section 4). In some of those cases reversible flower induction has been found[1] (cf. section 3). Perception of the photoperiodic stimulus is not dependent on intact leaves, since the stipules which protect the apical bud are fully effective, as concluded from experiments with continuously defoliated plants.[26,47]

The question arises as to whether or not we are dealing with a true photoperiodic response. This can be tested in two ways: by supplementing short days with light breaks during the night, and by replacing short days by long days of low intensity light. Very few experiments have been done on these lines and the

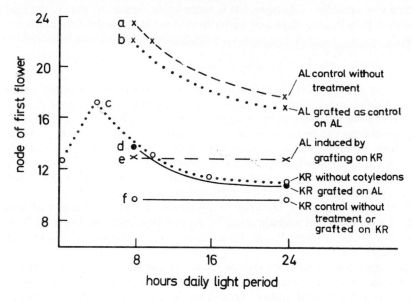

FIGURE 18–2. Flower initiation of peas as influenced by photoperiod. Early (KR) and late (AL) varieties with different treatments (after Köhler[26].) Curve b was added from comparable experiments, for completeness.

results are partly contradictory, pointing to more than one light effect being involved. On the one hand, in a late variety, lowering the light intensity in long days has no delaying effect on flower initiation[41] or even promotes it,[35] and short days plus light breaks can simulate the long-day effect.[41] However, in this clear case of true photoperiodism, vegetative branching is not equally influenced by light breaks, though also daylength dependent.[41] On the other hand, field experiments with some late varieties point more to the daily amount of light being the decisive factor.[45] With decotylized early peas, reducing the intensity of continuous light has the same retarding effect on flower initiation as shortening the photoperiod.[17] This latter effect may be interpreted as due to differences in photosynthesis. However, since reduced levels of sugar in the organic medium result in promotion rather than delay of flower initiation,[15] the photoperiod effect cannot be explained wholly in terms of photosynthesis. Perhaps, the so-called high energy reaction of photomorphogenesis takes part in this case. Again it is interesting to compare this response with the growth habit which, in contrast, responds here in different ways to reduced light intensity and reduced day length.[17]

The statement that the photoperiodic effect is quantitative rather than qualitative holds for flower initiation in peas in nearly all reports so far. For the development of flower primordia into fully grown flowers, however, there may also exist a qualitative effect, flower buds remaining undeveloped in short days.[54]

Photoperiod has a further, indirect effect on flowering in that, by altering the balance between reproductive and vegetative development, and by changing the extent of branching, photoperiod exerts a marked influence on the total number of flowers: this may be of horticultural interest.[1,10,41]

Finally, if photoperiodism in peas is compared with vernalization, there is a strong similarity between the effects of long days and those of cold on flower initiation.[41] These factors can also partly replace each other.[1] Since both factors act competitively rather than complementarily, it is not possible to assume a pattern x → vernalin → florigen.[1] It is remarkable, however, that with regard to vegetative growth long days and vernalization act in opposite directions to each other.[1]

13 Effects of Temperature

Apart from the effects of vernalization and devernalization by limited periods at low and high temperatures at an early stage, the temperature of growth may also influence flower initiation in late varieties,[1,9,41] early ones being not influenced.[12] No general rules can be formulated at the moment, as some of the results are contradictory. Whereas, in field experiments, higher temperatures have been shown to lower the first flowering node,[9] more recent investigations have shown higher temperatures to delay flowering by up to 6 nodes[1,41] (cf. Table 18–2). This latter effect is particularly marked if the night temperature is varied.[41]

There is an interaction between temperature and photoperiod and also between temperature and vernalization.[1,9] As can be seen from Table 18–2, differences due to photoperiod and vernalization are enlarged at higher growth temperature.

Thermoperiodic effects can also be found. In the late variety 'Greenfeast', the strong delay of flower initiation by short days compared with long days can be partly overcome by subdividing the 16-hour dark period into two 8-hour periods with temperatures differing by about 10°C; this is independent of whether the lower temperature precedes or succeeds the higher one, or whether alternating temperatures of 7 and 17°C or 17 and 26° are applied; nor has the temperature during the light period any bearing on the result.[42] Even though in these experiments only days to flowering were measured and the night temperature had a marked influence on the rate of node formation, the results seem to show true thermoperiodicity, as indicated by the importance of night temperature for node number to flowering.[41]

14 Effects of Mineral Nutrition

Since they initiate flowers so soon after germination, intact plants of early varieties would not be expected to show an effect of mineral nutrition on flowering. Such effects have to be investigated with late varieties or with decotylized early ones.

With intact late varieties, reduction in nutrient level[48] or, more specifically, in N,Mg, and perhaps P[41] enhances flower initiation by up to 2.5 nodes. No stronger effects have been found in plants of a late variety decotylized one week after soaking.[48]

If the early variety 'Kleine Rheinländerin' is decotylized during soaking, it is completely heterotrophic in organic and mineral nutrition, and it should be possible to detect any effects of nutrition on flower initiation in such plants. Indeed, media rich in nitrogen result in delayed flower initiation, irrespective of whether nitrogen is applied as nitrate, as a mixture of amino acids, as yeast extract or autolyzate, or as pea extract.[12,14] In contrast to the equivalent effects of different nitrogen sources on flower initiation, there is a differential effect on growth, the size of internodes and leaves being much more increased by organic than by inorganic nitrogen. Similarly plants grown in organic nitrogen contain much more nitrogen (in absolute as well as in relative amounts) than those grown in nitrate or under nitrogen deficiency.[15] Bearing this in mind, the delaying effect of nitrate on flower initiation is difficult to understand; it could be that a certain amount of nitrogen in any form in the medium is necessary for the uptake of another substance related to flower initiation.

The situation is further complicated by the finding that shortage of sugar in the medium also promotes flower initiation, at least in terms of node number.[15] Correspondingly, it has been found that in the early variety (Alaska), even with its cotyledons intact, addition of sugar delays flower initiation.[30] Thus, the classical hypothesis of Klebs of the significance for flowering of the C/N ratio cannot fit the results in peas; instead, it seems that deficiency in any one food factor can promote flower initiation. To ensure that the results observed in the above work[14,15,49a] were not a secondary effect of nutrient on rate of node formation, the latter was also measured (section 3).

Nutritional factors also greatly influence the number of flowers and pods which will develop after they have been initiated.[40]

16 Translocation of the Floral Stimulus

Whether or not a transmissible floral stimulus is formed in peas will be discussed in the next section; it is here anticipated that there is evidence for assuming such a substance. In normal grafts, this stimulus is translocated from stock to scion (e.g.[3,13,18,26,43]). However, downward translocation has also been found, though the stimulus is more effective if moving upward than if moving downward.[54] Furthermore, if a dwarf late variety is induced to flower by gibberellin (an exceptional case; see section 18), flowers appear first at the top of the main stem which is induced to grow out with long internodes, but then flowers are also initiated on the laterals which remain dwarfed, thus showing no direct gibberellin action. It is concluded that a floral stimulus, formed under the influence of gibberellin in the top, is translocated down the stem and up the laterals.[54]

17 Grafting Experiments

Grafting experiments have been done with the object of finding evidence for the transmission of hormone-like substances and whether a floral stimulus is supplied by plants already flowering or in an induced state, or whether a flower inhibitor is supplied by purely vegetative plants. Since external factors have less effect on flower initiation than genetic factors, most grafting experiments have made use of varietal differences.

When peas are grafted, the scion is isolated from its own cotyledons. First, therefore, the effect of decotylization needs to be known. Early varieties grown without cotyledons from the beginning of germination are delayed in flower initiation,[12] whereas in late varieties the same treatment results in flowering at an earlier physiological age.[3,43] This has been explained by the cotyledons containing a stimulus (florigen) in early and an inhibitor (colysanthin[1]) in late varieties respectively. The latter interpretation has been strengthened by the finding that rinsing young cuttings of a late variety in water for some days results in a further promotion of flower initiation. This is suggested to be due to leaching the colysanthin out of the plants.[50] Since decotylization can be compensated for (or even overcompensated) by supply of nitrogen in the late variety 'Supreme', the colysanthin hypothesis loses some of its significance.[48] The possibility of an indirect effect of arrested growth (section 3) should also be taken into account in explanations of leaching experiments.[26]

Early scions grafted on young late stocks are delayed in flowering to some degree.[3,43] If these grafts are performed with very young scions and if the results are compared with plants decotylized very early, no difference can be found between the delaying effects of the two treatments[12,17,26] (see Fig. 18-2). Hence, a specific flower-inhibiting effect of the cotyledons of the late stock cannot be demonstrated by this way, whereas the results point to a florigenic effect of the cotyledons of the early scion, which has been lost by both treatments in the same way.

Young late scions grafted on early stocks are promoted in flowering by several nodes.[43] The same result can be obtained using, as stocks, old plants of the late variety which already have initiated flower primordia or will do so very soon.[13] This has been explained simply as removal of the colysanthin from older plants, because there seemed not to be much difference between these grafts and isolated cuttings.[3,43] However, in repeated experiments, the flower-promoting effect exerted by early stocks clearly exceeded that due only to rooting the scions as cuttings or regrafting them on their own stocks.[13,18] Moreover, even stocks of a late variety in short days can be induced to earlier flowering by long-day induced scions.[54] This can hardly be explained by a reduced colysanthin supply due to grafting; but can readily be explained in terms of a stimulus to flowering passing from the early donor varieties to the late receptors.

This hypothesis is further strengthened by the results of modified grafts.[18] If receptors with and without their cotyledons are grafted on donors, in both cases marked flower promotion occurs. The effect is stronger in receptors without than in those with cotyledons, but no effect at all would be expected if only the colysanthin hypothesis were true. Furthermore, receptors have been grafted on interstocks which in turn have been grafted on stocks. If only the stock or the interstock is a donor, flower initiation of the receptor is always promoted in spite of the colysanthin source above or below the donor. From these experiments, preference must be given to the florigen hypothesis.[18] However, there are still some results which point to an additional participation of a colysanthin. Although it is possible that flower promotion in decotylized late varieties may be explained simply by removal of food reserves[48] or by temporarily arrested growth (which would correspond with the similar promotion of control grafts on their own stock[16]), it is still not clear why the flower promoting effect of the donor is reduced if the receptor has intact cotyledons or leaves.[18] Whether, here, we are indeed dealing with a colysanthin effect or only with inhibition of florigen translocation, cannot be decided yet. However, there is some evidence against a colysanthin function of the leaves: continuous defoliation has little or no effect on

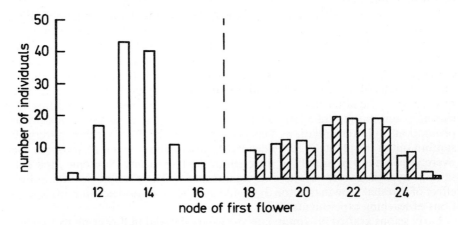

FIGURE 18–3. Frequency of nodes of first flower of a late pea variety grafted on an early one. Left group of columns (69% of the individuals; mean = 13.4): induction of the scion by the stock; right group (31% of the individuals; mean = 21.2): flower initiation not influenced by the stock. Hatched columns (mean = 21.3): control without treatment (after Köhler[26]).

flower initiation in late varieties, even though vegetative growth is as drastically inhibited as after the flower promoting decotylization.[26,47,cf.16]

More recent grafting experiments have led to the discovery of a different type of response.[26] If, under certain suboptimal conditions, receptors are grafted on donors, only a limited proportion of them is induced to earlier flowering, the rest being quite uninfluenced, as can be seen by comparing the two-peaked frequency distribution of node of first flower with the mean of the controls in Figure 18–3. This response seems to be comparable with the all-or-none induction of other plants and has been called a qualitative response. Only the induced plants can show a flower promoting response and this is called the quantitative response.

The qualitative response is markedly reduced if the receptor retains its leaves instead of being defoliated, if the donor is deprived of its cotyledons and leaves, and if the graft partners are grown in short days compared with long days (whether or not the donor has its leaves intact). The same factors also reduce the percentage of individuals in which the induction is irreversible but increase, relatively, the number of reversibly induced individuals (cf. section 3). In all these cases, the quantitative response of the induced individuals is not influenced by the factors in question (Table 18–4).

TABLE 18–4

Qualitative and quantitative response of late scions as receptors grafted on early stocks as donors, depending on daylength and on leaves of the stock. 'Alderman' as scion, 'Kleine Rheinländerin' as stock (after Köhler[26]).

		Short day	Long day
Donor with leaves	Overall percentage of induced receptors	93	98
	Percentage of irreversibly induced receptors	31	83
	Node of first flower of all induced receptors	12.5	13.0
Donor without leaves	Overall percentage of induced receptors	25	79
	Percentage of irreversibly induced receptors	16	60
	Node of first flower of all induced receptors	12.8	12.6

The qualitative response seems to reflect the amount of florigen supplied by the donor or the sensitivity to it of the receptor. Near the threshold, the amount of florigen relative to the sensitivity to it may suffice to induce only one to three nodes, resulting in reversible induction.[26]

In contrast, the quantitative response depends mainly upon the age of both donor and receptor and may reflect the ability of the receptor's apical meristem to respond faster or slower, or the rate of florigen formation in the stock:[26]

Though these results are not proof against any participation of a colysanthin, they rule out the need of it for explanation of the facts. Even the very important argument that late flowering (Sn) is dominant over early flowering (sn), suggesting a substance present in late flowering varieties, is not proof for colysanthin, a transmissible inhibitor of flower initiation. Rather, this Sn-substance may be an inhibitor, by itself not transmissible, of florigen formation.

The results concerning qualitative and reversible induction contribute not only to the question of florigen versus colysanthin, but also to a better understanding of the determination processes. Since those individuals which are not induced in a certain grafting experiment flower at the same node as the untreated controls, and since, in reversibly induced individuals, the second flower initiation also occurs at this same node, it is concluded that the pea has two different ways of initiating flowers, viz. determination solely by ageing versus induction by a donor, or, autonomous versus induced determination.[26] If this were true, a unified theory could be established to explain flower initiation in early and late varieties. Late varieties are normally autonomously determined, but they can be induced precociously by grafting to a donor. Early varieties are normally induced by their own cotyledons which contain sufficient florigen at a very early stage of development; however, if early plants are deprived of their source of florigen at the very beginning of their development, they must be autonomously determined. As a consequence, it should be possible to make a late variety flower as early as an early one and vice versa. However, graftings between swollen seeds, i.e. exchange of the plumules a few hours after beginning of soaking show marked differences: an induced late variety always flowers later than an induced early one (compare e with f in Fig. 18–2), and also autonomous determination always results in earlier flowering in the early than in the late variety (cf. a & b with c & d in Fig. 18–2). It is concluded, therefore, that there are also differences between early and late varieties in the ability of the apical meristem to become determined.[26]

18 Effects of Growth Regulators

Auxin has been reported to delay flower initiation in the early variety Alaska, amounting to 3–4 nodes with NAA at 10^{-6} M.[30,31] Arginine, malic acid, and even sugar, which by themselves delay flower initiation, can repromote the auxin-induced delay.[30] Similar to this rather complicated interaction is an interaction between auxin and vernalization, either of which factors delays flower initiation, but which, taken together, cancel each other. Thus, auxin-delayed early peas respond to vernalization as do late ones, by promotion of flower initiation. Consequently in auxin treated and vernalized plants, devernalization restores the delaying auxin effect.[30,31]

The hypothetical substance responsible for correlative inhibition of lateral buds, which sometimes acts antagonistically to auxin, seems to promote flower initiation.[32] These problems become still more complicated because there are also reports of auxin being ineffective,[12] or even promoting flower initiation in peas.[5]

Gibberellin, with one exception (see below), always delays flower initiation by about 1 to 3 nodes.[2,41] If dwarf and tall varieties are compared, there appear to be no significant differences in late strains, but in early ones, a dwarf is eventually more influenced than a tall[1] (but cf. [36]). This is interesting in view of some contradictory reports about the gibberellin content of tall and dwarf peas, the former having much more than the latter ones, if grown in light,[24,25] or no differences being found.[44]

In contrast to the auxin effect, there are no interactions with vernalization but only additive effects. Thus, promotion by vernalization can be cancelled by gibberellin which appears, superficially, like 'chemical devernalization'.[2,38] In early 'Massey' only gibberellin-delayed individuals respond to vernalization with flower promotion, but this need not be interpreted as an interaction, because the water controls initiate flowers so early that no promotion is possible. No interaction between gibberellin and photoperiod has been found, but only additive effects.[2]

Gibberellin antagonists are without effect[41] or, in the late 'Supreme', promote flowering somewhat; in this case, if applied together with gibberellin, the two effects cancel out each other.[49] The inhibitor of steroid biosynthesis, SK & F 7997, delays flowering in early varieties, amounting to about two nodes, but has little effect on late varieties. This compound seems neither to inhibit gibberellin biosynthesis nor to compete with applied gibberellins.[37] In one late strain a true promoting or even inducing effect of gibberellin has been referred to, comparable to its effect in other long day plants. Here, plants growing in short days are induced by GA_3 to flower like the untreated plants growing in long days.[54]

Besides its effect on flower initiation, gibberellin may also inhibit the development of flower primordia into flowers, i.e. they fail to complete their development, wither prematurely, and are aborted.[2,6,32a] Detailed analysis shows that the only primordia influenced in this way are those which have been initiated but are not more than three plastochrons old at the moment of gibberellin application.[48] Since abortion is an all-or-none response, it may be said also that gibberellin delays flower initiation quantitatively, but inhibits flower formation qualitatively.

20 Florigenic Extracts

No successful attempt has been made to extract florigenic substances. Diffusates of soaked seeds have been found to stimulate flower initiation in a late strain;[19] but since this effect is independent of whether this diffusate has been obtained from vernalized or unvernalized seeds, we are unlikely to be dealing with a true florigen. Other attempts[39] in this line are unconvincing because of very small effects.

Conclusion

Despite several apparently contradictory results and interpretations, some general conclusions on the factors controlling flower initiation in peas will be attempted (cf.[26]).

There are two possible ways in which the growing tip may initiate flowers, either autonomously or after induction.

Autonomous determination can be observed:

(*a*) in late varieties under normal conditions or in plants which, though grafted on a donor, did not respond to the induction or were induced only reversibly.

(*b*) in early varieties deprived of their cotyledons.

This autonomous determination seems to be an effect of ageing, but nothing is known about reactions underlying this process. It is promoted by long days and vernalization, delayed by gibberellin, but hardly influenced by the leaves. The range of dependence on promoting and delaying factors is fixed by the genetic constitution (cf. Fig. 18–2).

Induction of flower initiation can be observed:

(*a*) in early varieties under normal conditions by the older parts or when regrafted on donor stocks after decotylization.

(*b*) in late varieties when grafted on donor stocks.

Donors can be plants of early varieties of any age, or old plants of late-flowering varieties. This induction can be described as the proportion of plants which are induced to earlier flowering (qualitative response) or as the number of nodes until flower initiation (quantitative response).

The qualitative response is always 100 per cent in normally grown early peas; in graft inductions, however, the rate of induction of receptors depends on the day length, the leaves and cotyledons of the donor and receptor, and, to some extent, on the age of both donor and receptor. These factors also determine whether induction is reversible or irreversible. Thus, the qualitative response seems to reflect the amount of florigenic substances reaching the growing tip.

The quantitative response is independent of external factors (cf. Fig. 18–2). The number of nodes formed prior to flower initiation depends on the genetic constitution and the age of the receptor. This seems to reflect the speed with which the growing tip reacts to induction.

The reaction chains of autonomous and induced determination have in common the dependence on age and genetic constitution. There is, however, an important difference in the result; the autonomously determined plant can in turn induce another plant, whereas induced determination may be restricted to only one or a few nodes and cannot be transmitted in an unlimited way even within an individual. Accordingly, induction can be reversible, whereas autonomous determination seems to be always irreversible. If the latter is called an effect of ageing, the former cannot be a true induced ageing, i.e. an ageing effect of an older grafting partner on a younger one. This can be shown best by the fact that, sometimes, in the same individual, both kinds of determination can be observed successively without the physiological age of autonomous determination being influenced by the induction.

The difference between early and late flowering varieties seems to be in the earlier or later ageing (resulting in earlier or later autonomous determination), the sensitivity to induction, and the ability to induce a growing tip.

Concerning the problem florigen versus colysanthin, preference is given to the former. However, formation of florigen may be blocked by an inhibitor, resulting from the dominant Sn gene, which was thought to be a colysanthin but which seems to be not a transmissible hormone. It is quite possible that the influence of external factors on autonomous determination has something to do with this inhibitor as is suggested by Barber,[1] but the inhibitor is thought to act before and not after the florigen has been formed.

REFERENCES

[1] Barber, H. N. (1959). Physiological genetics of *Pisum* II. The genetics of photoperiodism and vernalization. *Heredity* **13**, 33.

[2] Barber, H. N., Jackson, W. D., Murfet, I. C. and Sprent, J. I. (1958). Gibberellic acid and the physiological genetics of flowering in peas. *Nature* **182**, 1321.

[3] Barber, H. N. and Paton, D. M. (1952). A gene-controlled flowering inhibitor in *Pisum. Nature* **169**, 592.

[4] Bonde, E. K. and Moore, T. C. (1958). Effects of gibberellic acid on the growth and flowering of Telephone peas. *Physiol. Plantar.* **11**, 451.

[5] Borgström, G. (1939). Anthogenesis in etiolated pea seedlings. *Bot. Notis., Lund* 830.

[6] Brian, P. W., Hemming, H. G. and Lowe, D. (1958). Effect of gibberellic acid on rate of extension and maturation of pea internodes. *Ann. Bot. N.S.* **22**, 539.

[7] Bünning, E. (1951). Über Langtagpflanzen mit doppelter photophiler Phase. *Ber. Deut. Bot. Ges.* **64**, 84.

[8] Doorenbos, J. (1954). Rejuvenation of *Hedera helix* in graft combinations. *Proc. Kon. Akad. Ned. Wetensch.* C **57**, 99.

[9] Fuchs, W. H. und Mühlendyck, E. (1951). Über den Einfluß der Aussaatzeit und der Temperatur auf die Entwicklung von Erbsensorten. *Z. Pflanzenzüchtg.* **30**, 172.

[10] Hänsel, H. (1954). Vergleich der Konstanz verschiedener 'Blühzeit' – Maße im Langtag im Hinblick auf Sortencharakteristik und Erbversuch bei *Pisum sativum*. *Der Züchter* **24**, 77.

[11] Hänsel, H. (1954). Versuche zur Vererbung der Nodienzahl-Blühzeit-Relation im langen Tag bei Erbsensorten. (*Pisum sativum* x *Pisum sativum* ssp. *arvense*). *Der Züchter* **24**, 97.

[12] Haupt, W. (1952). Untersuchungen über den Determinationsvorgang der Blütenbildung bei *Pisum sativum*. *Z. Bot.* **40**, 1.

[13] Haupt, W. (1954). Die Übertragung blühfördernder Prinzipien bei *Pisum sativum* durch Pfropfung. *Z. Bot.* **42**, 125.

[14] Haupt, W. (1954). Die stoffliche Beeinflussung der Blütenbildung bei *Pisum sativum*. I. Die Wirkung der Stickstoffernährung. *Ber. Deut. Bot. Ges.* **67**, 75.

[15] Haupt, W. (1955). Die stoffliche Beeinflussung der Blütenbildung bei *Pisum sativum*. II. Die Wirkung der Zuckerernährung. *Ber. Deut. Bot. Ges.* **68**, 107.

[16] Haupt, W. (1956). Förderung der Blütenbildung durch Hemmung der vegetativen Entwicklung. *Planta* **46**, 403.

[17] Haupt, W. (1957). Photoperiodische Reaktion bei einer als tagneutral geltenden Sorte von *Pisum sativum*. *Ber. Deut. Bot. Ges.* **70**, 191.

[18] Haupt, W. (1958). Die Blütenbildung bei *Pisum sativum*. Weitere Untersuchungen zur Übertragbarkeit eines Blühimpulses durch Pfropfung. *Z. Bot.* **46**, 242.

[19] Highkin, H. R. (1955). Flower-promoting activity of pea diffusates. *Plant Physiol.* **30**, 390.

[20] Highkin, H. R. (1956). Vernalization in peas. *Plant Physiol.* **31**, 399.

[21] Highkin, H. R. and Lang, A. (1966). Residual effect of germination temperature on the growth of peas. *Planta* **68**, 94.

[22] Ikegaya, Y. and Shinohara, S. (1957). Studies on the vernalization of leguminous plants II. *Bull. Shizuoka Agr. Expt. St.* **2**, 56.

[23] Inoue, Y. (1964). Studies on the flowering and fruiting in some leguminous vegetables. *Mem. Fac. Agric., College of Education, Tokyo* **10**, 157.

[24] Köhler, D. (1965). Über den Gibberellingehalt von Zwerg- und Normalerbsen im Rotlicht und die Wirkung von Chlorcholinchlorid auf das Wachstum der Erbsen. *Planta* **65**, 218.

[25] Köhler, D. (1965). Die Wirkung von schwachem Rotlicht und Chlorcholinchlorid auf den Gibberellingehalt normaler Erbsensämlinge und die Ursache der unterschiedlichen Empfindlichkeit von Zwerg- und Normalerbsensämlingen gegen ihr eigenes Gibberellin. *Planta* **67**, 44.

[26] Köhler, G. D. (1965). Die Physiologie der Blütenbildung bei *Pisum sativum*. *Z. Pflanzenphysiol.* **53**, 429.

[27] Kopetz, L. M. (1938). Photoperiodische Untersuchungen an Pflückerbsen. *Gartenbauwissensch.* **12**.

[28] Lamprecht, H. (1956). Ein Pisum-Typ mit grundständigen Infloreszenzen. *Agri. Hort. Genetica* **14**, 195.

[29] Leopold, A. C. (1949). Flower initiation in total darkness. *Plant Physiol.* **24**, 530.

[30] Leopold, A. C. and Guernsey, F. S. (1953). Flower initiation in Alaska pea. I. Evidence as to the role of auxin. *Amer. J. Bot.* **40**, 46.

[31] Leopold, A. C. and Guernsey, F. S. (1954). Flower initiation in the Alaska pea. II. chemical vernalization. *Amer. J. Bot.* **41**, 181.

[32] Libbert, E. (1955). Über mögliche Beziehungen zwischen Korrelationshemmstoff und Blütenbildung. *Naturwiss.* **42**, 610.

[32a] Lockhart, J. A. and Gottschall, V. (1961). Fruit-induced and apical senescence in *Pisum sativum* L. *Plant Physiol.* **36**, 389.

[33] McKee, R. (1935). Vernalization experiments with forage crops. *U.S. Dept. Agr., Circ.* **377**.

[34] Mendel, G. (1865). Versuche über Pflanzen-Hybriden. *Verhandl. Naturforsch. Verein Brünn* **IV**, 3.

[35] Moore, T. C. (1964). Effects of cotyledon excision on the flowering of five varieties of *Pisum sativum*. *Plant Physiol.* **39**, 924.

[36] Moore, T. C. (1965). Effects of gibberellin on the growth and flowering of intact and decotylized dwarf peas. *Nature* **206**, 1065.

[37] Moore, T. C. and Anderson, J. D. (1966). Inhibition of the growth of peas by tris-(2-diethylaminoethyl)-phosphate trihydrochloride. *Plant Physiol.* **41**, 238.

[38] Moore, T. C. and Bonde, E. K. (1958). Interaction of gibberellic acid and vernalization in the Dwarf Telephone pea. *Physiol. Plantar.* **11**, 752.

[39] Moore, T. C. and Bonde, E. K. (1962). Physiology of flowering in peas. *Plant Physiol.* **37,** 149.

[40] Mühleisen, R. (1951). Untersuchungen über den Blüten- und Hülsenansatz sowie über die Qualität der Erbsen. *Z.f. Acker- u. Pflanzenbau* **94,** 59.

[41] Nakamura, E. (1965). Studies on the branching in *Pisum sativum* L. *Special report of Laboratory of Horticulture, Shiga Agricultural College, Kusatsu,* 1.

[42] Paton, D. M. (1957). Thermoperiodic and photoperiodic control of flower initiation in a late pea variety. *Plant Physiol.* **32,** suppl. IX.

[43] Paton, D. M. and Barber, H. N. (1955). Physiological genetics of *Pisum.* I. Grafting experiments between early and late varieties. *Austral. J. Biol. Sci.* **8,** 231.

[44] Radley, M. (1958). The distribution of substances similar to gibberellic acid in higher plants. *Ann. Bot. N.S.* **22,** 297–307.

[45] Reath, A. N. and Wittwer, S. H. (1952). The effects of temperature and photoperiod on the development of pea varieties. *Proc. Amer. Soc. Hort. Sci.* **60,** 301.

[46] Rowlands, D. G. (1964). Genetic control of flowering in *Pisum sativum* L. *Genetica* **35,** 75.

[47] Sprent, J. I. (1966). Role of the leaf in flowering of late pea varieties. *Nature* **209,** 1043.

[48] Sprent, J. I. (1966). The effect of nutrient factors on the response of peas to gibberellic acid. *Ann. Bot. N.S.* **30,** 779.

[49] Sprent, J. I. (1969). In preparation.

[49a] Sprent, J. I. (1967). The effects of nutrient factors, water supply and growth regulating substances on the vegetative growth pattern of peas and its relationship to node of first flower. *Ann. Bot. N.S.* **31,** 607.

[50] Sprent, J. I. and Barber, H. N. (1957). Leaching of a flower inhibitor from late varieties of peas. *Nature* **180,** 200.

[51] Tedin, H. (1897). Nagra Synpunkter vid förädling af ärter. *Sver. Uts. för. Tidskr.* **7,** 111.

[52] Wellensiek, S. J. (1925). Genetic Monograph on *Pisum. Bibliographia Genetica* **2,** 343.

[53] Wellensiek, S. J. (1965). The use of induced mutations in plant breeding. *Rep. Meet. FAO, UN and IAEA,* 393.

[54] Wellensiek, S. J. (1969). *Z. Pflanzenphysiol.* (in press) and personal communication.

[55] Went, F. W. (1938). Transplantation experiments with peas. *Amer. J. Bot.* **25,** 44.

19

Lycopersicon esculentum Mill.

By S. H Wittwer and L. H. Aung

1 History of Use

The common tomato (*Lycopersicon esculentum* Mill.), which was once considered a highly poisonous plant because of its taxonomic membership in the Nightshade family, has found universal appeal and is today valued as one of the most important food crops.[86] The plant is of Latin American origin. From there it was carried by traders and explorers to Europe and Asia after its edibility and non-poisonous nature were recognized.

Sturtevant[68] recorded that the tomato, known in Italy as Pome d'oro (gold apple), was first introduced into that country in 1554 and used as food. Its presence in German, Belgian, French, and English gardens was noted about 1583. Currently, tomato production is world-wide, and its popularity has spread to all parts of the earth.

The tomato has been used extensively as an experimental plant in developmental and mineral nutrition studies, and treatment responses have often been appraised by differences in flowering and fruiting behaviour.[46] It is self-pollinated, and has well-defined and prominent flowering and fruiting organs. The plant is adapted to greenhouse and controlled environment culture. Light saturation of the leaves is reached at low intensities (1000–1500 f.c.). It is easy to culture and train and growth is rapid. Flowering and fruiting may occur at any season of the year. Nutritional requirements have been well defined and disorders are easily detected and corrected. There is relative freedom from insects and diseases. Finally, the tomato is responsive to a wide variety of growth factors, and the effects can be conveniently measured by marked differences in vegetative, flowering or fruiting behaviour. The tomato plant flowers under a wide variety of environmental conditions. The effects of photoperiod are not pronounced. Much of the early work relating to nutritional modifications of flowering dealt with the tomato, although the effects on flowering and subsequent fruiting were not clearly differentiated.[37]

2 Growing Techniques and Growth Habit

Growing techniques are precise and should be followed closely to produce plants of experimental acceptability.[8,78] All environmental variables modify the flowering behaviour. Hot water-treated (50°C for 25 minutes) or certified seeds, and samples which have been aged about one year, are recommended. Seeds of the desired variety may be sown in any suitable sterilized medium low in mineral nutrients and with a pH of 6.5–7.0. They are then covered with up to 1/2 cm of finely screened soil, sand, vermiculite, or peat, and sprinkled lightly with water. Germination temperatures should range between 18° and 24°C. Plants may be started by seeding directly into a medium in containers in which they are to be grown or transplanted with the appearance of the first true (plumule) leaves. After transplanting, the plants are spaced so that there is no crowding and overlapping of leaves. The optimal temperatures for growth and development range from 15° to 18°C at night and 18° to 27°C during the day. Appearance of the first flowers often occurs 45 to 60 days from seeding. The optimum night temperature range for fruit setting is 13° to 24°C, but is much narrower (16° to 21°C) for most commercially acceptable varieties. Control of growth should be achieved by regulating the water supply rather than by withholding mineral nutrients or lowering the temperature. Plants grown properly should be as wide as they are tall, the stems thick, the foliage dark green, and the nodes close together. An often neglected factor in tomato plant culture in greenhouse and growth chambers is the carbon dioxide level in the ambient atmosphere. Provision should be made for frequent air exchange, and supplementary carbon dioxide provided to maintain atmospheric levels of at least 300 ppm during the daylight hours.[84]

The tomato in its native habitat is a perennial. In the cultivated state, however, it is a short-lived herbaceous annual, with an erect or weak, trailing and much branched stem covered with glandular hairs.[11,13,25]

Cultivars differ in growth habit. In the erect types, the main stems are very thick, reaching a diameter of 2 cm or more, and some of the branches, which range from 10 to 17 in number, are over 2 metres in length. The trailing or semi-climbing types have smaller and weaker stems than the erect types. The branching is usually sympodial; the successive principal axes are developed from axillary buds. This mode of development is repeated many times until the axis is several metres long, bearing inflorescences and fruits throughout its length.

There are two flowering types. The terminal buds of determinate types differentiate into floral clusters or into abortive branches after the production of leaves at several nodes and a varying number of inflorescences. Each axillary bud then continues the vegetative shoot, producing leaves and floral clusters and finally terminates as an inflorescence. This pattern of growth is repeated by other lateral shoots.

The terminal buds in indeterminate types, which really originate as laterals to each successive inflorescence, continue to grow as the main growing point and produce leaves and floral clusters, alternating with each other. The axillary shoots exhibit a similar mode of development.

Went[73] noted that the bud in the axil of the leaf immediately below the lowest flower primordium was vegetative, and after growing out took over as the main axis of the plant. This lateral bud was observed to grow united to the basal portion of the petiole, and the leaf opposite the inflorescence invariably lacked an axillary bud. These facts suggested that the shoot above the floral cluster was of lateral origin.

3 Inflorescence Structure and Criteria of Flowering Response

Bouquet[2] classified the tomato inflorescences into three types: (1) simple raceme-like clusters; (2) dichotomous or two-forked clusters; and (3) polychotomous clusters or those having more than two forks or branches. Clusters of the last two groups were designated as compound. All three types may be found on the same plant. The simple raceme is genetically dominant over the compound type. Simple racemes occurred more frequently on the lower portion of the plant, while the compound type occurred more commonly on the upper parts.

There is no fixed or uniform size of inflorescence. Each cluster consists of a variable number of flowers. Inflorescence size is dependent on the type of cluster, its location on the plant, the vegetative growth of the plant, the season of the year, and the general structure of the cluster of the variety. Branched clusters have a blossom-producing area almost twice that of the simple type and the potential to produce more blossoms and fruits per cluster.

According to Lewis[43] the size of the inflorescence in tomatoes is controlled by a major gene, a system of polygenes which is responsible for the differences in mean number of flowers in cultivated varieties, and the growing environment.

The branching of the inflorescence is associated with the number of flowers, and this branching is the result rather than the cause of greater flower production.

A detailed study[28] with early Michigan State Forcing and late (Pennorange) tomato cultivars and their progeny suggests that earliness of flowering in the tomato is controlled by one major gene pair. The inheritance of the number of nodes preceding the first flower cluster, and of days from seeding to first anthesis, were examined with reciprocal crosses and selfing of hybrids between the two varieties. A very high correlation between the number of nodes formed before the first flower cluster and of days to first anthesis was noted.

Criteria employed for indexing flowering in the tomato vary with different workers. Generally, they are selected on the basis of personal preference and ease rather than on strict objectivity with regard to plant development. Among the criteria used are: (1) the total number of days from seeding to anthesis of the first flower on the earliest inflorescence; (2) the days from seeding to floral bud differentiation; (3) the number of blossoms per inflorescence; and (4) the number of leaf nodes between the cotyledons and the first inflorescence.

The number of nodes up to or preceding the first inflorescence is an objective measurement and is preferred as an index of flowering in the tomato. There is, however a high correlation between leaf nodes that precede the formation of the first flower cluster and days from seeding to anthesis.[28]

4 Effects of Plant Age

Age is not a decisive limiting factor in the flowering of the tomato. Flower differentiation and development can begin soon after cotyledon expansion. This developmental stage is usually reached within two weeks after germination. The age of seedlings, however, is critical in relation to the response of tomato plants to low temperatures and high light intensities. Both of these have strong modifying effects on earliness and flower production.[9,10]

FIGURE 19–1. The modification of tomato flowering by environmental or chemical factors. *Right.* More flowers, earlier flowering and fewer nodes induced by high light intensity, high nutrition, low temperature, a short photoperiod, growth retardants or a combination of these variables. *Left.* Fewer flowers, later flowering and more nodes induced by low light intensity, low nutrition, high temperature, a long photoperiod, gibberellin or a combination of these variables.

Exposure of tomato seedlings to various environmental conditions and chemical stimuli at different stages of development, modifies the number of flowers in the inflorescences located sequentially on the tomato stem (Fig. 19–1). Furthermore, the influence of any external factor is exercised on the particular inflorescence which is differentiating at the moment. Though flowering is modified quantitatively by the environment, it is apparent that the tomato plant will eventually produce flower primordia following cotyledon expansion irrespective of age or environment, even though numbers and position can be changed.

5 Vernalization and Devernalization

Prolonged exposure of partially germinated tomato seeds to near freezing temperatures (seed vernalization) has given variable results as measured by subsequent flowering behaviour. Stier[66] allowed tomato seed to imbibe water for 1–3 days and then held them at 0° to 2°C for 15, 30, and 45 days. Cold treatment for 15 days resulted in earlier flowering than in the control plants. There was, however, no significant effect on flowering for the 30 and 45-day treatments. The number of nodes that appeared before the first inflorescence was not altered by any of the vernalization treatments. Goodall and Bolas[24] found no difference in the time of first flowering due to vernalization of tomato seeds in an imbibed state at temperatures of 0°, 2°–3°, 7°, or 8°–11°C for periods ranging from 10–20 days. Similarly, Wittwer and Teubner[82] observed no difference in date of flowering in plants from chilled and non-chilled seeds.

6 Short-Day Vernalization

This is a possibility for the tomato. Seedlings (Michigan-Ohio Hybrid and WR-7 Globe cultivars), at the cotyledon expansion stage, exposed to an 18-hour photoperiod and high night temperature (18°C) were significantly delayed in flowering compared with those grown at a 9-hour photoperiod and a night temperature of 13°C. At the low temperature (13°C), however, there was no significant effect of photoperiod on the number of nodes that appeared before the first inflorescence. Nevertheless, the trend was for more nodes under the long photoperiod. The effects of a short photoperiod and low temperature, and of a long photoperiod and high temperature, were confounded.

Calvert[7] suggested that although the ambient temperature recorded on a thermograph remained constant during dark and light periods, the plants receiving a long light exposure (16-hour or more) might have a higher plant or leaf temperature than plants under an 8-hour photoperiod, since they were exposed to radiant energy for a longer period in each 24-hour cycle. Further studies, using night-interruption and with no heating effect from long day illumination, are needed to resolve the question of short day vernalization.

7 Photoperiod Response

The tomato plant initiates and forms floral buds irrespective of day length. It, has therefore been considered photoperiodically indifferent with respect to flowering and an example of a day-neutral plant. Nevertheless, photoperiod affects both reproductive growth and vegetative development.[38]

The assumption that the tomato is photoperiodically insensitive as to flowering behaviour is no longer valid. Some of the observed effects, however, are at variance.

Tomato plants in a 16-hour photoperiod showed greater plant height and increased dry weights of foliage and roots, and fewer days to first anthesis than plants in a photoperiod of 9–10 hours.[40] Saito et al.[61] also noted greater vegetative growth, earlier flower bud differentiation and increased flower numbers with photoperiods up to 16 hours. Continuous light, however, retarded growth and flowering. They concluded that 16 hours was the most favourable photoperiod for growth and flower formation in the tomato.

Cooper [15,16] found that plants under long days reached anthesis in fewer days than those exposed to a short photoperiod, and suggested that the tomato behaved as a weak long-day plant. The effects of long days and high light intensity during the summer months were not separated, and Cooper[16] did not rule out the possibility that the earlier flowering might be an effect of either total radiation or light duration.

Wittwer,[79] on the other hand, observed that tomato varieties differing widely in type and earliness flowered earlier in a photoperiod of 9 hours than in one of 18 hours. There were fewer nodes formed before the first inflorescence, and the time to the first anthesis was significantly reduced. He concluded that the tomato is a facultative short-day plant. Differences in total radiation may have caused earlier flowering under long days in some experiments, since Calvert has shown a progressive hastening of flowering with increase in light intensity[8] (Fig. 19–2).

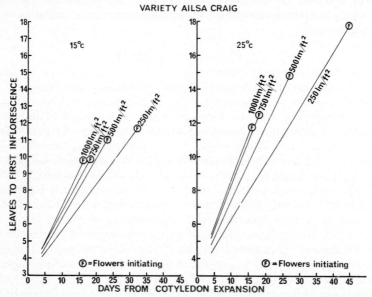

FIGURE 19–2. Effect of light intensity and temperature on number of leaves to first inflorescence and time of flower initiation in tomato (adapted from Calvert[8]).

This possibility was avoided by Wittwer[79] in the use of low light intensities (50–75 f.c.) for extending the light period beyond 9 hours. A true photoperiodic behaviour may reside in the cultivated tomato as a result of cross-pollination with short-day perennial species in the course of evolution of modern varieties.[11] There is no sound evidence against the proposal that the tomato is a facultative short-day plant.[79]

8 Spectral Dependence

Reinders–Gouwentak et al.[57] found that plants exposed daily for 9 hours to light from high pressure mercury vapor lamps had more flowers and a lower node of flowering than plants exposed to daylengths extended a further $7\frac{1}{2}$ hours with light from high intensity incandescent lamps.[56] The reduction in flowering of the plants receiving the additional illumination could be explained as resulting from either a higher temperature effect or an extended photoperiod, or a combination of the two.[5,6]

Helson[26] found that the dry weights of tomato stems and leaves were greater under cool-white than under Gro-Lux fluorescent lamps. However, when 35 per cent of the fluorescent wattage was added as incandescent light, plants under Gro-Lux plus incandescent had 34 per cent more flowers than those under cool-white and incandescent lamps. The increase in growth and number of flowers by the addition of incandescent light was attributed to an increased photosynthetic activity from greater light energy penetrating to the lower leaves. This, however, offers no explanation of the favourable effects on flowering when incandescent lighting was combined with Gro-Lux rather than cool-white fluorescent.

9 Endogenous Rhythms

No observations have been recorded as to changes in flowering behaviour induced by different light-dark cycles as they may interact with endogenous rhythms in the tomato plant. There is ample evidence that rhythms exist, and the marked differences manifest in vegetative growth[27,35,72] of plants on various cycle lengths were probably accompanied by equally pronounced variation in reproductive development.

11 Photoperiodic Inhibition

The results of defoliation experiments with tomato seedlings are of special significance as they relate to subsequent flowering responses. De Zeeuw[18,19] found that tomato seedlings which were partially, or completely and continuously defoliated since emerging, but with their cotyledons intact, initiated and developed flower clusters. Furthermore, flower initiation was advanced, the period from appearance of macroscopic flower primordia to the opening of the first flower was shortened, and the number of flowers increased two to threefold. However, if some young leaves immediately above the first cluster were allowed to develop, the elongation and development of the flower cluster was greatly inhibited. Leopold and Lam[41] similarly showed that the removal of young leaves had a promotive effect on tomato flowering while the removal of mature leaves had an inhibitory effect. Earlier flowering was especially pronounced for the late tomato varieties. De Zeeuw[18,19] removed not only the leaves but the young axillary buds. It is possible that the promotive effects of defoliation on flowering might be the combined influence of axillary bud and leaf removal.[1]

The inhibition of flowering in the presence of leaves and its release by leaf removal may have resulted from an inhibitor of flowering produced by the young leaves, or from their preferential mobilization of auxin.[18,19] If an inhibitor from the young leaf was the controlling factor in suppressing the growth of the inflorescence, such a substance may be isolated and correlated directly with the growth of the inflorescence. Auxin and flowering relationships in the tomato have not as yet been clearly defined, nor are the auxin effects clearly distinguishable from nutritional factors. It is entirely possible that the inhibition of flowering by young leaves is the result of a competition for the available substrates and nutrients.[22,31,32] Hussey[33] removed the young plumular leaves and advanced the rate of apical enlargement of the shoot. He explained this effect in terms of competition for available assimilates between the growing apex and the expanding leaves.

Removal of mature leaves decreased the number of flowers in the first inflorescence and to a lesser extent in the second and third inflorescences of the main stem of both early and late tomato varieties. Development of the flowers in the inflorescences was also suppressed. They tended to remain vegetative as shown by the poor development of the androecium and the elongated (lanceolate) leafy growth of the sepals.[1] The inhibition of inflorescence development and the retarded growth of the androecium was associated with a lack of carbohydrates.[22,23,29,30]

13 Effects of Temperature

Temperature profoundly modifies growth and flowering of the tomato. Went[74,75,76,77] found that stem elongation was greater in plants grown at different day and night temperatures than in those held at a constant temperature. The best growth rate for stems, over a two-week period, was obtained at a day temperature of 27°C and a night temperature of 19°C. These temperature treatments did not affect floral initiation or number, although the flower size was modified. At lower night temperature, flowers were larger, had a greater tendency to fasciate, and showed more phyllody of the calyx than those at higher temperatures.

Tomato seedlings can be vernalized and will produce greater numbers of flowers per inflorescence. Lewis[42,43] showed that a low temperature of 14°C in contrast to a high temperature of 25° or 30°C, given to tomato seedlings after cotyledon expansion, increased the flower number on the first inflorescence of four varieties. The low temperature effect, however, was less at high than at low light intensities. Subsequent reports by Calvert,[6,7] Lawrence,[39] Wittwer and Teubner,[80,81,82] and Wittwer[78] have confirmed and extended the beneficial or positive effects of low temperatures on tomato flowering. The modifications are twofold. Fewer leaves are formed prior to the first inflorescence and flower number is greatly increased (Fig. 19–1).

Exposure of tomato seedlings to relatively high temperatures (21°–24°C) following low temperature treatment did not nullify the effects of low temperatures. Seedlings which had received one or two weeks of 10°–13°C after cotyledon expansion and were then given four to five weeks of 18°–21°C were not devernalized. In fact the high temperature appeared to stabilize the cold effect and promoted flower production.[43,82] Promotion of flowering by the alternating low and high temperatures may have been a consequence of a greater assimilation rate from an increased photosynthetic surface.[33] The absence of devernalization may be attributed to the relatively low temperatures employed.

Exposure of tomato seedlings after cotyledon expansion to relatively low temperatures (10° to 13°C) results in greater flower numbers in the first inflorescence, and an advancement in development and flowering after fewer leaf nodes.[5,6,7,21,59,80] Low temperature determination of the position of the first flower cluster relative to node number precedes that of increasing the flower number. Flowers of the first cluster are differentiated shortly after cotyledon expansion. The low temperature effects on flowering are additive for both day and night exposures. In addition to a morphological lowering of the site on the main axis when the first flower cluster is initiated, the floral meristem is proliferated to give a larger inflorescence at the expense of vegetative development. There is a temperature-sensitive period for each inflorescence during which the low temperatures promote greater flower production.[5,39,80,81]

Lewis[43] indicated that the sensitive period for the temperature effect on the first inflorescence of the Kondine Red cultivar was between the 8th and 12th day after cotyledon expansion. He also noted that low temperatures (14°C) at cotyledon expansion and extending to the emergence of the first inflorescence significantly increased the number of flowers to the 5th inflorescence. Calvert[6] found that flower numbers increased in the first three inflorescences in Potentate with low temperatures (10°C night, 16°C day) during the 6 weeks subsequent to cotyledon expansion. The intervals between the temperature sensitive phases for the first three inflorescences were about one week. With Ailsa Craig only the first two inflorescences showed a significant increase in flower number, and the interval between their sensitive phases was two weeks.

The significance of the temperature-sensitive period in the production of more tomatoes for the early market is obvious. Commercially, plants with a high flower count and earlier flowering and fruiting may be produced by proper exposure to low temperatures during the sensitive period. This minimizes the retardation of growth from low temperature exposure and promotes an increase in early and total fruit yield.[81]

Differential treatment of tops and roots of tomato seedlings, during the sensitive period of flower formation for the first cluster, revealed that shoot temperatures determine the position of the first inflorescence, while root temperatures influence the number of flowers in the first cluster. Shoot temperatures of 10° to 13°C significantly reduced the number of nodes below the first inflorescence as compared with 16°–18° or 18°–21°C. On the other hand, root temperatures of 10°–13°C significantly increased flower numbers by comparison with 15°–18°C or 18°–21°C. The effect of root temperature in promoting greater flower production was graft-transmissible.[52]

14 Effects of Mineral Nutrition and Water

The classical studies of Kraus and Kraybill[37] on the role of mineral nutrition in the vegetative and reproductive physiology of the tomato plant were a milestone of progress in the plant sciences. The importance of various carbohydrate-nitrogen relationships was established as a base for classifying and predicting reproductive behaviour. Furthermore, their studies were a challenge to others and an impetus for further investigations.

Murneek[45] noted that tomato plants which received a high nitrogen supply in the nutrient solution were both vigorous in growth and fruitful, while plants grown without nitrogen showed poor growth and set only one or two fruits. In addition, he demonstrated the control of vegetative growth by the fruit. Control was determined by the number of fruits present, their proximity to the growing points, and the relative amount of available nitrogen. Thus, along with the concept that mineral nutrition may determine the course of reproductive development was the somewhat converse observation that reproductive development itself has profound effects upon carbohydrate-nitrogen relationships.

Salter[63] obtained the greatest vegetative growth on tomato plants with a small fruit load and high soil moisture. The weakest vegetative growth occurred with heavy fruiting and low moisture.

McIlrath[44] emphasized that the times of appearance of macroscopic floral buds, and just prior to and after anthesis, were periods of accelerated mineral nutrient absorption in the tomato. The greatest quantity of nutrients was absorbed during the fruiting stage.

Results from studies conducted in sand culture and in nursery beds have also demonstrated the need for high nutrient levels in stimulating vegetative growth and flower formation in the tomato.[60,61,62] A high concentration of nitrogen (120 ppm.) in the nutrient solution resulted in vigorous plant growth, earlier flower bud differentiation, increased flower number, and fewer nodes below the first flower cluster. Under a high light intensity (full daylight), high nitrogen promoted earlier flowering and greater flower numbers, but under a low light intensity (24 per cent of daylight), high nitrogen retarded vegetative growth and flower bud differentiation. High phosphorus (60 and 180 ppm.) gave results similar to those with high nitrogen. Growth was more vigorous, flowering earlier, and there were fewer nodes below the first flower cluster. High potassium (60 and 180 ppm.) also promoted early flowering, as compared with lower levels (0.5 and 10 ppm.); the reduction in leaf number preceding the first inflorescence was less evident than for the high nitrogen and phosphorus. Furthermore, Saito et al.[62] showed that for tomato seedlings grown in a fertile soil, an abundant water supply and wide spacing induced luxuriant growth, promoted earlier flower bud differentiation, increased flower numbers on the inflorescences and reduced the number of nodes before the first flower cluster. Plants grown under such conditions had high levels of both carbohydrates and nitrogen.

Eguchi et al.[20] found that tomato plants initiated flowers only in pots supplied with 4 (NPK), 2 (NPK), NPK or NP. Plants which received NK, PK, N, P, K or no fertilizer initiated no flowers. The mean number of days from seeding to flower differentiation was 28, 27, 31, and 33 for plants receiving 4 (NPK), 2 (NPK), NPK and NP, respectively. Nodes preceding the first flower cluster were also decreased by high nutrition.

Wittwer and Teubner[82] also noted that high nitrogen (440 ppm.) given throughout the life cycle of tomato plants grown in solution cultures, promoted flowering and reduced the number of nodes before the first cluster. Exposure of seedlings to low temperatures induced branching of the first flower clusters, and this effect was further enhanced by high levels of nitrogen in the root medium. Since flower formation is appreciably modified by mineral nutrition, the tomato plant has been classified as a 'nutritional type' in its flowering behaviour.[20]

15 Effect of Gas Composition

All developmental processes in tomato plants are accelerated by enhanced photosynthesis, as under high light intensities[9,54] and high concentrations of CO_2. Time from seeding to first anthesis may be reduced by seven to ten days in air with 1000 ppm. of carbon dioxide. First flowering occurs after fewer nodes and flower numbers are increased in the first inflorescence.[84]

17 Grafting Experiments

Results from reciprocal top-root grafting experiments with inherently early and late flowering tomato cultivars suggest the presence of both a stimulus and an inhibitor of flowering which are graft transmissible and arise in the leaves. Earlier flowering occurred on scions of both early and late cultivars when grafted on rootstocks of the early cultivar (Farthest North), and flowering was delayed with scions of both early and the late cultivars following grafting on rootstocks of the late cultivar (Pennorange). Plumule leaves were attached to the rootstocks in each instance.[50] The nature of the stimulus originating in the leaves of the early variety and of the inhibitor coming from the leaves of the late variety, and the velocity of their movement within the plant, are unknown.

Reciprocal top-root grafts, using an early and late tomato cultivar, demonstrated that flowering of scions was not influenced by hypocotyl or epicotyl grafting in the absence of leaves on the rootstock.[50]

18 Effects of Growth Substances and Growth Retardants

The presence[36] and identification of at least one auxin[58] and of gibberellin-like substances[4,49] in the tomato suggest that these naturally occurring chemical regulators may be involved in growth and reproductive development. A wide variety of synthetic plant growth substances applied at various stages of plant development also have a marked effect on flowering behaviour.[12,34,47,48,55,67,69,85]

Among the first studies on chemical modifications of flowering in the tomato were those of Zimmerman and Hitchcock.[87,88] Many others have repeated or supplemented their results. They showed that tomato plants treated with 2, 3, 5-triiodobenzoic acid in lanolin paste applied to the stem, sprayed on the foliage or applied directly to the soil produced greater flower numbers per cluster and caused vegetative axillary shoots, and the main growing point to terminate in flower clusters. The inflorescences had heavy peduncles and fasciated flowers mixed with small buds.

TABLE 19–1

Activity of several auxins in promoting earlier initiation and increased flower number in the first cluster of tomato plants (data from Wittwer and Bukovac[83]).

Auxins	Molar Concentrations			
	Nodes subtending 1st cluster		Number of flowers in 1st cluster	
	10^{-5}	10^{-3}	10^{-5}	10^{-3}
Control	6.0 †		7.0 †	
Indole-3-acetic acid	5.7	6.0	11.0*	9.6
α-(2-Naphthoxy)-phenylacetic acid..	6.2	2.9***	11.2*	23.6***
2,3,5-Triiodobenzoic acid.. ..	6.3	2.4***	13.2***	§
N-m-Tolylphthalamic acid ..	6.0	4.0**	7.0	24.4***

†Flower and node numbers differ significantly from control: * at 5%, ** at 1%, *** at 0.1% levels.
§Flowers and accessory tissues failed to diverge.

The effects of several auxins on flowering are detailed in Table 19–1. They greatly increased flower numbers when applied at certain concentrations and as foliar sprays to young tomato seedlings at the time of, or preceding, flower formation in the first flower cluster. All synthetic auxins also reduced the number of leaf nodes that formed before the first inflorescence. Numerous other N-arylphthalamic acids related to N-m-tolylphthalamic acid also increased flower formation in the tomato.[64,69,70,71] Derivatives, such as 2, 3-dichlorophenylphthalamic acid were very effective and caused flowers to form even at cotyledonary nodes. This potential also resides, but to a lesser degree, with a few other N-arylphthalamic acids, 2, 3, 5-triiodobenzoic acid, and α-(2-Naphthoxy)-phenylacetic acid. The magnitude of the induced increases in flower formation in the tomato with the various N-arylphthalamic acids is directly correlated with their promotion of parthenocarpic fruit growth as well as the growth induced in *Avena* coleoptile sections.[71]

It has further been demonstrated[17] that phenocopies of five recessive genetic characters in the tomato may be induced by treatment with N-m-tolylphthalamic acid, namely determinate growth, fasciation of the flowers, branching of flower clusters, leafy flower clusters, and sterility.

Treatment of tomato seedlings with gibberellin during the temperature-sensitive period of flower formation accelerates flowering in time, but morphologically flowering is delayed in that more nodes are formed before the first inflorescence, and fewer flowers develop.[3]

Flowering is delayed following treatment with the cytokinins. Both kinetin and benzyladenine result in an increase in nodes preceding the first inflorescence and days to the first anthesis.[83]

TABLE 19–2

Flowering of the tomato as affected by several plant growth substances. (data from Wittwer and Tolbert[85])

Treatment	Days to 1st anthesis	Nodes subtending 1st inflorescence	Flowers in 1st inflorescence
Control	53	6	6
2-Chloroethyl trimethyl-ammonium chlor-			
ide (10^{-3} M)	50*	5*	6
Amo-1618 (10^{-2} M)	53	6	6
Maleic hydrazide (10^{-3} M)	70*	10*	6
Phosphon D	61*	7	6
Gibberellin A$_3$ (10^{-4} M)	54	8	6
N-m-Tolylphthalamic acid (4×10^{-4} M)	54	5*	12*

*Significantly different from the control, $P < 0.05$.

Many growth retardants (Table 19–2) modify flowering in the tomato. 2-chloroethyl trimethylammonium chloride (CCC) and related compounds accelerate flowering by reducing the time to the first anthesis by as much as two weeks, and cause the first inflorescence to form one leaf earlier. Neither Amo-1618 (2-isopropyl-4-dimethylamino-5-methylphenyl, 1-piperidinecarboxylate methyl chloride) nor B–9 (N, N-dimethylamino succinamic acid) had an effect on flowering, while maleic hydrazide and phosphon D (2, 4-dichlorobenzyltri-butylphosphonium chloride) delay the first anthesis and increase the number of nodes before the first inflorescence.

There is no correlation between chemical inhibition or promotion of vegetative extension and flowering in the tomato. Auxins and CCC suppress growth but promote flowering. Gibberellins greatly stimulate vegetative extension, but markedly reduce flowering by increasing the node number at which the first flower cluster appears and reducing the number of flowers which form. Maleic hydrazide, phosphon D, and the cytokinins suppress both growth and flowering.

19 Effects of Metabolic Inhibitors

An inhibitor of steroid biosynthesis, tris-(2-diethylaminoethyl)-phosphate tri-hydrochloride (SK & F 7997), delays flowering in the tomato by significantly increasing the number of leaves which form before the first flower cluster is initiated, without having any effect upon vegetative growth.[51]

23 Inflorescence Differentiation

Chemical treatments (the N-arylphthalamic acids and 2, 3, 5-triiodobenzoic acid) have revealed that the potential for flowering in the tomato plant is present at every node. The morphological position of the first inflorescence, relative to the amount of preceding vegetation, is also a function of many environmental and chemical factors.

In the development of the tomato flower, a small protuberance of meristematic tissue develops from the pedicel of the preceding flower. The portion of this pedicel posterior to the protuberance becomes part of the peduncle. The meristematic protuberance or axis for the first flower of the cluster originates in the axil of the leaf. The pedicel which supports a single flower, as well as the peduncle from which it arises, is composed of a rather thick cortex, a ring of vascular tissue and a central portion of pith tissue.[14] Smith[65] similarly observed that the protuberance of the first flower of the inflorescence arose in the axil of the leaf. The succeeding flowers of the cluster each arise from similar protuberances which grow out from the pedicels of the preceding flower.

Differentiation of flower parts occurs after the following pattern: the protuberance is at first convex, then becomes flattened and broadened. The primordia of the first floral organs develop on the periphery of the flattened meristematic protuberance indicative of the calyx lobes. These rudimentary sepals are curved inward and arch over the apex of the axis. Swellings soon appear slightly higher on the axis and nearer the centre, alternating with the calyx lobes. These swellings develop into the corolla. Elevated areas of meristematic tissue soon arise on the axis and nearer the centre, opposite the calyx lobes and alternating with the petals. These elevated areas develop into stamens. The stamens are adnate to the interior of the corolla tube. Each primordium of the androecium consists of homogeneous tissue which later becomes differentiated into its various parts. The carpels are the last floral parts to differentiate. They arise from the centre of the floral axis and develop into a compound pistil consisting usually of six united carpels (gynoecium). The cavity of the ovary is formed as a result of the upward growth of the carpellary tissue.

An intriguing area for further study resides in chemical control of the differentiation of each component organ of the tomato flower. A recent report[53] suggests that stamen formation, as well as the viability of the pollen, is modified by gibberellin.

REFERENCES

[1] Aung, L. H. (1965). Influence of defoliation on vegetative, floral and fruit development in tomatoes (*Lycopersicon esculentum* Mill.). Ph.D. Thesis, Cornell Univ., Ithaca, N.Y.

[2] Bouquet, A. G. B. (1932). An anaylsis of the characters of the inflorescence and fruiting habit of some varieties of greenhouse tomatoes. *Cornell Agr. Exp. Sta. Memoir* **139**.

[3] Bukovac, M. J., Wittwer, S. H. and Teubner, F. G. (1957). Gibberellin and higher plants: VII. Flower formation in the tomato (*Lycopersicon esculentum*). *Mich. Agr. Ext. Sta. quart. Bul.* **40**, 207.

[4] Butcher, D. N. (1963). The presence of gibberellins in excised tomato roots. *J. Exptl. Bot.* **14**, 272.

[5] Calvert, A. (1955). Temperature effects on early growth and development in tomato. *14th International Hort. Congress*, 540.

[6] Calvert, A. (1957). Effect of the early environment on development of flowering in the tomato. I. Temperature. *J. Hort. Sci.* **32**, 9.

[7] Calvert, A. (1959). Effect of the early environment on the development of flowering in tomato. II. Light and temperature interactions. *J. Hort. Sci.* **34**, 154.

[8] Calvert, A. (1962). Critical phases of tomato plants. *Grower* **58**, 787.

[9] Calvert, A. (1964). Growth and flowering of the tomato in relation to natural light conditions. *J. Hort. Sci.* **39**, 182.

[10] Calvert, A. (1964). The effects of air temperature on growth of young tomato plants in natural light conditions. *J. Hort. Sci.* **39**, 194.

[11] Calvert, A. (1965). Flower initiation and development in the tomato. *N.A.A.S. Quart. Rev.* **70**, 79.

[12] Choudhury, B. and Singh, S. N. (1960). Seed treatment with plant regulators and their effect on the growth and yield of tomato (*Lycopersicon esculentum* Mill.). *Indian J. Hort.* **17**, 48.

[13] Cobley, L. S. (1956). *An Introduction to the Botany of Tropical Crops*, 302. Longmans Green & Co., Lond.

[14] Cooper, D. C. (1927). Anatomy and development of tomato flower. *Bot. Gaz.* **83**, 399.

[15] Cooper, A. J. (1962). Relations between day-length and annual patterns of plant development. *Nature* **195**, 1218.

[16] Cooper, A. J. (1964). The seasonal pattern of flowering of glasshouse tomatoes. *J. Hort. Sci.* **39**, 111.

[17] Cordner, H. B. and Hedges, G. (1959). Determinateness in the tomato in relation to variety and to application of N-metatolylphthalamic acid of high concentration. *Proc. Amer. Soc. Hort. Sci.* **73**, 323.

[18] De Zeeuw, D. (1954). De invloed van het blad op de bloei. (The influence of the leaf on flowering.) *Meded. Landbouwhogesch. Wageningen* **54**, (1) 1.

[19] De Zeeuw, D. (1956). Leaf induced inhibition of flowering in tomato. *Proc. Koninkl. Ned. Akad. van Wetenschap., Amsterdam*, **59**, 535.

[20] Eguchi, T., Matsumura, T. and Ashizawa, M. (1958). The effect of nutrition on flower formation in vegetable crops. *Proc. Amer. Soc. Hort. Sci.* **72**, 343.

[21] Fukushima, Y. and Masui, M. (1962). The effect of early environment on flower formation in tomato. I. On night temperature and soil moisture. *J. Jap. Soc. Hort. Sci.* **31**, 207.

[22] Goodall, D. W. (1945). The distribution of weight change in the young tomato plant. I. Dry weight changes of the various organs. *Ann. Bot.*, N.S. **9**, 101.

[23] Goodall, D. W. (1946). The distribution of weight change in the young tomato plant. II. Changes in dry weight of separated organs and translocation rates. *Ann. Bot.*, N.S. **10**, 305.

[24] Goodall, D. W. and Bolas, B. D. (1942). The vernalization of tomato seed. *Ann. Appl. Biol.* **29**, 1.

[25] Hayward, H. E. (1948). *The Structure of Economic Plants*, 550. The Macmillan Company, N.Y.

[26] Helson, V. A. (1965). Comparison of Gro-lux and cool-white fluorescent lamps with and without incandescent as light sources used in plant growth rooms for growth and development of tomato plants. *Canad. J. Plant. Sci.* **45**, 461.

[27] Highkin, H. R. and Hanson, J. B. (1954). Possible interaction between light-dark cycles and endogenous daily rhythms on the growth of tomato plants. *Plant Physiol.* **29**, 301.

[28] Honma, S., Wittwer, S. H. and Phatak, S. C. (1963). Flowering and earliness in the tomato. *J. Heredity* **54**, 212.

[29] Howlett, F. S. (1936). The effect of carbohydrate and of nitrogen deficiency upon microsporogenesis and the development of male gametophyte in the tomato, *Lycopersicum esculentum* Mill. *Ann. Bot.* **50**, 765.

[30] Howlett, F. S. (1939). The modification of flower structure by environment in varieties of *Lycopersicon esculentum*. *J. Agr. Research* **58**, 79.

[31] Hussey, G. (1963). Growth and development in the young tomato. I. The effect of temperature and light intensity on growth of the shoot apex and leaf primordia. *J. Exptl. Bot.* **14**, 316.

[32] Hussey, G. (1963). Growth and development in the young tomato. II. The effect of defoliation on the development of the shoot apex. *J. Exptl. Bot.* **14**, 316.

[33] Hussey, G. (1965). Growth and development in the young tomato. III. The effect of night and day temperatures on vegetative growth. *J. Exptl. Bot.* **16**, 373.

[34] Jackson, R. M., Brown, M. E. and Burlingham, S. K. (1964). Similar effects on tomato plants of Azotobacter inoculation and application of gibberellin. *Nature* **203**, 851.

[35] Ketellapper, H. J. (1950). Interaction of endogenous and environmental periods in plant growth. *Plant Physiol.* **35**, 238.

[36] Kramer, M. and Went, F. W. (1949). The nature of the auxin in tomato stem tips. *Plant Physiol.* **24**, 207.

[37] Kraus, E. J. and Kraybill, H. R. (1918). Vegetation and reproduction with special reference to the tomato. *Ore. Agri. Exp. Sta. Bull.* **149**, 5.

[38] Kristoffersen, T. (1963). Interactions of photoperiod and temperature in growth and development of young tomato plants (*Lycopersicon esculentum* Mill.).*Physiol. Plantar. Suppl.* **1**, 5.

[39] Lawrence, W. J. C. (1953). Temperature and tomato flowering. *John Innes Hort. Insti. Ann. Rept.*, 23.

[40] Learner, E. N. and Wittwer, S. H. (1953). Some effects of photoperiodicity and thermoperiodicity on vegetative growth, flowering and fruiting of the tomato. *Proc. Amer. Soc. Hort. Sci.* **61**, 373.

[41] Leopold, A. C. and Lam, S. L. (1960). A leaf factor influencirg tomato earliness. *Proc. Amer. Soc. Hort. Sci.* **76**, 543.

[42] Lewis, D. (1949). Temperature and fertility. *John Innes Hort. Insti.* 40th *Ann. Rept.* 13.

[43] Lewis, D. (1953). Some factors affecting flower production in the tomatoes. *J. Hort. Sci.* **23**, 207.

[44] McIlrath, W. J. (1956). Absorption of nutrient ions by the tomato plant at various stages of development. *Proc. Iowa Acad. Sci.* **63**, 339.

[45] Murneek, A. E. (1926). Effects of correlation between vegetative and reproductive functions in the tomato. *Plant Pysiol.* **1**, 3.

[46] Murneek, A. E. (1927). The selection of proper material for horticultural research. *Proc. Amer. Soc. Hort. Sci.* **24**, 201.

[47] Osborne, D. J. and Wain, R. L. (1950). Studies on plant growth-regulating substances. II. Synthetic compounds inducing morphogenic responses in the tomato plant. *J. Hort. Sci.* **26**, 60.

[48] Osborne, D. J. and Went, F. W. (1953). Climatic factors influencing parthenocarpy and normal fruit set in tomatoes. *Bot. Gaz.* **114**, 312.

[49] Pegg, G. F. (1966). Changes in levels on naturally occurring gibberellin-like substances during germination of seed of *Lycopersicon esculentum* Mill. *J. Exptl. Bot.* **17**, 214.

[50] Phatak, S. C. and Wittwer, S. H. (1965). Regulation of tomato flowering through reciprocal top-root grafting. *Proc. Amer. Soc. Hort. Sci.* **87**, 398.

[51] Phatak, S. C. and Wittwer, S. H. (1966). Unpublished data.

[52] Phatak, S. C., Wittwer, S. H. and Teubner, F. G. (1966). Top and root temperature effects on tomato flowering. *Proc. Amer. Soc. Hort. Sci.* **88**, 527.

[53] Phatak, S. C., Wittwer, S. H., Honma, S. and Bukovac, M. J. (1966). Gibberellin-induced anther and pollen development in a stamenless tomato mutant. *Nature* **209**, 635.

[54] Porter, A. M. (1937). Effect of light intensity on the photosynthetic efficiency of tomato plants. *Plant Physiol.* **12**, 225.

[55] Rappaport, L. (1957). Effect of gibberellin on growth, flowering, and fruiting of Earlypak tomato, *Lycopersicon esculentum*. *Plant Phsyiol.* **32**, 440.

[56] Reinders-Gouwentak, C. A. (1954). Growth and flowering of tomato in artificial light. II. Flower initiation. *Proc. Kon. Ned. Akad. Wetensh.* **57**, 594.

[57] Reinders-Gouwentak, C. A., Smeets, L. and Andeweg, J. M. (1951). Growth and flowering of the tomato in artificial light. I. Vegetative development. *Meded. Landbouwhogesch. Wageningen.* **51**, 63.

[58] Row, V. V., Sanford, W. W. and Hitchcock, A. E. (1961). Indole-3-acetyl-D, L-aspartic acid as naturally occurring indole compound in tomato seedlings. *Contrib. Boyce Thompson Inst.* **21**, 1.

[59] Saito, T. and Ito, H. (1962). Studies on growth and fruiting in the tomato. I. Effect of the early environment on growth and frutiing. I. Thermoperiods. *J. Jap. Soc. Hort. Sci.* **31**, 303.

[60] Saito, T., Hatayama, T. and Ito, H. (1963). Studies on growth and fruiting in the tomato. II. Effect of the early environment on growth and fruiting. 2. Light. *J. Jap. Soc. Hort. Sci.* **32**, 49.

[61] Saito, T., Hatayama, T. and Ito, H. (1963). Studies on the growth and fruiting in the tomato. III. Effect of the early environment on the growth and flowering. 3. Nutrition of nitrogen, phosphorus and potassium. *J. Jap. Soc. Hort. Sci.* **32**, 55.

[62] Saito, T., Konno, Y. and Ito, H. (1963). Studies on the growth and fruiting in the tomato. IV. Effect of the early environment on the growth and fruiting. 4. Fertility of the bed soil, watering and spacing. *J. Jap. Soc. Hort. Sci.* **32**, 38.

[63] Salter, P. J. (1958). The effects of different water regimes on the growth of plants under glass. 4. Vegetative growth and fruit development of the tomato. *J. Hort. Sci.* **33**, 1.

[64] Shen, J. Y. (1959). Modification of floral morphogenesis in the tomato (*Lycopersicon esculentum* Mill.) with a N-m-Tolylphthalamic acid. Ph.D. Thesis, Michigan State University, E. Lansing, Michigan.

[65] Smith, O. (1935). Pollination and life-history studies of the tomato (*Lycopersicon esculentum* Mill.). *Cornell Univ. Agr. Exp. Sta. Memoir* **184**, 3.

[66] Stier, H. L. (1938). Response of tomato (*Lycopersicon esculentum* Mill, var.' Marglobe') to certain vernalization treatments. *Proc. Amer. Soc. Hort. Sci.* **36**, 708.

[67] Stier, H. L. and Dubuy, H. G. (1938). The influence of certain phytohormone treatments on the time of flowering and fruit production of tomato plants under field conditions. *Proc. Amer. Soc. Hort. Sci.* **36**, 723.

[68] Sturtevant, E. L. (1889). The tomato. *Ann. Rep. Maryland Agr. Exp. Sta. of* 1888, 18.

[69] Teubner, F. G. and Wittwer, S. H. (1955). Effect of N-m-tolylphthalamic acid on tomato flower formation. *Science* **122**, 74.

[70] Teubner, F. G. and Wittwer, S. H. (1957). Effect of N-arylphthalamic acids on tomato flower formation. *Proc. Amer. Soc. Hort. Sci.* **69**, 343.

[71] Teubner, F. G., Wittwer, S. H. and Shen, J. Y. (1961). Relationship of molecular structure to biological activity in N-arylphthalamic acids. In *4th Intern. Conf. Plant Growth Regulation*, 259. The Iowa State Univ. Press, Ames, Iowa.

[72] Tukey, H. B., Jr. and Ketellapper, H. J. (1963). Length of the light-dark cycle and plant growth. *Amer. J. Bot.* **50**, 110.

[73] Went, F. W. (1944). Morphological observations of the tomato plant. *Torrey Botan. Club Bull.* **71**, 77.

[74] Went, F. W. (1944). Plant growth under controlled conditions. II. Thermoperiodicity in growth and fruiting of the tomato. *Amer. J. Bot.* **31**, 135.

[75] Went, F. W. (1944). Plant growth under controlled conditions. III. Correlation between various physiological processes and growth in the tomato plant. *Amer. J. Bot.* **31**, 597.

[76] Went, F. W. (1945). Plant growth under controlled conditions. V. The relation between age, light, variety, and thermoperiodicity of tomatoes. *Amer. J. Bot.* **32**, 469.

[77] Went, F. W. (1945). Plant growth under controlled conditions. VI. Comparisons between field and air-conditioned greenhouse culture of tomatoes. *Amer. J. Bot.* **32**, 643.

[78] Wittwer, S. H. (1960). Practices for increasing the yields of greenhouse tomatoes. *Michigan Agr. Expt. Sta. Cir. Bul.* **228**.

[79] Wittwer, S. H. (1963). Photoperiod and flowering in the tomato (*Lycopersicon esculentum* Mill.). *Proc. Amer. Soc. Hort. Sci.* **83**, 688.

[80] Wittwer, S. H. and Teubner, F. G. (1956). Cold exposure of tomato seedlings and flower formation. *Proc. Amer. Soc. Hort. Sci.* **66**, 369.

[81] Wittwer, S. H. and Teubner, F. G. (1956). New practices for increasing the fruit crop of greenhouse-grown tomatoes. *Michigan Agr. Expt. Sta. Quart. Bul.* **39**, 198.

[82] Wittwer, S. H. and Teubner, F. G. (1957). The effects of temperature and nitrogen nutrition on flower formation in the tomato. *Amer. J. Bot.* **44**, 125.

[83] Wittwer, S. H. and Bukovac, M. J. (1962). Exogenous plant growth substances affecting floral initiation and fruit set. *Proc. Plant Sci. Symposium* (1962), 65. Campbell Soup Co., Camden, N.J.

[84] Wittwer, S. H. and Robb, W. (1964). Carbon dioxide enrichment of greenhouse atmospheres for food crop production. *Econ. Bot.* **18**, 34.

[85] Wittwer, S. H. and Tolbert, N. E. (1960). (2-Chloroethyl) trimethylammonium chloride and related compounds as plant growth substances. III. Effect on growth and flowering of the tomato. *Amer. J. Bot.* **47**, 560.

[86] Work, P. (1945). *The Tomato*. Orange Judd Publishing Co., Inc. N.Y.

[87] Zimmerman, P. W. and Hitchcock, A. E. (1942). Flowering habit and correlation of organs modified by triiodobenzoic acid. *Contr. Boyce Thompson Inst.* **12**, 491.

[88] Zimmerman, P. W. and Hitchcock, A. E. (1949). Triiodobenzoic acid influences on flower formation of tomatoes. *Contr. Boyce Thompson Inst.* **15**, 353.

20

Cestrum nocturnum L.

By Roy M. Sachs

1 History of Use

Photoperiodic responses of *C. nocturnum* were first reported by Sachs.[8–12] Subsequent work is limited to that by Griesel,[3–6] who has also studied flowering responses in *C. aurantiacum*, *C. diurnum*, *C. elegans*, *C. parqui*, and *C. reflexum*.

2 Growing Techniques and Growth Habit

Cestrum species are woody shrubs in the family Solanaceae, indigenous to the tropical and warm temperate regions of Central and South America.[14] Some species are found at relatively high altitudes in the tropical zones and may be adapted to relatively low temperatures.

They may be propagated from seed or cuttings. Terminal and subterminal green wood cuttings dipped in a solution of 4000 ppm indole butyric acid struck roots in two weeks under mist. During the course of development of seedlings and cuttings of *C. nocturnum* leaf shape and size changes progressively from an elliptical outline less than 35 mm long to an ovate or lanceolate form up to 200 mm long. The leaves are alternate; petioles are approximately one-tenth the length of the blade on slender, flexuose branches which are capable of secondary growth. Axillary buds are usually flanked by one or two smaller buds which have bract-like leaves at their base. Axillary branches develop near the crown of the plant after the main shoot has about 20 nodes.

Sachs' studies were with seedlings 3 months old, terminal cuttings two months after rooting, and re-used plants in which the old shoot was removed and a new axillary branch developed from the crown. In all cases single-branched plants were used and all were cultivated initially for one to three months at an average temperature of 23°C with an 8-hour photoperiod.

Griesel used clonal material mainly, and also re-used the plants; more than one branch was permitted to develop on each plant. After removing the old shoot system Griesel placed the plants in the new experimental conditions where the new shoot system developed.

In early experiments by Sachs and in all of Griesel's studies the plants were grown in quart containers in a mixture of vermiculite and gravel frequently irrigated with half strength Hoagland's solution. At an average temperature of 23°C a new leaf was initiated every two days and stems elongated more than 1 cm per day.[8] Thus, the plants achieved a relatively large size with many leaves, and short periods of wilting were common on bright days about 10 weeks after rooting, even when water was applied up to four times daily. This fact is emphasized because growth of *C. nocturnum* was checked by water stress, and results with growth retardants suggest that the flowering response of *C. nocturnum* and other species is greatly modified by these substances. Also, there are many observations by nurserymen that water stress promotes flower initiation. Growing plants with severely restricted root systems also introduces the possibility of hormonal imbalance in the shoot system,[2,7] which may in turn affect flowering responses. Griesel's studies have been on plants with several branches and an overall plant height of 60–180 cm; observations on flowering have been made from 16 to 50 weeks after cutting back. Sachs' studies were confined to single-branched plants between 40 and 80 cm tall, defoliated to 5 fully expanded leaves (16 leaves over-all); observations on flowering were completed generally within 3 weeks after the seedlings were introduced into experimental conditions.

3 Inflorescence Structure and Criteria of Flowering

The flowers of *C. nocturnum* occur singly or, more commonly, in clusters of 3 to 5 with as many as 20 clusters on one axillary branch (Fig. 20–1). Flowers appear at axillary positions usually 10 to 20 nodes below the apex. Terminal flowering is common under optimal conditions. Flowering also occurs at basal positions after leaf abscission.[3]

FIGURE 20–1. Flowers of *Cestrum nocturnum*. Each flower is about 2 cm long.

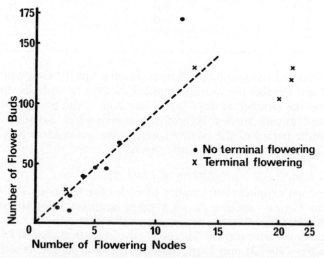

FIGURE 20–2. Relation between numbers of flowers and number of flowering nodes in *C. nocturnum* (Sachs[8]).

Quantitative estimation of the flowering response has been accomplished in several ways: (1) percent flowering is most suitable for measuring differences among treatments which bracket the critical requirements for floral initiation; (2) number of nodes bearing flowers per plant is useful for differentiating among treatments in which all plants initiate flowers; it is the preferred method when flower primordia are observed by microdissection 7 days after the end of induction; (3) the number of flowers per plant is closely related to the number of flowering nodes (Fig. 20–2), although there is a break in the curve when terminal flowering occurs. The 7 to 10 nodes in the terminal cluster usually bear one to three flowers per node whereas the lower axillary shoots usually bear 30 flowers.

TABLE 20–1

The number of days required for LD and SD induction in *C. nocturnum* (adapted from Sachs[9]).

LD induction – 8 hours natural light plus 8 hours of mixed fluorescent-incandescent light (700 f.c. at plant height); SD induction – 8 hours natural light. Temperature conditions were 8 hours at 26°C and 16 hours at 20°C. For Part A, the plants received 7 SD after exposure to LD and in Part B, 15 LD before exposure to SD.

No. of Days	% Flowering	Nodes Flowering/Plant
A. Long Day Induction		
4	0	0
5	67	1
7	100	7
8	100	9
9	100	17
10	100	20
18	100	32
B. Short Day Induction		
1	0	0
2	100	15
3	100	18
4	100	22
7	100	23

Griesel also counted the number of flower clusters, but for comparative studies with species and hybrids the average number of days to anthesis, the standard deviation, and the number of days for 99 per cent of the population to bloom were calculated for each species. Hybrid populations which did not flower within the 99 percentile period of the parent species were assumed to be significantly different in flowering response from the parent.

4 Effects of Plant Age

No minimum age or minimum number of nodes for flowering has been determined for any *Cestrum* species. At an average temperature of about 23°C (26° day, 20° night) seedlings attained maximum sensitivity to photoperiodic induction two or three months after sowing. Three-month old seedlings had at least 30 nodes and three leaves 140–200 mm long.[8] The results of experiments with branches from cut back plants suggested that plants were maximally responsive to photoperiodic treatments when they had three to five leaves in excess of 140 mm long (usually there were 13 to 16 additional leaves in various stages of expansion).[8] Thus, plant age may be related to photosynthetic capacity or adequate nutritional status permitting initiation and development of flowers.

Griesel noted considerable differences in flowering dates between *C. elegans* and *C. nocturnum* and hybrids grown in constant daylength conditions.[5] In part, the differences in days to anthesis may have reflected differences in time to develop sensitivity to daylength treatments as well as differences in response of the mature plant.

5 Vernalization and Devernalization

Although Griesel has found low temperature promotion of flowering in *Cestrum* species,[6] the low temperature treatments have been given for long periods, past the time of initiation and, hence, are probably not equivalent to vernalization.

6 Shortday Vernalization

This term probably does not apply to *Cestrum* species, although Griesel has shown that a temperature drop satisfies the SD requirement.

7 Photoperiod Response

C. nocturnum was shown to be a long-short day (LSD) plant at 23°C, requiring a minimum of 5 LD followed by 2 SD (Table 20–1). The critical daylength for LD induction was between 11.5 and 12.5 hours, and the critical nightlength for SD induction between 11 and 12 hours (Fig. 20–3). LD conditions were satisfied partially by incandescent light of 10 f.c. intensity at the plant tops for 16 hours as a

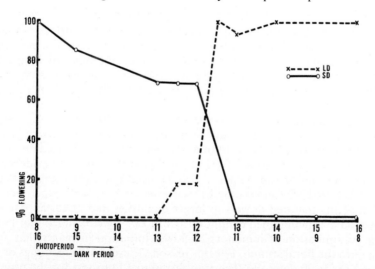

FIGURE 20–3. Light and dark period requirements for LD and SD induction in *C. nocturnum*. Note that the critical photoperiod for LD induction is between 11 and 13 hours, and the critical dark period for SD induction is also between 11 and 13 hours (Sachs[9]).

supplement to an 8 hour exposure to natural light, but there was considerably greater response with supplementary light of 700 f.c. intensity. A 1-hour interruption in the middle of a 16-hour dark period with 700 f.c. light also satisfied partially the LD requirement (Table 20–2). A 10-minute interruption with 500 f.c. incandescent light in the middle of a 16-hour dark period inhibited slightly, and a 60-minute interruption completely inhibited SD induction. Considerable caution must be exercised in estimating effective light intensities in *Cestrum* since, even in

TABLE 20–2

Promotion of long-day induction by supplementary light and by interruption of the dark period; inhibition of short-day induction by interruption of the dark period and by auxin (adapted from Sachs[9]).

Treatment	% Flowering	Nodes Flowering/Plant
A. Long Day Induction		
1. Supplementary Light		
None	0	0
16 hrs, 10 f.c.	40	1
16 hrs, 700 f.c.	100	6
2. Light Interruption		
None	0	0
1 hr, 700 f.c.	60	3
16 hrs, 700 f.c.	100	17
B. Short Day Induction		
1. Light Interruption		
60 min, 500 f.c.	0	0
10 min, 500 f.c.	80	15
None	100	22
2. Auxin		
NAA, 5×10^{-4} M	57	1
Control	100	10

a single-branched plant, the intensity falls below 1 f.c. at the surface of the tenth leaf below, when there is 10 f.c. at the apex. There was, moreover, a marked difference in flowering response at different times of the year in temperature-controlled greenhouses in which light intensity was the main variable. LD induction in the winter months proved much less effective than during the summer.[8]

Griesel found that *C. nocturnum* flowered after 15 to 20 weeks with continuous cultivation in daylengths of 12 hours or greater; sporadic, but heavy flowering periods were observed with 16 to 18 hour day-lengths, with reduced flowering at longer and shorter day-lengths.[4] Griesel concluded that this was evidence for a LD response in *C. nocturnum* with a critical daylength between 8 and 12 hours.

Griesel has tested SD followed by LD sequences in long term experiments and found that plants initiated flowers in larger quantities and at earlier dates than they would have if maintained continuously in LD.[4] He concluded that LD may cause the accumulation of inhibitors of flower initiation in plants that are too young to form the floral stimuli. For this reason Griesel raised seedlings or shoot systems in SD for 90 days and then transferred to LD to test for the promotive effects of LD, and found that all plants flowered 137 days later.[5]

Griesel has also found LSD responses in *C. aurantiacum*, *C. diurnum*, and *C. reflexum*. The last species does not flower at temperatures above 19°C and shows the LD and LSD response below 19°C. In addition, he found that *C. nocturnum* was day neutral at temperatures above 24°C and flowered in continuous LD if there was an 8°C temperature drop after 90 days at 27°C. *C. diurnum* flowered under continuous SD at 23°C, in LSD, or in continuous LD if there was an 8°C temperature drop. Thus, for long-term experiments at least, temperature change is nearly as important as the daylength sequence in regulating floral initiation. An 8°C drop from 27° to 19° or from 23° to 15° with plants in LD conditions is equivalent to a transfer to SD.[6]

Griesel noted a shift with age in the critical daylength for the SD response in *C. diurnum* when it was grown in continuous light and transferred to shorter daylengths; SD induction in 6-month old shoot systems was satisfied by 8-hour dark periods, whereas 3-month old shoot systems required 12-hour dark periods. The effect of temperature on flowering responses suggests, too, that daylength requirements are intimately involved with other aspects of plant growth, a theme reiterated in studies on the effects of gibberellic acid and growth retardants on flowering in *C. nocturnum*.

Griesel has investigated the behaviour of inter-specific hybrids (as well as F_2 and backcross progenies) between *C. elegans*, a day neutral plant, and *C. nocturnum*.[5] His data suggest that there are at least 2 independent genes or gene groups controlling flower initiation in *C. nocturnum*. All F_1 hybrids responded to LSD induction, although there were notable quantitative differences between some of the clones; nevertheless, Griesel concluded that a single dominant gene controls this response. None of the F_1 hybrids, 2 of 12 F_2 hybrids, and 3 of 17 in the backcross to *C. nocturnum* produced flower primordia in SD followed by LD induction, the special treatment which Griesel used to test for response to LD induction. Also, none of the F_1 plants flowered in response to a temperature drop. Hybrids between *C. reflexum* (a LSD plant at temperatures below 19°C) and *C. nocturnum* responded to LD and LSD induction regardless of temperature.[6] Griesel concluded that the LD requirement is controlled by one or more recessive genes and that action of these genes is apparently temperature-dependent, since at lower temperatures flowering in *C. nocturnum* was daylength independent and occurred in LD with a temperature drop.

10 Fractional Induction

No studies on alternate LD–SD–LD–etc. treatments have been published; however, Sachs found that SD interpolated between LD inhibited LD induction. Also, a 13-hour light/13-hour dark cycle was ineffective, even though both light and dark periods exceeded the threshold values.[13]

11 Photoperiodic Inhibition

The evidence for daylength-induced inhibition of flowering is limited to the observation that continuous light was less effective than a 16-hour daylength for LD induction,[10] and that SD preceding LD is better than continuous LD in *C. nocturnum*. SD inserted in the LD induction treatment inhibited flower initiation.[13] Griesel has shown that a temperature drop or constant low temperature induced flowering in *C. nocturnum* in otherwise noninductive daylength conditions and suggests that a temperature-dependent inhibitor is formed in LD and LSD conditions.[16]

13 Effects of Temperature

The recent studies of Griesel, discussed above, indicate that temperature is as important as daylength in controlling flower initiation in *C. nocturnum* and other *Cestrum* species. Earlier, work had shown that LD induction was most effective when the temperature of the 16-hour photoperiod was above 17°C; the temperature of the associated 8-hour dark period had very little effect upon LD induction. The effectiveness of SD induction decreased when the temperature of the 16-hour dark period was below 14°C; on the other hand, SD induction was relatively unaffected by temperature variations during the 8-hour photoperiod.[11] Again, it is important to note the differences in technique between Griesel's studies and those of Sachs. Griesel maintained plants for relatively long periods (up to 250 days) at continuous temperatures (or with temperature drops after 60–90 days) and at continuous daylengths, whereas Sachs' temperature treatments were applied for a maximum of 18 days (LD induction) and for as few as 3 days (SD induction).

16 Translocation of the Floral Stimulus

Completely defoliated plants of *C. nocturnum* did not initiate flowers in any daylength.[9] Also, defoliation at the end of LD induction prevented flower initiation even though the plants developed new leaves and subsequently received SD induction. If some material were translocated from the leaves and accumulated in the buds or stems, floral initiation should have occurred after the new leaves had received SD induction. Also, flower initiation did not occur if some leaves received LD induction and others on the same branch received SD induction. Thus, the floral stimulus was not synthesized or not translocated from leaves, unless the leaves received both LD and SD induction.

Timed defoliation[8] following the short day induction revealed that translocation of floral stimulus in quantities required for minimal floral initiation occurs between 3 and 8 hours after the end of the second long dark period and continues for 20 to 70 hours thereafter (Table 20–3). There was, however, considerable variation in translocation among plants in the same experiment and between experiments. Sachs[9] and Griesel[3] have shown that the floral stimulus is translocated acropetally and basipetally in one and two-branched plants.

TABLE 20–3

Translocation of the floral stimulus from the leaves of *C. nocturnum*. Time of defoliation is the number of hours after the end of the second dark period of SD induction (adapted from Sachs[8]).

Time of defoliation	% Flowering	Flowering Nodes/Plant
Expt. 1		
−21	0	0
3	0	0
27	14	1.1
51	100	11.1
123	100	15.4
Expt. 2		
8	100	4.3
22	83	14.5
31	100	13.2
46	100	22.3
70	100	28.5
Expt. 3		
0	0	0
8	29	0.6
25	29	0.3
48	71	10.7

17 Grafting Experiments

Griesel[3] has made a thorough study of inter-specific grafts between *C. nocturnum* and *C. diurnum* and concluded that the floral stimulus was not interchangeable between species. There did not appear to be a translocation block due to inadequate graft union between the two species, since an intergraft of *C. nocturnum* between two shoots of *C. diurnum* did not prevent translocation of the floral stimulus from the induced donor to the receptor branch. Both the intact and defoliated branches of *C. diurnum* produced floral buds regardless of the presence or absence of leaves on the interstock.

18 Effects of Growth Substances and Retardants

Gibberellic acid (100 ppm, sprayed weekly) inhibited floral initiation in *C. nocturnum* plants receiving LSD induction; stem elongation was increased about 10 per cent by such treatments.[13] The growth retardant 1, 1-dimethylamino succinamic acid (2000 ppm, sprayed thrice weekly) promoted floral initiation in LD conditions after 3 to 5 weeks of treatment and reduced stem elongation by 50 per cent.[13] These results are contrary to those reported by Zeevaart and Lang[15,16] for *Bryophyllum daigremontianum*, another LSD plant.

The dramatic effects of gibberellin and growth retardants upon floral initiation in *C. nocturnum* suggest strongly that modification of vegetative growth may be an important factor in regulating photoperiodic responses in *Cestrum*.

Aqueous solutions of 5×10^{-4} M naphthalene acetic acid sprayed on plants prior to SD induction severely inhibited floral initiation in *C. nocturnum* (Table 20–2); the auxin treatments caused temporary epinasty of the younger leaves, but there were no enduring effects.

21 Induction of Excised Apices

Recently Caplin and Griesel[1] have investigated photoperiodic responses of explants of *C. diurnum* which flower in SD conditions. Single leaves with an axillary bud and short stem section have been cultured on White's medium.

Young, not fully expanded, leaves produced only vegetative growth from axillary positions. Vegetative growth occurred in axillary buds of old, fully expanded leaves. However, with recently expanded leaves (20–30 days after leaf initiation) flowering occurred at the axillary bud. Old leaves caused flowering when they were inserted, upside down, in the nutrient medium. Flower initiation occurred with light intensities as low as 1 f.c. Increased flowering response, as measured by the number of flowers initiated, was observed up to 80 f.c., but higher light intensities reduced flowering.

23 Inflorescence Differentiation

A stage system for flower development from the fourth to eighth day after the start of SD induction is illustrated in Figure 20–4. The rate of development of flower primordia in SD conditions (8 hours natural light at 26°C and 16 hours darkness at 20°C) is shown in Figure 20–5. Flower development occurred at the same rate regardless of the conditions of LD induction and, if the temperature was near the optimum for growth, independently of SD induction (Table 20–4).

TABLE 20–4

Flower development is not influenced by the intensity of long-day or short-day induction (adapted from Sachs[8]).

No. LD	% Flowering	Flowering Nodes/Plant	Flower stage*
7	29	1.5	6.0
9	100	7.5	6.5
No. SD			
2	100	15	4.9
3	100	18	5.0
4	100	22	4.6
7	100	23	3.9

* Each figure in this column is the mean stage of development of the most advanced flower at each node bearing at least one flower.

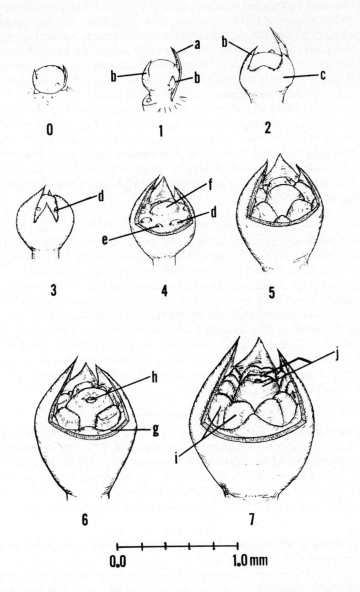

FIGURE 20-4. Development of floral primordia in axillary positions in *C. nocturnum*. Seven stages selected arbitrarily to fit rate of development studies illustrated in Fig. 20–5;0– vegetative bud, youngest leaf primordia are stubs on either side of apical meristem; 1 – floral bud, apex expanded and raised on short peduncle, youngest leaf primordium (a) is arched around bud, calyx primordia (b) are apparent; 2 – apex larger, calyx tube has formed (c); 3 – calyx tube almost encloses bud, stamen primordia can be seen (d); 4 – calyx tube partially removed; corolla primordia appear (e) between stamen primordia, central mass reduced to hemisphere (f); 5 – two calyx lobes removed, stamen and corolla primordia cover entire space between central hemispheres and calyx; 6 – corolla tube appears (g); central hemisphere invaginated, forming ovary (h); 7 – stamens divided into two lobes (i), two carpels become evident (j) enclosing ovary (adapted from Sachs[8]).

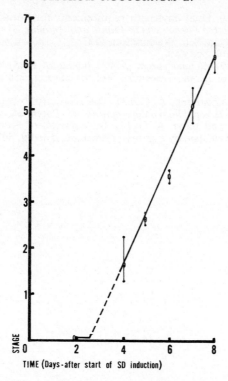

STAGE

TIME (Days-after start of SD induction)

FIGURE 20–5. Rate of development of flower primordia in axillary position of *C. nocturnum*. Plants received 18 LD and then transferred to SD; dissections started at the end of the second SD (adapted from Sachs[8]).

There were differences in time of initiation of flower primordia within a cluster and at different nodes. Also, the rate of flower development was influenced by post-inductive photoperiodic conditions; that is, after SD induction was complete flowers developed somewhat more rapidly in LD than in SD (Table 20–4).

REFERENCES

[1] Caplin, S. and Griesel, W. O. (1966). Personal communication.
[2] Carr, D. J., Reid, D. M. and Skene, K. G. M. (1964). The supply of gibberellins from the root to the shoot. *Planta* **63**, 382.
[3] Griesel, W. O. (1963). Photoperiodic responses of two *Cestrum* species and non-interchangeability of their flowering hormones. *Plant Physiol.* **38**, 479.
[4] Griesel, W. O. (1965). Initiation of floral primordia in *Cestrum diurnum* and *Cestrum nocturnum* in response to various photoperiodic patterns. *Ibid.* **40**, 268.
[5] Griesel, W. O. (1966). Inheritance of factors affecting floral primordia initiation in *Cestrum*; hybrids of *C. elegans* and *C. nocturnum*. *Ibid.* **41**, 111.
[6] Griesel, W. O. (1966). Temperature effect on floral initiation in the genus *Cestrum*. *Ibid. Proc. Ann. Meetings*, xxvii. University of Maryland, College Park, Maryland.
[7] Phillips, I. D. J. and Jones, R. L. (1964). Gibberellin-like activity in bleeding-sap of root systems of *Helianthus annuus* detected by a new dwarf pea epicotyl assay and other methods. *Planta* **63**, 269.
[8] Sachs, R. M. (1955). Floral initiation in *Cestrum nocturnum*. Ph.D. dissertation. California Institute of Technology, Pasadena, Calif.
[9] Sachs, R. M. (1956). Floral initiation in *Cestrum nocturnum*. I. A long-short day plant. *Plant Physiol.* **31**, 185.
[10] Sachs, R. M. (1956). Floral initiation in *Cestrum nocturnum*, a long-short day plant. II. A 24-hour *versus* a 16-hour photoperiod for long day induction. *Ibid.* **31**, 429.
[11] Sachs, R. M. (1956). *Ibid.* III. The effect of temperature upon long day and short day induction. *Ibid.* **31**, 430.

[12] Sachs, R. M. (1959). Dual daylength requirements for floral initiation. In *Photoperiodism and Related Phenomena in Plants and Animals*, 315. Ed. R. B. Withrow. Amer. Assoc. Advan. Sci., Washington, D.C.
[13] Sachs, R. M. Unpublished data.
[14] Schulz, O. E. (1909). *Solanacearum genera nonnulla*. In *Symbolae Antillanae sen Fundamenta Floral Indiae Occentalis*, Vol. 6, chap. 5, 254. Ed. I. Urban. Borntraeger, Leipzig.
[15] Zeevaart, J. A. D. and Lang, A. (1963). The relationship between gibberellin and floral stimulus in *Bryophyllum daigremontianum*. *Planta* **58**, 531.
[16] Zeevaart, J. A. D. and Lang, A. (1963). Suppression of floral induction in *Bryophyllum daigremontianum* by a growth retardant. *Ibid.* **59**, 509.

21

Bryophyllum

By Jan A. D. Zeevaart

1 History of Use

Various *Bryophyllum* species can usually be found in Botanical Gardens and greenhouses, mainly as a curiosity because of the plantlets developing along the margins of the leaves. Although the time of flowering is listed in books on gardening as late autumn or winter, suggesting a response to daylength, the actual discovery of photoperiodic control of flower formation in *Bryophyllum* was made rather late.

In a survey of various *Crassulaceae* for response of growth habit and flowering to photoperiod, von Denffer[7] noticed that *B. crenatum* Bak. flowered neither in 9-hour SD, nor in natural LD. In a footnote added later it is stated, however, that all plants kept on natural days showed flower buds in early November, whereas plants in SD were still vegetative at that time. From these observations von Denffer[7] concluded incorrectly that *B. crenatum* is a LDP. By November 1 the photoperiod in Göttingen is less than 10 hours which is SD for *Bryophyllum* (section 12). Thus von Denffer's plants actually produced flower buds in response to the gradual change in natural daylength from LD → SD.

It remained for Dostál[8,9] in Czechoslovakia to discover in the late 1940's that *B. crenatum* and *B. tubiflorum* Harv. (= *B. verticillatum* Scott-Elliott) have a dual daylength requirement. Both species remained vegetative if kept in continuous I D or SD for two years, but the shift LD → SD did result in flower formation. This work was confirmed and extended to *B. daigremontianum* (R. Hamet *et* Perrier) Berger, and to certain species of *Kalanchoë* and *Aloë* by Resende[23] in 1952. Thus a new class of photoperiodically sensitive plants, the long-short-day plants was established.

Experimentation with *Bryophyllum* is rather cumbersome since these succulent plants have a long juvenile phase, grow slowly, and a long period of time elapses between photoperiodic induction and the actual appearance of flower buds. This is undoubtedly the main reason why *Bryophyllum* has not been used widely in research on flowering. The late Prof. Resende at the University of Lisbon had a long-lasting interest in various aspects of flower bud initiation and further development of *Bryophyllum* and other succulents, beginning in 1944 (Resende[22]) until his untimely death in 1967. He also carried out numerous grafting experiments with *Bryophyllum* and species of related genera.[26,28]

Soon after gibberellic acid (GA₃) was discovered as a chemical which could induce flowering in certain LDP and cold-requiring plants, Bünsow and Harder[2] in Göttingen reported that GA_3 can substitute for the LD, but not for the SD requirement in *Bryophyllum*. This discovery was followed up by an extensive study of the effect of GA_3 on flower formation in *Bryophyllum* by the same group.[5,19]

Dostál[8,9] already performed grafting experiments and reported that the floral stimulus could be transmitted from a donor to a receptor in *B. crenatum* and *B. tubiflorum*. Zeevaart[38] extended these observations to *B. daigremontianum*. His later work in collaboration with Lang at the California Institute of Technology, Pasadena, dealt with the relationship between GA_3 and the floral stimulus,[42] the effect of growth retardants,[43] and the juvenile phase.[39]

Despite the relatively small amount of work done so far with *Bryophyllum*, some important facts have emerged. In particular our knowledge of the role of gibberellins (GA) in flower formation, and of the physiological basis of the juvenile phase in herbaceous plants, has been significantly advanced by the use of *B. crenatum* and *B. daigremontianum* as experimental plants.

2 Growing Techniques and Growth Habit

Bryophyllum can be easily propagated by means of adventitious buds, called pseudobulbils or leaf plantlets, which are produced along the margins of the leaves in *B. crenatum* and *B. daigremontianum*, or near the tips of the subcylindrical leaves of *B. tubiflorum*. The plantlets arise from a few meristematic cells in the serrations of the leaves. Although these primordia are always present, their outgrowth into plantlets is under strict photoperiodic control in *B. daigremontianum* and *B. tubiflorum*: plantlets will develop in LD, but not in SD.[29] On detached leaves of both species, or on leaves of decapitated plants, however, plantlets will develop in SD, or even in total darkness, suggesting a correlative inhibition by other parts of the plant.[14] Finally, plantlets will also grow out on attached leaves of *B. daigremontianum* under SD conditions after treatment with 6-benzylaminopurine.[12] This effect is strictly localized in the leaves to which the cytokinin is applied.

In other species of *Bryophyllum*, including *B. crenatum*, plantlet formation is not controlled by photoperiod,[29] but will occur rapidly when the leaves are detached from the plant. Catarino[6] observed, however, that spraying with kinetin caused plantlet formation on leaves *in situ* on several *Bryophyllum* species.

For vegetative propagation the plantlets are readily detached from the leaves and will root if placed on soil or moist vermiculite. Later they are transplanted to soil, or a mixture of gravel and vermiculite. Even large *B. daigremontianum* plants two years old can easily be kept growing in quart containers if watered 3 times per week with half strength Hoagland solution. Excessive watering should be avoided since this can cause stem rot, particularly under winter conditions of low intensity light and high relative humidity.

Many species of the *Crassulaceae*, including those of *Bryophyllum*, exhibit striking differences in growth habit under SD and LD conditions.[7] In plants of *B. daigremontianum* (Fig. 21–1) kept permanently in SD, the internodes and petioles are very short, the blades are twisted with the edges downwards, and there is a well developed shield at the leaf base. The leaves are dark green with sharply outlined patches of anthocyanin on the lower epidermis. No plantlets are formed on new leaves, but plantlets are sometimes formed on old ones.

In LD (Fig. 21–1) the internodes and petioles are much longer than in SD; the leaf blades are straight and point upwards; the shield at the leaf base is less developed than in SD. The leaf color is light green. Numerous plantlets develop along the margins of the young leaves.

Induction of flower formation caused by the sequence LD → SD is accompanied by a marked increase in length of the newly developing internodes (Fig. 21–1). The bracts are smaller than ordinary leaves and do not produce plantlets. The terminal inflorescence is a dichasium.

The morphological differences between SD and LD individuals are even more striking in *B. crenatum*.[7,10,19] In SD the internodes are very short so that the plants have the appearance of rosettes (Fig. 21–3). The leaves are sessile, round and very succulent. Plants permanently in LD have much longer internodes and leaves with petioles; the blades are elliptical. Downward bending ('drooping') of the stem tip is a conspicuous sign of the beginning of floral initiation in this species.[10]

The blue variety of *B. crenatum*, so called because of its high anthocyanin content, is much less dwarfed in SD than the normal strain.[3] Due to the longer internodes (average length 11 mm *versus* 2.4 mm in the normal variety) and to the fact that the petioles do not break off easily, the blue variety is quite suitable for SD treatment of individual leaves with bags of black cloth[3] (sections 12, 16 and 18.2).

FIGURE 21–1. Growth habit of *B. daigremontianum* as affected by photoperiod. See text. *Left*: Permanently in SD. *Middle*: Permanently in LD. *Right*: After sequence LD → SD (from Resende[27]).

The blue variety of *B. crenatum* shows a weak flowering response after one year of growth in continuous SD. Much more abundant flowering is induced, however, by the shift LD → SD, so that it is appropriate to call this plant a quantitative LSDP.[3] Dostál[10] also observed that specimen of *B. crenatum* in SD produced a single flower occasionally.

In *B. tubiflorum* internodes are shorter in SD than in LD, and no plantlets are formed at the tips of the leaves in SD.

3 Criteria of Flowering Response

Several criteria for measuring flowering response in *Bryophyllum* have been used:

(*a*) The percentage of plants which ultimately responds with flower formation to a given treatment.[19]

(*b*) The number of days from the beginning of inductive treatment until appearance of flower buds or inflorescence.[17,19,42]

(*c*) Number of days from the beginning of treatment until opening of first flower.[19]

(*d*) Number of flower buds or flowers produced per plant.[17,19]

(*e*) Penner[19] used a numerical system with a scale from 0 to 6 to indicate the various degrees of inflorescence development in *B. crenatum* and *B. daigremontianum* (Fig. 21–2):

Stage 0. Plants completely vegetative, no axillary shoots.

„ 1. Axillary shoots grown out partially.

„ 2. Vegetative inflorescence: axillary shoots fully developed, but no flower buds.

„ 3. Inflorescence with a few flower buds; bracts show phyllody.

„ 4. No phyllody, but inflorescence with very short internodes.

„ 5. Normal inflorescence.

„ 6. Normal inflorescence with additional inflorescences arising from the upper leaf pairs.

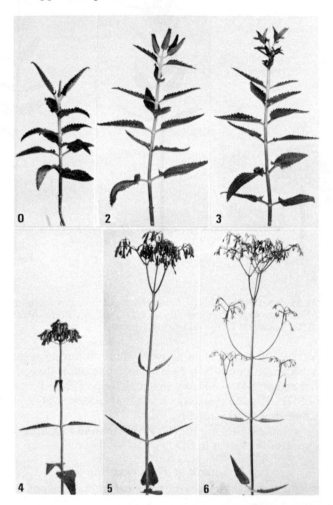

FIGURE 21–2. Various degrees of inflorescence development induced in *B. daigremontianum* after treatment in SD with different dosages of GA_3. Figures indicate stages of inflorescence development. See text (from Penner.[19] courtesy Dr. R. Bünsow, Göttingen).

(*f*) As can be seen from Figure 21–2, there is a close relation between inflorescence stage, and internode elongation. Zeevaart and Lang[42] therefore used the length of the 3rd and 4th internode (as counted above the youngest leaf pair marked at the beginning of an experiment) as a quantitative measurement which was closely correlated with the flowering response.

4 Plant Age

The juvenile phase

All *Bryophyllum* species have a juvenile phase during which they cannot be induced to flower by the shift LD → SD. In Penner's experiments[19] *B. crenatum* produced flower buds after the transfer LD → SD when 5 months old. In *B. daigremontianum* it takes much longer to reach the stage of ripeness-to-flower: more than one year according to Penner,[19] or even two years according to Resende (personal communication). A better criterion than age for ripeness-to-flower is probably size. In my own experience *B. daigremontainum* plants with at least 12 to 15 leaf pairs in LD will flower after the transfer to SD.

Resende and Viana[34] observed that *B. proliferum* Bowie required 6 years of vegetative growth before flowering took place.

Plants of *B. calycinum* Salisb. (= *Kalanchoë pinnata* Pers.) did not flower under the natural conditions of Delhi, India, until they were 2 years old and had produced at least 37 leaf pairs.[37]

The following two possibilities have been suggested to explain why juvenile plants cannot be induced to flower:[39]

(*a*) The leaves of the juvenile plants cannot respond to the inductive day-length with production of the floral stimulus.

(*b*) The growing points of juvenile plants are insensitive to a supply of the floral stimulus.

The latter alternative was tested by grafting young *B. daigremontianum* plants retaining their 3rd leaf pair onto flowering stocks. All these young plants produced flower buds rapidly and flowered profusely later on. The average number of leaf pairs produced by grafted juvenile plants in LD and SD was 7.3 and 7.4, respectively. None of the ungrafted juvenile plants formed flower buds after the transfer LD → SD. The results demonstrate convincingly that the growing points of juvenile plants can respond to a supply of floral stimulus. Thus, the second possibility suggested above is ruled out and it can be concluded then that juvenile plants cannot be induced to flower because their leaves are incapable of producing the floral stimulus.

Flowering in juvenile plants of *B. daigremontianum* can also be induced by two other methods:

(*a*) Penner[19] discovered that juvenile plants reach the stage of ripeness-to-flower sooner if first grown in SD and then transferred to LD, than when kept in LD continuously. In his experiments plants grown for 9 months in SD were exposed to LD for 2 months, and then returned again to SD. This sequence, SD → LD → SD caused flowering in all plants. On the other hand, control plants of the same age shifted directly from LD → SD remained vegetative.

(*b*) Flower formation in juvenile plants can be obtained by treatment with GA_3. Three-months-old *B. daigremontianum* plants were induced to flower in SD by a minimal amount of 2.5 μg GA_3 per plant.[19] Early flowering under SD conditions following GA_3 treatment has also been observed in young plants of *B. proliferum*,[34] and of *B. calycinum*.[37] In the latter species more GA_3 was required to induce flowering in three-months-old plants than in nine-months-old ones, viz. 50 and 5 μg per plant, respectively.[37]

Bryophyllum in LD cannot be induced to flower with GA_3 (section 18). But if juvenile plants in LD were treated with GA_3 and kept in LD for another 4 months, flower formation took place after transfer to SD, while untreated controls remained vegetative.[19] Thus, GA_3 shortens the juvenile phase of *B. daigremontianum* not only in SD, but also in LD. The after-effect of GA_3 persists in

LD for at least 4 months. The possible nature of the juvenile phase in *Bryo-phyllum* will be discussed further in section 18.

Flowering of plantlets

As described in section 2, plantlets on the leaves of intact *B. daigremontianum* plants are produced only under LD conditions. So, when *Bryophyllum* is trans-ferred from LD → SD, no plantlets develop on the newly produced leaves which precede the inflorescence. If, however, the inflorescence and axillary branches are removed, plantlets will develop on these leaves. Kröner (p. 412)[14] observed that some of these plantlets produced flower buds while still attached to the leaves. Resende[22,25] made similar observations, but stressed that only those plantlets produced *de novo*, i.e. at the base of such leaves where they would never develop normally, flowered. However, in a later paper by Resende[30] it can be seen in his Figure 4 that removal of the inflorescence caused flowering of most plantlets produced along the margins of the two upper leaves.

Flowering plantlets have also been observed on detached leaves treated with GA_3 and kept permanently in SD[41].

These observations on flowering plantlets are of considerable interest since they show that the growing point of *Bryophyllum* is responsive to the floral stimu-lus at a very early stage. For example, it appears from Figures 37 and 41 in Resende[22] that only 2 very small leaf pairs were produced prior to the terminal flower bud. It is probable therefore that the meristems receive the floral stimulus from the leaf in whose serrations they are localized as soon as they start to pro-duce plantlets following the removal of the inflorescence. Already existing plant-lets grow further, but do not produce flower buds after the inflorescence has been removed.[22] This may be because such plantlets have reached some degree of autonomy, at least as far as supply of organic material is concerned, thus pre-venting movement of the floral stimulus.

12 Dual Photoperiod Responses

Discovery

Dostál[8,9] described the dual daylength requirement of *B. crenatum* and *B. tubi-florum* in 1949. Resende,[20] working at the same time with *B. daigremontianum*, assumed this species to be a SDP since it produces macroscopically visible flower buds by the end of October in Lisbon when the natural daylength has become less than 11 hours. Resende[27] later observed that none of the plants kept perma-nently in SD or in LD showed any signs of flower formation for at least 5 years. If, on the other hand a LD treatment was given and the plants were then returned to their former SD environment, flowering did take place.[23,27] Thus, *B. daigre-montianum* has a dual daylength requirement and Resende[23] introduced the term long-short-day plant (LSDP) to describe this new response type.

Number of cycles necessary for photo-induction

The minimum number of LD and SD cycles required for flower formation varies with the time of the year. Resende[23] reported originally that *B. daigremontianum* plants kept in SD had to be exposed to LD for one month. Later he stated that 1 to 2 months were required in summer and more than 3 months in winter.[24] The difference seems to be due to light intensity rather than to temperature diff-erences. SD had to be given for 2 to 4 weeks at all times. Continuous darkness could not replace SD treatment. In reasonable agreement with Resende's data is Penner's report[19] that *B. daigremontianum* needs at least 60 LD, followed by approximately 15 SD.

The requirements for photoperiodic induction in the normal variety of *B. crenatum* are a minimum of 20 LD, followed by 9 to 12 SD.[19] The blue variety is considerably more sensitive than the normal one and needs fewer LD and SD to reach a comparable flowering stage.[3]

Lightbreaks

The effect of night interruptions on flowering of *Bryophyllum* has not been studied systematically. However, Penner[19] used a 2-hour night interruption at an intensity of a few hundred lux routinely to prevent plants from flowering during the SD of winter. Resende[27,31] similarly observed a LD effect with a night interruption of 1 to 2 hours.

Critical daylength

The critical daylength for SD induction of *B. daigremontianum* has both an upper and a lower limit. Extremely short photoperiods of less than 3 hours of light per day were ineffective as SD following LD treatment, but 3 hours of light were sufficient for flower formation.[27] The upper limit of the photoperiod which still acts as SD is approximately 12 hours; 12.5 hours of light have a clear-cut LD effect. The borderline area between SD and LD, i.e. 12 hours light and 12 hours darkness (12 : *12* hr), can act both as LD and as SD, depending upon the conditions to which the plants were previously exposed. *B. daigremontianum* moved from LD to a 12-hour photoperiod produced flower buds.[27] Thus, 12 : *12* hours acts as SD for plants grown in LD. Plants raised in SD, then shifted to 12 : *12* hours and subsequently returned to SD also flowered.[27] Since only the shift LD → SD can induce flower formation in *Bryophyllum*, it follows that 12 : *12* hours acted as LD for the SD specimen. In view of these findings Resende[27] maintained *B. daigremontianum* in 12 : *12* hours for 19 months to see if this intermediate photoperiod could fulfill both the LD and SD requirement for flower formation. Plants kept under these conditions showed a mixed SD and LD habit of growth, and a weak flowering response was indeed obtained. LD characteristics were enhanced by high light-intensity and high temperature, and SD became more expressed under conditions of low intensity light and lower temperature. Since 12 hours of light is the only permanent photoperiod in which *B. daigremontianum* will flower, one might also consider this LSDP as an intermediate day plant,[1] or as a SDP with a very narrow margin between the upper and lower limit of the critical daylength. This margin is less than one hour, since 11.5 : *12.5* hours has a SD effect only, and 12.5 : *11.5* hours clearly acts as LD.

In its native habitat in Southern Madagascar at 25° S.L. *B. daigremontianum* is exposed to natural daylengths ranging from 10.5 to 13.5 hours. It follows from Resende's data that this annual variation in photoperiod is sufficient to fulfill both the LD and SD requirements for flowering.

The situation with respect to critical day length is quite similar in *B. crenatum*[19] except that in this species 12.5 : *11.5* hours instead of 12 : *12* hours can fulfill either the LD or the SD requirement, depending upon the length of the preceding photoperiod. The data in Table 21–1 show that 12 and 13 hours light act as SD and LD, respectively. A photoperiod of 12.5 hours is active as SD for plants grown in LD, and as LD for plants grown in SD. *B. crenatum* has not been maintained continuously in a daylength of 12.5 hours, but in view of the behaviour of *B. daigremontianum* under 12-hour photoperiods, flowering would probably occur.

Light intensity

According to Resende and Viana[33] a light intensity above a certain limit (*ca.* 1000 f.c.) is necessary for production of the floral stimulus in *B. daigremontianum*. By

TABLE 21–1

Flower formation in *B. crenatum* grown continuously in LD or SD, followed by exposure to photoperiods between 12 and 13 hours for 4 weeks. + = flower formation. − = vegetative (from Bünsow *et al.*[5]).

Treatment	Flower response
SD → 12.0 hr → SD	−
SD → 12.5 hr → SD	+
SD → 13.0 hr → SD	+ +
LD → 12.0 hr → LD	+ +
LD → 12.5 hr → LD	+
LD → 13.0 hr → LD	−

differential treatments of the leaves and the shoot tips, it could be established that for normal development of the inflorescence the mature leaves must be exposed to strong light. In low intensity light flowering plants reverted to vegetative growth.

Dostál[10] also observed the ineffectiveness of short photoperiods of low intensity light in inducing flower formation in *B. crenatum*. Very weak light given during 16-hour photoperiods did not substitute for the SD requirement of plants grown in LD.

Localization of induction

Totally defoliated plants of *B. daigremontianum* failed to produce flower buds when exposed to LD → SD.[22] Although nutritional factors may have played a role also, this observation suggests that leaves are necessary for perceiving the daylength. More conclusive evidence was provided by Penner[19] who used LD individuals with 1 or 2 leaf pairs to show that only the leaf pair closest to the shoot apex must receive SD to cause flower formation. This shows that photo-induction is localized in the leaves, but the question remains whether LD and SD can be perceived simultaneously or successively by different leaves, or must be perceived successively by one and the same leaf. The latter alternative was found in the LSDP *Cestrum nocturnum* and Bünsow *et al.*[5] state that the same holds true for *Bryophyllum*. The review by Bünsow *et al.* is based on the experimental work of Penner, and although his data definitely show that LD → SD given to the same leaf induces flower formation, they do not show unequivocally that exposing one leaf of a pair to LD and at the same time the other to SD, fails to do so. Such an experiment, combined with various GA_3 treatments, has been reported for *B. daigremontianum* (Table 11 in Penner[19]), but since these plants were still in the juvenile phase the negative results are inconclusive. The simplest experimental approach to this problem is to grow plants in SD, defoliate them to a single leaf pair, then transfer the plants to LD and subject one of the leaves to SD by daily darkening with a bag of black cloth. Thus, one leaf is subjected to SD → LD, the other to SD → SD. This treatment never caused flower formation in *B. crenatum*.[3,19] It is possible that the leaf area exposed to different photoperiods was insufficient in these experiments, but it is also conceivable that the stem and shoot tip in LD inhibited flowering.[3] It should be noticed, however that subjecting a single leaf to SD treatment on plants otherwise in LD, did cause flower formation (section 16). Leaves on SD specimens of *B. crenatum* are quite small and one might therefore consider subjecting several leaves simultaneously to LD and SD. This approach seems to be doomed as well, since the flowering response of terminal shoots is controlled by the uppermost leaf pair (section 16). Thus, the important question whether or not the shift LD → SD applied to the same leaf is the only treatment which will induce flowering in *Bryophyllum*, remains unanswered at present.

Be that as it may, if one assumes that LD and SD control different steps in the series of processes leading to flower formation, *a priori* it is most likely that the same leaf of a LSDP has to perceive both daylengths. In this concept presence of the product of LD is a prerequisite for SD action. In *Cestrum nocturnum* the former is immobile whereas the latter gives rise to the transmissible floral stimulus (p. 430).

An alternative interpretation of LD and SD action in LSDP given in Bünsow et al.[5] deserves consideration here. These authors postulate that minimal amounts of two independent substances, one produced in LD, and the other in SD, must be present simultaneously to induce flowering. Since *Bryophyllum* requires more LD than SD for photo-induction, it is assumed that the SD material is produced at a higher rate than the LD product. Indirect evidence further suggests that the SD product has the shorter life-time of the two. This would explain for example why SD → LD does not induce flower formation: the SD product would have disappeared before the LD material could reach the level necessary for flowering. The effect of GA_3 (section 18) would consist of maintaining a high level of the LD substance. As will be discussed in section 17, data obtained in grafting experiments are at variance with the idea that LD and SD each induce the production of a separate, transportable substance.

Further work will be required to decide between the chain hypothesis and that of Bünsow et al.[5] of two independent substances with different kinetic characteristics for production and metabolism. It is of interest, however, to note that the latter hypothesis also fits the experimental data on fractional induction which is possible in LDP (LD product with long life-time can accumulate), but not in SDP (SD product has disappeared during intercalated LD before the next SD cycle is perceived).

13 Effects of Temperature

A striking effect of temperature during SD induction of *B. daigremontianum* was first noticed by Zeevaart and Lang.[42] Natural daylight was given for 8 hours at 23°C, and darkness at 11°, 15°, or 19°C. Flower formation took place at the two lower temperatures, but not at 19°C. There is no explanation for this low temperature optimum in the dark period of SD induction in *B. daigremontianum*, but it contrasts sharply with the much higher optimum dark-period temperature for induction of SDP.

Preliminary observations suggest that the temperature optimum for induction of *B. crenatum* is also relatively low. This species flowered in SD when the temperature was kept at 10° or 15°C throughout, but flowering was delayed at 20°C, and fully suppressed at 28°C.[16]

Resende[31] found that the action of SD was not absolutely essential for flower induction in *B. daigremontianum* and that flowering could also take place in LD, provided the night temperature was kept at 10° to 12°C. These results were further confirmed and extended with a small number of plants grown in controlled environments.[32] Again it was found that normal flowering took place in *B. daigremontianum*, but not in *B. crenatum*, grown continuously in a LD regime of 14 : 10 hours with a 22° day and 7°C night temperature. Continuous exposure to 7°C in LD did not result in flower formation. In contrast to Zeevaart and Lang's results, flower formation also took place after the shift LD → SD at a night temperature of 22°C, although the inflorescences showed phyllody.[32] These conflicting results may be due to different clones used by the different workers.

Once floral induction of B. *daigremontianum* has been completed, subsequent inflorescence development will take place in SD, or in LD with a low night temperature. In LD with warm nights the inflorescences tend to revert to vegetative growth.[31]

16 Translocation of the Floral Stimulus

Translocation of the floral stimulus in *Bryophyllum* plants, as evident from photo-inducing only one leaf pair and observing the flower response in the shoot apex, was clearly demonstrated by Penner.[19] If two leaf pairs of the same orthostichy were retained on the plant, flower formation could only be obtained by induction of the leaf pair closer to the apex. Induction of the lower leaf pair never resulted in flowering. Thus, non-induced leaves located between induced ones and the receptor bud exert a flower-inhibiting effect in *Bryophyllum*. Non-induced leaves did not inhibit flowering if they were located below the induced leaf pair.[19]

Bünsow and Kruse[3] repeated these experiments with the blue variety of B. *crenatum* and obtained similar results. In addition, if one leaf of the upper pair was kept in LD, and the other subjected to LD → SD, inflorescences with uni-lateral flowering above the induced leaf were formed. A surprising result was observed with intact plants in LD when a single, not yet fully mature leaf on the 5th node (counted from the tip) was exposed to SD. This caused formation of a terminal inflorescence bearing flowers only on the side of the induced leaf. The failure of LD leaves located between the donor leaf and the receptor tip to prevent flower formation was perhaps due to the fact that these leaves were still immature when induction was started.

Inhibition of flowering by mature LD leaves located between induced ones and the receptor tip has also been observed and studied in the related SDP *Kalanchoë*, in which little or no lateral transport takes place from vascular bundles leading to and from the leaf. If this holds for *Bryophyllum* as well, the most obvious interpretation of the flower-inhibiting effect exerted by non-induced leaves is as follows. Of two leaf pairs in the same orthostichy, the upper one is the main supplier of photosynthates to the shoot apex and the floral stimulus moves along with this flow of assimilates. Thus, when the lower leaf pair is induced, the floral stimulus is prevented from reaching the receptor shoot by the stream of assimilates coming from the non-induced upper leaf pair.

An alternative interpretation is that leaves in LD produce a flower-inhibiting substance which would nullify the effect of the floral stimulus in the shoot apex. Since the lower leaf pair kept in LD does not inhibit flowering, this explanation is less probable.

An implication of the hypothesis by Bünsow et al.,[5] discussed at the end of section 12, would be that the products of LD and SD induction are different, so that characteristics of their movements might also be different. However, since data of grafting experiments (section 17) do not support this idea, it will not be considered further here.

17 Grafting Experiments

Cleft-grafting *Bryophyllum* shoots onto stocks of the same species is easy to perform and almost complete success can be obtained.[38,42] Furthermore, grafts can also be established between *Bryophyllum* and species of the related genus *Kalanchoë*. A compilation of the cases in which flower formation has been induced in B. *daigremontianum* via grafting is given in Table 21-2.

B. *daigremontianum* stocks with several leaf pairs induced either by the shift LD → SD, or with GA_3 in SD, functioned as donors, and defoliated scions as receptors. Transmission of the flowering condition occurred irrespective of

whether the receptors were in LD or SD. Single leaf pairs taken from flowering
plants and grafted onto vegetative stocks also caused flowering, but in this case
receptors in LD responded more readily than those in SD.[42]

The results of these grafting experiments also have a bearing on the hypothesis
of two independent substances produced in LD and SD[5] (section 12). SD individuals of *B. daigremontianum* shifted to LD do not function as donors for plants

TABLE 21-2

Successful transfer of the floral stimulus from different donors to *B. daigremontianum* receptors.

Donor			Bryophyllum Receptor in	References
Species	Response type	Induced by		
B. daigremon-tianum	LSDP	LD → SD	SD	Zeevaart,[38] Zeevaart and Lang[42]
" "	"	LD → SD → LD	LD	Zeevaart,[38] Zeevaart and Lang[42]
" "	"	SD + GA$_3$	SD	Zeevaart and Lang[42]
" "	"	SD + GA$_3$ → LD	LD	Zeevaart and Lang[42]
Kalanchoë velutina	SDP	SD → LD	LD	Resende[26]
Kalanchoë blossfeldiana	"	SD	SD	Zeevaart[38]
" "	"	SD → LD	LD	Zeevaart[38]

in LD,[42] but plants induced by the sequence LD → SD → LD rapidly transmit
the floral stimulus to LD receptors. According to the hypothesis of two independent substances LD receptors would contain the LD substance, but would still
need the SD substance from the donor before flower formation could take place.
Obviously, the missing factor is not supplied by plants shifted from SD → LD.
Since induced plants returned to LD do effectively function as donors, it follows
that the shift LD → SD results in the production of something, the floral stimulus, which is more than the sum of the separate effects of LD and SD. Thus, these
data do not support the idea that the floral stimulus in *Bryophyllum* consists of
two different substances produced independently in LD and SD.

It is of interest that *Bryophyllum* plants in LD in which flower formation had
been induced by grafting, could themselves again function as donors in grafting
experiments.[42] So far, this phenomenon is known only in the SDP *Xanthium*
(Ch. 2) and in the LDP *Silene*, apart from *Bryophyllum*.

Transmission of the floral stimulus from an induced to a non-induced partner
has also been achieved by Dostál[8,9] in *B. crenatum* and in *B. tubiflorum*, and by
Resende[28] in hybrids between different species of *Bryophyllum*.

It is also possible to use plants of a different response type as donor for *Bryophyllum*. As listed in Table 21-2, flowering was induced in *Bryophyllum* receptors
in LD as well as in SD after grafting with the SDP donors *Kalanchoë velutina* and
K. blossfeldiana. The number of responding receptor plants was small in these
experiments, and further experimental work is needed with these graft combinations. Nevertheless, the tentative conclusion may be drawn that the floral stimulus is interchangeable and thus probably identical in the two response types.

18 Growth Substances and Growth Retardants

18.1 Auxin

Resende's auxin/anti-auxin hypothesis—Resende has repeatedly pointed out[21,22,24,28] that *Bryophyllum* plants in LD have much longer internodes and petioles than in SD (Fig. 21–1), and inferred from these morphological differences that the auxin level is higher in LD than in SD individuals. He did not believe that a specific flower hormone determines floral initiation. Instead, according to Resende's working hypothesis, the differences between vegetative and flowering plants are due to quantitative differences in their auxins and anti-auxins.[21,24,26] The level of both groups of substances is supposedly low in SD, and considerably higher in LD. In order to induce flowering, the level of auxin and anti-auxin has to be kept above a certain minimum. Although this level is exceeded in LD conditions, the optimal difference between anti-auxin and auxin can be established only by the shift LD → SD. It should be realized that Resende's use[22] of the term auxins and anti-auxins was quite broad, meaning all growth-promoting and growth-inhibiting substances, respectively. Nowadays, the former would also include gibberellin-like substances, and the latter chemicals such as abscisic acid.

Formulation of this hypothesis was based on circumstantial evidence and on the morphological appearance of the plants. For example, root formation on darkened portions of the stem can occur in LD, but not in SD.[24] Furthermore, an inverse correlation was found to exist between floral initiation and root formation in *Bryophyllum* plants held horizontally, while being photoinduced.[20] Only 45 per cent of the horizontal plants flowered, as compared to 72 per cent of the vertical ones. The horizontal plants bent upwards, and produced roots in the curved portions of their stems. None of the flowering horizontal plants produced roots. Resende[24] interpreted this to indicate that auxin is needed for flower formation, and if used in this process, it cannot induce root formation.

Applied auxins and anti-auxins—More direct evidence in support of Resende's hypothesis was obtained with *Kalanchoë rotundifolia*, another LSDP, which was induced to flower in SD by spraying with 0.01 per cent IAA.[35] However, other workers[3] using Resende's strain of *K. rotundifolia* were unable to reproduce this result and observed that IAA had no effect, or slightly inhibited flower formation.

Applications of auxins and anti-auxins to *B. daigremontianum* did not give spectacular results.[11] Plants were moved from LD → SD for one month, or kept permanently in LD. Auxins (IAA, NAA, 2,4-D), or anti-auxins (TIBA, 2,4-dichloranisole) were applied continuously to the 3rd leaf pair by submerging the leaves in the solutions. Flowering never occurred in LD conditions. All plants flowered after the shift LD → SD, and only small quantitative differences due to the applied growth regulators were observed. Anti-auxins slightly promoted flowering, whereas auxins delayed appearance of flower buds and inhibited development of the inflorescences.

Spraying *B. crenatum* every other day with solutions of 10, 50, or 100 mg/l IAA did not cause flower formation in either SD or LD, but it did have a slight flower-inhibiting effect in plants induced by the shift LD → SD, or by GA_3 under SD conditions.[3]

Endogenous auxin—Extraction of *B. crenatum* leaves grown in SD and LD, and determination of the IAA content by paper chromatography gave yields of 3 and 70 μg IAA per 100 g leaves, respectively.[15] Unfortunately, no data were presented for plants subjected to the shift LD → SD. Chromatograms of extracts of SD leaves also showed an intense spot at an Rf-value similar to that of the inhibitor β. This spot was absent when extracts of LD leaves were chromatographed. Although the authors[15] considered the data in agreement with

Resende's hypothesis, one should be cautious, since none of the spots localized on the chromatograms was tested for biological activity. In conclusion, it appears that there is no conclusive evidence that flower formation of *Bryophyllum* is controlled by the auxin level of the plant.

A further objection that can be raised against Resende's hypothesis is that it does not account for all the experimental facts. For example, the transfer from LD → SD which induces flowering is accompanied by a striking elongation of the terminal internodes.[30,42] Thus, one would infer that the change LD → SD does not result in a drop of the auxin level, as assumed by Resende, but rather in a rise.

18.2 Gibberellins

General effects—GA's are the only chemicals known so far which can induce flower formation in *Bryophyllum* kept in permanent SD. This was first reported

FIGURE 21–3. *B. crenatum* grown continuously in SD. (a) Control. (b) Treated with approximately 35 μg GA₃. Photographed 60 days after beginning of GA₃ treatment (courtesy Dr. R. Bünsow, Göttingen).

by Bünsow and Harder[2] for both *B. crenatum* (Fig. 21–3) and *B. daigremontianum*. Since then, GA_3-induced flowering under SD conditions has also been observed in *B. proliferum*,[34] *B. tubiflorum*,[19] and in *B. calicynum*,[37] as well as in the LSDP *Kalanchoë rotundifolia*.[3,34]

The earliest response to GA_3 is stem elongation, soon followed by appearance of flower buds. Chemical control of flowering in *Bryophyllum* is quite spectacular and at optimal GA_3 doses the effect is indistinguishable from photo induced flowering. Penner[19] obtained a weak flowering response in *B. crenatum* with as little as 0.15 μg GA$_3$ per plant, whereas 0.75 μg per plant caused normal flowering. In studies by Bünsow and Kruse[3] the normal variety of *B. crenatum* needed 0.1–0.5 μg GA$_3$ per plant for optimal flowering, whereas the blue variety required 1 to 5 μg per plant for a comparable response. Thus, there was a tenfold difference in sensitivity between the two strains.

In the order of 10 μg GA$_3$ per plant was necessary to induce normal flowering in *B. daigremontianum* and *B. tubiflorum.*[19]

An extract of bean seeds containing GA-like substances also induced flower formation in *B. crenatum* in SD.[4]

The relative effectiveness of nine different gibberellins in causing flower formation in *B. crenatum* in SD was reported by Michniewicz and Lang.[18] The order of effectiveness was: GA$_3$ = GA$_4$ = GA$_7$ > GA$_9$ > GA$_1$ = GA$_2$ = GA$_5$ > GA$_6$ ≫ GA$_8$. The minimal amount to cause flowering in this particular strain of *B. crenatum* was 1.5 μg for the most active gibberellins, and 50 μg in the case of the least active one, GA$_6$. GA$_8$ was incapable of inducing flowering at all concentrations studied.

Of considerable interest is the fact that GA$_3$ can induce flowering in *Bryophyllum* kept permanently in SD (Table 21–3, *a*), but never when the plants are kept in LD (Table 21–3, *b*). Likewise, in the short-long-day plant (SLDP) *Coreopsis grandiflora* GA$_3$ can replace the LD, but not the SD requirement for floral induction.[13] Thus, in LSDP as well as in SLDP GA$_3$ substitutes for the LD,

TABLE 21–3

Flower formation in *Bryophyllum* as affected by daylength and gibberellin. + = flower formation. − = vegetative (from Bünsow *et al.*[5]).

	Flower response	
Treatment	− GA$_3$	+ GA$_3$
(a) SD	−	+ + +
(b) LD	−	−
(c) LD → SD	+ + +	+ + +
(d) LD → SD → LD	+	+ +
(e) SD → LD	−	±

even though the order in which the photoperiodic treatments must be perceived is the reverse in the two reaction types.

Effects of GA$_3$ under conditions of suboptimal photo-induction—An optimal flowering response induced by the transfer LD → SD is neither inhibited nor promoted by applied GA$_3$ (Table 21–3, *c*). However, suboptimal photoinduction of *Bryophyllum* is enhanced by application of GA$_3$ (Table 21–3, *d*). The effects of chemical and photoperiodic induction thus appear to be additive. Such conditions are encountered when the number of SD given is insufficient for a normal flowering response. As shown in Table 21–4, 6 SD will result in formation of a vegetative inflorescence without flower buds, but plants receiving 6 SD + 15 μg GA$_3$ produced 18 flower buds per plant. The flower-promoting effect of GA$_3$ diminished with increasing number of SD. For optimal flowering 15 SD were required whereas in the presence of GA$_3$, 9 SD sufficed to obtain the same response. Thus, under these experimental conditions GA$_3$ could substitute for a few SD.

An enhancement of flowering by GA_3 was also observed under photoperiods close to the critical one.[19] For *B. crenatum* grown in LD, photoperiods of 12.0 or 12.5 hours still act as SD, and GA_3 has little effect on the response (Table 21–5). On the other hand a daylength of 13 hours is LD, but even then GA_3 can

TABLE 21–4

Flower formation in *B. crenatum* as induced by different numbers of SD in the absence or the presence of GA_3. A total amount of 15 μg GA_3 applied per plant (from Penner[19]).

Number of SD	GA_3 treatment	Days until appearance of inflorescence	Number of flower buds per plant	Inflorescence stage
0	−	∞	0	0
	+	∞	0	0
3	−	23	0	2.4
	+	20	0	2.2
6	−	20	0	3.0
	+	18	18	4.0
9	−	19	20	4.0
	+	16	30	5.4
12	−	18	22	4.0
	+	18	28	5.6
15	−	17	28	5.6
	+	15	28	5.8

induce a slight flowering response. This shows that GA_3 not only substitutes for LD treatment, but under these circumstances at least, also partly for SD treatment. Alternatively, one could say that treatment with GA_3 increases the critical daylength for SD induction.[5]

GA_3 and the transfer SD → LD—The transfer SD → LD never causes flowering in *Bryophyllum* on its own, but may induce a weak flowering response when combined with GA_3 treatment, depending upon plant age and time of application (Table 21–3, *e*). In *B. crenatum* plants of all ages tested, GA_3 induced 100 per cent flower formation if the treatment was followed by at least 6 more SD.[19] The percentage of plants which produced inflorescences became smaller as GA_3 was applied nearer the time of transfer SD → LD. With plants of 8 months or older, some would still produce inflorescences if GA_3 was given 4 to 5 days after the shift SD → LD, i.e. flowering was induced with GA_3 under LD conditions! Penner[19] interpreted this finding as an indication that a weak SD after-effect persisted for approximately 5 days if old plants of *B. crenatum* were moved to LD conditions (also section 12).

Dostál[10] never observed flowering in *B. crenatum* when GA_3 was applied in lanolin simultaneously with the transfer SD → LD. However, SD individuals treated with TIBA formed ring fasciations and lateral shoots. The latter flowered after GA_3 treatment, even if the plants were simultaneously moved to LD.

GA_3 effects on plants with 1 or 2 leaf pairs—If *B. crenatum* plants were defoliated so that 2 pairs of the same orthostichy remained, flower formation was determined by the leaf pair closer to the apex.[19] As in intact plants, flowering occurred only after this leaf pair received LD → SD, or SD + GA_3.

TABLE 21–5

Effect of photoperiod and GA_3 application on flower formation in *B. crenatum* kept in different photoperiods for 28 days. Plants in LD before and after experimental treatment. A total of 12.5 μg GA_3 applied per plant (from Penner[19]).

Photoperiod	GA_3 treatment	Days until appearance of inflorescence	Number of flower buds per plant	Inflorescence stage
12.0 hr	−	19	22	5.0
	+	18	32	5.0
12.5 hr	−	24	21	5.0
	+	19	26	5.0
13.0 hr	−	∞	0	0
	+	33	0*	2.5

* Flower buds initiated, but not further developed.

Juvenile *B. daigremontianum* retaining only one leaf pair, with one leaf in SD and the other in LD, could be induced to flower by GA_3 application to either leaf. The response was slower after treating the leaf in LD than the one in SD. Penner[19] mentioned that applied GA_3 was readily transported throughout the plant, and it is probable therefore that when GA_3 was applied to the LD leaf, it acted nevertheless in the SD leaf.

An interesting observation with *B. crenatum* was that plants of the normal variety defoliated to one or two leaf pairs and treated with GA_3 under LD conditions showed a beginning of transition towards the reproductive phase (stage 1 or 2), but flower buds were never formed.[3,19] Plants of the blue variety never produced vegetative inflorescences in response to GA_3 treatment, although stem elongation was stimulated.[3] Intact plants of *B. crenatum* always remained strictly vegetative in LD when treated with GA_3.

GA and florigen—Although GA_3 can induce flower formation in *Bryophyllum* in SD, it fails to do so in LD. On the other hand, grafting of vegetative *Bryophyllum* plants on induced individuals results in flower formation regardless of whether the former are kept in continuous LD or continuous SD.[38] GA_3 therefore cannot be identical with florigen, the hypothetical hormone responsible for flowering, the existence of which has been inferred from physiological experiments.

An attempt to clarify the relationship between GA and the floral stimulus in *B. daigremontianum* has been made by Zeevaart and Lang.[42] Flower formation was induced in SD with GA_3 and plants were then used as donors in grafting experiments. Receptors kept in SD or LD responded equally well with flower formation (Table 21–2 and Fig. 21–4). In the case of SD receptors it could be argued

FIGURE 21–4. Transmission of floral stimulus in *B. daigremontianum*. Donor stocks induced by the shift LD → SD (left), or by GA_3 treatment in SD (right), then both transferred to LD. Receptor scions kept permanently in LD. Arrows indicate graft union (from Zeevaart and Lang[42]).

that flowering was due to residual GA_3 transmitted via the graft union, but this reasoning does not hold for the LD receptors since GA_3 by itself does not cause flowering in LD. These results demonstrate that GA_3-induced plants do produce the floral stimulus. In a physiological sense GA_3 can therefore be considered as the precursor of florigen. Both LD → SD and SD + GA_3 induce elongation of the younger internodes (Table 21–6), and it was postulated therefore that with

TABLE 21–6

Shoot and internode growth of *B. daigremontianum* as affected by photoperiod and GA_3. The youngest leaf pair with leaves longer than 5 cm was marked at the beginning of treatments. Measurements were taken 47 days later. Internodes numbered in acropetal direction (from Zeevaart and Lang[42]).

Treatment	Total shoot length mm	Length of 3rd internode mm
SD	68	14
SD + GA_3	442	117
LD	212	48
LD → SD	324	108

the shift LD → SD the endogenous GA level increases to that necessary for production of the floral stimulus. In order to test this directly, Skene and Lang[36] extracted *B. daigremontianum* plants kept permanently in LD or in SD, and plants subjected to LD → SD. Under LD conditions a substance like GA_1 and one like GA_5 were found. The level of both these substances was very low in SD. The transfer LD → SD caused a rise in the GA_5-like material prior to floral initiation in the apices and upper leaves; no changes in the level of the GA_1-like material during induction were observed. These results would support the suggestions made by Zeevaart and Lang.[42] They further show that a good correlation exists between internode length and extractable GA. However, a substantial increase in the GA_5-like material was also found under continued LD treatment, at least in some experiments. Further work is therefore needed.

Site of GA action—If it is true that the GA level has to be increased in SD leaves for florigen production to take place, one would predict that exogenously applied GA_3 has to exert its effect in the leaves.

The following lines of evidence suggest that in order to induce flowering in *Bryophyllum*, GA_3 must act in a SD leaf:

(*a*) In *B. crenatum* grown in SD a minimal leaf area of 3 or more leaf pairs per plant was necessary for GA_3-induced flowering. In case only 1 or 2 leaf pairs were retained, GA_3 applied to the upper pair failed to induce flowering.[3]

(*b*) In plants of *B. daigremontianum* with only two leaves, one in LD and the other in SD, flower formation was earlier after GA_3 application to the SD leaf than to the one in LD.[19] This strongly suggests that GA_3 must act in the SD leaf. If the hormone acted in the growing point, appearance of flower buds should be independent of the site of application, since GA_3 would be expected to move with equal ease to the apex from either leaf.

(*c*) Flower formation in LD receptors of *B. daigremontianum* was obtained by grafting with a single leaf pair taken from a donor which had been induced in SD with GA_3.[42]

(*d*) Detached SD leaves of *B. daigremontianum* treated with GA_3 sometimes produce a few flowering plantlets, demonstrating directly the presence of floral stimulus in these leaves[41] (also section 4).

Further evidence that GA_3 acts exclusively in the leaves of *Bryophyllum* in SD could probably be obtained in grafting experiments with LD receptors and the following donors: detached leaves treated with GA_3, or decapitated and continuously de-budded plants in SD + GA_3.

GA and the juvenile phase—As discussed in section 4, juvenile *Bryophyllum* plants cannot produce the floral stimulus after the transfer LD → SD. GA_3, however, is capable of inducing flowering in plants only 3 months old.[19] In view of the foregoing discussion it would appear therefore that GA is the limiting factor for florigen production in juvenile plants. The nature of the juvenile phase in *Bryophyllum* can then be defined as the stage during which the sequence LD → SD does not induce an increase in endogenous GA which is a prerequisite for production of the floral stimulus.[39] This idea is supported by the observation that internodes formed during the first year are quite short[19] as compared to those of older *Bryophyllum* plants.

The flower-promoting effect of GA_3 on juvenile plants persisted in LD for at least 4 months.[19] This interesting observation is hard to interpret, but it is improbable that a naturally occurring compound such as GA_3 had not been fully metabolized after a period of 4 months. Could this mean that the treatment with GA_3 had activated the production of endogenous GA?

18.3 *Cytokinins*

Treatment of *B. crenatum* with kinetin up to a dosage of 0.375 µg per plant did not cause floral initiation in SD or in LD individuals. In flowering plants, induced by the shift LD → SD, or with GA_3 treatment in SD, kinetin applications also remained without effect.[3]

18.4 *Growth retardants*

Growth retardants usually have effects on plants opposite to those caused by GA_3. As far as the mode of action is concerned, at least three of the retardants, viz. Amo-1618, CCC, and Phosfon D, are known to block GA biosynthesis in higher plants.[40] Thus, these chemicals effectively lower the endogenous GA level without exerting any noticeable harmful side effects. Since photoinduction of *Bryophyllum* appears to be associated with an increase in GA synthesis (see above), inhibition of flower formation in *Bryophyllum* by retardants would further support the idea that endogenous GA plays a crucial role in the control of flowering. Such studies, undertaken by Zeevaart and Lang,[43] showed that the flower-inducing effect of the sequence LD → SD could be completely suppressed in *B. daigremontianum* by CCC in a highly specific way. Although the plants did not produce any flower buds, vegetative growth, as measured by the number of leaf pairs produced, was not affected. CCC was applied in these experiments at 5-day intervals via the roots during exposure to 25 SD. *Bryophyllum* plants which received at least 1 g CCC in this manner remained vegetative. GA_3 reversed the flower-inhibiting effect completely when applied simultaneously with the retardant. The lowest dosage tested, i.e. 1.5 µg GA_3 per plant was fully effective, but 10 times as much GA_3 was necessary to restore full stem elongation in CCC-treated plants.

It can be concluded from these results that the growth retardant CCC suppresses flower formation and stem elongation in *Bryophyllum* by inhibiting the GA biosynthesis following the shift LD → SD. Thus, work with the growth retardant CCC supplies further evidence that endogenous GA is directly involved in the processes leading towards floral initiation.

Other work on the effect of the growth retardant phosfon D on flowering in *B. tubiflorum* is less conclusive.[17] Flowering was induced in this species in permanent SD by GA_3, and this effect was only slightly inhibited by phosfon D. This is not surprising since the GA level in SD individuals was raised by exogenous GA_3 application, and the growth retardants do not compete with GA as such.

Flower formation induced by the sequence LD → SD was inhibited somewhat by phosfon D, but never fully suppressed.[17] However, the retardant was applied as a single treatment during the natural LD in summer, whereas photoinduction due to the shortening daylength did not take place until fall. Thus, a long period of time elapsed between the phosfon treatment and actual photoinduction, undoubtedly explaining why the retardant did not inhibit flowering more actively.

When CCC was applied via the roots and GA_3 to the shoots of juvenile *B. calicynum* plants, the growth retardant did not interfere with GA_3-induced flowering. It did, however, prevent the inhibitory effects caused by an application of 150 μg GA_3 per plant.[37]

Conclusion

The interesting aspect of floral induction in *Bryophyllum* is that representatives of this genus have a dual photoperiodic requirement which can be fulfilled only if LD precedes SD.

In *B. daigremontianum* there is a borderline area around 12 hours light per day which can act both as LD and as SD. Since a relatively long dark period is essential for floral induction, it would be appropriate to indicate LSDP as SDP with a very narrow margin between the upper and lower limit of the critical photoperiod.

There is no conclusive evidence to indicate whether LD and SD affect different steps in a series of processes in the same leaf, or independent processes which may be localized in different leaves.

Various lines of evidence suggest that the LD process results in maintaining a high level of gibberellin-like substances which is essential for the SD process to proceed. This is also supported by the fact that small amounts of applied GA_3 induce completely normal flowering in SD individuals. Indications are that GA must act in the leaves rather than in the growing point.

Flower formation following the shift LD → SD, or SD + GA_3, is due to the production of a graft-transmissible stimulus which causes flower formation in both LD and SD receptors.

The juvenile phase in different species of *Bryophyllum* varies from a few months to several years. The physiological basis of the juvenile phase is the inability of the leaves to produce the floral stimulus following the shift in LD → SD. This in turn is due to the low gibberellin level in juvenile plants.

REFERENCES

[1] Allard, H. A. (1938). Complete or partial inhibition of flowering in certain plants when days are too short or too long. *J. agric. Res.* **57,** 775.

[2] Bünsow, R. und Harder, R. (1956). Blütenbilding von *Bryophyllum* durch Gibberellin. *Naturwiss.* **43,** 479.

[3] Bünsow, R. und Kruse, J. Unpublished data.

[4] Bünsow, R., Penner, J. und Harder, R. (1958). Blütenbildung bei *Bryophyllum* durch Extrakt aus Bohnensamen. *Naturwiss.* **45,** 46.

[5] Bünsow, R., Penner, J. und Harder, R. (1962). Die Wirkung der Gibberellinsäure auf die photoperiodisch bedingten Blühvorgänge bei Lang-Kurztagpflanzen. In *Eigenschaften und Wirkungen der Gibberelline*, 101. Symp. Oberhess. Ges. Natur- und Heilkunde, Naturw. Abt., Gieszen, 1960. Ed. R. Knapp. Springer-Verlag, Berlin.

[6] Catarino, F. M. (1965). Some effects of kinetin on growth, breaking of dormancy, and senescence in *Bryophyllum*. *Portug. Acta biol.* A **9,** 211.

[7] Denffer, D. von (1941). Ueber die photoperiodische Beeinfluszbarkeit von Habitus und Sukkulenz bei einigen Crassulaceeen Arten. *Jahrb. wiss. Bot.* **89,** 543.

[8] Dostál, R. (1949). On photoperiodism and correlations in *Bryophyllum crenatum*. *Rozpravy II. tr. České Akad.* **59,** 1.

[9] Dostál, R. (1950). Morphogenetic experiments with *Bryophyllum verticillatum*. *Acta Acad. Sci. Nat. Moravo-Siles.* (Brno) **22,** 57.

[10] Dostál, R. (1966). On morphogenesis in *Bryophyllum* with respect to its dual photo-periodic conditionality. *Adv. Front. Plant Sci.* **14**, 11.

[11] Esteves-de-Sousa, A. (1952). On the action of synthetic phytohormones upon the flowering stimulus of *Bryophyllum daigremontianum*. *Portug. Acta biol.* A **3**, 323.

[12] Heide, O. M. (1965). Effects of 6-benzylaminopurine and 1-naphthaleneacetic acid on the epiphyllous bud formation in *Bryophyllum*. *Planta* **67**, 281.

[13] Ketellapper, H. J. and Barbaro, A. (1966). The role of photoperiod, vernalization and gibberellic acid in floral induction in *Coreopsis grandiflora* Nutt. *Phyton* **23**, 33.

[14] Kröner, E. (1955). Experimentelle Beiträge zum Photoperiodismus der vegetativen Vermehrung der Gattung *Kalanchoë*. *Flora* **142**, 400.

[15] Linskens, H. F. und Resende, F. (1961). Beitrag zur Charakterisierung des Langtag- und Kurztag-Habitus von *Bryophyllum crenatum* Bak. *Portug. Acta biol.* A**6**, 141.

[16] Linskens, H. F. and Resende, F. (1966). About the action of temperature on the floral impulse in *Bryophyllum* (LSDP) (Preliminary note). *Portug. Acta biol.* A **9**, 305.

[17] Marcelle, R. et Sironval, C. (1964). Action du phosphon D et de la gibbérelline sur la croissance et la floraison de *Bryophyllum tubiflorum* Harv. *Physiol. vég.* **2**, 409.

[18] Michniewicz, M. and Lang, A. (1962). Effect of nine different gibberellins on stem elongation and flower formation in cold-requiring and photoperiodic plants grown under non-inductive conditions. *Planta* **58**, 549.

[19] Penner, J. (1960). Ueber den Einfluss von Gibberellin auf die photoperiodisch bed-ingten Blühvorgänge bei *Bryophyllum*. *Planta* **55**, 542.

[20] Resende, F. (1948). Suculentas Africanas. X. Auxin and the floral initiation. *Port. Acta biol.* A **2**, 250.

[21] Resende, F. (1949). Auxin and antiauxin, the hormones responsible for the change of the vegetative into floral phenotypes. *Bol. Soc. Portug. Cienc. Nat.* 2a, *Sér.* **2**, 174.

[22] Resende, F. (1950). Contribution to the physiology of development of the inflor-escence and of the single flower (*Bryophyllum* and *Kalanchoë*). *Portug. Acta biol.* A, *R. Goldschmidt-Volume*, 729.

[23] Resende, F. (1952). 'Long-short' day plants. *Portug. Acta biol.* A **3**, 318.

[24] Resende, F. (1953). Acerca do impulso floral em plantas de 'dia longo-curto' e plantas de 'dia curto-longo'. *Rev. Fac. Cienc. Lisboa* **3**, 447.

[25] Resende, F. (1954). Vegetative and flowering leaf plantlets at short daylength (*Bryo-phyllum*). *Proc. First. Intern. Photobiol. Congress, Amsterdam*, 70.

[26] Resende, F. (1955). Gradaçao floral e comportamento das PDLC na transmissão do estado floral entre 'Donor' e 'Acceptor' (*Bryophyllum* e *Kalanchoë*). *Portug. Acta biol.* A **4**, 272.

[27] Resende, F. (1956). Acerca do comportamento de *Bryophyllum daigremontianum* (PDLC) vivendo permanentemente em condições fotoperiódicas de 12h luz e 12h de escuridão. *Rev. de Biol.* **1**, 32.

[28] Resende, F. (1959). On the transmission of the 'Floral State', through grafting, from LSDP- or SDP-donors to LSDP-acceptors in LD and SD. *Portug. Acta biol.* A **6**, 1.

[29] Resende, F. (1959). Ueber die Brutknospen-Entwicklung bei *Bryophyllum* und ihre Vererbung. *Ber. deutsch. bot. Ges.* **72**, 3.

[30] Resende, F. (1964). Senescence induced by Flowering (Revision). *Portug. Acta biol.* A **8**, 248.

[31] Resende, F. (1965). Acção do frio (10-12°C) durante o escotoperiodo no impulso floral e realização da inflorescância de *Bryophyllum daigremontianum* (R. Hamet et Perr.) Berg. – PDLC. *Rev. de Biol.* **5**, 115.

[32] Resende, F. and Pereira-da-Silva, M. J. (1965). Photo- and thermoperiodism, their interaction for the phenogenesis. II. About floral impulse in two species of long-short-day plants (LSDP). *Rev. de Biol.* **5**, 203.

[33] Resende, F. and Viana, M. J. (1948). Suculentas Africanas. IX. The role played by the intensity of illumination during the development of the inflorescence of *Bryo-phyllum daigremontianum* (R. Hamet et Perr.) Berg. *Portug. Acta biol.* A **2**, 211.

[34] Resende, F. and Viana, M. J. (1959). Gibberellin and sex expression. *Portug. Acta biol.* A **6**, 77.

[35] Silva, M. H. T. da, e Resende, F. (1956). *Kalanchoë rotundifolia* (PDLC) florescendo em permanente DC pela acção de auxina (AIA). *Rev. de Biol.* **1**, 63.

[36] Skene, K. G. M. and Lang, A. (1964). Native gibberellins and flower formation in *Bryophyllum daigremontianum*. *Plant Physiol.* **39**, Suppl. XXXVII.

[37] Wadhi, M. and Mohan Ram, H. Y. (1967). Shortening the juvenile phase for flowering in *Kalanchoë pinnata* Pers. *Planta* **73**, 28.

[38] Zeevaart, J. A. D. (1958). Flower formation as studied by grafting. *Meded. Land-bouwhogeschool Wageningen* **58**(3), 1.

[39] Zeevaart, J. A. D. (1962). The juvenile phase in *Bryophyllum daigremontianum*. *Planta* **58**, 543.

[40] Zeevaart, J. A. D. (1966). Reduction of the gibberellin content of *Pharbitis* seeds by CCC and after-effects in the progeny. *Plant Physiol.* **41**, 856.

[41] Zeevaart, J. A. D. Unpublished data.

[42] Zeevaart, J. A. D. and Lang, A. (1962). The relationship between gibberellin and floral stimulus in *Bryophyllum daigremontianum*. *Planta* **58**, 531.

[43] Zeevaart, J. A. D. and Lang, A. (1963). Suppression of floral induction in *Bryophyllum daigremontianum* by a growth retardant. *Planta* **59**, 509.

22

The Nature of Flower Induction

By L. T. Evans

Some Definitions

The word induction appears in the title and on many pages of this book, in several contexts. Its usage has, perhaps, been stretched beyond useful limits. Thus, before considering the nature of flower induction as a conclusion to the preceding case histories, we might usefully examine the word itself.

In molecular biology induction refers to the *de novo* synthesis of an enzyme in the presence of a substance which is often its substrate. In embryology it refers to the process whereby one tissue can influence the developmental pathway of a neighbouring tissue. Photoperiodic induction could come under this definition except that the two tissues, the perceptive leaf and the responding shoot apex, are not adjacent. In photosynthesis induction originally referred to the phenomena occurring when plants were first moved from darkness to light. It was in this context that the term photoperiodic induction was introduced into flowering physiology by Lubimenko and Szeglova[79] in 1932, for the after-effect of a period in long or short days. They applied it to effects on growth as well as to those on reproductive development, and to both positive (accelerating) and negative (retarding) effects. The persistence of photoperiodic induction was thought to be due to changes in protoplasmic structure which were stable enough to influence the subsequent rate of development.

Moshkov[89] proposed that it was the leaves which underwent an irreversible change at photoperiodic induction, and the term was subsequently used for events in the leaf which commit plants to flowering. Induction is still used widely in that context, but it has also come to be used for events at the shoot apex following the arrival there of the floral stimulus, but before the differentiation of flowers begins. The term has also been used for the changes wrought by cold vernalization (thermoinduction).

The events in the leaf and those at the shoot apex are likely to be so different that it is neither logical nor lucid to use the one word for both. On the grounds of priority, the term photoperiodic induction should be used for the processes occurring in the leaf. Those at the shoot apex would then need to be qualified as apex induction, or given a new term. One suggested long ago by Waddington for comparable events in embryology seems appropriate: *evocation*. In the sense of calling forth memories and summoning to new energies and a higher fate, evocation is an apt term to replace shoot apex induction. It has the further advantage that Waddington has repeatedly emphasized its separation from the succeeding processes of differentiation.[132]

Terms for the substances which evoke flowering are considered in more detail later, but some distinctions are desirable at this point. I will use floral stimulus as an uncommitted term for any translocated substance which evokes flowering. The term florigen is restricted to the immediate product(s) of leaves undergoing photoperiodic induction which cause(s) evocation, the sense in which Chailahjan introduced it. Flower hormone will be used as the term for the graft-transmissible substance(s) from photoperiodically induced plants which evoke(s) flowering in non-induced receptors. Whether or not florigen and the flower hormone are identical is discussed below.

Outline of the Argument

Central to much of our thinking about floral evocation and the processes leading to it is the concept, originated thirty years ago, that there is one substance, made in the leaves and common to all higher plants, which specifically evokes flowering. This concept has had an enormous influence on our approach to the physiology of flowering. Trying to reconcile it with the variety of behaviour we have seen in the case histories causes much of the agony of flowering physiologists, and the scepticism of others. While the concept of a unique, specific floral stimulus has occasionally been queried,[18,32,55,77,78] it is still widely accepted and we can read 'The existence of florigen is so obvious from physiological experiments that its isolation and identification seem long overdue'.[144]

Reviews of the physiology of flowering often give an account of the grafting experiments which are so suggestive of a common flower hormone near their beginning and proceed with that as background, with the added assumption that the graft-transmissible flower hormone is the same as the florigen generated by the leaves during photoperiodic induction.

Here, we begin by querying the concept of specific organ-forming substances in plants, and present evidence for a broad spectrum of action by the floral stimulus, i.e. we query the specificity of floral evocation. Then we query the concept of one pathway to floral evocation by examining the evidence for evocation by a variety of environmental pathways, by application of a wide array of growth regulators, or by excision of the shoot apex or removal of inhibitory organs.

Evidence for more than one mobile floral stimulus is then considered.

All these are arguments against a unique, specific floral stimulus. The crucial grafting experiments are then discussed, and two alternatives to the florigen concept are considered; first, Chailahjan's hypothesis of complementary primary photoperiodic stimuli; then, Carr's distinction between primary florigen(s) and a secondary flower hormone.

Finally, attention is focussed on what little we know of the nature and sequence of changes at the shoot apex during evocation, as evidence that it may be controlled by age-evolving or environmentally-imposed changes in the pattern and timing of interaction at the shoot apex of a number of hormones.

Organ-forming Substances

Julius Sachs many years ago suggested that there may be specific organ-forming substances in plants, and the florigen concept is simply an extension of this idea. Indeed, Lang[68] writes of the grafting experiments, 'the results of these experiments reveal a situation ubiquitous in flowering plants, thus fully confirming ideas expressed by J. Sachs as early as 1880–1882, but for a time not accepted and even vigorously disputed by plant biologists'. The florigen concept is highly compatible with present day notions of mechanisms for the control of gene action derived from molecular biology. Florigen would specifically release from inhibition the genes controlling floral development (Zeevaart's floral genes[142]), presumably in some defined step-by-step sequence in a grand operon. Heslop-Harrison[54] has presented several models of this kind for the control of flower differentiation in plants. Among insects, the hormone ecdysone possibly acts in this way, inducing sequential activation of gene transcription, evident in the patterns of puffing and dependent on ecdysone concentration.[28,29,30]

However, no specific organ-forming inducer has yet been identified in plants. The known plant hormones – auxins, gibberellins, cytokinins, abscisin – all have an extremely wide spectrum of action, and interact quantitatively to control many responses, including differentiation. With tobacco stem callus grown *in vitro*, for example, a high auxin/cytokinin ratio leads to root formation, whereas a high cytokinin/auxin ratio results in shoot formation.[117] Auxins and cytokinins also interact in controlling the release of axillary buds from apical dominance. Auxin from the shoot apex prevents development of the axillary buds, but this inhibition can be overcome in the presence of cytokinin.[136] This interaction may have particular relevance to flower evocation, one consequence of which is the precocious development of axillary buds. Auxin concentration interacts with that of gibberellin in the differentiation of vascular tissue. High auxin favours xylem differentiation, whereas high gibberellin levels favour phloem differentiation.[33] In cultured callus of several species, both auxin and sugar are necessary for the induction and differentiation of xylem and phloem, high sucrose levels favouring phloem, low sucrose levels favouring xylem, and intermediate concentrations allowing the evocation of both, with a cambium between.[135] Similarly, abscisin interacts quantitatively with gibberellin in the control of bud dormancy in *Ribes*,[34] with auxin in the abscission of *Perilla* leaves,[34] and with cytokinins in the growth of *Lemna*[100] and the senescence of radish leaf disks.[4]

These examples suffice to indicate that the evocation, differentiation and growth of tissues and organs in plants can be controlled by the quantitative interplay of known plant hormones and assimilates. These hormones do not seem to act at the organ or tissue level, or even at the level of processes such as cell division or extension, but rather by the regulation of the synthesis of proteins, of the various kinds of RNA, and of DNA.[3,72,100,118] Merely because the known plant hormones act in this way is not sufficient reason to assume that the floral stimulus also does. But other evidence, which we now consider, leads us to question its specificity of action.

Multiple Effects of the Photoperiodic Stimulus

Daylength controls many plant responses besides flower initiation. Flower development, sex expression and breeding system may be affected by daylength, as may germination, growth rate, cambial activity, leaf shape, dormancy, senescence, and tuberization. Control of tuberization, for example, was among the earliest effects noted by Garner and Allard. It is a true photoperiodic response, light breaks preventing the evocation of aerial tubers in *Begonia evansiana*,[35] and of subterranean tubers in *Helianthus tuberosus*.[93] Moreover, the response involves substances translocated from the leaves perceiving the daylength to the responding tissue. In *Helianthus*, for example, scions of *H. annuus* can cause tuberization in stocks of *H. tuberosus* when the grafted plants are held in short days, but not in long days. Yet *H. annuus* alone forms no tubers, and its flowering is indifferent to daylength.

Are we to assume that each of these transmissible effects of daylength is caused by a specific hormone? Or that a specific hormone evokes flowering whereas the other responses are controlled by the interplay of substances whose production varies with daylength? Or are all daylength responses controlled by such interplay? The grafting experiments on tuberization in *Helianthus*[93] strongly suggest that the daylength-dependent stimulus to tuberization is non-specific since it is generated by a plant incapable of forming tubers. What of the floral stimulus?

Earlier work with *Kalanchoë*[50] suggested that the effects of daylength on flowering and on leaf shape were due to different stimuli, but in *Sedum ellacombianum* they appear to be caused by only one.[141] Lettuce seeds implanted in the petioles of *Xanthium* leaves and then wrapped in aluminium foil germinated to a far greater extent on plants in short days than on those in long days.[15,80] Thus, at least one component of the short-day stimulus translocated from *Xanthium* leaves can influence germination as well as flowering, and is therefore not highly specific in its action.

Many of the responses to daylength can be controlled by growth regulators whose level of activity is in turn controlled by daylength. Abscisin, for example, which is produced in greater amounts in short days, can cause a cessation of extension growth, the formation of resting buds, accelerated senescence of leaves, tuberization, the inhibition of flowering in long-day plants, and the promotion of flowering in several short-day plants.[34]

In many of the species treated in this book, flower evocation is particularly sensitive to daylength, flower differentiation less so. With soybean, however, normal development of the microspores requires exposure to more short days than does evocation (p. 66). The flower buds produced on *Pharbitis* plants by exposure to one short day may abort unless further short days are given, or unless the other flower buds are removed (p. 113). In *Cynosurus cristatus*, exposure to 3 long days is sufficient for the evocation of flowering, but normal inflorescence development requires at least 14 long days.[39] Flower development in peas has more exacting long-day requirements than does evocation (p. 399), and more exacting short-day requirements in *Cannabis* (p. 211) and *Chrysanthemum* (p. 275). Then there are plants, such as *Caryopteris clandonensis*,[103] which are indifferent to daylength for flower evocation, but have absolute photoperiodic requirements for flower differentiation. Such a range of behaviour suggests that flower evocation, like earlier or later steps in development, can be limited in certain plants and certain daylengths by the supply from the leaves of compounds with a broad spectrum of activity.

One of the earliest changes at floral evocation is a general activation of shoot apex metabolism. This is apparent in early increases in the number of ribosomes in the already active cells of the peripheral zone of the apex (Fig. 5–7) of the SDP *Perilla*[65] and *Pharbitis*,[53] and in increased RNA and protein synthesis in the leaf initials and summit cells of the apex of *Lolium temulentum*.[43] RNA synthesis in expanding leaves, which could hardly be regarded as a target for a highly specific floral stimulus, also increased at the time of evocation.[106]

Experiments on changes in terminal buds at that time are also suggestive of early increases in the activity of young leaves. Take, for example, the buds of *Chenopodium amaranticolor* harvested immediately after exposure to 2 short days, which showed a 7-fold increase in the specific activity of the RNA extracted from them, compared with that from vegetative plants.[133] In these buds, which had a fresh weight of about 1 mg, the shoot apex together with the youngest leaf primordium probably comprised less than 0.3 per cent of the tissue, on the basis of the structure of the *Lupinus* bud.[119] If the increase in specific activity was confined to the shoot apex, it must have been more than 2000-fold to account for the observed rise. More likely, there was a general increase in much of the tissue of the apical bud.

A temporary rise in the rate of leaf initiation occurs at about the time of floral evocation in many plants, e.g. the SDP *Perilla* (p. 149), soybean,[71] *Pharbitis*,[131] *Chenopodium amaranticolor*,[123] and *C. album*,[47] and the LDP *Spinacea* and *Trifolium*.[124] Such changes can occur even when the photoperiodic exposures are below the threshold for flower evocation, as in young plants of *Lolium temulentum*.[38] In *Cannabis*, exposure to 4 short days can affect leaf shape and serration without causing flower induction (p. 213). This pleiotropism in the early effects of evocation suggests a general increase in apical activity by the floral stimulus. In fact, the earliest steps in the development of flowers differ from those of vegetative buds more in their pace and timing than qualitatively (e.g. in *Anagallis*, p. 390).

Consider also the effect of inductive photoperiods beyond the number required for flower evocation. In *Xanthium* and in *Lolium temulentum* exposure to only one short or long day, respectively, is required for photoperiodic induction. Flowering is evoked the following day, yet exposure to additional 'inductive' days causes a progressive increase in the subsequent rate of inflorescence development. No discontinuity is apparent between the effect of the first 'inductive' day and of those subsequent to it, even those after flower initiation has begun. (Fig. 14–3). With *L. temulentum* this is true even when the additional long days are given after several intervening short days.[39] Again, such results suggest that, in both SDP and LDP, inductive photoperiods generate a general stimulus to apical activity rather than a highly specific stimulus to flower evocation.

The quantitative expression of the intensity of photoperiodic induction varies greatly between species, depending particularly on the position and structure of their inflorescences, as may be seen in the preceding chapters. The axillary flowers of *Anagallis*, like the terminal inflorescences of *Xanthium* and *Lolium*, respond to more extended induction with faster development, whereas those of *Cestrum* do not. *Cestrum*, like a great many species, responds with the formation of more flowers, whereas in *Fragaria* flower number is not a function of the intensity of induction. In soybean (SDP) and *Anagallis* (LDP) flower number increases in proportion to the number of inductive days, presumably because more axillary bud sites become competent to respond to the floral stimulus as the period of induction is extended. On return to non-inductive conditions the plants revert to the vegetative state, rapidly in soybean and *Anagallis*, more slowly in *Cannabis*. Such differences may reflect differences in the lability of the floral stimulus, or in the pattern of its translocation from the induced leaf to the competent bud.

In some plants, more extended induction increases the number of flowers by increasing the degree of branching in the inflorescence. In *Kalanchoë blossfeldiana*, for example, additional short days increase the order of branching in the dichasium, so that flower number increases logarithmically with increase in the number of short days (Fig. 9–3). Such a relation probably reflects inflorescence structure more than the kinetic nature of increase in the floral stimulus.

In some plants with axillary flowers, highly effective induction leads to the formation of a terminal flower, as in *Cestrum* and *Pharbitis*. There is, however, an interesting difference between varieties of *Pharbitis*, in that the dwarf variety Kidachi is unable to form terminal flowers (p. 93). The most extreme requirement for terminal flowering is in *Geum urbanum*, in which the axillary buds flower after normally saturating vernalization treatments whereas terminal flowers are formed only after plants are vernalized for a whole year.[27] Terminal flowers can also be evoked in species which do not normally form them by continuous removal of all axillary buds and flowers, as in *Impatiens balsamina*[91] and peas.[76] With *Impatiens* this was thought to be due to conservation of the floral stimulus, in peas to the prevention of apical senescence. In *Sinapis* and *Arabidopsis*, minimal photoperiodic induction leads to the differentiation of the terminal inflorescence, and the lateral ones are formed only after more extended long day induction.

These few examples suffice to indicate that, while there is considerable variation between plants in the mode of expression, flower evocation is a quantitative response. Earlier work, in which the criterion of flowering response was often the proportion of plants which initiated flowers, tended to emphasize the qualitative nature of evocation. We either see a flower primordium on a plant, or we do not. This all-or-none concept was compatible with that of action by a specific flower hormone. Adherents to these concepts could argue that increases in the numbers of flowers, or in the rate of their development, with more extended exposures to inductive photoperiodic conditions, are due to a direct and separate effect of these conditions on flower development. However, the great volume of recent work with plants requiring only a single inductive cycle has shown that comparable variations in rate of development or in flower number result from variations in the efficiency of a single inductive cycle. The induced state is thus a quantitative one and, as we have seen, one which has early effects on tissues which could hardly be viewed as primary targets for a highly specific flower hormone.

Flower Evocation: Alternate Environmental Pathways

Flowering in many plants is either indifferent to photoperiod or not strictly controlled by it. On the other hand, most work on the physiology of flowering has been with the minority of plants in which flower evocation is under strict photoperiodic control. While this has great experimental advantages, it may incline us to a too absolute view of the need for a specific photoperiodic stimulus to evocation. Moreover, even our most used experimental plants yield many examples of less absolute environmental control of flower evocation than might be expected. Some examples follow:

Among SDP, *Pharbitis* will flower in continuous light at low temperatures (15°C optimum) if given sucrose.[120] *Perilla* will also flower in continuous light, provided the intensity is not too high (p. 123), or in long days when the photoperiod is at a low temperature (p. 129 and Table 5–3). In *Chenopodium rubrum* flowering in continuous light will occur in certain strains if the temperature is low (15°C) or high (30°C) (Fig. 6–2), or if the proportion of phytochrome in the P_{fr} form is kept low (p. 164, Table 6–1). *Lemna perpusilla* 6746 will also flower in continuous light, in the absence of EDTA and with cupric ions present in the medium, if the temperature is below 28°C (p. 198). Strawberry plants flower in long days when the temperature is 15°C or less, or following transplanting, drought or nutritional check. *Xanthium* plants will flower in 16-hour days if part of the light period, particularly the second half, is at a low temperature,[95,140] or if plants are subjected to high CO_2 pressures after a sub-critical dark period (p. 44). Soybean plants will also flower in long days if the young, expanding leaves are continuously removed.[45,52] Another classical short-day plant, Maryland Mammoth tobacco, flowers in long days when the night temperature is low.[107]

Thus, many short-day plants can flower in long days, even in continuous light, under a variety of conditions, and particularly at low temperatures. This may suggest an equivalence of long dark periods and low temperatures, comparable to that found in several vernalizable plants, where short days may substitute for low temperature vernalization. Alternatively, a temporary stasis may be the operative factor, since drought or nutritional stress can sometimes accomplish the same result.

Long-short-day plants can also be induced to flower in long days, *Bryophyllum daigremontianum* by night temperatures of 10–12°C (p. 443), *Cestrum nocturnum* by drought, restriction of the root system, or low night temperatures (p. 428).

A number of long-day plants can form flowers in continuous darkness, e.g. *Silene armeria* (p. 355), *Pisum sativum* (p. 398), and *Vicia faba*.[36] With peas, continuous darkness was not as inhibitory as short days. *Hyoscyamus niger* plants deprived of all their leaves flowered in both short days and continuous darkness,[66] as rapidly in the latter condition as in continuous light.[69] Vernalized plants of *Raphanus sativus*,[121] *Beta vulgaris*,[44] *Spinacia oleracea*,[128] and *Trifolium subterraneum*[37] will also flower in continuous darkness as well as in long days.

As with several SDP, low night temperatures extend the range of daylengths in which a number of LDP will flower.[68] A few LDP will also flower in short days at high temperatures, such as *Bouvardia humboldtii*,[108] *Rudbeckia bicolor*,[90] and *Silene armeria* if the night temperature is above 30°C. *Silene* will even flower in short days when only the temperature of the roots is high (p. 357). Among plants requiring vernalization but indifferent to photoperiod, a comparable case is that of *Scrofularia alata*, which will flower without vernalization if grown for a period at 32°/27°C or higher.[25]

Thus, even among the minority of plants with pronounced environmental requirements for flowering, there are many examples of apparently alternative pathways to evocation. A striking example of this is *Silene armeria*, for which exposure to long days, to short days at low temperatures (5°C), to short days at high temperatures (30°C), or to GA_7, each leads to evocation. All these conditions are additive in their effects and result in effective donors for graft transmission of the flower hormone (p. 359). Either the floral stimulus can be produced by a great variety of alternative pathways, or these are the conditions in which an inhibitor is *not* produced, or a variety of conditions can lead to the particular interplay of influences at the shoot apex which is conducive to flower evocation.

Flower Evocation: Some Effects of Growth Regulators

Not long after the genesis of the florigen concept, Cholodny[22] wrote 'we must form no hasty conclusion regarding special organ forming substances . . . we must first test whether some of the already known phytohormones are endowed with the faculty to induce the physiological effect under observation'. Some examples of this faculty follow.

Among short-day plants, flowering in long days or in sub-threshold conditions has been evoked by:

sugars—in defoliated plants of *Chenopodium amaranticolor*,[77] and in *Pharbitis* at 15°C or lower.[120] In *Chenopodium rubrum*, glucose and sucrose increased the flowering response particularly with lengths of the dark period unfavourable to flowering, damping out the rhythmic response to dark period length (Chapter 6). The presence of adjuvant leaves in continuous light had a similar effect in *Xanthium*.[88]

gibberellic acid—in *Chrysanthemum morifolium*;[6] it also hastens flowering considerably in *Perilla* under suboptimal conditions (p. 142).

zeatin—in *Wolffia microscopica*.[82]

kinetin—in *Perilla* (pp. 144–145), in *Chenopodium rubrum* (p. 178), and in *Pharbitis* plants inhibited by far-red light at the beginning of a dark period or by a red break at the mid point (p. 110).

adenine—in *Perilla* (p. 145).

uracil—in *Chenopodium rubrum* (p. 178).

eosin—in *Perilla* (p. 141).

abscisin—in *Pharbitis*, *Chenopodium rubrum*, *Ribes* and *Fragaria*[34].

CCC—in strawberry[34] and *Pharbitis*.[143]

maleic hydrazide—in *Perilla* (p. 143).

TIBA—in soybeans (p. 84) and *Xanthium* (p. 46).

nicotine sulphate—in soybeans (p. 84).

mineral salts—by the iron salt of ethylene diamine-di-o-hydroxyphenyl acetic acid in *Wolffia*,[81] and by cupric ions in the absence of EDTA in *Lemna perpusilla* (p. 199).

Among the long-short-day plants, B995 can evoke flowering in *Cestrum* in long days (p. 431), whereas GA_3 can evoke flowering in *Bryophyllum* in short days, and also in photoperiods slightly longer than those critical for the short-day response (pp. 448–449). In the short-long-day plant, *Coreopsis grandiflora*, GA_3 can replace the requirement for long days.[60]

Among LDP, flowering in short day or subthreshold conditions has been evoked by application of:

auxins—in *Silene, Hyoscyamus*,[75] and *Lolium temulentum*.[41]
gibberellic acid—in at least 23 species of long day plants.[68]
furfuryl alcohol—in *Rudbeckia speciosa*.[94]
kinetin—in *Arabidopsis thaliana*.[87]
vitamin E—in *Arabidopsis*[87] and *Calendula officinalis*.[8]
sucrose—in excised shoot tips of *Sinapis alba* (Table 13–5).

Applied gibberellins can also replace the need for vernalization in at least 17 plants,[68] as can Vitamin E in *Cichorium intybus*[86] and Petkus rye.[16]

A final example is the evocation of flowering in pineapple by ethylene. Apparently, auxin-evoked flowering in this plant is mediated by the ethylene produced following auxin treatment.[17]

The previous examples have been given to emphasize the great variety of compounds whose application has resulted in flowering in non-inductive conditions. They hardly suggest control by a single limiting factor.

Consider some of the effects of applied gibberellins and their antagonists. At first it was thought that flowering in LDP and SDP was affected in opposite ways by gibberellic acid, just as it was by phytochrome in the P_{fr} form. Whereas flowering was evoked in many LDP by gibberellins, it was inhibited by them in *Kalanchoë blossfeldiana*[51] and other SDP. Now, as with phytochrome P_{fr}, the pattern of response to GA is seen to be more complex, with many similarities between SDP and LDP. While flowering is evoked in many LDP by application of GA_3, it is inhibited by GA_3 in a long-day variety of *Fuchsia hybrida*[111] and in *Proserpinaca palustris*,[31] and delayed in peas (p. 404). With the LDP *Samolus parviflorus*, in which GA_3 evokes flowering in plants in short days, application of Amo-1618 or CCC, which inhibit gibberellin biosynthesis, prevents flowering in plants exposed to long days. The more Amo applied, and the fewer the long days, the greater is the amount of GA_3 needed to restore flowering.[5] These results suggest that relatively high GA levels are necessary for the production of the floral stimulus in this LDP. However, in another LDP, *Lolium temulentum*, comparable experiments have given a quite different result. GA_3 evokes flowering in short days, but CCC has no effect on the flowering of plants exposed to only one long day, and even increases the flowering response to applied GA_3, in both long and short days (p. 341).

Among SDP, flowering in *Xanthium* was increased by GA_3 applied before the critical night length,[112] or with debudded plants retaining their young leaves.[73] Young *Perilla* plants which need exposure to 12 short days will flower after only 9 SD when treated with gibberellic acid.[105] With *Pharbitis* too, GA_3 application increased flowering under marginally inductive conditions, especially when applied just before the dark period.[99] It is not surprising, therefore, that both CCC and B995 inhibit flowering in *Pharbitis*, this inhibition being overcome by application of GA_3.[143,145] Yet CCC alone could also promote flowering in certain conditions. In this species, then, gibberellins promote, and appear essential for, evocation, yet compounds inhibiting gibberellin synthesis and action may also evoke flowering. In *Chenopodium rubrum* the picture is equally complex. Application of GA_3 can inhibit flowering, and so can inhibition of GA synthesis by treatment with CCC. GA_3 will overcome this inhibition by CCC, as will applied kinetin, which alone is inhibitory.[122]

Such results suggest it is too simple to think of gibberellin as florigen or as a precursor of florigen. Rather, it may be one component whose variations in concentration at the shoot apex, both in time and in space, interact with those of other endogenous regulators to control the evocation of flowering. That gibberellins may also be involved in the photoperiodic processes occurring in leaves is evident from a number of experiments, e.g. with *Bryophyllum* (p. 450) and *Lolium* (p. 340).

Shoot Apex Excision

While there has been relatively little work on the culture of excised shoot apices, some of it leads us to query whether flowering is evoked only by the arrival of a specific stimulus. When shoot apices of the SDP *Perilla frutescens* were cultured, explants with unfolded leaves behaved like intact plants, producing flowers in short days and remaining vegetative in long days. When stripped of their unfolded leaves, however, they initiated inflorescences not only in short but also in long days.[104]

There are no directly comparable results with long-day plants, but in *Lolium temulentum* excision of vegetative shoot apices, followed by culture in darkness, led to activation of RNA and protein synthesis at the axillary bud sites, one of the earliest events following flower evocation in intact plants.[43]

Among plants requiring chilling, a comparable result has been obtained with excised apical buds of *Iris*.[109] With intact plants, previous exposure to low temperatures (around 13°C) is required before flower initiation will occur at 25°C. Excised apical buds with part of a fleshy scale attached to them behave similarly, but apical buds with only primordial leaves attached can initiate flowers without pretreatment at 13°C. Buds without primordial leaves were slower to initiate, but GA_3 could replace the effect of the primordial leaves. Auxin, on the other hand, was very inhibitory.

These experiments all cast doubt on the existence of an absolute requirement for a specific floral stimulus in plants with well defined requirements for daylength or low temperature. They also indicate an inhibitory effect on flower evocation of young leaves in non-inductive conditions.

Photoperiodic Inhibition

Examples of inhibition of flowering under non-inductive photoperiods have been given in section 11 of many of the preceding chapters. The term inhibition has been used for several quite different phenomena, even in the purely passive sense of non-evocation of flowering. There can be an active inhibition by non-inductive daylengths, the initial effect of which is operative within the leaves exposed to the unfavourable conditions, even though the measured effect is on the flowering response; i.e. no transmissible inhibitor of evocation is involved. Photoperiodic inhibition in *Silene* is thought to act in this way (Ch. 15), but the fact that flower evocation can occur in short days when only the roots are at a high temperature (p. 357) complicates the analysis. Experiments on fractional induction, in which non-inductive photoperiods are interpolated between inductive ones, cannot, on their own, resolve whether the inhibition is transmissible or not. However, experiments of this kind with *Kalanchoë* have been interpreted on the assumption that the inhibition is operative within the leaves (Ch. 9).

There is a considerable body of evidence for inhibitory action outside the leaves held under non-inductive photoperiods. These effects could arise from two quite different causes, which are not easy to disentangle. They may be due to the export by leaves in non-inductive photoperiods of a substance inhibitory to floral evocation. Or the leaves in non-inductive conditions might interfere with translocation of the floral stimulus to the shoot apex. While this latter effect can probably be ruled out in some cases, e.g. in the SDP *Fragaria* and LDP *Lolium*, there are other cases where it may be the dominant component. In *Kalanchoë*, for example, leaves in long days were shown to be highly inhibitory to evocation, the more so the more of them and the older they were, but only if they were inserted between the leaves exposed to short days and the responding meristem. Also, the long-day leaves were most inhibitory when in the same orthostichy as the short-day leaves.[50]

These results with *Kalanchoë* have often been used to interpret the results of experiments with other plants, forcing the conclusion that a transmissible inhibitor of evocation has not been demonstrated. In the next section we consider evidence that the velocity and pattern of movement of the floral stimulus may differ between plants in very real ways, suggesting caution in the application of the *Kalanchoë* analysis to other plants.

A resolution between effects on stimulus translocation and on inhibitor production cannot be made for several defoliation experiments. The results of early experiments by Hamner and Bonner[49] on *Xanthium* plants with two branches, one in short days and one in long days, were suggestive of an inhibitory action by long days, since only half of a mature leaf could prevent flowering in the long day branch, unless young leaves were also present. However, the young and old leaves in these experiments could have exerted their influence on flowering through effects on the pattern of assimilate movement. Such effects seem unlikely to explain the inhibitory influence of long-day leaves in the experiments of Lam[63] and Searle,[113] and particularly in those of Lincoln *et al.*[74] (p. 40). In both *Perilla*[130] and a short-day variety of *Chrysanthemum*[129] flowering could be evoked in continuous light by the continuous removal of lateral shoots and young leaves. If these results are interpreted in terms of these organs competing with the shoot apex for the flow of assimilates and floral stimulus, one must further assume that the floral stimulus in these SDP can be generated in continuous light.

An interpretation of this kind has been offered by Lang[68] for the experiments of Lona,[77] in which plants of *Chenopodium amaranticolor* flowered in long days if their leaves were removed and the plants supplied with sugar. Lang suggests that the stem tissue, even in long days, produces enough florigen to cause evocation, provided leaves are not present to prevent it reaching the apex. Why the stem tissue should do in long days what the leaves cannot, and why long-day leaves should be so much more effective than short-day leaves in preventing florigen from reaching the apex, since the stem can make enough of it in both long and short days, is not clear. Lona's simpler explanation is that substance(s) inhibitory to evocation are produced by leaves in long days.

With *Pharbitis*, the experiments of Imamura[56] in which one cotyledon was exposed to a short day while the other was exposed to a long day under a variety of conditions suggest that the inhibitory effect of the cotyledon in long days was not due to its effects on the translocation of the short-day stimulus, or on the movement of assimilates, but to the production of a transmissible inhibitor. It was noted above (p. 462) that soybean plants will flower in long days if the young, expanding leaves are continuously removed. Further evidence for a long-day inhibitor in soybeans comes from experiments with dodder.[46] The dodder itself flowered on plants in short days, but not on those in long days unless their leaves were removed. When dodder was used to connect soybean plants in long days with plants in short days, the plants in long days remained vegetative, while those in short days were delayed in their flowering (p. 80). The induction of inflorescence initiation in excised apices of *Perilla* under long days by the removal of the unfolded leaves suggests that induction in long days is prevented by an inhibitory substance from these leaves, as noted above (p. 465). The inhibitory effect of pairs of long-day leaves on plants undergoing short-day induction, in both *P. crispa*[13] and *P. ocymoides*,[7] supports this interpretation.

Fragaria provides some of the clearest evidence for a transmissible long-day inhibitor of evocation in SDP, in the acceleration of flowering in mother plants in short days by defoliation of connected daughter plants in long days (p. 256). Another SDP in which there is evidence for the transmissibility of the long-day inhibition to evocation is *Rottboellia exaltata*.[40]

Among LDP, the evocation of flowering in *Hyoscyamus* plants in short days following removal of the leaves[66] is most simply interpreted in terms of inhibitor export by the short-day leaves, but other interpretations can be made.[67] Similarly, the experiments of Withrow *et al*.[137] with spinach plants, in which the lower leaves in short days inhibited the flowering response to upper leaves in long days, suggest action by a short-day inhibitor of evocation in this LDP. The strongest evidence for the export of such an inhibitor from leaves in short days comes from experiments with *Lolium temulentum* (pp. 336–337). In this plant there is also evidence for the export of a floral stimulus from long-day leaves, and therefore of a dual response to daylength.

A dual response to daylength is also evident in LSDP and SLDP, but with these it is not yet clear whether both the short and long-day processes result in transmissible products. With *Cestrum*, the fact that the long and short days must be given successively to the same leaves argues against the long-day processes resulting in a transmissible product (p. 430). A similar conclusion was at first drawn from the work with *Bryophyllum daigremontianum*, but this can still be questioned (Chapter 21). With SLDP such as rye, *Scabiosa succisa*[23] or *Campanula medium*,[134] the requirement for prolonged short-day treatment precludes investigation of whether the preliminary short days act via a transmissible product. Since short days can be replaced for *Scabiosa succisa* by vernalization at low temperatures, which presumably acts at the shoot apex, the product of the short days may likewise act at the shoot apex. Further work with a plant such as *Trifolium repens*, certain clones of which require only 3 short days followed by 1 long day for induction,[125] could clarify whether the long and short days produce independent transmissible stimuli.

On balance, the evidence is suggestive that, in SDP, LDP and plants with dual photoperiod requirements, daylength controls the production in leaves of more than one transmissible substance with a controlling influence on flower evocation. Which of these limits evocation depends on the plant and on the conditions in which it is grown. In some plants, such as *Kalanchoë* and *Xanthium*, the requirement for a positive stimulus may be dominant. In others, such as *Lolium*, the promotive and inhibitory effects may be balanced, while in others, such as the strawberry, the inhibitory effects may be dominant and limiting.

The almost unassimilable complexities of phytochrome action on flowering will not be discussed in this chapter, but some of them might be resolvable if we consider that daylength, and phytochrome-P_{fr} level and action, may control the production of more than one key substance, and that these may have different rhythms of synthesis and different P_{fr} requirements.

Finally, the point should be made that there is no need to assume that the photoperiodic inhibitor specifically inhibits flower evocation, or that there is only one such substance. A compound which inhibits evocation in one plant or condition, as abscisin does in *Lolium* plants exposed to long days (p. 337), may evoke flowering in another situation, as abscisin does in several SDP in long days (p. 463).

Evidence of More than One Stimulus to Flowering

Velocity and pattern of translocation

In one LDP, *Lolium temulentum*, several kinds of evidence indicate that the floral stimulus, or at least its slowest-moving component, is translocated at about 2 cm/hr and independently of assimilate movement (p. 339). On the other hand, in the SDP *Pharbitis nil*, the velocity of movement of the stimulus is much higher, up to 50 cm/hr (p. 108). We have confirmed the higher velocity of the *Pharbitis* stimulus, and shown it to be comparable to that of simultaneously translocated assimilates.[61] Thus, both the velocity and the mechanism of translocation of the floral stimulus may differ between LDP and SDP.

Grafting experiments with tobacco plants also suggest a difference in the mechanism of translocation of the stimulus in LDP and SDP. The stimulus generated by the LDP *Nicotiana sylvestris* in long days can move either acropetally into scions or basipetally into stocks of the SDP Maryland Mammoth, and can do so even in the presence of leaves on receptor stocks. The SD stimulus from Maryland Mammoth donors, on the other hand, caused flowering in *N. sylvestris* receptors only when the latter were defoliated.[141] In *Perilla* too, acropetal movement of the floral stimulus is apparently inhibited by the presence of leaves on the scion (Table 5–5), while there is evidence that acropetal movement of the substance (inhibitor) from leaves in long days is not reduced by the presence of other leaves nearer the shoot apex (p. 128).

Florigenic extracts

Not only may the floral stimuli of LDP and SDP be different, but each may be comprised of more than one active component. The evidence at the moment is very slender. Flower-evoking activity of extracts of both *Xanthium* and sunflower appears to occur both in the ether and water-soluble acidic fraction and in the water soluble–ether insoluble neutral fraction.[85] This result could be due either to inadequate separation techniques, or to there being more than one active component. Similarly, while a crude chloroform extract of flowering chrysanthemum plants did not cause any flowering in *Xanthium* and chrysanthemum plants under non-inductive conditions, three of eight fractions of the crude extract caused some flower initiation in *Xanthium*, and two of them in *Chrysanthemum*.[14] The fact that the crude extract caused no initiation suggests that, besides the active fractions, it might also contain an inhibitor of evocation. The presence of several active components could explain why the florigenic activity of such extracts appears to be lost on further purification, which would preclude any synergism.

A possibly relevant observation is that 5FU can act at the shoot apex to inhibit evocation in *Xanthium* before the floral stimulus is exported from the leaves (p. 49). It could do this by inhibiting some necessary preparatory process. Alternatively, since defoliation treatments tell us only when the slowest component of the floral stimulus is being exported, the 5-FU could be inhibiting the action at the apex of a faster moving product of photoperiodic induction.

There are no comparable results from florigenic extracts of LDP. A number of LDP, e.g. *Anagallis* and *Brassica*, require high light intensities throughout the photoperiod for long days to have their maximal inductive effect, suggesting that evocation requires a continuing supply of energy substrates to the shoot apex concurrent with the supply of the photoperiodic stimulus (cf. pp. 369 and 385). In *Sinapis*, exposure to a single 12-hour day is sufficient to release the meristematic cells from the G_2 phase, one of the components of evocation,[12] although a longer photoperiod is required to initiate flowering (Fig. 13–3). Either there is one LD stimulus, with different threshold levels for release from G_2 and for evocation, or there is more than one component of the long-day stimulus.

Grafting Experiments

The tenor of the preceding sections has been that flowering, like many other plant responses, may be controlled by the interplay of a number of endogenous growth regulators, none uniquely concerned with the evocation of flowering. The concept of one substance specifically evoking flowering arose from grafting experiments, which should now be considered. Lang[68] has reviewed these comprehensively, and has listed the many examples of successful transfers of the floral stimulus from induced donors to non-induced receptors of the same photoperiod response type, and to receptors of a different response type. It is these latter successes which are most suggestive of the existence of a universal flower hormone. For example, short-day species of *Kalanchoë* have evoked flowering in LDP *Sedum* species in short days, and in LSDP such as *Bryophyllum* species in either long or short days. Flowering in SDP Maryland Mammoth tobacco in long days has been evoked by the LDP *Nicotiana sylvestris* and *Hyoscyamus niger*, and by some day neutral varieties of *Nicotiana tabacum*, as donors. Similarly, flowering in the LDP *Hyoscyamus niger* and *Nicotiana sylvestris* in short days has been evoked by grafting to Maryland Mammoth donors in short days. With four of these cases of successful graft transmission of the floral stimulus between different photo-period response types it has also been shown that receptors were evoked only when the donors were in inductive conditions. These are the four crucial examples that have to be accounted for by any alternative to the florigen hypothesis.

Against them we have to place a few unsuccessful attempts to transfer the floral stimulus. As is often the fate of apparently negative results, fewer may have been reported than have occurred in spite of adequate techniques. In *Cestrum*, there is clear failure of transfer between species even though intergrafts of *C. nocturnum* did not prevent translocation of the stimulus from donor to receptor *C. diurnum* (p. 430). There is a similar failure of transfer from *Phaseolus* to soybean (p. 83) and from *Perilla* to several other plants (p. 141). In tobacco, the day neutral variety of *N. tabacum*, Delcrest, could evoke flowering in defoliated receptors of LDP *N. sylvestris* in short days, but not in defoliated receptors of SDP Maryland Mammoth in long days.[141] If there is only one flower hormone and it is graft transmissible to *N. sylvestris*, it should also be graft transmissible to Maryland Mammoth, especially to defoliated scions. Another very interesting case, mentioned by Carr,[18] is the ability of leaves of *Sedum* (LDP) plants transferred to short days to evoke flowering in *Kalanchoë* plants, but not in their own shoot apices. Again, if there is only one flower hormone the *Sedum* apex should have been induced.

Complementary Photoperiodic Stimuli

Besides the florigen hypothesis, two other explanations of the grafting experiments have been put forward. One has been developed particularly by Chailahjan,[20] the originator of the florigen hypothesis. The usual fate of such originators is to be left defending their hypothesis when others wish to drop it, but such is the contrary nature of flowering physiology that the originators of both vernalin and florigen wish to drop them when others want to preserve them. What Chailahjan wishes to change is the concept of florigen as one universal substance. Rather, he now proposes that the primary photoperiodic stimulus may consist of two complementary groups of substances. One of these (the gibberellins) is more limiting in short-day conditions, particularly in LDP, while the other (the anthesins) is more limiting in long-day conditions, particularly in SDP.

Lang[67] considered this possiblity in 1952 and rejected it on the grounds that donors of one photoperiod response type should evoke flowering in receptors of the other type even when the donor was in non-inductive conditions. Few such grafts have been examined, since they are awkward to set up, and most have given negative results. However, both Lang[67] and Zeevaart[141] have found that vegetative Maryland Mammoth tobacco (SDP) in long days could evoke some flowering in defoliated scions of *Nicotiana sylvestris* (LDP). Eighteen out of thirty-seven such scions flowered in Zeevaart's experiments, although ungrafted and comparably defoliated plants of *N. sylvestris* remained vegetative in long days. Vegetative Maryland Mammoth stocks in long days also evoked some flowering in unvernalized biennial *Hyoscyamus niger* scions.[67] Yet another case is that quoted by Carr[18] of leaves of the LDP *Sedum* being unable to support flowering in defoliated scions of *Sedum* when returned to short days, but still able to cause flowering in the SDP *Kalanchoë*.

Considering how few of these grafts have been examined, these results suggest that Lang's rejection of complementary action may have been premature. Extraction experiments may support this conclusion. For example, extracts of vegetative *Perilla* and Maryland Mammoth plants grown in long days could evoke flowering in *Rudbeckia* (LDP) in short days.[21]

Moreover, while Chailahjan originally thought in terms of two complementary substances, he subsequently broadened his concept to two groups of substances. Flowering in LDP was favoured by high sugars, auxins, and gibberellins, and by a low content of nitrogenous compounds, while that in SDP was favoured by a prevalence of nitrogen compounds and nucleic acid metabolites, and by lower sugar levels. While we may argue about the composition of these groups of substances, which hark back to Klebs and Kraus and Kraybill, the point is that not only is the concept of complementary factors still viable, but the broadening of their composition to include a number of components makes a failure of reciprocal grafts in non-inductive conditions a less critical test of Chailahjan's hypothesis.

Different Primary Stimuli, a Common Secondary One

Carr[18] has developed an alternative hypothesis on the basis that 'we cannot assume that the substances which cause a grafted receptor plant to flower are the same as those which caused the donor to flower in the first place'. He goes on to suggest that the term florigen should be reserved for the diffusible, labile immediate products of photoperiodic induction of the leaf, which may differ from plant to plant, as Chailahjan supposes. These may be quite different from the 'contagiously-propagated change' transmitted by grafting from plants already evoked to flower, or from secondarily induced leaves, which he calls the flower hormone. As evidence of such secondary induction Carr cites his experiments with *Xanthium* in which the leaf, after exporting the product of the long dark period, was temporarily incompetent as a donor, but regained that competence if attached to the parent plant while it was coming into flower, and then remained an effective donor. If the movement of the graft-transmissible flower hormone is as dependent on the pattern of assimilate movement as it often appears to be, it is difficult to see how it could move from the shoot apex, past young leaves, to the old donor leaf. It is clear, however, that young leaves of *Xanthium*, as they enlarge, can become secondarily induced in the presence of older, previously induced leaves (p. 46). This phenomenon of secondary induction occurs also in *Silene* (even in defoliated plants (p. 360)) and in *Bryophyllum* (p. 445).

In *Xanthium*, detached, expanding leaves can be photoperiodically induced.[141] However, in plants with all buds removed before exposure to short days, the presence of the flowering stimulus could be demonstrated by graft transmission only if young leaves were also present on the donor during short-day treatment. This effect of the young leaves was greatly enhanced by treatment with GA_3, but GA_3 could not replace the requirement for the young leaves.[73] The young leaves (or possibly meristematic tissue) were required for either the storage or the conversion of the primary photoperiodic stimulus, or for the supply of another essential component of the stimulus to flowering. Whatever their function, it

sed by 250
vith tran-
P) the
t in

presumably occurred in detached, *expanding* leaves but not in mature leaves of *Xanthium*. Apparently, the primary photoperiodic stimulus requires interaction with meristematic tissue (not necessarily at the shoot apex) for stabilization as a graft-transmissible hormone.

The situation is rather different in *Perilla*. Excised *mature* leaves can be permanently induced in the absence of any attached bud or meristematic tissue (p. 137), and young leaves which expand after the short-day treatment is completed are not secondarily induced, even though the induced leaf continues to function as an effective donor of the floral stimulus in grafting experiments (p. 139). If only half of the leaf is exposed to SD, not even the other half can function as an effective donor in grafting experiments (p. 139).

Superficially, these experiments with *Perilla* do not support the generality of Carr's hypothesis. However, other *Perilla* experiments may support his central proposition of a difference between the immediate photoperiodic product, florigen, and the graft-transmissible flower hormone. To evoke flowering in *Perilla*, exposure to about 8 SD is required, depending on age and variety (p. 122). The experiments of Zhdanova (p. 132) suggest, however, that the primary photoperiodic stimulus moves out of the leaves each day (or at least every 2 days), and that its summation occurs at the shoot apex, as it does also in the LDP *Rudbeckia*. A comparable conclusion was reached for the primary photoperiodic stimulus in the SDP *Rottboellia exaltata*.[40] Zhdanova's experiments further show that floral evocation depends not so much on the amount of stimulus received at the apex as on the period over which it is received, which must be at least 8 days. Floral evocation may therefore be assumed to occur on about the 9th day, yet leaves require exposure to a minimum of 14 SD (and optimally a month in SD) before they can function as effective graft donors of the flower hormone (p. 138). While the length of the period of photoperiodic induction and the time of removal of the induced leaves are not entirely clear from the original description[146] of Zhdanova's critical experiments, such results strongly suggest that permanent photoperiodic induction of *Perilla* leaves occurs after floral evocation. An important difference from Carr's hypothesis, however, is that secondary induction in *Perilla* appears to be independent of floral evocation since it can occur in excised leaves. This can happen in *Xanthium* too, and some of the differences in flowering behaviour between the two plants, such as vegetative reversion in *Perilla* in spite of the presence of a permanently induced leaf, may be due more to differences in translocation patterns than to differences in the nature of induction and evocation.

Carr's hypothesis is flexible enough to explain many of the difficulties with the original florigen hypothesis which have been outlined above. However, there is little evidence of secondary induction in the flowering behaviour of plants such as soybean, *Cannabis* and *Anagallis*, although graft-transmission of a floral stimulus has been shown to occur in both soybean and *Cannabis*.

What may be a powerful example of secondary induction is the gradient in the ability of stem segments from tobacco plants to form flowers *in vitro*. Segments from vegetative plants, or from proximal regions of flowering plants, form only vegetative buds, but with progressively more distal segments, more flower buds are formed, segments close to the inflorescence giving rise directly to flowers with small or no bracts.[2,24] This gradient is evident only in varieties with no absolute photoperiod requirements, and not in either the SDP Maryland Mammoth or the LDP *N. sylvestris*.[1] An observation by Haupt (p. 406) may be very relevant at this point. In peas, the photoperiodically-induced determination of flowering is reversible and not graft-transmissible, whereas autonomous determination (with age) is irreversible and graft-transmissible. If the secondary flower hormone, generated with age in peas and in the non-photoperiodic tobacco plants, is responsible for the gradient in flower-forming ability, plants induced to flower by photoperiodic treatment will not reveal such gradients until autonomous or secondary induction has occurred.

The Site of Floral Evocation

The preceding arguments can be summarized as follows. Inductive photoperiodic conditions lead to the export from leaves of floral stimuli which may differ between plants. Non-inductive conditions can lead to the export of inhibitors of flower evocation, whose production is also under photoperiodic control. Besides these primary photoperiodic stimuli there may also be produced a more stable, and possibly more universal, graft-transmissible flower hormone. This can be generated, independently of floral evocation, by extended photoperiodic induction of leaves (*Perilla*), or by secondary induction of young leaves (*Xanthium*) or defoliated stems (*Silene*), or simply with increasing age (peas). There is thus a multiplicity of floral stimuli, and what is a positive stimulus to floral evocation in one plant or condition may be inhibitory to it in another, as are the gibberellins and abscisin. This suggests that the alternative environmental pathways to floral evocation arise because it is controlled by interactions between a number of photoperiodic hormones, just as root or shoot initiation depends on relative auxin/cytokinin concentrations. The likely site of these interactions is the shoot apex, and the interactions may be both spatial and temporal. Unfortunately, we know far too little about shoot apex metabolism to formulate a coherent theory of floral evocation.

Spatial interactions

That marked morphogenetic gradients exist at the site of evocation can be deduced from the effect of single leaf induction in *Kalanchoë* (Fig. 9–2), and from the phenomenon of one-sided evocation in *Perilla* (p. 135). Such phenomena indicate the strong effect of vascular pattern and connections on evocation.

Fully expanded leaves, besides supplying the floral stimulus in some plants (e.g. *Lolium* and *Perilla*) may, depending on their position, also supply assimilates to the apex throughout the period of high intensity light, and for some hours afterwards. In short days they may also supply abscisin to the apex. In *Hyoscyamus* they can influence mitotic activity at the shoot apex, and the degree of orientation of the mitotic spindles following treatment with GA_3.[70,92] They may also inhibit floral evocation in their axillary buds, as in *Cestrum* where basal axillary inflorescences are formed only when the leaves abscise (p. 425).

Expanding leaves, a source of auxins, gibberellins and probably other hormones, also exert a powerful influence on the shoot apex. As noted above, their removal under non-inductive conditions can lead to flowering in soybean, *Perilla* and *Chrysanthemum*, and in the LDP *Scrofularia arguta*.[26] In tomatoes their removal increased the rate of apical enlargement (p. 414). Experiments with TIBA suggest that at least part of the inhibitory effect of expanding leaves is due to their export of auxin. TIBA inhibits auxin transport and promotes flower initiation in tomatoes, but only if young leaves are present on the plant; when these are removed, TIBA is inhibitory to flowering.[139] Treatment of tomatoes with the most effective inhibitors of auxin transport can even result in flower initiation at the cotyledonary node (p. 418). With soybeans too, in which the young leaves are inhibitory to flowering, applications of TIBA can increase the flowering response (p. 84).

The role of roots in flower evocation is not clear. Roots are not necessary for evocation in *Perilla* (p. 137), in *Lolium* (p. 344), and possibly in the LDP *Rudbeckia bicolor*.[19] In tomatoes, more flowers are formed if the roots are at low

s, an effect which is graft-transmissible (p. 416). In *Silene*, on the
, high root temperatures evoke flowering in short days (p. 357). Roots
o generate substances, possibly gibberellins or cytokinins, which can in-
ce flower evocation at the shoot apex in some circumstances.

Besides the gradients at the shoot apex imposed by young and old leaves, there
are also gradients imposed by the shoot meristem itself, from which auxins, cytokinins and other endogenous hormones may diffuse. Destruction of the meristem
in *Phaseolus* leads to shoot initiation from cells which would normally have given
rise to the next leaf primordium.[102] Comparable results had previously been obtained in ferns, with incisions isolating the terminal meristem. They suggest that
the kind of organ initiated at the shoot apex is determined by gradients set up by
the pattern of supply of hormones and assimilates. This example is of real relevance to flower induction, the consequence of which is, in essence, the precocious
initiation of axillary buds (cf. pp. 160, 229, 345, 382). In *Pharbitis* photoperiodic
induction leads to an early acceleration of axillary bud development, even at
positions where flower initiation does not occur.[131] In *Chrysanthemum*, removal
of the shoot apex leads to flowering of the laterals (p. 273). Destruction of the
terminal meristem in *Geum urbanum* resulted in rapid flower initiation in unvernalized plants,[126] an effect which could be mimicked to some extent by the application of kinetin.

Precocious development at the axillary bud sites is, in a way, an unexpected
result of floral evocation, which also leads to an early rise in the activity of the
terminal meristem and could therefore be expected to increase apical dominance.
This emphasizes the marked changes in correlative effects which must occur in
the evoked shoot apex.

The most striking change in the pattern of activity in evoked dicotyledonous
shoot apices is activation of the cells of the central zone, at the very summit of
the apex (Fig. 5–7). In the vegetative apex these cells have thicker walls, a much
lower mitotic index, and a lower RNA and ribosome content than the cells of the
surrounding peripheral zone, which periodically give rise to the leaf primordia.[10,96] Soon after evocation there is a marked increase in the ^{3}H-thymidine-
labelling and mitotic activity of the cells of the central zone, and in nucleolar size,
pyroninophilia, and ribosome number.[11,53,65] While there is no inactive central
zone in the vegetative shoot apex of *Lolium*, the repressed axillary bud sites are
comparable, and also show an early rise in activity at evocation.[43] However, activation of the central zone also occurs in a number of dicotyledonous plants when
held for a long period in non-inductive conditions, e.g. in the LDP *Aster sinen-
sis*,[64] *Sinapis alba*,[9] *Rudbeckia bicolor*,[58] and *Hyoscyamus niger*,[114] in the
vernalization-requiring *Geum urbanum*,[126] and in the SDP *Chenopodium album*,[48]
Perilla nankinensis,[97] and *Amaranthus retroflexus*.[98] Shoot apex structure in
Cannabis also passes to the intermediate stage in continuous light, correlated with
the shift to a spiral phyllotaxis and the evocation of abortive flower primordia.
When plants exposed to a short day episode revert to vegetative growth in long
days, their apex structure reverts to the intermediate stage (p. 223).

Many plants, e.g. *Kalanchoë*, *Perilla* and *Lolium*, require exposure to progressively fewer inductive photocycles as they age. The progressive activation of
the central zone with age might account for this increasing sensitivity to photoperiodic induction. However, this does not seem to be the case in *Perilla* (p. 149),
and in both *Bryophyllum* (p. 439) and *Lolium* (p. 332) juvenile insensitivity is associated with the response of leaf rather than of apex.

Activation of the central zone does not, alone, lead to flower initiation. A less
dramatic, but perhaps more characteristic, early change in evoked apices is an increase in the activity of the already active peripheral zone (Fig. 5–7). In *Sinapis*

alba (LDP) the proportion of nuclei labelled with ³H-thymidine incre̶a̶
per cent in the central zone, and by 116 per cent in the peripheral zone,
sition from the vegetative to the prefloral state. In *Perilla nankinensis* (SD
proportion increased by 103 per cent in the central zone, and by 25 per ce
the peripheral zone.[11] In this species, over the same interval, the number of ribosomes increased by 105 per cent in the central zone, and by 25 per cent in the
peripheral zone.[65] In *Pharbitis* over a similar interval, the number of ribosomes
in the central zone increased by 117 per cent, while that in the peripheral zone
increased by 30 per cent.[53] Similarly, in *Lolium temulentum* at the time of evocation RNA synthesis increased by 184 per cent at the axillary bud sites, and by 43
per cent at the already active summit.[43]

As a result of these changes, a meristematic mantle covers the entire shoot
apex. One could imagine that this elimination of the vegetative zonation of activity is a necessary prelude to the imposition of the new, floral geometry, like
a child cleaning her slate before making a new drawing. However, the meristematic mantle is not as uniform in activity as, superficially, it appears. The
changes that occur at evocation suggest more a progressive redistribution of activity in the shoot apex than a wholly new geometry.

As might be expected from the variety of response to environment and applied
growth substances, the morphogenetic field which permits flower evocation may
be reached in a number of ways. An example is the formation of flower buds
directly on excised segments of flowering stems of some tobacco varieties.[2] A
more striking example, is the formation of such flowers on excised segments of
the root of *Cichorium intybus*. Earlier work[101] suggested that flowers were produced only by explants from vernalized roots. However, with larger explants and
higher sugar levels in the medium flowers could be evoked in the absence of vernalization.[84] There was an interaction between the sugar level and the level of
nitrate, and it was also found that the degree of hydration of the medium had a
major influence on whether or not flowers were evoked.[83] Thus, whereas flowering
of the intact plant only occurs in certain environmental conditions, it can be induced directly on tissue which normally would never bear flowers by an apparently fortuitous interaction of a number of factors.

Interactions in time

These may be considered on three scales, in terms of weeks, of days, and of
hours. Many plants require more the passage of time than specific environmental
conditions for flowering to be evoked. This is Haupt's autonomous determination (p. 405). Progress towards evocation appears to be progressive, at least in
heteroblastic plants such as *Cannabis* (Fig. 8–3), strawberry,[115] and *Vicia faba*.[36]
In *Vicia*, for example, leaf form changes progressively at a rate determined by
both daylength and temperature, and flower evocation always coincides with the
reaching of a particular leaf form. In *Cannabis* and in *Sinapis*,[10] there is some
evidence that the progressive change in leaf form reflects changing apical organization, and therefore that flowering may be evoked by changing apical correlations.

Plants which require exposure to several inductive photocycles also yield evidence of changing reactions during the course of evocation. This is particularly
evident in the marked effect that the time at which long days are interpolated in
an inductive sequence of SD has on the flowering response. In *Perilla crispa* and
Salvia occidentalis, for example, long days were most inhibitory when interpolated
just before plants had been exposed to the minimum number of SD required for
evocation (p. 127). The same was true for *Rottboellia* whether the long day was
interpolated or given to lower leaves while an upper one was in short days.[40] On

the other hand, long days interpolated between the first two SD, or given to lower leaves while an upper one received its second short day, increased the flowering response. Optimum evocation in this SDP thus requires a changing balance in the products of long and short-day leaves. Even *Xanthium* may show a similar, but less marked, trend.[113] In LSDP such as *Bryophyllum* this trend is still further developed.

Flowering in several SDP can be evoked by a temporary stress to growth – by drought, transplanting, nutrient stress, low temperatures, or the application of growth retardants or abscisin. It seems quite possible that a comparable stress is one component of short day induction in these plants, the stress being relieved on return to long days, or by adaptation to short-day conditions. A comment by Ursprung[127] is of interest in this context, namely, that unequal cell divisions can occur only when mitosis in the neighbouring tissue has come to a halt. Such unequal cell divisions could well be a necessary component of flower initiation in some plants.

Short term, hourly, changes in metabolic activity at the apex are little known, but likely. They can be very marked in other organs.[62] Incorporation of RNA and protein precursors by shoot apices of *Lolium* varied with time of day, and suggested that the rhythms of protein and RNA synthesis might be different.[42,106] The effect evoked by the floral stimulus could well depend on when it reached the apex in relation to the rhythms of synthetic activity. This would particularly be so where several substances under photoperiodic control are being exported by the leaves, and moving at different velocities. The apparent lability of the floral stimulus in some conditions may simply reflect the need for close synchronization of a number of apical processes if flowering is to be evoked. The sharp time-dependence for the inhibitory effect of some metabolic inhibitors, such as actinomycin in *Lolium* (Fig. 14–7), and thiouracil in *Sinapis* (Fig. 13–5), may arise from a similar cause. These show not only that RNA synthesis at the apex is an essential component of evocation, but that it must occur at a particular time, possibly in synchrony with other events. Similarly, the marked effect of time of application of growth regulators on flower evocation may also reflect the need for synchronization of several processes. Applied GA_3, for example, shows an approximate 24-hour periodicity in its effect on flowering in *Lolium* plants exposed to one long day.[41] The lack of effect from applications at other times, even only 3 hours earlier or later, may not be due to lability but rather to incorrect synchronization. Application of GA_3 is known to cause a persistent synchronization of cell divisions in shoot apices of *Samolus*[110] and *Rudbeckia*,[59] Cytokinin application may also result in synchronization of cell division, in callus tissue.[138]

It will be only too obvious by now that while there may be strong arguments for proceeding beyond the attractive but inadequate simplicity of the florigen hypothesis, we are by no means in a position to formulate a coherent alternative. To assert that flowering is evoked by the spatial pattern and temporal sequence of interaction at the shoot apex of endogenous hormones not specifically concerned with flowering is not enough. However, our insight into the localization and sequence of events during evocation is increasing, and may soon allow us to formulate hypotheses more commensurate with the complexity, and the fascination, of the processes of flower induction and evocation.

REFERENCES

[1] Aghion, D. (1962). Conditions expérimentales conduisant à l'initiation et au développement de fleurs à partir de la culture stérile de fragments de tige de Tabac. *C. R. Acad. Sci.* (*Paris*) **255**, 993.

[2] Aghion-Prat, D. (1965). Néoformation de fleurs *in vitro* chez *Nicotiana tabacum*. *Physiol. Veget.* **3**, 229.

[3] Armstrong, D. J. (1966). Hypothesis concerning the mechanism of auxin action. *Proc. Natl. Acad. Sci.* **56**, 64.

[4] Aspinall, D., Paleg, L. G., and Addicott, F. T. (1967). Abscisin II and some hormone-regulated plant responses. *Aust. J. Biol. Sci.* **20**, 869.

[5] Baldev, B. and Lang, A. (1965). Control of flower formation by growth retardants and gibberellin in *Samolus parviflorus*, a long day plant. *Amer. J. Bot.* **52**, 408.

[6] Barbat, I. and Ochesanu, C. (1964). The action of gibberellin A$_3$ on *Chrysanthemum morifolium* in non-inductive photoperiodic conditions. *Naturwiss.* **51**, 316.

[7] Barbat, I. and Ochesanu, C. (1965). The nature of the photoperiodical induction. The presence of a flowering hormone or a flowering inhibitor. *Naturwiss.* **52**, 458.

[8] Baszynski, T. (1967). The effect of vitamin E on flower initiation in *Calendula officinalis* L. grown in short day. *Naturwiss.* **54**, 339.

[9] Bernier, G. (1962). Evolution of the apical meristem of *Sinapis alba* L. (long day plant) in long days, in short days, and during the transfer from short days to long days. *Caryologia* **15**, 303.

[10] Bernier, G. (1966). The morphogenetic role of the apical meristem in higher plants. In *Les Phytohormones et L'Organogenèse*, 151. Univ. Liège.

[11] Bernier, G. (1966). Evolution of nucleic acid metabolism during the ontogenetic development of apical meristems. In *Differentiation of apical meristems and some problems of ecological regulation of development of plants*, 151. Academia Praha.

[12] Bernier, G., Kinet, J. M. and Bronchart, R. (1967). Sudden release of the meristematic cells from G$_2$ as an associate effect of flower induction in *Sinapis. Plant Physiol.* **42**, S–21.

[13] Bhargava, S. C. (1965). A transmissible flower bud inhibitor in *Perilla crispa. Proc. Koninkl. Nederl. Akad. Wetensch. Ser. C.*, **68**, 63.

[14] Biswas, P. K., Paul, K. B. and Henderson, J. H. M. (1966). Effect of chrysanthemum plant extract on flower initiation in short day plants. *Physiol. Plantar.* **19**, 875.

[15] Bogorad, L. and McIlrath, W. J. (1959). A correlation of photoperiodic response of *Xanthium* and germination of implanted lettuce seed. In *Photoperiodism*, 301. Ed. R. B. Withrow, A.A.A.S. Washington, D.C.

[16] Bruinsma, J. and Patil, S. S. (1963). The effects of 3-indoleacetic acid, gibberellic acid, and vitamin E on flower initiation in unvernalized Petkus winter rye plants. *Naturwiss.* **50**, 505.

[17] Burg, S. P. and Burg, E. A. (1966). Auxin-induced ethylene formation: its relation to flowering in the pineapple (*Ananas sativus*) *Science* **152**, 1269.

[18] Carr, D. J. (1967). The relationship between florigen and the flower hormones. *New York Acad. Sci. Ann.* **144**, 305.

[19] Chailahjan, M. K. (1961). Photoperiodic sensitivity of plants deprived of stems and roots. *Dokl. Akad. Nauk. S.S.S.R. Bot. Sci. Transl.* **135**, (1–6) 249.

[20] Chailahjan, M. K. (1961). Principles of ontogenesis and physiology of flowering in higher plants. *Can. J. Bot.* **39**, 1817.

[21] Chailahjan, M. K. and Loznikova, V. N. (1959). The influence of gibberellin-like substances, extracted from the leaves of various plants, on the growth and flowering of *Rudbeckia. Dokl. Akad. Nauk. S.S.S.R.* **128**, 1309.

[22] Cholodny, N. G. (1939). The internal factors of flowering. *Herb. Rev.* **7**, 223.

[23] Chouard, P. (1957). La journée courte ou l'acide gibberellique comme succédanés du froid pour la vernalization d'une plante vivace en rosette, le *Scabiosa succisa* L. *C. R. Acad. Sci.* (*Paris*) **245**, 2520.

[24] Chouard, P. and Aghion, D. (1961). Modalités de la formation de bourgeons floraux sur des cultures de segments de tige de Tabac. *C. R. Acad. Sci.* (*Paris*) **252**, 3864.

[25] Chouard, P. and Larrieu, C. (1964). Un nouveau type de vernalisation exigeant le froid ou le chaud, présenté par une plante vivace, *Scrofularia alata* Gilib. *C. R. Acad. Sci.* (*Paris*) **259**, 2121.

[26] Chouard, P. and Lourtioux, A. (1959). Correlations et reversions de croissance et de mise à fleurs chez la plante amphicarpique *Scrofularia arguta* Sol. *C. R. Acad. Sci.* (*Paris*) **249**, 889.

[27] Chouard, P. and Tran Thanh Van, M. (1962). Nouvelles récherches sur l'analyse des mécanismes de la vernalisation d'une plante vivace, le *Geum urbanum* L. (Rosacées). *Bull. Soc. Bot. France* **109**, 145.

[28] Clever, U. (1964). Actinomycin and puromycin: effects on sequential gene activation by ecdysone. *Science* **146**, 794.

[29] Clever, U. (1965). The effect of ecdysone on gene activity patterns in giant chromosomes. In *Mechanisms of Hormone Action*, 142. Ed. P. Karlson. Academic Press, N.Y.

[30] Clever, U. and Romball, C. G. (1966). RNA and protein synthesis in the cellular response to a hormone, ecdysone. *Proc. Natl. Acad. Sci.* **56**, 1470.

[31] Davis, G. J. (1967). *Proserpinaca*: Photoperiodic and chemical differentiation of leaf development and flowering. *Plant Physiol.* **42**, 667.

[32] von Denffer, D. (1950). Blühormon oder Blühemmung. *Naturwiss.* **37**, 296, 317.

[33] Digby, J. and Wareing, P. F. (1966). The effect of applied growth hormones on cambial divisions and the differentiation of cambial derivatives. *Ann. Bot. N. S.* **30**, 539.

[34] El-Antably, H. M. M., Wareing, P. F. and Hillman, J. (1967). Some physiological responses to D, L abscisin (dormin). *Planta* **73**, 74.

[35] Esashi, Y. (1961). Studies on the formation and sprouting of aerial tubers in *Begonia evansiana*. Andr. VI. Photoperiodic conditions for tuberisation and sprouting in the cutting plants. *Sci. Rep. Tohoku Univ. Ser.* 4, **27**, 101.

[36] Evans, L. T. (1959). Environmental control of flowering in *Vicia faba*. *Ann. Bot. N. S.* **23**, 521.

[37] Evans, L. T. (1959). Flower initiation in *Trifolium subterraneum* L. I. Analysis of the partial processes involved. *Aust. J. Agric. Res.* **10**, 1.

[38] Evans, L. T. (1960). Inflorescence initiation in *Lolium temulentum* L. I. Effect of plant age and leaf area on sensitivity to photoperiodic induction. *Aust. J. Biol. Sci.* **13**, 123.

[39] Evans, L. T. (1960). The influence of environmental conditions on inflorescence development in some long-day grasses. *New Phytol.* **59**, 163.

[40] Evans, L. T. (1962). Daylength control of inflorescence initiation in the grass *Rottboellia exaltata* L.f. *Aust. J. Biol. Sci.* **15**, 291.

[41] Evans, L. T. (1964). Inflorescence initiation in *Lolium temulentum* L. V. The role of auxins and gibberellins. *Aust. J. Biol. Sci.* **17**, 10.

[42] Evans, L. T. and Rijven, A. H. G. C. (1967). Ibid. XI. Early increases in the incorporation of ^{32}P and ^{35}S by shoot apices during induction. *Aust. J. Biol. Sc.* **20**, 1033.

[43] Evans, L. T., Knox, R. B. and Rijven, A. H. G. C. (1968). The nature and localization of early events in the shoot apex of *Lolium temulentum* during floral induction. In *Cellular and Molecular Aspects of Floral Induction*. Ed. G. Bernier. *In press*.

[44] Fife, J. M. and Price, C. (1953). Bolting and flowering of sugar beets in continuous darkness. *Plant Phsyiol.* **28**, 475.

[45] Fisher, J. E. (1955). Floral induction in soybeans. *Bot. Gaz.* **117**, 156.

[46] Fratianne, D. G. (1965). The interrelationship between the flowering of dodder and the flowering of some long and short day plants. *Amer. J. Bot.* **52**, 556.

[47] Gifford, E. M. and Tepper, H. B. (1961). Ontogeny of the inflorescence in *Chenopodium album*. *Amer. J. Bot.* **48**, 657.

[48] Gifford, E. M. and Tepper, H. B. (1962). Histochemical and autoradiographic studies of floral induction in *Chenopodium album*. *Amer. J. Bot.* **49**, 706.

[49] Hamner, K. C. and Bonner, J. (1938). Photoperiodism in relation to hormones as factors in floral initiation and development. *Bot. Gaz.* **100**, 388.

[50] Harder, R. (1948). Vegetative and reproductive development of *Kalanchoë blossfeldiana* as influenced by photoperiodism. *Symp. Soc. Exp. Biol.* **2**, 117.

[51] Harder, R. and Bünsow, R. (1956). Einfluss des Gibberellins auf die Blütenbildung bei *Kalanchoe blossfeldiana*. *Naturwiss.* **23**, 544.

[52] Haupt, W. (1954). Blütenbildung einer Kurztagpflanze im Dauerlicht. *Naturwiss.* **14**, 340.

[53] Healey, P. L. (1964). Histochemistry and ultrastructure in the shoot of *Pharbitis* before and after floral induction. Ph.D. Thesis Univ. Calif., Berkeley.

[54] Heslop-Harrison, J. (1963). Sex expression in flowering plants. In *Meristems and Differentiation*. Brookhaven Symp. Biol. No. 16, 109.

[55] Hillman, W. S. (1963). *The physiology of flowering*. Holt, Rinehart and Winston, N.Y.

[56] Imamura, S-I. (1961). The nature of inhibition of flowering by the leaves illuminated continuously during the inductive dark treatment of other leaves in short day plants. *Recent Adv. Bot.* **2**, 1287.

[57] Imamura, S-I. and Takimoto, A. (1956). Transmission rate of the photoperiodic stimulus across the graft union in *Pharbitis Nil Chois*. *Bot. Mag.* (*Tokyo*) **69**, 23.

[58] Jacqmard, A. (1964). Action comparée de la photopériode et de l'acide gibbérellique sur le méristème caulinaire de *Rudbeckia bicolor* Nutt. *Bull. Acad. roy. Belg. Ser.* 5, **50**, 174.

[59] Jacqmard, A. (1967). Etude cinétique de la stimulation de l'activité mitotique dans le bourgeon terminal de *Rudbeckia bicolor* traité par l'acide gibbérellique. *C. R. Acad. Sci.* (*Paris*) **264**, 1282.

[60] Ketellapper, H. J. and Barbaro, A. (1966). The role of photoperiod, vernalization, and gibberellic acid in floral induction in *Coreopsis grandiflora* Nutt. *Phyton* **23**, 33.

61 King, R. W., Evans, L. T. and Wardlaw, I. F. (1968). Translocation of the floral stimulus in *Pharbitis Nil* in relation to that of assimilates. *Z. Pflanzenphysiol.* **59**, 377.

62 Klyachko, N. L. and Kulaeva, O. N. (1965). The periodicity of protein synthesis in tobacco leaves. *Dokl. Bot. Sci.* (*Transl.*) **164**, 115.

63 Lam, S-L. (1965). Movement of the flower stimulus in *Xanthium*. *Amer. J. Bot.* **52**, 924.

64 Lance, A. (1958). Recherches cytologiques sur l'évolution de quelques méristèmes apicaux et sur ses variations provoquées par des traitements photoperiodiques. *Ann. Sci. Nat. Bot. Ser.* 11, **18**, 91.

65 Lance-Nougarède, A. and Bronchart, R. (1965). Métabolisme des acides nucleiques dans le méristème apical du *Perilla nankinensis* au cours des diverses phases du développement. *C. R. Acad. Sci.* (*Paris*) **260**, 3140.

66 Lang, A. (1941). Über die Bedeutung von Licht und Dunkelheit in der Photoperiodischen Reaktion von Langtagpflanzen. *Biol. Zentral.* **61**, 427.

67 Lang, A. (1952). Physiology of flowering. *Ann. Rev. Pl. Physiol.* **3**, 265.

68 Lang, A. (1965). Physiology of flower initiation. *Handb. Pflanzenphysiol.* **15**, (1) 1380.

69 Lang, A. and Melchers, G. (1943). Die photoperiodische Reaktion von *Hyoscyamus niger*. *Planta* **33**, 653.

70 Lang, A., Sachs, R. M. and Bretz, C. (1959). Effets morphogenetiques de la gibberelline. *Bull. Soc. Franc. Physiol. Veget.* **5**, 1.

71 Langer, R. H. M. and Bussell, W. T. (1964). The effect of flower induction on the rate of leaf initiation. *Ann. Bot. N. S.* **28**, 163.

72 Letham, D. S. and Ralph, R. K. (1967). A cytokinin in soluble RNA from a higher plant. *Life Sciences* **6**, 387.

73 Lincoln, R. G. and Hamner, K. C. (1958). An effect of gibberellic acid on the flowering of *Xanthium*, a short day plant. *Plant Physiol.* **33**, 101.

74 Lincoln, R. G., Raven, K. A. and Hamner, K. C. (1956). Certain factors influencing expression of the flowering stimulus in *Xanthium*. I. Translocation and inhibition of the flowering stimulus. *Bot. Gaz.* **117**, 193.

75 Liverman, J. L. and Lang, A. (1956). Induction of flowering in long day plants by applied indoleacetic acid. *Plant Physiol.* **31**, 147.

76 Lockhart, J. A. and Gottschall, V. (1961). Fruit induced and apical senescence in *Pisum sativum*. *Plant Physiol.* **36**, 389.

77 Lona, F. (1948). La fioritura della brevidiurne *Chenopodium amaranticolor* Coste et Reyn. coltivata in soluzione nutrizizia con saccharosio, in assenza di stimulo fotoperiodico euflorigeno. *Nuov. Giorn. Bot. Ital. N. S.* **55**, 559.

78 Lona, F. (1949). La fioritura delle brevidiurne a notte continua. *Nuov. Giorn. Bot. Ital.* **56**, 479.

79 Lubimenko, V. N. and Szeglova, O. A. (1932). Sur l'induction photopériodique dans le processus du développement des plantes. *Bull. Jardin. Bot. Acad. Sci. U.R.S.S.* (*Leningrad*) **30** (1–2) 1.

80 McIlrath, W. J. and Bogorad, L. (1958). Photoperiodic floral induction of *Xanthium* and germination of lettuce seeds implanted in the petioles. *Bot. Gaz.* **119**, 186.

81 Maheshwari, S. C. and Seth, P. N. (1966). Induction of flowering in *Wolffia microscopica* by the iron salt of ethylene diamine-di-o-hydroxyphenyl acetic acid (Fe-EDDHA). *Z. Pflanzenphysiol.* **55**, 89.

82 Maheshwari, S. C. and Venkataraman, R. (1966). Induction of flowering in duckweed – *Wolffia microscopica* – by a new kinin, zeatin. *Planta* **70**, 304.

83 Margara, J. and Bouniols, A. (1967). Comparaison *in vitro* de l'influence du milieu, liquide ou gélosé, sur l'initiation florale, chez *Cichorium intybus* L. *C. R. Acad. Sci.* (*Paris*) **264**, 1166.

84 Margara, J., Rancillac, M. and Bouniols, A. (1966). Recherches expérimentales sur la néoformation de bourgeons inflorescentiels ou végétatifs *in vitro* à partir d'explantats d'endive (*Cichorium intybus*. L.). *Ann. Physiol. Veget.* **8**, 285.

85 Mayfield, D. L. (1964). Floral-inducing extracts of *Helianthus* and of *Xanthium*: some chemical and physiological properties. In *Régulateurs Naturels de la Croissance Végétale*, 621. CNRS. Paris.

86 Michniewicz, M. and Kamienska, A. (1964). Flower formation induced by kinetin and vitamin E treatment in a cold-requiring plant (*Cichorium intybus* L.) grown under non-inductive conditions. *Naturwiss.* **51**, 295.

87 Michniewicz, M. and Kamienska, A. (1965). Flower formation induced by kinetin and vitamin E treatment in long day plant (*Arabidopsis thaliana*). *Naturwiss.* **52**, 623.

88 Mitchell, W. D. (1964). Endogenous circadian rhythm in *Xanthium*. *Plant Physiol. Supplement* **39**, xxxviii.

[89] Moshkov, B. S. (1937). Photoperiodism and a hypothesis as to hormones of flowering. *C. R. (Dokl.) Acad. Sci. U.R.S.S.* **15**, 211.

[90] Murneek, A. E. (1940). Length of day and temperature effects in *Rudbeckia. Bot. Gaz.* **102**, 269.

[91] Nanda, K. K. and Purohit, A. N. (1967). Experimental induction of apical flowering in indeterminate plant *Impatiens balsamina* L. *Naturwiss.* **54**, 230.

[92] Negbi, M., Baldev, B. and Lang, A. (1964). Studies on the orientation of the mitotic spindle in the shoot apex of *Hyoscyamus niger* and other rosette plants. *Israel J. Bot.* **13**, 134.

[93] Nitsch, J. P. (1966). Photopériodisme et tubérisation. *Bull. Soc. Franc. Physiol. Veget.* **12**, 233.

[94] Nitsch, J. P. and Harada, H. (1958). Production de fleurs en jours courts par l'alcool furfurylique chez le *Rudbeckia speciosa. Bull. Soc. Bot. France* **105**, 319.

[95] Nitsch, J. P. and Went, F. W. (1959). The induction of flowering in *Xanthium pensylvanicum* under long days. In *Photoperiodism*, 311. Ed. R. B. Withrow, A.A.A.S., Washington.

[96] Nougarède, A. (1967). Experimental cytology of the shoot apical cells during vegetative growth and flowering. *Int. Rev. Cytol.* **21**, 203.

[97] Nougarède, A., Bronchart, R., Bernier, G. and Rondet, P. (1964). Comportement du méristème apical du *Perilla nankinensis* (Lour.). Decne. en relation avec les conditions photopériodiques. *Rev. Gen. Botan.* **71**, 205.

[98] Nougarède, A., Gifford, E. M. and Rondet, P. (1965). Cytohistological studies of the apical meristem of *Amaranthus retroflexus* under various photoperiodic regimes. *Bot. Gaz.* **126**, 281.

[99] Ogawa, Y. (1961). Über die Wirkung des Gibberellins auf die Blütenbildung von *Pharbitis Nil.* Chois. *Plant & Cell Physiol.* **2**, 311.

[100] van Overbeek, J., Loeffler, J. E. and Mason, M. I. R. (1967). Dormin (Abscisin II), inhibitor of plant DNA synthesis. *Science* **156**, 1497.

[101] Paulet, P. and Nitsch, J. P. (1964). La néoformation de fleurs sur cultures *in vitro* de racines de *Cichorium intybus* L.: études physiologiques. *Ann. Physiol. Veget.* **6**, 333.

[102] Pellegrini, O. (1961). Modificazione delle prospettive morfogenetiche in primordi fogliari chirurgicamente isolati dal meristema apicale del germoglio. *Delpinoa N. S.* **3**, 1.

[103] Piringer, A. A., Downs, R. J. and Borthwick, H. A. (1963). Photocontrol of growth and flowering of *Caryopteris. Amer. J. Bot.* **50**, 86.

[104] Raghavan, V. and Jacobs, W. P. (1961). Studies on the floral histogenesis and physiology of *Perilla*. II. Floral induction in cultured apical buds of *P. frutescens. Amer. J. Bot.* **48**, 751.

[105] Razumov, V. I. (1960). Acceleration of flowering of short day plants treated with gibberellin. *Fiziol. Rast. (Transl.)* **7**, 294.

[106] Rijven, A. H. G. C. and Evans, L. T. (1967). Inflorescence initiation in *Lolium temulentum* L. X. Changes in ^{32}P incorporation into nucleic acids of the shoot apex at induction. *Aust. J. Biol. Sci.* **20**, 13.

[107] Roberts, R. H. and Struckmeyer, B. E. (1938). The effects of temperature and other environmental factors upon the photoperiodic responses of some of the higher plants. *J. Agric. Res.* **56**, 633.

[108] Roberts, R. H. and Struckmeyer, B. E. (1939). Further studies on the effects of temperature and other environmental factors upon the photoperiodic responses of plants. *J. Agric. Res.* **59**, 699.

[109] Rodrigues Pereira, A. S. (1962). Physiological experiments in connection with flower formation in Wedgewood Iris (Iris c.v. Wedgewood). *Acta Bot. Néerl.* **11**, 97.

[110] Sachs, R. M., Bretz, C. F. and Lang, A. (1959). Shoot histogenesis: the early effects of gibberellin upon stem elongation in two rosette plants. *Amer. J. Bot.* **46**, 376.

[111] Sachs, R. M., Kofranek, A. M. and Shyr, S-Y. (1967). Gibberellin-induced inhibition of floral initiation in *Fuchsia. Amer. J. Bot.* **54**, 921.

[112] Salisbury, F. B. (1959). Influence of certain growth regulators on flowering of the cocklebur. In *Photoperiodism*, 381. Ed. R. B. Withrow. A.A.A.S., Washington.

[113] Searle, N. E. (1965). Physiology of flowering. *Ann. Rev. Plant Physiol.* **16**, 97.

[114] Seidlova, F. and Jurakova, J. (1964). Ein Vergleich der Struktur des Vegetationskegels mit der Länge der photoperiodischen Induktion bei *Hyoscyamus niger. Naturwiss.* **51**, 442.

[115] Sironval, C. (1951). Recherches organographiques et physiologiques sur le développement du Fraisier des quatre-saisons à fruits rouges. *Mem. Acad. Roy. Belg. Cl. Sci.* **26**, (4) 1.

116 Skinner, B.F. (1963). *Science and Human Behaviour*, Macmillan, N.Y.
117 Skoog, F. and Miller, C.O. (1957). Chemical regulation of growth and organ formation in plant tissues cultured *in vitro. Symp. Soc. Exp. Biol.* **11**, 118.
118 Skoog, F., Armstrong, D. J., Cherayil, J. D., Hampel, A. E. and Bock, R. M. (1966). Cytokinin activity: localization in transfer RNA preparations. *Science* **154**, 1354.
119 Sunderland, N. and Brown, R. (1956). Distribution of growth in the apical region of the shoot of *Lupinus albus. J. Exp. Bot.* **7**, 127.
120 Takimoto, A., Tashima, Y. and Imamura, S. (1960). Effect of temperature on flower initiation of *Pharbitis Nil* cultured *in vitro. Bot. Mag. (Tokyo)* **73**, 377.
121 Tashima, Y. (1953). Flower initiation in total darkness in a long day plant, *Raphanus sativus* L. *Proc. Jap. Acad.* **29**, 271.
122 Teltscherova, L., Havlickova, H. and Krekule, J. (1967). Effect of (2-chloroethyl) trimethylammonium chloride (CCC) and gibberellic acid (GA_3) on the flowering of *Chenopodium rubrum* L. *Biol. Plantar. (Praha)* **9**, 317.
123 Thomas, R. G. (1961). Correlations between growth and flowering in *Chenopodium amaranticolor*. I. Initiation of leaf and bud primordia. *Ann. Bot. N. S.* **25**, 138.
124 Thomas, R. G. (1961). The relationship between leaf growth and induction of flowering in long day plants (LDP). *Naturwiss.* **48**, 108.
125 Thomas, R. G. (1961). Flower initiation in *Trifolium repens* L.: a short-long-day plant. *Nature* **190**, 1130.
126 Tran Thanh Van, M. (1965). La vernalization de *Geum urbanum* L. *Ann. Sci. Nat. Ser.* 12, *Bot.* **6**, 373.
127 Ursprung, H. (1966). The formation of patterns in development. *Symp. Soc. Devel. Biol.* **25**, 177.
128 Vlitos, A. J. and Meudt, W. (1955). Interactions between vernalization and photoperiod in spinach. *Contrib. Boyce Thompson Inst.* **18**, 159.
129 Volodarskij, N. I. (1957). (Flowering of chrysanthemum in continuous illumination.) *Dokl. Akad. Nauk. S.S.S.R.* **117**, 504.
130 Volodarskij, N. I. (1961). (Flowering of short day plants under continuous illumination.) *Dokl. Akad. Nauk. S.S.S.R.* **138**, 473.
131 Wada, K. (1967). Studies on the flower initiation in *Pharbitis* seedlings. I. Ages of shoot apices and initiation rates of leaf primordia at the shoot apex. *Bot. Mag. (Tokyo)* **80**, 161.
132 Waddington, C. H. (1966). Fields and gradients. *Symp. Soc. Devel. Biol.* **25**, 105.
133 Watson, J. D. and Matthews, R. E. F. (1966). Effect of Actinomycin D and 2-thiouracil on floral induction and nucleic acid synthesis in the bud in *Chenopodium amaranticolor. Aust. J. Biol. Sci.* **19**, 967.
134 Wellensiek, S. J. (1960). Flower formation in *Campanula medium. Meded. Landbouwhogesch. (Wageningen)* **60**, (7) 1.
135 Wetmore, R. H. and Rier, J. P. (1963). Experimental induction of vascular tissues in callus of angiosperms. *Amer. J. Bot.* **50**, 418.
136 Wickson, M. and Thimann, K. V. (1958). The antagonism of auxin and kinetin in apical dominance. *Physiol. Plantar.* **11**, 62.
137 Withrow, A., Withrow, R. and Biebel, J. P. (1943). Inhibiting influence of the leaves on the photoperiodic response of Nobel spinach. *Plant Physiol.* **18**, 294.
138 Yeomans, M. M. and Evans, P. K. (1967). Growth and differentiation of plant tissue cultures. II. Synchronous cell divisions in developing callus cultures. *Ann. Bot. N. S.* **31**, 323.
139 de Zeeuw, D. (1956). Leaf-induced inhibition of flowering in tomato. *Koninkl. Nederl. Akad. Wetenschap. Proc.* **59**, 535.
140 de Zeeuw, D. (1957). Flowering of *Xanthium* under long day conditions. *Nature* **180**, 558.
141 Zeevaart, J. A. D. (1958). Flower formation as studied by grafting. *Meded. Landbouwhogesch. (Wageningen)* **58**, (3) 1.
142 Zeevaart, J. A. D. (1963). Climatic control of reproductive development. In *Environmental Control of Plant Growth*, 289. Ed. L. T. Evans. Academic Press, N.Y.
143 Zeevaart, J. A. D. (1964). Effects of the growth retardant CCC on floral initiation and growth in *Pharbitis nil. Plant Physiol.* **39**, 402.
144 Zeevaart, J. A. D. (1966). Hormonal regulation of plant development. In *Cell Differentiation and Morphogenesis*, 144. Nth. Holland, Amsterdam.
145 Zeevaart, J. A. D. (1966). Inhibition of stem growth and flower formation in *Pharbitis nil* with N-dimethylaminosuccinamic acid (B995). *Planta* **71**, 68.
146 Zhdanova, L. P. (1948). (On the rate of export of flower hormone in photoperiodic induction.) *Dokl. Akad. Nauk. S.S.S.R.* **61**, 553.

Index of Species

Subject Index